INTRODUCTORY
MATHEMATICAL
ANALYSIS

INTRODUCTORY MATHEMATICAL ANALYSIS

Third Edition

EDGAR D. EAVES

Professor of Mathematics
University of Tennessee

ALLYN AND BACON, INC., BOSTON

Fifth printing . . . November, 1971

Library of Congress Catalog Card Number:
77-86998

PRINTED IN THE UNITED STATES OF AMERICA

CONTENTS

I	LOGIC AND SETS	1
1.	INTRODUCTION	1
2.	LOGIC, PROPOSITIONS, AND CONNECTIVES	2
3.	CONJUNCTIONS, DISJUNCTIONS, NEGATIONS, AND IMPLICATIONS	4
4.	EQUIVALENCES AND RELATED PROPOSITIONS	10
5.	SETS, ELEMENTS, AND MEMBERSHIP	12
6.	METHODS OF CONSTRUCTING SETS	13
7.	THE UNIVERSAL SET AND THE EMPTY SET	15
8.	SUBSETS	17
9.	VENN DIAGRAMS	19
10.	EQUIVALENT SETS	20
11.*	COUNTABLE SETS	23
12.	SET OPERATIONS	26
13.	THE CARTESIAN PRODUCT OF TWO SETS	32
14.	OPEN STATEMENTS	35
15.*	QUANTIFIERS	37

II	NUMBER SYSTEMS	40
1.	INTRODUCTION	40
2.	REAL NUMBERS	40

  3. MATHEMATICAL SYSTEMS 44
  4. THE REAL NUMBER SYSTEM 45
  5. SOME BASIC THEOREMS 50
  6. SOME PRODUCTS AND QUOTIENTS INVOLVING ZERO 53
  7. MULTIPLICATION OF NONZERO NUMBERS 55
  8. MULTIPLICATION AND DIVISION OF FRACTIONS 57
  9. ADDITION AND SUBTRACTION OF FRACTIONS 60
10. SYMBOLS OF GROUPING 61
11. THE ORDER RELATIONS 63
12. THE ABSOLUTE VALUE OF A REAL NUMBER 66
13. THE NUMBER LINE 67
14. RECTANGULAR COORDINATE SYSTEM 69
15. COMPLEX NUMBERS 75

III   ELEMENTARY ALGEBRAIC PROCESSES **80**

  1. THE TERMINOLOGY OF ALGEBRA 80
  2. ADDITION AND SUBTRACTION OF ALGEBRAIC
     EXPRESSIONS 81
  3. EXPONENTS AND RADICALS 83
  4. MULTIPLICATION OF ALGEBRAIC EXPRESSIONS 89
  5. SPECIAL PRODUCTS AND FACTORING 90
  6. DIVISION OF ALGEBRAIC EXPRESSIONS 94
  7. ALGEBRAIC FRACTIONS 96
  8.* MATHEMATICAL INDUCTION 101
  9. THE BINOMIAL THEOREM 105

IV   POLYNOMIALS, EQUATIONS, AND INEQUALITIES **111**

  1. INTRODUCTION 111
  2. POLYNOMIALS IN ONE VARIABLE 111
  3. EQUATIONS 112
  4. SOLUTIONS AND SOLUTION SETS 114
  5. QUADRATIC EQUATIONS IN ONE VARIABLE 119
  6. THE METHOD OF FACTORING 120
  7. THE METHOD OF COMPLETING THE SQUARE 122
  8. THE QUADRATIC-FORMULA METHOD 124
  9. FACTS ABOUT THE ROOTS OF THE QUADRATIC
     EQUATION $ax^2 + bx + c = 0$ 127
10. EQUATIONS IN QUADRATIC FORM 128
11. POLYNOMIALS: TWO MAJOR PROBLEMS 130
12. SYNTHETIC SUBSTITUTION 131
13. THE ZEROS OF A POLYNOMIAL 132
14. THE REMAINDER THEOREM 134
15. COMPLEX ROOTS OF A POLYNOMIAL EQUATION 137
16. NUMBER OF ROOTS 138

17. THE UPPER AND LOWER LIMITS OF THE REAL ROOTS
    OF A POLYNOMIAL EQUATION   139
18. DESCARTES' RULE OF SIGNS   140
19. RATIONAL ROOTS   142
20. EQUATIONS CONTAINING FRACTIONS   145
21. EQUATIONS INVOLVING RADICALS   149
22. GRAPHS OF POLYNOMIALS   151
23. IRRATIONAL ROOTS OF A POLYNOMIAL EQUATION   154
24. INEQUALITIES IN ONE VARIABLE   157
25. LINEAR INEQUALITIES IN ONE VARIABLE   159
26. QUADRATIC INEQUALITIES   161
27. INEQUALITIES IN ONE VARIABLE INVOLVING
    POLYNOMIALS OF DEGREE $n > 2$ AND
    INEQUALITIES INVOLVING FRACTIONS   165

V   RELATIONS, FUNCTIONS, AND GRAPHS   **171**

 1. A PREVIEW   171
 2. RELATIONS   172
 3. THE FUNCTION CONCEPT   173
 4. FUNCTIONAL NOTATION   174
 5. RULES USED IN DEFINING FUNCTIONS   176
 6. FUNCTIONS DEFINED BY A FORMULA OR AN EQUATION   176
 7. FUNCTIONS DEFINED BY A TABLE OF VALUES   178
 8. GRAPHS OF RELATIONS AND FUNCTIONS   181
 9. GRAPHS OF EQUATIONS INVOLVING TWO VARIABLES   185
10. LENGTH AND MIDPOINT OF A LINE SEGMENT   189
11. THE SLOPE OF A LINE   193
12. EQUATIONS OF STRAIGHT LINES   198
13.* EQUATIONS OF CIRCLES, PARABOLAS, ELLIPSES
    AND HYPERBOLAS   203
14. GRAPHS OF LINEAR INEQUALITIES IN TWO VARIABLES   214

VI   AVERAGE RATES, INSTANTANEOUS RATES,
     AND LIMITS   **217**

 1. AVERAGE RATES   217
 2. INSTANTANEOUS RATES FOUND GRAPHICALLY   218
 3. MORE ABOUT AVERAGE RATES   222
 4. AVERAGE RATES OVER A FLEXIBLE INTERVAL   224
 5. THE LIMIT CONCEPT   226
 6. SOME THEOREMS CONCERNING LIMITS   230
 7. CONTINUOUS FUNCTIONS   232
 8. POLYNOMIAL FUNCTIONS   232
 9. THE CONCEPT OF INFINITY   235
10. INSTANTANEOUS SPEED   237

11. ACCELERATION   238
12. TANGENT LINE TO A CURVE AT A POINT   239
13. SLOPE OF A CURVE AT A POINT   240
14. INSTANTANEOUS RATES IN GENERAL   241

VII   DIFFERENTIATION   **244**

1. THE DERIVATIVE OF A FUNCTION   244
2. Δ NOTATION   245
3. RULES FOR DIFFERENTIATION   247
4. DERIVATIVES OF PRODUCTS, QUOTIENTS, AND POWERS   250
5. IMPLICIT DIFFERENTIATION   256
6. SOME IMPORTANT THEOREMS   259
7. INTERPRETATIONS OF A DERIVATIVE   262
8. SUCCESSIVE DIFFERENTIATION   265
9. INCREASING AND DECREASING FUNCTIONS   266
10. MAXIMA AND MINIMA VALUES   271
11. APPLIED PROBLEMS IN MAXIMA AND MINIMA   277
12.* THE CHAIN RULE FOR DIFFERENTIATION   280
13.* RELATED RATES   281

VIII   INTEGRATION   **284**

1. INTRODUCTION   284
2. DIFFERENTIATION REVERSED   285
3. SOME INTEGRATION FORMULAS   285
4. SPEED AND DISTANCE   288
5. FREELY FALLING BODIES   290
6. THE EQUATION OF A CURVE   293
7. INTEGRAL NOTATION   294
8. THE DIFFERENTIAL OF A FUNCTION   297
9. AREAS FOUND BY INTEGRATION   301
10.* VOLUMES OF SOLIDS   309

**IX   SIMULTANEOUS, LINEAR EQUATIONS AND
         INEQUALITIES, LINEAR PROGRAMMING**   **312**

1. SYSTEMS OF TWO LINEAR EQUATIONS
     IN TWO VARIABLES   312
2. GRAPHICAL METHOD FOR EQUATIONS AND
     INEQUALITIES IN TWO VARIABLES   313
3. THE METHOD OF ELIMINATION BY ADDITION AND
     SUBTRACTION FOR EQUATIONS   314
4. THE METHOD OF DETERMINANTS   319

5. SYSTEMS OF LINEAR INEQUALITIES 329
6.* LINEAR PROGRAMMING 332

X TRIGONOMETRIC FUNCTIONS 341

1. ANGLES 341
2. TRIANGLES 344
3. THE TRIGONOMETRIC FUNCTIONS 345
4. RELATED ANGLES 348
5. BASIC IDENTITIES AMONG THE TRIGONOMETRIC
   FUNCTIONS 350
6. THE TRIGONOMETRIC FUNCTIONS OF $0, \pi/6, \pi/4, \pi/3$,
   AND $\pi/2$ 353
7. TABLES OF TRIGONOMETRIC FUNCTIONS 355
8. SOLUTION OF RIGHT TRIANGLES 358
9. ANGLES OF ELEVATION AND ANGLES OF DEPRESSION 360
10. PROJECTIONS, VECTORS, AND COMPONENTS
    OF VECTORS 362
11. OBLIQUE TRIANGLES 367
12.* FUNCTIONS OF $(A + B)$, $(A - B)$, AND $2A$ 371

XI SIMPLE AND COMPOUND INTEREST 378

1. INTRODUCTION 378
2. PERCENTAGE 379
3. SIMPLE INTEREST DEFINED 381
4. PRESENT VALUE AT SIMPLE INTEREST 382
5. COMPOUND INTEREST DEFINED 384
6. SOME TERMINOLOGY 385
7. A FORMULA FOR COMPOUND AMOUNT 385
8. PRESENT VALUE 387
9. EQUATION OF VALUE 389

XII SEQUENCES, SERIES, AND ANNUITIES 392

1. SEQUENCES 392
2. ARITHMETIC PROGRESSIONS 393
3. ARITHMETIC MEANS 395
4. GEOMETRIC PROGRESSIONS 396
5. GEOMETRIC MEANS 397
6. GEOMETRIC SERIES 398
7. ANNUITIES DEFINED 401
8. TYPES OF ANNUITIES 401
9. ANNUITIES CERTAIN 402
10. THE PRESENT VALUE OF AN ANNUITY 404

11. FINDING THE VALUE OF AN ANNUITY ON ANY DATE   407
12. AMORTIZATION OF A DEBT   411

XIII   EXPONENTIAL AND LOGARITHMIC FUNCTIONS   414

1. INTRODUCTION   414
2. COMPOUNDING CONTINUOUSLY   415
3. EXPONENTIAL FUNCTIONS   418
4. NATURAL LOGARITHMS DEFINED   420
5. THE USE OF A NATURAL-LOGARITHM TABLE   421
6. THE LAWS OF NATURAL LOGARITHMS   422
7. THE DERIVATIVE OF e^u AND $\ln u$ 425
8. THE INTEGRALS $\int e^u\,du$ AND $\int (du/u)$ 426
9.* LOGARITHMS TO ANY BASE   428

XIV   PROBABILITY AND STATISTICS   430

1. INTRODUCTION   430
2. PROBABILITY   430
3. PERMUTATIONS AND COMBINATIONS   433
4. THE BINOMIAL EXPANSION; PROBABILITY RULES   437
5. MATHEMATICAL EXPECTATION   441
6. PROBABILITY DISTRIBUTIONS   443
7. MEAN VALUE, VARIANCE, AND STANDARD DEVIATION   448
8. POPULATIONS AND SAMPLES   453
9: NORMAL PROBABILITY DISTRIBUTIONS   455

TABULAR APPENDIX   461

TABLE I.   NATURAL TRIGONOMETRIC FUNCTIONS   462
TABLE II.   COMPOUND AMOUNT   485
TABLE III.   PRESENT VALUE   491
TABLE IV.   EXPONENTIAL FUNCTIONS   497
TABLE V.   NATURAL LOGARITHMS   503
TABLE VI.   AMOUNT OF AN ANNUITY OF 1 PER ANNUM   505
TABLE VII.   PRESENT VALUE OF 1 PER ANNUM   511

ANSWERS TO ODD-NUMBERED EXERCISES   517

INDEX   547

PREFACE

The purpose of this book, as in the case of the two earlier editions, is to provide a text which will give those students who take only one year of college mathematics an opportunity to obtain as broad a background in mathematics as is possible in the two semesters, or three quarters these students have available. The book gives a modern integrated treatment of the basic concepts of algebra, trigonometry, analytic geometry, and elementary calculus with simple applications to problems within the range of the student's understanding and experience.

In this revision the order of some of the topics has been changed, several of the sections have been rewritten, new topics have been included, and many new problems added.

The author feels that a student will be more able to read and follow the logical steps in the given proof of a theorem and to formulate a proof for himself if he has been exposed to the general principles of elementary logic. He also feels it desirable to be able to use the language and concept of sets when to do so helps to simplify or to make more meaningful the theory under discussion. For these reasons Chapter I is devoted to a brief discussion of logic and sets.

Chapter II presents the systems of real and complex numbers from an axiomatic point of view and the basic properties of real numbers and complex numbers are listed and emphasized.

Chapters III and IV provide a thorough review of the important topics of elementary algebra, including a rather detailed and systematic treatment of methods for the solution of polynomial equations and polynomial inequalities. A section on Mathematical Induction is also included in Chapter III.

Chapter V is devoted to a detailed discussion of relations, functions, and their graphs, including the definitions and standard form equations of the conic sections.

Chapter VI lays the foundation for the material on the calculus treated in Chapters VII and VIII. The approach to the calculus is through the notion of an instantaneous rate defined as the limit of an average rate.

Chapters VII and VIII present from the rate standpoint the theory of differentiation and integration of algebraic functions with applications to problems from geometry and physics with which the student already has some familiarity.

Chapter IX treats methods for solving systems of linear equations and linear inequalities including the method of determinants. One section is devoted to linear programming. A brief study of trigonometry with applications is presented in Chapter X.

Chapters XI and XII treat simple and compound interest, sequences, series, and annuities. The formula for compound interest is used in Chapter XIII as a stepping stone to the law of growth and the exponential and logarithmic functions.

Chapter XIV gives a brief treatment of probability and statistics.

Answers to most of the odd-numbered exercises appear at the end of this volume; answers to the even-numbered exercises are provided in a separate booklet.

Teachers who are pressed for time may omit any or all starred sections without loss of continuity.

I wish to thank my former co-author, Dr. Robert L. Wilson, who has been on an assignment in Nigeria for the past two years and was unable to assist with this revision, for graciously granting free use of the material from the Second Edition.

I deeply appreciate the help given me by my colleagues Mrs. Elizabeth Carlson, Mr. Michael Carter, Miss Margaret Mason, and Mrs. Lucile Scott in reading and correcting the manuscript. Particular thanks go to Mrs. Frank A. Brown, III and to Mrs. Garland Hart who did the typing. Also, special thanks are due the many teachers who have used the Second Edition for their many helpful suggestions.

It is a pleasure to acknowledge the valuable assistance and complete cooperation of the staff of Allyn and Bacon.

Edgar D. Eaves

INTRODUCTORY
MATHEMATICAL
ANALYSIS

I

LOGIC AND SETS

1 INTRODUCTION

In developing any mathematical theory, which is the prime function of a textbook in mathematics, one has to decide where to start. In an elementary text such as this the usual procedure is to start by defining some words or terms that are to be used and by listing certain statements that are to be assumed true. By the word "statements" we mean declarative sentences. These statements are called axioms and may or may not seem true intuitively. From these assumed truths or axioms we hopefully deduce many other truths by a mental process called logical reasoning. These deduced truths are usually stated as conclusions of propositions called theorems. We affirm the conclusion of a theorem by *proving* the *theorem*. How does one reason logically? How does one know when his argument is valid?

Many discussions in elementary mathematics can often be greatly simplified and at the same time be made more meaningful to the student by the use of the language and concept of sets. In fact, the concept of sets is one of the important fundamental concepts in modern mathematics and one which permeates many branches of mathematics.

In an attempt to shed some light on the two questions raised in the first paragraph above, and in order to be able to use the language and concept of sets whenever needed in later chapters, a brief discussion of logic and sets is given in this first chapter.

1

2   LOGIC, PROPOSITIONS, AND CONNECTIVES

In our routine daily lives most of us must make certain decisions based upon our ability to reason. To be sure, many of these decisions are made more or less subconsciously and without any thought or realization as to whether we are or whether we are not reasoning correctly. In mathematics we must reason correctly if the conclusions based on our reasoning are to be valid.

How can one be sure that he is reasoning correctly? This is where formal logic comes to our aid. Logicians have very carefully worked out formal rules designed to help us draw valid conclusions from a given set of known facts. By a known fact is meant a declarative statement concerning which it can be said that the statement is true or that the statement is false but not both. For convenience we shall refer to such a statement as a *proposition*. Thus *a statement is a proposition if one and only if one of the terms "true" or "false" can be meaningfully applied to it*. If a proposition is true we say that it has truth value T (true), if the proposition is false its truth value is F (false). For a statement to be a proposition it is not necessary that we know which of the two truth values actually applies to the statement. The important thing to know is that one and only one of the truth values does apply. For example, the student is probably familiar with one of the standard processes for obtaining a decimal approximation to the square root of a number that is not a perfect square. If such a process is repeated over and over a result may be obtained that contains as many decimal places as is desired, even a thousand or more decimal places if we were willing to waste a sufficient amount of time in such an activity. Thus the statement "the digit in the 100th decimal place in a decimal approximation to $\sqrt{2}$, that contains more than 100 decimal places, is 7," is a proposition because either the statement is true or the statement is false even though we do not know which. Other examples of propositions are the following.

(1)   Dallas is the capital of Texas.
(2)   7 is a prime number.
(3)   If a triangle is equilateral it is equiangular.
(4) $8 + 5 = 12$.
(5)   All rectangles are squares.

It is obvious that propositions (1), (4), and (5) are all false, hence each has truth value F. Propositions (2) and (3) are both true, hence the truth value of each is T.

The first grade student after learning the names of the counting numbers and learning to recognize the symbols which represent these numbers then is confronted with the problem of learning how to combine two or more numbers. That is, he has to learn how to add, subtract, multiply and divide. He perhaps memorizes an addition table and a multiplication table. In short he has to learn the four fundamental operations of arithmetic. When two or more numbers are combined using one or more of the fundamental operations the result in general is a number whose value is determined by the kinds of operations used and by the values of the numbers involved in the combination. For example, if two counting numbers are added the result is always another counting number called the sum of the first two. Furthermore, the value of the sum is determined by the values of the two numbers being added. Likewise, two or more propositions may be combined to form a new proposition whose truth value may be determined from the truth values of the propositions from which the new one is being formed. In arithmetic the combinations are formed by using one or more of the fundamental operations. In the case of propositions, combinations are formed by the use of certain words or terms called connectives. The most common connectives, and the ones which we shall discuss here, are the words *and, or, if-then, if and only if,* and *not.* Two definitions are in order at this point.

Definition 1.1.   *A proposition that contains no connectives is called a simple proposition.*

Definition 1.2.   *A proposition that contains one or more connectives is called a compound proposition.*

As an example of how the connectives listed above may be used to form compound propositions from simple propositions, let us consider the two simple propositions (1) "a horse is a four legged animal," and (2) "2 times 3 is 5." From (1) and (2) we can construct the new compound propositions: "a horse is a four legged animal and 2 times 3 is 5," "a horse is a four legged animal or 2 times 3 is 5," "if a horse is a four legged animal, then 2 times 3 is 5," "a horse is a four legged animal if and only if 2 times 3 is 5." Finally, from the proposition "2 times 3 is 5" we can form the new proposition "2 times 3 is not 5." It should be observed that in the last case (1) we used only one of the two given propositions in forming our new proposition and (2) the new proposition is a denial of the old. We say that the new proposition is the negative of the old or a negation of the old. In other words, the connective word *not* applied to a given proposition gives us a new proposition whose truth value is opposite of the truth value of the given proposition. For example, the proposition "2 times 3 is 5" obviously is false, hence has truth value F whereas the proposition "2 times 3 is not 5" has truth value T. To even include the word *not* as a connective may seem arbitrary but suffice it to say that it is most important in mathematics to be able to form a proposition that denies or negates a given proposition. Negation will be discussed more fully in a later section.

In the succeeding sections we shall consider each of the connectives one at a time and define the truth values of compound propositions involving them. However, before we start our discussion of each of the connectives some general remarks are in order. First, we want to emphasize the fact that in symbolic logic we are not concerned with the meaning of propositions but only with their truth values. This being the case, the truth value of a compound proposition is determined by the truth values of its components. To simplify our discussion, suppose that we have a compound proposition formed from the two unspecified propositions p and q. Obviously proposition p is either true or false. Likewise proposition q is either true or false. Thus for each of our connectives the only possible combinations of truth values of p and q are the following.

(a) p true and q true,
(b) p true and q false,
(c) p false and q true,
(d) p false and q false.

We shall now define the truth value for each of the compound propositions "p and q," "p or q," "if p then q," and "p if and only if q," in each of the four cases, (a), (b), (c), and (d) listed above.

3   CONJUNCTIONS, DISJUNCTIONS, NEGATIONS, AND IMPLICATIONS

The compound proposition "p and q," denoted symbolically as "$p \wedge q$" is called the *conjunction* of p and q. It should be intuitively obvious that the conjunction "$p \wedge q$" is true when and only when both p and q are true. But to be more explicit we define the truth values of the conjunction as shown in the following table, called a truth table. See Fig. 1.1.

Conjunction

p	q	$p \wedge q$
T	T	T
T	F	F
F	T	F
F	F	F

FIGURE 1.1

The compound proposition "p or q," denoted symbolically as "$p \vee q$" is called the *inclusive disjunction* of p and q and is false when and only when both p and q are false. In ordinary language the compound statement "p or q" is often used to mean p is true or q is true but not both. Such a disjunction is called an *exclusive* disjunction and denoted symbolically as "$p \underline{\vee} q$." Unless otherwise stated disjunctions used in this text should be interpreted as inclusive disjunctions. The truth tables for the two types of disjunction are shown in Figs. 1.2 and 1.3.

Inclusive Disjunction			Exclusive Disjunction		
p	q	$p \vee q$	p	q	$p \veebar q$
T	T	T	T	T	F
T	F	T	T	F	T
F	T	T	F	T	T
F	F	F	F	F	F

FIGURE 1.2   FIGURE 1.3

A typical example of an inclusive disjunction as used in mathematics is the following.

Example. If p and q are the propositions

p: $x^2 - 1$ is positive for all real numbers x greater than 1.
q: $x^2 - 1$ is positive for all real numbers x less than -1.
$p \vee q$: $x^2 - 1$ is positive for all real numbers x greater than 1 or less than -1.

As an example of an exclusive disjunction consider the following.

Example. Suppose two basketball teams, Team A and Team B, are scheduled to play each other in a game with the understanding that overtimes will be used if necessary to prevent the game ending in a tie. If p and q are the propositions

p: Team A will win the game
q: Team B will win the game

then the proposition "Team A or Team B will win the game" would be correctly symbolized as "$p \veebar q$."

As was pointed out in the last section, it is often desirable to form a proposition that negates, or denies a given proposition. To be able to form such a proposition it is necessary that we state precisely what is meant by the negation of a proposition. Suppose p is a given proposition. By the negation of p is meant the proposition, denoted symbolically as "$\sim p$" and read "not p," such that

(a) if p is true, then $\sim p$ is false
(b) if p is false, then $\sim p$ is true.

Negation

p	$\sim p$
T	F
F	T

FIGURE 1.4

The truth table is shown in Fig. 1.4. Often there are several equivalent ways of forming the negation of a given proposition. For example let p be the proposition "the weather is hot." The negation "$\sim p$" could take either of the following forms.

(a)   The weather is not hot.
(b)   It is false that the weather is hot.
(c)   The weather is cool.

It should be noted that one needs to exercise a certain amount of care in forming the negation of a proposition. To see that this is true let p be the proposition "all men are honest." Now consider the following propositions as possibilities for $\sim p$.

(a)   All men are not honest.
(b)   Not all men are honest.
(c)   Some men are dishonest.
(d)   All men are dishonest.
(e)   It is false that all men are honest.

Which of the propositions (a), (b), (c), (d), and (e) is a negation of the given proposition p? In making our decision we must use the definition of the negation of a proposition, namely, if p is true, then $\sim p$ is false and if p is false, then $\sim p$ is true. Let us now apply this test to propositions (a), (b), (c), (d), and (e), keeping in mind that the statement "All men are honest" means that each and every man is honest.

   Suppose p is true, then obviously (a), (b), (c), (d), and (e) are all false. Next suppose p is false. This means that at least one man is not honest. That is, p can be false without each and every man being dishonest. Thus, if p is false, then propositions (b), (c), and (e) are definitely true. But propositions (a) and (d) are not necessarily true. We therefore conclude that either of the propositions (b), (c), and (e) is the negation of p.

   In a later section the symbol used above to denote negation, namely "$\sim$," will be used to denote that two sets are equivalent but this double usage will not cause any confusion. Also, negation is sometimes denoted by the symbol "/," called a *slash*. For example, to negate the statement "$3 = 5$" we would write "$3 \neq 5$."

It often happens that instead of making an outright assertion one feels that it is necessary or at least desirable to qualify his statement by inserting a condition. Most everyone has made, or heard, or read such statements as "If I go to Nashville tomorrow, I will go by plane"; "If $x = y$, then $x^2 = y^2$"; "If the diagonals of a parallelogram are equal, then it is a rectangle." Each of these statements is a compound proposition formed from two simple propositions by use of the connective "if-then," called the *conditional connective*.

Suppose p and q are propositions. The compound proposition "if p then q," denoted symbolically as "$p \rightarrow q$," is called an *implication*. The truth values of the implication are defined in the truth table of Fig. 1.5.

Implication

p	q	$p \rightarrow q$
T	T	T
T	F	F
F	T	T
F	F	T

FIGURE 1.5

The alert student, upon careful examination of Fig. 1.5, may question the last two entries in the third column. The first two entries in the third column are intuitively obvious. That is, if p and q are both true, then $p \rightarrow q$ is obviously true. Likewise, if p is true and q is false it is equally obvious that $p \rightarrow q$ is false. But what about the cases where p is false? On first thought, one might be inclined to leave these cases undefined. However, to do so would violate our basic principle that a proposition is true or it is false. So, quite arbitrarily, the implication $p \rightarrow q$ is defined as true whenever p is false regardless of the truth value of q. This is a definition and we accept it as such.

It should be observed that the order in which p and q occur in the implication is important. That is, the implication "$p \rightarrow q$" does not have the same meaning as the implication "$q \rightarrow p$." A more precise way of saying this is made possible with the following definition.

Definition 1.3. *Two compound propositions are said to be logically equivalent if they have the same truth values in every possible case.*

A comparison of the truth tables given in Fig. 1.5 and 1.6 shows that the third columns are not identical. Hence, according to Definition 1.3, the implications "$p \rightarrow q$" and "$q \rightarrow p$" are not logically equivalent.

Implication

q	p	$q \rightarrow p$
T	T	T
F	T	T
T	F	F
F	F	T

FIGURE 1.6

Associated with each implication, "$p \rightarrow q$" are three other implications defined as follows.

Definition 1.4. *The implication "$q \rightarrow p$" is called the* converse *of the implication "$p \rightarrow q$."*

Definition 1.5. *The implication "$\sim q \rightarrow \sim p$" is called the* contrapositive *of the implication "$p \rightarrow q$."*

Definition 1.6. *The implication "$\sim p \rightarrow \sim q$" is called the* inverse *of the implication "$p \rightarrow q$."*

> **Example.** *Implication:* If a parallelogram is a square, then it is a rectangle.
> *Converse:* If a parallelogram is a rectangle, then it is a square.
> *Contrapositive:* If a parallelogram is not a rectangle, then it is not a square.
> *Inverse:* If a parallelogram is not a square, then it is not a rectangle.

It can be shown by comparing truth tables that any implication and its contrapositive are logically equivalent.

EXERCISES

1. Assume the following statements are compound propositions. Find their simple components. Denoting one component as p and the other as q, express each compound proposition in symbolic form.
   a. Jack is late and I am going to town.
   b. Mathematics is difficult or English is easy.
   c. Bill is a senior and Mary is smart.
   d. If John is studious he will pass his French course.
   e. If Tom is not rich, then Jane will not marry Tom.
   f. Smith is dull and Jones is not happy.
2. Write the following propositions in symbolic form, letting p be "Frank is tall" and q be "Joan is tall."
   a. Frank is tall and Joan is short.
   b. Joan is tall and Frank is short.
   c. Frank and Joan are both short.

     d. Frank is tall or Joan is short.

     e. Neither Frank nor Joan is tall.

     f. It is not true that Frank and Joan are both short.

3. Assume that Frank and Joan are both tall. Determine which of the compound propositions in Exercise 2 are true.

4. Let p be "the triangle ABC is isosceles" and let q be "the angle C is a right angle." Write in words a translation for each of the following.

     a. $p \wedge q$.   **f.** $p \leftrightarrow q$.

     b. $p \wedge \sim q$.   **g.** $\sim(p \wedge q)$.

     c. $\sim p \wedge \sim q$.   **h.** $\sim(p \vee q)$.

     d. $\sim p \vee q$.   **i.** $\sim p \rightarrow q$.

     e. $p \rightarrow q$.   **j.** $\sim(\sim p \vee \sim q)$.

5. Form the conjunction, disjunction, and two implications for each pair of propositions.

     a. History is difficult. Math is uninteresting.

     b. 7 is a prime. $3 + 2 = 5$.

     c. 7 is a prime. $3 + 2 = 6$.

     d. 7 is not a prime. $3 + 2 = 5$.

     e. 7 is not a prime. $3 + 2 = 6$.

6. Discuss the truth values of the implications called for in Exercise 5.

7. Form the negation of the following propositions.

     a. The diagonals of any rectangle are perpendicular.

     b. $3 + 2 = 6$.

     c. It is false that the lines are parallel.

     d. Some men are rich.

     e. All blondes are beautiful.

     f. All triangles are not isosceles.

     g. Not all triangles are isosceles.

8. Write the converse, the contrapositive, and the inverse of the following implications.

     a. If two triangles are congruent, then they are similar.

     b. If $a = b$, then $a^2 = b^2$.

     c. If two triangles are congruent, then the corresponding angles are equal.

     d. If a triangle is equilateral, then the angles are all equal.

     e. If the diagonals of a parallelogram are equal, then it is a rectangle.

9. By comparing truth tables show that any implication and its contrapositive are logically equivalent.

10. By using truth tables show that the converse and the inverse of any implication are logically equivalent.

11. By using truth tables verify that the following table is correct.

	Given Proposition	Negation
Conjunction	$p \wedge q$	$(\sim p) \vee (\sim q)$
Disjunction	$p \vee q$	$(\sim p) \wedge (\sim q)$
Implication	$p \rightarrow q$	$p \wedge (\sim q)$

12. By referring to the table in Exercise 11, form the negation of the following compound propositions.

     a. John is sick and Harry is hungry.

     b. Alice or Mary will be here on time.

     c. If 7 is a prime, then $2 + 3 = 6$.

     d. Only if $x = 3$, then $x + 5 = 7$.

     e. The polygon is a square or it is not a rectangle.

13. Suppose p, q, and r are three simple propositions. Complete the truth table shown below.

p	q	r	$p \wedge r$	$q \wedge r$	$p \vee r$	$q \vee r$	$p \wedge (q \wedge r)$	$p \wedge (q \vee r)$	$p \vee (q \wedge r)$
T	T	T							
T	T	F							
T	F	T							
T	F	F							
F	T	T							
F	T	F							
F	F	T							
F	F	F							

14. Construct truth tables for the following compound propositions.

    a. $p \to (q \vee r)$.   **b.** $(p \vee \sim q) \wedge r$.

15. The truth table for a proposition formed from two simple propositions has four rows, and the truth table for a proposition formed from three simple propositions has eight rows. How many rows would the truth table for a proposition formed from four simple propositions have? For n?

4   EQUIVALENCES AND RELATED PROPOSITIONS

The fifth and last connective which we shall discuss here is the one consisting of the words "if and only if." Given any two propositions p and q, the compound proposition "p if and only if q" and denoted symbolically as "$p \leftrightarrow q$" is called the *equivalence* of p and q. This proposition is true when and only when p and q are both true or both false. In fact, the proposition "$p \leftrightarrow q$" is the conjunction of the two propositions "$p \to q$" and "$q \to p$," that is, the conjunction of an implication and its converse. The truth values of the "equivalence" are defined in the truth table shown in Fig. 1.7.

Equivalence

p	q	$p \leftrightarrow q$
T	T	T
T	F	F
F	T	F
F	F	T

FIGURE 1.7

In mathematics the implication "$p \to q$" is called a *theorem*. If $p \to q$ we say that "p is a sufficient condition for q" and that "q is a necessary condition for p." In the equivalence "$p \leftrightarrow q$" we say that "p is both a necessary and sufficient condition for q." It should be observed here that an equivalence is indeed the combination of two theorems into one, and that to prove a theorem which is an equivalence one has to prove each of the two theorems from which it was formed. For example, suppose a and b are numbers and we have the theorem "$a^2 = b^2$ if and only if $a = b$ or $a = -b$." This theorem is equivalent to the two theorems

A.   "If $a^2 = b^2$, then $a = b$ or $a = -b$"

and

B.   "If $a = b$ or $a = -b$, then $a^2 = b^2$."

To prove the original theorem one must prove both Theorem A and Theorem B. It should be noted that Theorem B is the converse of Theorem A and vice versa.

In the remainder of the text we shall encounter many theorems of the form "$p \leftrightarrow q$." It is therefore most important that you recognize the form and also the general procedure used in the proof of such a theorem. This general procedure consists of two steps and can be summarized briefly as follows.

To prove: p if and only if q.

Proof: Step 1.   Assume p is true. Prove q is true.

Step 2.   Assume q is true. Prove p is true.

We shall end this section by listing without verification the following two sets of equivalent propositions.

Proposition	*Equivalent Propositions*
If p, then q	p is a sufficient condition for q q is a necessary condition for p If not q, then not p Only if q, then p
p if and only if q	p is a necessary and sufficient condition for q q if and only if p q is a necessary and sufficient condition for p

EXERCISES

1.   Use truth tables to show that the propositions "$p \leftrightarrow q$" and "$(p \rightarrow q) \wedge (q \rightarrow p)$" are logically equivalent.
2.   Show that $p \leftrightarrow q$ and $q \leftrightarrow p$ are logically equivalent.
3.   Use truth tables to show that the negation of $p \leftrightarrow q$ is $p \leftrightarrow (\sim q)$ or $(\sim p) \leftrightarrow q$.
4.   Form the negation of the following propositions.
     a.   A parallelogram is a rectangle if and only if its diagonals are equal.
     b.   A necessary and sufficient condition that a parallelogram be a rectangle is that a vertex angle be a right angle.
     c.   A necessary and sufficient condition that $x^2 - 3x = 0$ is that $x = 0$ or $x = 3$.

d. A necessary condition that x^2 be greater than 4 is that x be greater than 2.

e. A sufficient condition that an integer be an even integer is that it be a multiple of 4.

5. A husband said to his wife, "I will buy you a new car only if I get a raise." He got the raise but did not buy his wife the car. Was she logically justified in thinking her husband had lied to her?

6. A notice sent to all members of a sandlot softball team had printed on it: "The softball game on Friday will not be played only if the weather is not fair."

    a. State in other words precisely what this statement says and only what it says.

    b. It was fair Friday. Should there have been a game?

    c. There was a game. What was the weather like?

7. By appropriately identifying p and q with the simple propositions from which the compound propositions is formed write each of the following compound propositions in the form $p \rightarrow q$ or $p \leftrightarrow q$, whichever applies.

    a. $7x + 3 = 10$ only if $x = 1$.

    b. A sufficient condition that $x^2 = 9$ is that $x = 3$.

    c. A necessary condition that a triangle be a right triangle is that no angle be greater than 90°.

    d. A polygon is a parallelogram if and only if a pair of opposite sides are both parallel and equal.

    e. A necessary and sufficient condition that a triangle be equiangular is that it be equilateral.

8. Smith and Brown are running for Mayor. Let p be "Smith is smart," let q be "Brown is stupid," and let r be "Smith will win the election." For each of the following propositions find a symbolic form, and then construct a truth table.

    a. If Smith is smart and Brown is stupid, Smith will win the election.

    b. Smith will win the election if and only if either he is smart or Brown is stupid.

5 SETS, ELEMENTS, AND MEMBERSHIP

Few words in the English language are more common than the word *set* as it applies to a collection of *things*. In an attempt to be as general and as inclusive as possible, we shall use the word *element* to mean the most general notion associated with such words as *things*, *entities*, *objects*, and the like. That is, an element may be any definite distinct object of our perception or of our thought. For example, an element could be a book, a house, a number, a theorem in geometry, a mathematical symbol, a word, a paragraph, a thought, a sound, a color, or a day of the week.

In general, we shall think of a *set* as any collection of elements, and we shall always think of elements as members of sets. The elements in the collection which form a particular set are said to *belong* to that set, or to be *members* of that set. An element which belongs to a set is said to be *contained* in the set. For example, consider the set consisting of the vowels in the alphabet. The elements are a, e, i, o, and u. The letter a is a member of this set, or it belongs to this set. The set called the set of vowels contains the letters *a, e, i, o, u.*

As has been suggested above, the notion of a set, or of belonging to a set, is common knowledge gained from experience. It is not at all uncommon in our daily conversation to use or hear such phrases as *a set of books, a set of dishes, a set of tools, a set of boys,* and so forth. In fact, almost everyone is interested in some kind of set. The 2-year-old child is interested in his set of toys. The history student may be interested in a particular set of events or in a set of historical dates. The teacher of elementary arithmetic is concerned with the set of counting numbers. The student of mathematics is interested in many different sets—the set of real numbers, a set of points, a set of axioms, a set of formulas, a set of operations, to name just a few. However, to be useful in mathematics, it is necessary that a set be well defined. That is, we must be able to say of a given set and a given element that the element does belong to the set or that it does not belong to the set. This implies that a set is determined by some rule or property which completely characterizes the set. For example, the set consisting of the capitals of the 50 states in the United States is a well-defined set because it is possible to say of any element that it does or does not belong to the set. Nashville is a member of the set; Knoxville is not a member of the set. On the other hand, the set consisting of the five happiest persons in Tennessee is not well defined, because it is impossible to say exactly who belongs to this set. Thus, in constructing a well-defined set, it is necessary to describe its elements so precisely that there is no question about what elements the set contains. Methods of doing this will be discussed in the following section.

6 METHODS OF CONSTRUCTING SETS

In our daily life we find it convenient, if not absolutely necessary, to give names to everything around us—people, food, our possessions, our emotions, and things in general. This obviously makes it much easier for us to identify, describe, or single out any object or concept under consideration in a conversation, discussion, or discourse. Hence it seems natural, when discussing sets, to give particular sets names and then to refer to them by name. It is more or less conventional to use capital letters as names of sets and small letters as names of elements. This convention will be followed here except in special cases where other names are self-explanatory and more appropriate. We shall also use braces, { }, to denote sets, and the symbols within the braces either will be a list of the names of the elements of the set or will describe the properties of the elements of the set. The symbol $\in$ will be used to indicate that an element belongs to a particular set. For example, if S is a set and a is an element, we write $a \in S$, which is read "a belongs to S" or "a is a member of S." If we wish to indicate that an element d does not belong to a set S, we write $d \notin S$, which is read "d does not belong to S" or "d is not a member of S." Note that the slash used in the last symbol is in keeping with the familiar use of the slash to denote unequal quantities, as when we write $a \neq b$ (read "a is not equal to b"). In general, when it is used "over" other symbols, we shall interpret the slash as a denial. Other uses of the slash will be indicated later.

As mentioned above, for a set to be useful in mathematics it must be described so clearly that everyone interested in the set will know exactly what elements it contains. What method or methods may one use to describe a set precisely? One obvious way is, where possible, to list the names of all the elements in the set. For example, let A be the set consisting of the names of three persons: George Washington, Abraham Lincoln, and Woodrow Wilson. We write this in abbreviated form:

$A = \{\text{George Washington, Abraham Lincoln, Woodrow Wilson}\}.$

Some other examples are:

$B = \{\text{Knoxville, Nashville, Chattanooga, Memphis}\},$
$C = \{\text{Tom, Dick, Harry}\},$
$H = \{a, b, c, d, e\},$
$J = \{\text{boy, dog, gun}\},$
$K = \{1, 2, 3, 4, \cdots, 99\}.$

This method is feasible only if the number of elements in the set to be defined is relatively small; it is impossible if the number of elements is infinite. Notice that in defining set K we used a shortcut, namely three dots. These three dots indicate that we are to include in set K all the counting numbers from 1 to 99 inclusive. Another method of defining the set K is given by the following notation:

$K = \{x \mid x \text{ is a counting number less than } 100\},$

which is read "K is the set consisting of all the elements x such that x is a counting number less than 100." Note the interpretation of the vertical line, which is read "such that." Another very important point to be emphasized regarding the latter method of defining the set K is the meaning of the letter x. Here the letter x is used not as the name of a particular element of the set but to represent an arbitrary element of the set; it is called a variable.

Definition 1.7. *A letter used to represent an arbitrary element of a set (containing more than one element) is called a* variable. *If a set contains only a single element, the letter used to represent this element is called a* constant.

Consider each of the following sets.

1. $R = \{c \mid c \text{ is an even counting number less than 4}\}$ is read "R is the set consisting of all the elements c such that c is a counting number less than 4." Since there is only one even counting number less than 4, namely 2, then

set R contains only one element. It follows from Definition 1.7 that c is a constant. It would be correct to write $c = 2$.

2. $T = \{x \mid x$ is the name of a state in the United States$\}$ is read "T is the set consisting of all the elements x such that x is the name of a state in the United States." In this case the set T contains 50 elements; that is, the variable x has 50 different possible values. One such value is $x =$ Tennessee.

3. $N = \{n \mid n$ is a counting number$\}$ is read "N is the set consisting of all the elements n such that n is a counting number." Another method that is often used for describing this set is $N = \{1, 2, 3, 4, 5, \cdots\}$. The three dots in this case are placed last in the braces and may be read "and so on without end." This is interpreted to mean that if the counting numbers are arranged in natural order, there is no last, or largest, such number. We say that the set N contains infinitely many elements, or more briefly, N is an infinite set.

4. $S = \{p \mid p$ is a point on a line segment 1 inch long$\}$ is read "S is the set consisting of all the elements p such that p is a point on a line segment 1 inch long." This is another example of an infinite set.

Definition 1.8. *A set of elements is said to be finite if there exists a fixed counting number, denoted by M, such that the number of elements in the set is M. A set that is not finite is said to be infinite.*

Sets A, B, C, H, J, and K defined above are finite sets. Set A contains 3 elements, hence in this case $M = 3$. For set B, $M = 4$; for set C, $M = 3$; for set H, $M = 5$; for set J, $M = 3$; for set K, $M = 99$. Likewise, sets R and T are finite, while N and S are infinite.

7 THE UNIVERSAL SET AND THE EMPTY SET

Consider the following sets $A = \{x \mid x$ is a student in the University of Tennessee$\}$, $B = \{x \mid x$ is a freshman in the University of Tennessee$\}$, $C = \{x \mid x$ is a student enrolled in Mathematics at the University of Tennessee$\}$, and $D = \{x \mid x$ is an Engineering student in the University of Tennessee$\}$. Here set A is a type of overall set which contains all the elements with which one might be concerned in any discussion involving one or more of the sets B, C, and D. Such a fixed overall set as A, when used in a particular discussion, is called a universal set for that discussion.

Definition 1.9. *In discussing particular sets, we may assume or have specified some fixed overall set of elements to which all elements under consideration must belong. Such a fixed set is called the universal set for that discussion. A universal set is always denoted by the capital letter U.*

It should be emphasized here that the universal set for a particular discussion is usually determined by the nature of the discussion and the elements involved. In a particular case one may choose the universal set to suit his purpose or convenience. The basic use of the universal set is one of restriction; that is, it is designed to keep a discussion within the desired bounds. This is especially true in the case of mathematical discussion. For example, if $B = \{x \mid x$ is a counting number less than 20$\}$ is being considered by a class in fourth-grade arithmetic, the universal set would most probably be the set of all counting numbers. However, for a class of college freshmen the universal set might be the set of all real numbers.

We have already had an example of a set that contains only one element. Is it possible to have a set that has no elements? Consider the set consisting of all the counting numbers less than 5, each of which is exactly divisible by 7. Since the counting numbers less than 5 are the numbers 1, 2, 3, 4 and none of these is exactly divisible by 7, our set contains no elements. It is an empty set. If such a set at first seems a bit artificial, suffice it to say that for purposes of complete generality it is convenient and desirable to define the empty set and to include it in our general discussion of sets. The empty set is also called the *null* set. In a certain sense the empty set plays a role somewhat analogous to that played by the number zero in the real number system.

Definition 1.10.   *By the* empty *or* null *set, denoted by the symbol $\emptyset$, is meant any set that contains no elements. The null set is sometimes denoted by empty braces thus:* { }.

   Example.   The set of all the students in your class who are over 10 feet tall is an empty set.

To indicate that a set A is not an empty set we would write $A \neq \emptyset$.

EXERCISES

1.   Label each of the following sets as being finite, infinite, or a null set. For the sets in **(a), (b),** and **(c),** find the number of elements M in each.
   a.   The set consisting of all the letters in the English alphabet.
   b.   The set consisting of all the senators in the United States Congress.
   c.   The set consisting of all the even counting numbers less than 20.
   d.   The set of men now living who fought in the War of 1812.
   e.   The set consisting of all the people now living in the world. Is this set well defined?
   f.   The set of stars in the Milky Way.
   g.   The set of all the even counting numbers less than 20 each of which is exactly divisible by 7.
   h.   The set of all the counting numbers each of which is exactly divisible by 1379.
2.   Give an example, not given in the text, of each of the following kinds of sets.
   a.   A finite set.
   b.   An infinite set.
   c.   An empty set.
   d.   A set that is not well defined.

3. For each of the following sets write the set in set notation using braces and within the braces list the elements of the set.
   a. The set consisting of the names of all the states in the United States whose names begin with M.
   b. The set of all counting numbers which lie between 2 and 11.
   c. The set of all counting numbers less than 50, each of which is the square of a counting number.
   d. The set of all counting numbers less than 10, each of which is the square root of a counting number.
   e. The set consisting of the first name of each member of your immediate family.
   f. The set consisting of the names of the states bordering Tennessee.
4. Describe in words each of the following sets.
   a. $A = \{$Alabama, Alaska, Arizona, Arkansas$\}$.
   b. $B = \{1, 2, 3, \cdots, 30\}$.
   c. $C = \{x \mid x + 3 = 5\}$.
   d. $D = \{2, 4, 6, 8, 10, \cdots\}$.
   e. $E = \{y \mid y$ is an even counting number less than 20$\}$.
   f. $F = \{y \in E \mid y$ is exactly divisible by 3$\}$.
   g. $G = \{x \mid x$ is the name of a baseball team which belongs to the American League$\}$.
5. The sets mentioned below are defined in Exercise 4 above. Label each of the following statements as T (true) or F (false).
   a. $17 \in B$.
   b. $1478 \in D$.
   c. $20 \in E$.
   d. Argentina $\notin A$.
   e. $2 \in C$.
   f. Atlanta Braves $\in G$.
   g. $15 \in F$.
   h. New York Yankees $\notin G$.
6. For each of the following sets give a possible universal set that could be useful in a discussion involving the elements of the set.
   a. $L = \{x \mid x$ is a city in Texas with population over 100,000$\}$.
   b. $M = \{x \mid x$ is a vowel in the English alphabet$\}$.
   c. $P = \{y \mid y$ is a woman over forty years of age$\}$.
   d. $Q = \{x \mid x$ is a teacher of mathematics$\}$.
   e. $R = \{x \mid x$ is a college freshman$\}$.

8 SUBSETS

Consider the two sets $A = \{1, 2, 3\}$ and $B = \{1, 2, 3, 4, 5\}$. Every element of A is also an element of B, but there are elements of B that do not belong to A. We say that A is a *proper subset* of B.

Definition 1.11. *A set A is said to be a* proper subset *of a set B when every element of A is also an element of B and there is at least one element of B that does not belong to A. This relation is denoted by the special symbol $A \subset B$, which is read "A is a proper subset of B."*

It may happen that set A and set B are identical—that is, that every element of A belongs to B and every element of B belongs to A; in this case we say that set A is equal to set B.

Definition 1.12.   *Two sets, A and B, are said to be* equal *if, and only if, they have exactly the same members. We indicate this relation by writing A = B.*

The set A is said to be a *subset* of B if either $A \subset B$ or $A = B$. We usually combine these two symbols into the single symbol $A \subseteq B$, and read "A is a subset of B." This relation is convenient when we do not have enough information to be more specific. For example, suppose that A is the set consisting of all the boys in your math class and B is the set consisting of all the students in your math class: without further information, one is certainly correct in writing $A \subseteq B$. Let us now write this definition in symbolic notation.

Definition 1.13.   *A is a* subset *of B if, and only if, for every element a such that $a \in A$ it is also true that $a \in B$. We indicate this relation by writing $A \subseteq B$. Note that Definition 1.5 can now be restated in the simple form: if $A \subseteq B$ and $B \subseteq A$, then $A = B$.*

The empty set, or null set, is considered to be a subset of every set. Similarly, every set is a subset of itself; that is, $A \subseteq A$.

From the set $A = \{1, 2, 3\}$ let us form all the possible subsets. First, there is the empty set, $\{\ \ \}$. Next, the subsets with only one element are $\{1\}$, $\{2\}$, $\{3\}$. Next, the subsets with two elements are $\{1, 2\}$, $\{1, 3\}$, $\{2, 3\}$. Then, last, we have the set itself, $\{1, 2, 3\}$. A quick count shows that $A = \{1, 2, 3\}$ has exactly 2^3, or 8, subsets. It can be shown that for every set of n elements there are exactly 2^n subsets.

Next consider the two sets $A = \{a, c, e, g\}$ and $B = \{a, b, e, f, h\}$. Some elements of A also belong to B, but there are elements of A not contained in B. There are also elements in B which do not belong to A. We say that the sets A and B are *overlapping*.

Definition 1.14.   *Any two sets are said to be* overlapping *if, and only if, they have at least one element in common but neither is a subset of the other.*

Another possible relation between two sets is that they have no elements in common: $A = \{$Chicago, Cleveland, Dallas$\}$ and $B = \{$Alabama, Georgia, Tennessee$\}$ are two such sets, and they are said to be *disjoint*.

Definition 1.15.   *Two sets are said to be* disjoint *if and only if* (a) *both are nonempty and* (b) *they have no elements in common.*

In the above remarks we have noted that two sets may be related in any one of four principal ways. In fact, any two sets must be related in one and only one of the four ways: (a) the two sets are equal, (b) one set is a proper subset of the other, (c) the two sets overlap, (d) the two sets are disjoint.

9 VENN DIAGRAMS

In studying sets and subsets it is often helpful to have a pictorial representation of them. A very convenient one is a diagram called a Venn Diagram after the English logician John Venn (1834–1883). A Venn diagram uses regions bounded by suitable closed curves, usually circles, to graphically represent sets. The usual procedure is to draw a rectangle and to let the region inside the rectangle represent the universal set U and then to draw circular regions inside the rectangle to represent each subset of U under consideration. For example, suppose Professor Smith has one chemistry class of about 100 students; some have blue eyes, some have brown eyes and some have eyes that are neither blue nor brown. Suppose further we are discussing the students of this class who have blue eyes and those who have brown eyes. For purposes of our discussion we could define the following three sets

$U = \{x \mid x$ is a student in Professor Smith's chemistry class$\}$,
$A = \{x \in U \mid x$ has blue eyes$\}$,
$B = \{y \in U \mid y$ has brown eyes$\}$.

It is obvious that $A \subset U$, $B \subset U$, and sets A and B are disjoint. The relationships among the sets U, A, and B can be made readily apparent and emphasized by means of the Venn diagram shown in Fig. 1.8.

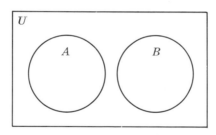

FIGURE 1.8

Observe that in the Venn diagram of Fig. 1.8, the name of each subset is placed inside the region representing that subset. Also, since A and B are disjoint the regions representing them must not overlap. In fact, one of the important features of any Venn diagram representing a universal set and its subsets is that the diagram shows at a glance which subsets are disjoint, which are overlapping, and which are proper subsets of others. As a further illustration, consider Fig. 1.9 which shows the Venn diagram of the following universal set and subsets.

$U = \{x \mid x$ is a student in the University of Tennessee$\}$,
$A = \{x \in U \mid x$ is a freshman$\}$,

$B = \{x \in U \mid x \text{ is enrolled in Mathematics}\},$
$C = \{x \in U \mid x \text{ is studying Engineering}\},$
$D = \{x \in U \mid x \text{ is a senior Law student}\},$
$E = \{x \in D \mid x \text{ is a girl}\}.$

The Venn diagram in Fig. 1.9 emphasizes at a glance the following facts regarding students at the University of Tennessee: (a) some freshmen, but not all, are enrolled in mathematics; (b) some freshmen, but not all, are studying engineering; (c) some engineering students who are not freshmen are enrolled in mathematics; (d) some students are enrolled in mathematics who are neither freshmen nor studying engineering; (e) some freshmen are enrolled in mathematics and are studying engineering (see shaded region); (f) no senior law student is a freshman, is enrolled in mathematics, or is studying engineering; (g) $E \subset D$.

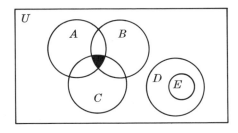

FIGURE 1.9

Venn diagrams have their greatest value as an aid in the discussion of sets, like those represented in Fig. 1.9, where the number of elements in-involved is too large for a listing to be practical or sets where such a listing would be impossible. In such a case it is convenient, but not necessary, to think of the "points" which make up the region representing a set as the elements of the set. It should be emphasized, however, that no significance is to be attached to the relative sizes of the regions used to represent subsets of a given universal set. In fact, it must be clearly understood that Venn diagrams are strictly schematic representations and nothing more.

10 EQUIVALENT SETS

Consider the sets $A = \{1, 2, 3\}$ and $B = \{a, b, c\}$. Obviously, the only property that these sets have in common is that they have the same number of elements, namely 3. Since A and B are disjoint, they are not equal in the sense of our definition of the equality of two sets; that is, they are not identical. We often use the word *equivalence* to indicate the sense of "equal in some respects" but not identical. So we say the sets A and B are equivalent.

Before we make a precise definition of equivalent sets, let us consider another example. Let S be the set of students in Professor Smith's chemistry class and let T be the set of chairs in his classroom. At the first meeting of the class, Professor Smith does not need to count either students or chairs to decide whether or not he has the same number of students as chairs. He simply asks the students to be seated. If every chair is occupied and no student is left standing, his conclusion is that the number of students is the same as the number of chairs. The mental process used in arriving at this conclusion was one of pairing students and chairs. In mathematical language we say that a correspondence has been set up between students and chairs. To each student there corresponds one and only one chair, namely the chair occupied by the student. Conversely, to each chair there corresponds one and only one student, namely the student occupying the chair. This type of pairing is called *one-to-one correspondence*.

Definition 1.16.   *Two sets A and B are said to be in* one-to-one correspondence *when it is possible to find a pairing of the elements of A and B such that each element of A corresponds to one and only one element of B and each element of B corresponds to one and only one element of A.*

We are now ready to define equivalent sets.

Definition 1.17.   *Two sets A and B are said to be* equivalent *when the elements of A and the elements of B can be placed in one-to-one correspondence. We denote this relation by the symbol $A \sim B$, read "A is equivalent to B."*

In the example given above, if Professor Smith finds that he has exactly the same number of students as chairs, then $S \sim T$.

It should be pointed out that the common property of two or more equivalent sets is that they each contain the same number of elements. That is, two finite sets A and B are equivalent if the number of elements in A is the same as the number of elements in B. Hence if $A = B$, then $A \sim B$. However, the converse is not necessarily true. A may be equivalent to B when A is not equal to B. For example, the sets $A = \{1, 2, 3\}$ and $B = \{a, b, c\}$ are equivalent but not equal.

A very important aspect of our definition of equivalent sets is that it gives us a means of comparing the number of elements in each of two sets when each set contains infinitely many elements. As a matter of fact, when we say that one infinite set has the same number of elements as a second infinite set we simply mean that the two sets are equivalent.

Example.   Let $N = \{1, 2, 3, \cdots\}$ and $E = \{2, 4, 6, \cdots\}$. It is easy to show that $N \sim E$. We need to show that the elements of N and E can be placed in one-to-one correspondence. To do this, let x represent an arbitrary element of N. Then certainly there is an element $y \in E$ such that $y = 2x$. Now, if we pair with each

$x \in N$ the number $2x \in E$, then to each element of N there corresponds one and only one element of E and to each element of E there corresponds one and only one element of N. Thus, by definition the elements of N and E have been placed in one-to-one correspondence. Hence, $N \sim E$. We often indicate this particular equivalence by saying that there are as many even counting numbers as there are counting numbers. The pairing of the elements of N with the elements of E described above can be exhibited as follows:

$$
\begin{array}{ccccccc}
1 & 2 & 3 & 4 & \cdot\ \cdot\ \cdot & x & \cdot\ \cdot\ \cdot \\
\updownarrow & \updownarrow & \updownarrow & \updownarrow & & \updownarrow & \\
2 & 4 & 6 & 8 & \cdot\ \cdot\ \cdot & 2x & \cdot\ \cdot\ \cdot
\end{array}
$$

Example. Let us prove that a line segment one-half inch long has the same number of points as a line segment one inch long.

Proof: First we construct the two segments, one above the other as shown in Fig. 1.10. Denote the endpoints of the one-inch segment by A

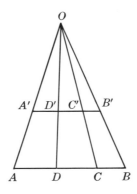

FIGURE 1.10

and B and the endpoints of the one-half inch segment by A' and B'. Now let S be the set consisting of points A and B and all points between them on segment AB, and let T be the set consisting of points A' and B' and all points between them on segment $A'B'$. The two segments have the same number of points if $S \sim T$. To show this is true draw lines AA' and BB' and let O be their point of intersection. The elements of S and T can be put into a one-to-one correspondence in the following manner: Let C be an arbitrary point of set S. Pair with each such point C of set S the point C' of set T which is obtained as the point of intersection of lines OC and $A'B'$. Similarly, pair with each point D' of set T the point of intersection of lines OD' and AB which we denote by D. Thus to each point C of set S there corresponds, by this procedure, one and only one point of set T, namely C' and conversely to each point D' of T there corresponds one and only one point of set S, namely D. Thus a one-to-one correspondence has been established between the elements of the sets S and T and hence $S \sim T$. That is to say there are as many points in T as in S.

If the sets A and B are equivalent, it follows from the definition of equivalent sets that each of the following statements is true.

1. $A \sim A$; each set is equivalent to itself.
2. If $A \sim B$, then $B \sim A$.
3. If $A \sim B$ and $B \sim C$, then $A \sim C$.

These three relations may be stated in words: the property of equivalence of sets is reflexive, symmetric, and transitive.

11* COUNTABLE SETS

In one of the examples of Section 10 it was shown that the set $N = \{1, 2, 3, 4, \cdots\}$ and the set $E = \{2, 4, 5, 8, \cdots\}$ are equivalent. That is, it was shown that the elements of set N can be put into a one-to-one correspondence with the elements of set E. The set E is obviously a proper subset of N. Here we have the surprising result of the elements of a set being put into a one-to-one correspondence with the elements of a proper subset of itself. This is not a rare case. In fact, every infinite set can be put into one-to-one correspondence with *some* proper subset of itself. This is one of the characteristic properties of an infinite set and is often used in defining such a set.

It is easy to see how such sets as $K = \{51, 52, 53, 54, \cdots\}$, $L = \{1000, 2000, 3000, 4000, \cdots\}$ and $M = \{7, 14, 21, 28, \cdots\}$ can be put into a one-to-one correspondence with the set N of counting numbers. For example the correspondence between N and K could be shown as follows:

$$1 \leftrightarrow 51, \quad 2 \leftrightarrow 52, \quad 3 \leftrightarrow 53, \quad 4 \leftrightarrow 54, \quad \cdots, \quad n \leftrightarrow n + 50, \quad \cdots.$$

For the correspondence between N and M we could use $1 \leftrightarrow 7$, $2 \leftrightarrow 14$, $3 \leftrightarrow 21$, $4 \leftrightarrow 28$, $\cdots$, $n \leftrightarrow 7n$, $\cdots$. Each of the sets K, L, and M is a proper subset of N. Let us now consider the set

$$P = \{-5, -4, -3, -2, -1, 0, 1, 2, 3, 4, \cdots\}.$$

In this case $N \subset P$ and $N \sim P$. To show this equivalence between N and P, we could pair the elements thus: $1 \leftrightarrow -5$, $2 \leftrightarrow -4$, $3 \leftrightarrow -3$, $4 \leftrightarrow -2$, $\cdots$, $n \leftrightarrow n - 6$, $\cdots$. Note here that the relation $n \leftrightarrow n - 6$ serves as a formula for the correspondence which may be used to determine quickly the number in P that is paired with a specific number in N or vice versa. For example, $735 \in N$, the number in P that is paired with 735 is $735 - 6$, or 729.

As a slightly more complicated case let us show that the set

$$I = \{\cdots, -4, -3, -1, 0, 1, 2, 3, 4, \cdots\}$$

can be put into a one-to-one correspondence with set N. One method is the following.

$$
\begin{array}{cccccccccccccc}
1 & 2 & 3 & 4 & 5 & 6 & 7 & 8 & 9 & 10 & 11, & \cdots, & 2K, & 2K+1, & \cdots \\
\updownarrow & \updownarrow & \updownarrow & \updownarrow & \updownarrow & \updownarrow & \updownarrow & \updownarrow & \updownarrow & \updownarrow & \updownarrow & & \updownarrow & \updownarrow & \\
0 & -1 & 1 & -2 & 2 & -3 & 3 & -4 & 4 & -5 & 5, & \cdots, & -K, & K, & \cdots
\end{array}
$$

In this case we really need two formulas to express the correspondence between the elements of N and I. If $n \in N$ and $n = 2K$ where K is a counting number, then $-K \in I$ and $2K \leftrightarrow -K$, but if $n \in N$ and $n = 2K + 1$, where K is either zero or a counting number, then $K \in I$ and $2K + 1 \leftrightarrow K$. It should be noted that since n is a counting number, to say that $n = 2K$ simply means that n is an even counting number. To say that $n = 2K + 1$ means that n is an odd counting number and that $n = 1$ if and only if $K = 0$.

The above discussion suggests that many infinite sets possess this common property, namely that each can be put into a one-one-one correspondence with the set N of counting numbers. Any infinite set having this property is said to be a countably infinite set.

Definition 1.18.   *A set whose elements can be put into a one-to-one correspondence with the elements of the set of counting numbers is called a countably infinite set.*

Definition 1.19.   *A set is said to be countable if* (a) *it is the empty set, or* (b) *it is a finite set, or* (c) *it is a countably infinite set.*

We may ask, are all infinite sets countable? That is, are all infinite sets countably infinite? The answer is no. To justify this answer we shall show that the set S consisting of all the real numbers lying between 0 and 1 is not a countably infinite set. To make our proof we shall need to make use of the fact that every real number between 0 and 1 can be written uniquely as a nonending decimal if we agree to write fractions like 0.5, 0.37, 0.854, etc., as $0.4999 \cdots, 0.369999 \cdots, 0.8539999 \cdots$, etc. We shall use an indirect method of proof. That is, we shall assume that set S is a countably infinite set and show that this assumption leads us to a contradiction. If S is a countably infinite set then its elements can be put into a one-to-one correspondence with the elements of N; and let us suppose that such a correspondence has been set up. Further, let us denote by r_1 the number in S that corresponds to 1, denote by r_2 the number in S that corresponds to 2, denote by r_3 the number in S that corresponds to 3, and so on. Thus $\{r_1, r_2, r_3, \cdots, r_n, \cdots\} \subseteq S$. Next, we express r_1, r_2, r_3, etc., as nonending decimal fractions and denote them as follows.

$$
\begin{aligned}
1 &\leftrightarrow r_1 = 0.a_{11}\, a_{12}\, a_{13}\, a_{14}\, \cdots\, a_{1n}\, \cdots \\
2 &\leftrightarrow r_2 = 0.a_{21}\, a_{22}\, a_{23}\, a_{24}\, \cdots\, a_{2n}\, \cdots \\
3 &\leftrightarrow r_3 = 0.a_{31}\, a_{32}\, a_{33}\, a_{34}\, \cdots\, a_{3n}\, \cdots \\
&\quad \cdots\cdots\cdots\cdots\cdots\cdots\cdots\cdots\cdots \\
&\quad \cdots\cdots\cdots\cdots\cdots\cdots\cdots\cdots\cdots \\
&\quad \cdots\cdots\cdots\cdots\cdots\cdots\cdots\cdots\cdots
\end{aligned}
$$

$$n \leftrightarrow r_n = 0.a_{n1}\, a_{n2}\, a_{n3}\, a_{n4} \cdots a_{nn} \cdots$$
$$\cdots\cdots\cdots\cdots\cdots\cdots\cdots\cdots\cdots\cdots$$
$$\cdots\cdots\cdots\cdots\cdots\cdots\cdots\cdots\cdots\cdots$$
$$\cdots\cdots\cdots\cdots\cdots\cdots\cdots\cdots\cdots\cdots$$

where each symbol of the form a_{ij} represents some one of the digits 0, 1, 2, 3, 4, 5, 6, 7, 8, 9. If our assumption that set S is countable is true, then each number between 0 and 1 must be one of the numbers $r_1, r_2, r_3, \cdots$ listed above. We shall now show that there is a number which lies between 0 and 1 and which does not occur in the above list and hence does not correspond to one of the counting numbers. For example, consider the number $s = 0.b_1b_2b_3 \cdots b_n \cdots$ where each of the symbols $b_1, b_2, b_3,$ and so on represents some one of the digits 0, 1, 2, 3, 4, 5, 6, 7, 8, 9 and is determined as follows. If $a_{11} \neq 1$, then $b_1 = 1$, if $a_{11} = 1$, then $b_1 = 2$; if $a_{22} \neq 1$, then $b_2 = 1$, if $a_{22} = 1$, then $b_2 = 2$; if $a_{33} \neq 1$, then $b_3 = 1$, if $a_{33} = 1$, then $b_3 = 2$; or in general $b_K = 1$ if $a_{KK} \neq 1$, but $b_K = 2$ if $a_{KK} = 1$. Obviously $s \in S$. Also $s \neq r_1$ since $b_1 \neq a_{11}$, $s \neq r_2$, since $b_2 \neq a_{22}$, $s \neq r_3$, since $b_3 \neq a_{33}$, and so on. Therefore s does not correspond to one of the counting numbers and hence the correspondence is not one-to-one, a contradiction of our assumption that set S is countable. We must conclude therefore that not all infinite sets are countable.

EXERCISES

1. Determine which of the following pairs of sets are equal and which are equivalent but not equal.
    a. $A = \{x \mid x$ is a letter in the word "Tennessee"$\}$ and $B = \{y \mid y$ is a letter in the word "nest"$\}$.
    b. $C = \{b, d, t\}$ and $D = \{$boy, dog, toy$\}$.
    c. $E = \{1, 2, 3, \cdots, 30\}$ and $F = \{3, 6, 9, \cdots, 90\}$.
    d. $G = \{x \mid x + 5 = 7\}$ and $H = \{x \mid x + 1 = 3\}$.
    e. $I = \{x \mid x$ is a vowel in the English alphabet$\}$ and $J = \{x \mid x$ is a letter in the word "eight"$\}$.
2. Let the universal set U consist of all people now living in the world. Next let A be the set of all people living in Russia, B the set of all people living in the United States, and C the set of all people living in Tennessee. Draw a Venn diagram representing U, A, B, and C.
3. Write all the subsets of the set $A = \{1, 2, 3, 4\}$. How many subsets of A are there?
4. a. If $S = \{a, b, c, d, e\}$, write four proper subsets of S that are equivalent but not equal.
    b. Write a proper subset of $N = \{1, 2, 3, 4, 5, \cdots\}$ that is equivalent to N.
5. $U = \{$all quadrilaterals$\}$, $R = \{$all rectangles$\}$, $S = \{$all squares$\}$, and $T = \{$all parallelograms$\}$. Draw a Venn diagram representing U, R, S, and T.
6. For the sets of Exercise 5, label each of these statements T (true) or F (false).
    a. $S \subset U$.
    b. $R \subset T$.
    c. $S \subseteq R$.
    d. $T \subseteq U$.
    e. $S \subset T$.
    f. $T \subset R$.
    g. $R \subseteq U$.
    h. $R = T$.
    i. $R = S$.

7. If $N = \{1, 2, 3, 4, 5, \cdots\}$ and $T = \{5, 10, 15, 20, 25, \cdots\}$, show that $N \sim T$. Is the statement $T \subset N$ true or false? One characteristic property of an infinite set is that it have a proper subset equivalent to itself.

8. If $E = \{2, 4, 6, 8, \cdots\}$, find a proper subset of E that is equivalent to E.

9. Construct a Venn diagram to represent the following subsets of the set of all triangles: all right triangles, all isosceles triangles, all equilateral triangles.

10. Suppose that X, Y, and Z are sets such that $X \subset Y$ and $Y \subset Z$. Show that $X \subset Z$.

11. A, B, and C are three sets such that $a \in A$, $b \in B$, $A \subset C$, and $B \subset C$.

   a. By drawing Venn diagrams exhibit as many different possible relations as you can which could exist among the sets A, B, and C, yet still preserve the given relations.
   b. Does $a \in C$?
   c. Does $b \in C$?
   d. Could $a \in B$?
   e. Could there exist an element c such that $c \in C$, $c \notin A$, and $c \notin B$?
   f. Could A, B, and C satisfy the given relations and yet be such that if $c \in C$ then either $c \in A$ or $c \in B$ but not both? If so, give an example of three such sets.

12. List all of the possible ways in which the elements of the two sets $\{a, b, c\}$ and $\{1, 2, 3\}$ can be paired in a one-to-one correspondence.

13. Suggest a method for showing that the semi-circular arc $\overset{\frown}{ACB}$, and the diameter AB, Fig. 1.11, have the same number of points.

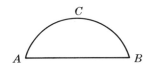

FIGURE 1.11

14. Give examples of the following pairs of sets:
   a. Two sets that are overlapping.
   b. Two sets one of which is a proper subset of the other.
   c. Two sets which are disjoint.
   d. Two sets which are equal.
   e. Two sets which are equivalent but not equal.

15. Prove: If for any three sets A, B, and C, $A = B$ and $B = C$, then $A = C$.

16. Establish a one-to-one correspondence between the sets {Carolyn, Joan, Mary, Ruth} and {Jim, Joe, Bob, Tom}.

17. Show that each of the following sets is countable.
   a. $A = \{7, 14, 21, 28, \cdots\}$. d. $D = \{\cdots, -4, -3, -2, -1, 0, 1, 2, 3\}$.
   b. $B = \{\frac{1}{1}, \frac{1}{2}, \frac{1}{3}, \frac{1}{4}, \cdots\}$. e. $E = \{4, 9, 14, 19, 24, 29, \cdots\}$.
   c. $C = \{\frac{1}{2}, \frac{2}{3}, \frac{3}{4}, \frac{4}{5}, \cdots\}$. f. $F = \{1, \frac{1}{2}, \frac{1}{4}, \frac{1}{8}, \frac{1}{16}, \cdots\}$.

12 SET OPERATIONS

In the previous sections we have seen how two sets may be related. In this section we wish to introduce three operations that may be performed on sets.

These operations may be regarded as set-forming operations, for the result of performing each of these operations is to form a set.

The first of these operations is that of combining into one set all of the elements of two sets. The operation is called the *union* of the two sets.

Definition 1.20.   *The* union *of two sets A and B is the set of all elements belonging to A or B or to both A and B. The operation of union is represented by the symbol $A \cup B$ and is read "A union B" or "A cup B" or "the union of A and B."*

Although union was defined as an operation on two sets, the notion obviously can be extended to any number of sets simply by combining them two at a time. That is, we define

$$A \cup B \cup C = (A \cup B) \cup C,$$

and then define

$$A \cup B \cup C \cup D = (A \cup B \cup C) \cup D, \text{ etc.}$$

The final result in each case is one set.

It is obvious from the definition of the union of two sets that the order in which the sets are considered does not matter. That is,

1. $A \cup B = B \cup A.$
2. $(A \cup B) \cup C = A \cup (B \cup C).$

Property (1) is called *the commutative law for the union of two sets*, and Property (2) is called *the associative law for the union of three sets*.

Example.   Let $G = \{1, 2, 3\}$, $H = \{3, 4, 5\}$, and $K = \{7, 8\}$. Find **(a)** $G \cup H$, **(b)** $H \cup K$, and **(c)** $G \cup H \cup K$.

$$G \cup H = \{1, 2, 3, 4, 5\},$$
$$H \cup K = \{3, 4, 5, 7, 8\},$$
$$G \cup H \cup K = \{1, 2, 3, 4, 5, 7, 8\}.$$

The shaded area in each of the Venn diagrams in Fig. 1.12 represents the set $A \cup B$ in the three important cases, namely that A and B are overlapping sets, that $B \subset A$, and that A and B are disjoint.

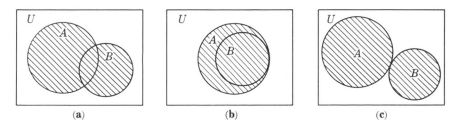

(a)   (b)   (c)

Figure 1.12

The second set-forming operation we wish to consider is that of the *intersection* of two sets.

Definition 1.21. *The* intersection *of two sets A and B is the set of all the elements which are in both A and B. We denote the operation of intersection by the symbol ∩ and write A ∩ B, which is read "the intersection of A and B" or "A cap B."*

The commutative and associative laws are valid also for this operation. That is,

$$A \cap B = B \cap A$$
$$(A \cap B) \cap C = A \cap (B \cap C).$$

The set $A \cap B$ is represented by the shaded area in the Venn diagrams in Fig. 1.13.

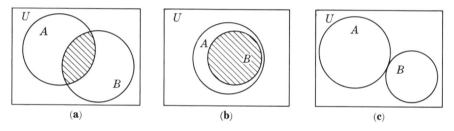

FIGURE 1.13

It often happens in mathematical discussions that it is desirable to talk about the set which is called the *complement* of a set S relative to a universal set U. Such a set is defined as follows.

Definition 1.22. *By the* complement *of a set S relative to a universal set U is meant the set S̄ containing all the elements in U not contained in S.*

Example. Suppose that S is the set of all the students in your school that are enrolled in at least one mathematics course. Suppose further that the universal set U is the set of all students enrolled in your school. Then $\bar{S}$ is the set consisting of all the students enrolled in your school who are not taking mathematics.

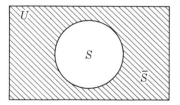

FIGURE 1.14

The Venn diagram in Fig. 1.14 shows the relation between any set S and its complement $\bar{S}$ relative to a universal set U. The shaded area represents $\bar{S}$ and the rectangle represents U.

EXERCISES

1. If $A = \{1, 2, 3, 4, 5\}$, $B = \{2, 5, 7, 9\}$, $C = \{3, 5, 6, 7, 8\}$, find each of the following sets.

   a. $A \cup B$.
   b. $A \cup C$.
   c. $B \cup C$.
   d. $A \cap C$.
   e. $B \cap C$.

   f. $A \cup B \cup C$.
   g. $A \cup (B \cap C)$.
   h. $(A \cup B) \cap (A \cup C)$.
   i. $A \cap (B \cup C)$.
   j. $(A \cap B) \cup (A \cap C)$.

2. Show that
   a. If $A = B$, then $A \cup B = A \cap B = A$.
   b. If $A \subset B$, then $A \cup B = B$ and $A \cap B = A$.
   c. If A is any set and $\varnothing$ is the empty set, then $A \cup \varnothing = A$ and $A \cap \varnothing = \varnothing$.

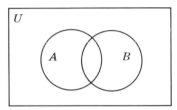

FIGURE 1.15

3. Two subsets A and B of a universal set U are related as shown in the Venn diagram of Fig. 1.15. Use a separate copy of this Venn diagram and shading to represent each of the following sets.

   a. $A \cap B$.
   b. $\bar{A}$.
   c. $\bar{B}$.

   d. $\overline{A \cup B}$.
   e. $\bar{A} \cup \bar{B}$.

4. If the universal set $U = \{x \mid x$ is a letter in the English alphabet$\}$, $A = \{a, e, i, o, u, w, y\}$, and $B = \{u, v, w, x, y, z\}$ find each of the following sets.

   a. $\bar{A}$.
   b. $\bar{B}$.
   c. $\overline{A \cup B}$.

   d. $\bar{A} \cup \bar{B}$.
   e. $\overline{A \cap B}$.
   f. $\bar{A} \cap \bar{B}$.

5. Three subsets A, B, and C of a universal U are related as shown in Fig. 1.16.

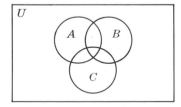

FIGURE 1.16

Use a separate copy of this Venn diagram and shading to represent each of the following sets.

a. $A \cup C$.   **d.** $A \cup (B \cap C)$.
b. $B \cap C$.   **e.** $(A \cup B) \cap (A \cup C)$.
c. $(A \cap B) \cap C$.

Compare the Venn diagrams of the sets in Parts **(d)** and **(e)**. What conclusion?

6. Repeat Parts **(d)** and **(e)** of Exercise 5 for the following two cases.

Case 1. A, B, and C are related as shown in Fig. 1.17.

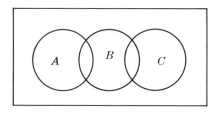

FIGURE 1.17

Case 2. A, B, and C are related as shown in Fig. 1.18.

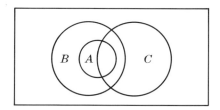

FIGURE 1.18

What relation between $A \cup (B \cap C)$ and $(A \cup B) \cap (A \cup C)$ is suggested by the Venn diagrams of these two sets in Case 1 and Case 2?

7. There are many possible ways in which three sets A, B, and C might be related. Three such possibilities are exhibited in Figs. 1.16, 1.17, and 1.18. It was shown in Exercises 5 and 6, by use of Venn diagrams, that for the three cases considered

$$A \cup (B \cap C) = (A \cup B) \cap (A \cup C).$$

This equation states a law called the *distributive law of union over intersection* which can easily be proved without the use of Venn diagrams to be true in general. For convenience in making such a proof, let $S = A \cup (B \cap C)$ and $T = (A \cup B) \cap (A \cup C)$. First prove that if $x \in S$, then $x \in T$ and hence $S \subseteq T$. Do this by considering two cases.

Case 1. $x \in S$ and $x \in A$, hence $x \in A \cup B$ and $x \in A \cup C$. That is, $x \in T$. Why?

Case 2. $x \in S$ and $x \notin A$, therefore $x \in B \cap C$, that is, $x \in B$ and $x \in C$, hence $x \in A \cup B$ and $x \in A \cup C$. Thus $x \in T$. Why?

Conclusion: $S \subseteq T$.

Next, prove that if $y \in T$, then $y \in S$ and hence $T \subseteq S$. Again consider two cases.

Case 1. $y \in T$ and $y \in A$.
Case 2. $y \in T$ and $y \notin A$.

Complete the argument as above.

8. Using the method of Exercise 7, prove the *distributive law of intersection over union*.

$$A \cap (B \cup C) = (A \cap B) \cup (A \cap C).$$

9. DeMorgan's Laws
   a. $\overline{(A \cup B)} = \overline{A} \cap \overline{B}.$ **b.** $\overline{(A \cap B)} = \overline{A} \cup \overline{B}.$
   Use the method of Exercise 7 to prove DeMorgan's laws.

10. The difference, $A - B$, between the two sets A and B is defined as the set consisting of all the elements of A that do not belong to B, or in symbols $A - B = \{x \mid x \in A, x \notin B\}$. Represent the set $A - B$ by means of Venn diagram and shading for each of the following cases.
    a. A and B are overlapping sets.
    b. A and B are disjoint.
    c. $B \subset A.$ **d.** $A \subset B.$ **e.** $A = B.$

11. If $A = \{a, b, c, d, e\}$ and $B = \{b, d, f, h, j\}$, and $C = \{a, c, f, g, h\}$ find
    a. $A - B.$ **d.** $B - A.$
    b. $A - C.$ **e.** $C - B.$
    c. $B - C.$ **f.** $(A \cup C) - B.$

12. Let $N(A)$ denote the number of elements in set A. For example, if $A = \{1, 3, 4, 7, 9, 11\}$, $N(A) = 6$ and if $B = \{x \mid x$ is a U.S. senator$\}$, $N(B) = 100$.
    a. Give an example of two sets A and B such that $N(A \cup B) = N(A) + N(B)$.
    b. Give an example of two sets A and B such that $N(A \cup B) \neq N(A) + N(B)$.
    c. Give an example of two sets A and B such that $N(A - B) = N(A) - N(B)$.

13. If A and B are any two overlapping sets, use a Venn diagram to show that $N(A \cup B) = N(A) + N(B) - N(A \cap B)$. Would this be true for any two sets?

14. A total of 50 boys enrolled in a summer camp. Each boy had to participate in at least one of the three sports: swimming, tennis, and softball. After registration it was found that 22 had signed up for swimming, 20 for tennis, and 25 for softball. Also, it was found that 5 had signed up for both swimming and tennis, 4 had signed up for swimming and softball but not for tennis, and 3 had signed up for all three. Let the universal set U consist of the 50 boys enrolled in the camp, and subsets B, S, and T defined as follows.

$$B = \{x \in U \mid x \text{ signed up for softball}\}$$
$$S = \{x \in U \mid x \text{ signed up for swimming}\}$$
$$T = \{x \in U \mid x \text{ signed up for tennis}\}$$

Use a Venn diagram representation of the three subsets B, S, and T as an aid in finding each of the following.
    a. $N(B \cap S \cap T).$ **e.** $N(S \cup T).$
    b. $N[(S \cap T) - (B \cap S \cap T)].$ **f.** $N(B - S \cup T).$
    c. $N[(B \cap S) - (B \cap S \cap T)].$ **g.** $N[(B \cap T) - (B \cap S \cap T)].$
    d. $N[S - (B \cup T)].$ **h.** $N(T - B \cup S).$

15. Referring to Exercise 14 and using the information found there, answer the following questions.
    a. How many boys signed up for swimming and tennis but not for softball?
    b. How many signed up for swimming and softball?

    c. How many signed up for at least two of three sports?
    d. How many signed up for tennis only?
    e. How many signed up for softball only?

13   THE CARTESIAN PRODUCT OF TWO SETS

In the previous section we discussed some operations which we called set-forming operations. The result of each operation was a set; that is, $A \cup B$ is a set, $A \cap B$ is a set, and $\overline{A}$ is a set, assuming, of course, a universal set U. If the universal set is determined, then the operation of union, intersection, or complement performed upon subsets of U always gives rise to a set which is a subset of U. For example, if $C = A \cup B$, then the elements of C are also elements of U. Furthermore, these operations were applied to the sets rather than to the elements in the sets.

In this section we shall show how two sets A and B may give rise to a third set each of whose elements is a pair, (a, b), of elements, such that $a \in A$ and $b \in B$. We shall refer to the pair (a, b) as an ordered pair because, in general, the pair (a, b) will not be the same as the pair (b, a). In other words, the order in which the pair is written may and generally does affect whatever the pair represents. We are familiar with this fact from elementary arithmetic; the number resulting from combining a pair of integers may depend upon the order in which you combine the integers. For example, an ordinary fraction may be thought of as a number pair, say $\frac{2}{3}$. We could even use the above notation by agreeing that the two symbols (2, 3) and $\frac{2}{3}$ mean the same thing, that $(2, 3) = \frac{2}{3}$. Now certainly, if we change the order in the number pair, we get a different fraction for $(3, 2) = \frac{3}{2} \neq \frac{2}{3}$. So you see, if we define fractions as number pairs, we have to define them as ordered number pairs, lest we get into difficulty.

In referring to an ordered pair, say (x, y), we call x the first element of the pair and y the second element of the pair. This is easy to remember, for the element written first is the first element, assuming of course that in writing we use the natural order in which we write words, from left to right.

Now suppose we have the two sets $A = \{1, 2, 3\}$ and $B = \{2, 4\}$. How many simple fractions can be formed from these two sets if the numerator must be an element of A and the denominator must be an element of B? Obviously, there are as many different fractions as there are possible number pairs, if the first number in each pair has to be from A and the second number from B. Writing down all the possible pairs as described, we get (1, 2), (1, 4), (2, 2), (2, 4), (3, 2), and (3, 4). Hence there are exactly six different such fractions possible. We now consider these ordered pairs as being the elements of a set, say C. We may write

$$C = \{(1, 2), (1, 4), (2, 2), (2, 4), (3,2), (3, 4)\}.$$

This new set C, which we have formed from A and B, is called the "Cartesian product of A and B." It is customary, instead of giving this new set a name, to denote it by $A \times B$, read "A cross B." This leads us to the definition.

Definition 1.23.   *By the* Cartesian product set *of two sets A and B is meant the set of all ordered pairs (a, b) such that $a \in A$ and $b \in B$. In symbols, this becomes $A \times B = \{(a, b) \mid a \in A$ and $b \in B\}$.*

It should be noted that the definition just given for the Cartesian product of two sets does not specify any relation between the two sets forming the product. The two sets could be the same or they could be different. They both, of course, must be nonempty. Also, the elements of the two sets need have no relation. However, the real usefulness in mathematics of such a product will be found in cases in which the elements of both sets are related. For example, we shall be interested in the case in which the elements of both sets are real numbers.

Example.   Let $A = \{1, 2\}$; then $A \times A = \{(1, 1), (1, 2), (2, 1), (2, 2)\}$.

Example.   Let $A = \{a, b, c\}$ and $B = \{d, e\}$; then
$$A \times B = \{(a, d), (a, e), (b, d), (b, e), (c, d), (c, e)\}.$$
$$B \times A = \{(d, a), (d, b), (d, c), (e, a), (e, b), (e, c)\}.$$

A very convenient way of representing graphically a Cartesian cross-product is illustrated in Fig. 1.19, the cross-product is $S \times T$, where $S = \{a, b, c\}$ and $T = \{d, e\}$. By definition,

$$S \times T = \{(x, y) \mid x \in S \text{ and } y \in T\}.$$

To obtain the graph shown in Fig. 1.19, two mutually perpendicular lines

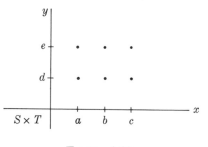

FIGURE 1.19

are drawn. Just as a matter of convenience, one is drawn horizontal and the other vertical. The horizontal line is labeled at the far right with an x and is referred to as the x axis. The vertical line is labeled with a y and is referred to as the y axis. Three arbitrary but distinct points are chosen on the x axis, to represent the elements of the set S; one represents the element a, one the element b, and one the element c. Which point is associated with which element of S is of no particular significance, except that one point of the x axis is associated with only one element of S. In a similar manner two distinct points were chosen on the y axis, to represent the two elements d and e of the set T. Each of the three points on the x axis is labeled with the name of the element it represents, and so is each of the two points on the y axis. Next, to represent the element (a, d) of the crossproduct $S \times T$, a point is placed vertically above a and on the same level as d. Similarly, to represent the element (a, e), a point is placed vertically above a and on the same level with e. This scheme is repeated until six points, representing the six ordered pair elements of $S \times T$ are located. Points arranged in this manner are called lattice points.

To read the graph, which is to find the ordered pairs associated with a particular point, one reverses the procedure just described. The first element of the ordered pair represented by a particular lattice point is the element on the x axis vertically below the given point. The second element of the ordered pair is the element on the y axis and on the same level as the given point.

A graph of the type just described can, of course, be constructed for any cross-product, regardless of the kind of elements involved. However, the lattice-type graphs that are of most interest to mathematicians are those in which the elements x and y of the given sets are real numbers and, hence, the elements of the cross-product are ordered pairs, (x, y), of real numbers. Then it is customary to select an arbitrary unit of measure for measuring distances and to associate with each number $x \in S$ a point on the x axis that is x units to the right of the y axis, assuming x a positive number, and to associate with each number $y \in T$ a point on the y axis that is y units above the x axis if y is a positive number. The number elements x and y of the ordered pair (x, y) are then called the coordinates of the lattice point with which the number pair is associated. The lattice point associated with the number pair $(3, 2)$ is located three units to the right of the y axis and two units above the x axis. It is quite obvious that such a scheme would associate with $(2, 3)$ a point different from the one associated with $(3, 2)$. Hence in considering a pair of elements (x, y) the order is as important as the elements themselves. Graphs of cross-products whose elements are real numbers will be discussed in a later chapter.

Example. Construct the graph of the cross-product $A \times B = \{(x, y) \mid x \in A$ and $y \in B\}$, where $A = \{1, 2, 3, 4, 5\}$ and $B = \{1, 2, 3, 4\}$. See Fig. 1.20.

EXERCISES

1. Let $A = \{3, 4, 5\}$ and $B = \{2, 7\}$.
   a. Find $A \times B$, $A \times A$, $B \times B$, and $B \times A$.
   b. How many elements are in each set of Part (a)?
2. If $N(A) = x$ and $N(B) = y$, find $N(A \times B)$.
3. If one coin is tossed, it will fall heads (H) or tails (T). If two coins are tossed, what is the set of possible outcomes, expressed as a cross-product?

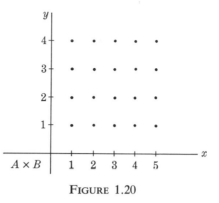

FIGURE 1.20

4. An ideal die is a perfect cube with six faces. One face has one dot, a second face has two dots, a third face three dots, and so on, the sixth face having six dots. Associate with each face a number corresponding to the number of dots on the face and let S be a set consisting of the numbers $S = \{1, 2, 3, 4, 5, 6\}$. If two dice are rolled, $S \times S$ is the set of possible outcomes. Draw a lattice graph representing $S \times S$.

5. Let A and B be two sets. Discuss the possibility that $A \times B = B \times A$.

6. The school cafeteria serves three kinds of salads: tossed, head lettuce, and tomato. There is also a choice of three kinds of dressing: thousand-island, French, and mayonnaise. Treating the salads as the elements of a set A and the three dressings as elements of a second set B, draw a lattice graph representing $A \times B$. Label one or two of the lattice points with the kind of salad they represent.

7. Figure 1.20 represents $A \times B$ where $A = \{1, 2, 3, 4, 5\}$ and $B = \{1, 2, 3, 4\}$. List the elements of each of the following subsets of $A \times B$.
   a. $C = \{(x, y) \mid (x, y) \in A \times B$ and x is less than $4\}$.
   b. $D = \{(x, y) \mid (x, y) \in A \times B$ and x is 1 and y is even$\}$.
   c. $E = \{(x, y) \mid (x, y) \in A \times B$ and $x = y\}$.
   d. $F = \{(x, y) \mid (x, y) \in A \times B$ and $x + y = 4\}$.
   e. $G = \{(x, y) \mid (x, y) \in A \times B$ and $xy = 30\}$.
   f. $H = \{(x, y) \mid (x, y) \in A \times B$, x is greater than 3 and y is less than $3\}$.

8. Referring to Exercise 4, list the elements in each of the following subsets of $S \times S$.
   a. $M = \{(a, b) \mid (a, b) \in S \times S$ and $a + b = 7\}$.
   b. $N = \{(a, b) \mid (a, b) \in S \times S$ and $a + b$ is at least $7\}$.
   c. $Q = \{(a, b) \mid (a, b) \in S \times S$ and $a + b \neq 8\}$.
   d. $K = \{(a, b) \mid (a, b) \in S \times S$ and $a \neq 6, b \neq 6\}$.
   e. $L = \{(a, b) \mid (a, b) \in S \times S$ and $a = 6, b \neq 6\}$.
   f. $J = \{(a, b) \mid (a, b) \in S \times S$ and $a = 6$ or $b = 6$, but not both$\}$.

9. If $A = \{$John, Paul$\}$ and $B = \{$Alice, Mary$\}$, what are (a) all the elements of $A \times B$ and (b) all the subsets of $A \times B$?

14   OPEN STATEMENTS

In Section 2 we discussed a special kind of statement which we called a proposition. It will be recalled that a proposition was defined as a statement for which it could be said that the statement is true or the statement is false but not both. Then in Section 6 we defined a variable as a letter used to represent an arbitrary element of some given or implied set. In this section we want to define a second special kind of statement called an *open* statement. As we shall see, open statements are statements involving one or more variables and it is this fact which makes them important in mathematics. For example, in mathematics we often need to write and use such statements as:

1. $2x + 4 = 10$.
2. $x^2 > 4$ (Read "x^2 is greater than 4").
3. $(x - 2)(x - 5) = 0$.
4. $2x < 6$ (Read "$2x$ is less than 6").
5. $x + y = 5$.

It is obvious that, as it stands, neither of the five statements listed above is a proposition, because it is not possible to say of either statement that it is true or that it is false. However, in each case if a specific number is substituted for x, or in statement 5 if a number is substituted for x and a number for y, then the statement becomes a proposition.

Definition 1.24.   *An open statement is a statement which contains a variable and which becomes a proposition when the variable is replaced by any one of its possible values.*

Example.   Let $N = \{1, 2, 3, 4, \cdots\}$ and suppose $x \in N$. Then the statement

$$2x + 4 = 10$$

is an open statement. For, first the statement contains the variable x and second, if x is replaced by any specific element of N the statement becomes a proposition. In fact $2x + 4 = 10$ is a true statement when x is replaced by 3 and the statement is false when x is replaced by any other specific number from the set N.

In our discussion of propositions we used the letters p, q, r, $\cdots$, to designate unspecified propositions. It seems quite natural therefore, to designate unspecified open statements involving the variable x by p_x, q_x, r_x, etc. In keeping with this notation we shall use the corresponding capital letters to designate the truth sets of open statements. That is, we shall designate by the capital letter P the set of elements x for which p_x is a true statement, by the capital letter Q is the set of all elements x for which q_x is a true statement, and so on.

Example.   Let p_x be the statement "$(x - 1)(x - 3) = 0$," then

$$P = \{x \mid (x - 1)(x - 3) = 0\} = \{1, 3\}.$$

Example.   Let p_x be the statement "$x + 5 = 7$" and let q_x be the statement "$5x = 10$." Then

$$P = \{x \mid x + 5 = 7\} = \{2\}$$

and

$$Q = \{x \mid 5x = 10\} = \{2\}.$$

In this case we see that $P = Q$. In such a case we say that p_x and q_x are equivalent and denote this fact symbollically as $p_x \leftrightarrow q_x$.

Definition 1.25. *Two open statements p_x and q_x whose truth sets are respectively P and Q are said to be equivalent if and only if $P = Q$.*

Remark: All of the statements given above as examples of open statements are either statements which are commonly known as "equations," or are statements known as "inequalities." In fact, our chief concern with open statements in the remaining chapters of this text will be with those which are either equations or inequalities. For example, we shall discuss methods for determining the solution sets of certain types of equations and inequalities. We shall discover that in determining such solution sets the role played by equivalent open statements is a very important one.

15* QUANTIFIERS

A statement that involves a variable isn't necessarily an open statement. It may be a proposition. For example, in a course in high school algebra where it is generally understood that, unless otherwise specified, the universal set is the set consisting of all the real numbers, statements similar to the following are quite commonplace.

For all x, $3x + 4x = 7x$.
For every x, $x^2 + 1 > 0$.
For each integer x, $2x$ is an even integer.

Obviously, all three of the above statements are true and hence each is a proposition. In mathematics it often happens that we need to express the fact that a certain property is true for each and every element x in some suitably restricted set. This is usually done by use of one of the phrases "for all x," "for every x," or "for each x." We shall regard these three phrases as having the same meaning. Each is called a *universal quantifier* and each is symbolized by the common symbol "$\forall_x$." By using this quantifier symbol the examples listed above can be written

$$\forall_x[3x + 4x = 7x]$$
$$\forall_x[x^2 + 1 > 0]$$
$$\forall_x[x \text{ an integer, } 2x \text{ is an even integer}].$$

The symbol "$\forall_x$" is most often read "for all x," but either of the phrases "for every x," or "for each x," would be equally appropriate.

Another type of quantifier that is most useful in mathematics is one illustrated by such statements as:

There exists an x such that $x + 2 = 5$.

For some x, $x^2 - 5x + 6 = 0$.

There is at least one integer x such that $\dfrac{x}{x} \neq 1$.

Here we have used the three phrases "there exists an x," "for some x," and "there is at least one x," to express one central fact, namely, that there exists at least one element x which belongs to an implied universal set and for which our statement is true. That is to say, these three phrases are regarded as having the same meaning. They are called *existential quantifiers* and each is symbolized by the common symbol "$\exists_x$." By using this symbol the above three statements can be written

$$\exists_x[x + 2 = 5]$$
$$\exists_x[x^2 - 5x + 6 = 0]$$

$$\exists_x\left[x \text{ an integer}, \frac{x}{x} \neq 1\right].$$

The symbol "$\exists_x$" is most commonly read "there exists an x," but it could just as well be read "for some x," or "there is at least one x."

An important problem in connection with propositions involving quantifiers is that of writing the negation of such a statement. This problem is easily solved provided we keep in mind the definition of the negation of a proposition; namely, the negation of a proposition p_x is a proposition $\sim p_x$ such that:

(a)   If p is true, then $\sim p$ is false.
(b)   If p is false, then $\sim p$ is true.

Let x be an element of a universal set U, and let p_x be a proposition whose truth set is P, then $P \subseteq U$. Furthermore, the truth set of $\sim p_x$ is $\bar{P}$, the complement of P. Now consider the statement $\forall_x(p_x)$. If $\forall_x(p_x)$ is true, then $P = U$, $\bar{P} = \varnothing$, and hence $\exists_x(\sim p_x)$ is false. On the other hand, if $\forall_x(p_x)$ is false, then $P \neq U$, $\bar{P} \neq \varnothing$, and therefore $\exists_x(\sim p_x)$ is true. In other words, a correct negation of $\forall_x(p_x)$ is $\exists_x(\sim p_x)$. Similarly, suppose the statement $\exists_x(p_x)$ is true, then $P \neq U$, $\bar{P} \neq \varnothing$, and thus $\forall_x(\sim p_x)$ is false. Next, suppose $\exists_x(p_x)$ is false, then $P = \varnothing$, $\bar{P} = U$, and accordingly $\forall_x(\sim p_x)$ is true. It follows then from the definition of negation that the negation of $\exists_x(p_x)$ is $\forall_x(\sim p_x)$. In summary, we have shown that the negations of propositions involving quantifiers are given by the following equivalences:

$$\sim\forall_x(p_x) \leftrightarrow \exists_x(\sim p_x)$$
$$\sim\exists_x(p_x) \leftrightarrow \forall_x(\sim p_x).$$

Example.   Write the negation of the proposition

$$\text{"}\exists_x\left[x \text{ an integer}, \frac{x}{x} \neq 1\right].\text{"}$$

Solution.   The negation is "$\forall_x \left[x \text{ an integer, } \dfrac{x}{x} = 1 \right].$"

EXERCISES

1. Find the truth set for each given open statement.
    a. x is a prime less than 10.   **c.** $x + 4 = 0$.
    b. $2x + 3 = x + 5$.   **d.** x is a U.S. Senator.
    e. x is a baseball team in the National League.

2. Write four open statements, that are not equations, involving a variable x and in each case state a universal set to which x belongs.

3. Replace each given open statement with an equivalent one containing the phrase "for all x." (The given statements are not necessarily true.)
    a. For each prime number x greater than 2, $x + 1$ is an even integer.
    b. For every real number x, $x^2 - 4x + 7$ is positive.
    c. If $x > 2$, then $x^2 > 4$.
    d. No man is 8 feet tall.
    e. The square of every odd integer is an odd integer.

4. By using quantifiers express the negation of each statement in Problem 3.

5. For each of the following open statements write an open statement equivalent to it. (See definition of equivalent open statements.)
    a. $2x + 3x = 10$.   **c.** $2x + 5 = 2x + 7$.
    b. $x^2 - 3x + 2 = 0$.   **d.** $3x < 6$.

6. Express each of the following open statements using the quantifier "there exists an x." (The given statements are not necessarily true.)
    a. For some prime number x, $x + 1$ is a prime number.
    b. Some men are rich.
    c. There is at least one number x such that $x^2 = 1$.
    d. In the set of all triangles in the plane some are isosceles.
    e. For some number x, $1 - 17x - 5x^2$ is positive.

7. By using quantifiers write the negation of each statement in Problem 6.

II

NUMBER SYSTEMS

1 INTRODUCTION

It is the purpose of this chapter to study in some detail the characteristic properties of the real number system and the complex number system. We shall exhibit the elements, the axioms, and the definitions which determine these two systems, and use these axioms and definitions in proving some theorems that are basic in the study of elementary mathematics. For some, much of this chapter may be a review. If so, it is nevertheless well for the student not to take the review lightly, but rather to be certain that all the topics covered are clear to him, for these topics furnish the background of the material that is to follow.

2 REAL NUMBERS

The concept of numbers is basic in mathematics and every student has studied about, and worked with numbers since his grade school days. In fact, the mathematical objects called numbers are so commonplace in all our lives that most are apt to take them for granted without really knowing or understanding their characteristic properties. Since a knowledge and a clear understanding of these properties are so essential as background for further study of mathematics, we feel it worthwhile to give a brief discussion of such properties at this point.

Our experience in working with numbers started in early childhood when we learned to count. In the counting process we became acquainted with the set of natural numbers, $\{1, 2, 3, 4, \cdots\}$, also known as counting numbers or as positive integers. Then in grade school we learned to add, subtract, multiply and divide natural numbers and we soon discovered that we can add any two natural numbers or multiply any two natural numbers and the result of either operation is always a natural number. However, with only natural numbers to work with, the operations of subtraction and division are not always possible. For example, it is not possible to subtract 5 from 3 or to divide 7 by 2 if our arsenal of numbers contains only natural numbers. To remedy this situation, that is, to extend the operations of subtraction and division it was necessary to include in our set some new elements. First, we included *zero* (0), and then the *negatives of the natural numbers* $\{-1, -2, -3, -4, \cdots\}$, which together with the natural numbers form the set of integers $\{\cdots, -3, -2, -1, 0, 1, 2, 3, \cdots\}$. Next, we included such elements as $\frac{1}{5}$, $\frac{2}{3}$, $-\frac{4}{7}$, etc., called *fractions*. A number that can be expressed in the form a/b, where a and b are both integers and $b \neq 0$ is called a *rational number*. Obviously, every integer is a rational number. Thus the set of rational numbers consists of all the integers together with all the fractions which do not represent integers but whose numerators and denominators are integers.

Definition 2.1.   *A natural number b is called a* factor *or a* divisor *of a natural number a if there is a natural number c such that a is the product of b and c, that is $a = bc$. In this case c is likewise a factor of a.*

Since 1 is a factor of every natural number, it follows that each natural number has at least two factors, namely itself and 1.

Definition 2.2.   *A natural number is called a* prime *if it is greater than 1 and has only itself and 1 as factors. A natural number greater than 1 and not a prime is called a* composite.

Example.   Numbers such as 2, 3, 7, 17, etc., are primes, while numbers such as 6, 9, 12, 14, etc., are composites.

We next state without proof, two very useful theorems, the second of which is a consequence of the first.

Theorem 2.1.   Unique Factorization Theorem.   *A natural number greater than 1 can be expressed as the product of factors, which are primes, in one and only one way except for the order in which the factors are written in the product.*

Theorem 2.2.   *Suppose that a and p are natural numbers and p is a prime. If p is a factor of a^2, then p is a factor of a.*

Definition 2.3.   *If two natural numbers a and b have the same natural number c as a factor, then c is called a* common factor *of a and b.*

Example.   2 is a common factor of 6 and 10; 2, 3, 5, 6, 10, and 15 are common factors of 30 and 60.

Definition 2.4.   *If two natural numbers have no common factors other than* 1, *the two numbers are said to be relatively prime.*

Definition 2.5.   *A fraction whose numerator and denominator are natural numbers is said to be in simplest, or lowest form, if the numerator and denominator are relatively prime.*

Example.   The fractions $\frac{2}{3}$, $\frac{4}{9}$, $\frac{8}{15}$, and $\frac{10}{21}$ are in simplest form, while $\frac{4}{6}$, $\frac{9}{12}$, and $\frac{14}{21}$ are not in simplest form.

In the study of arithmetic we learned that each rational number is expressible as an infinite decimal. For example,

$$2 = 2.00000\cdots$$
$$\tfrac{1}{2} = 0.50000\cdots$$
$$\tfrac{1}{3} = 0.33333\cdots$$
$$\tfrac{7}{22} = 0.3181818\cdots$$
$$\tfrac{2}{7} = 0.285714285714\cdots.$$

In each of the decimal representations listed above, it is seen that a fixed digit or a fixed set of digits repeat indefinitely; for this reason such decimals are called *repeating decimals*. It can be shown that if a rational number is expressed as an infinite decimal it will be a repeating decimal and conversely that every repeating infinite decimal is the expansion of some rational number. It is easy to exhibit infinite decimals that are not repeating decimals and hence are not rational numbers. For example, $0.25303003000300003\cdots$.

Definition 2.6.   *A number whose infinite decimal expansion is not a repeating decimal is called an* irrational number.

It is obvious from the definition of an irrational number that the set of rational numbers and the set of irrational numbers are disjoint. That is, no number can be both rational and irrational.

Theorem 2.3. $\sqrt{3}$ *is not a rational number.*

We shall give an indirect proof. That is, we shall assume the theorem false and show that this assumption leads to a contradiction.

Proof: Assume $\sqrt{3}$ is a rational number. Then it follows from the definition of a rational number that there must exist two integers a and b, which we shall assume to be relatively prime, such that

(1)
$$\frac{a}{b} = \sqrt{3},$$

hence

(2)
$$a^2 = 3b^2.$$

This last equation implies that the prime number 3 is a factor of a^2 and thus 3 is a factor of a (Theorem 2.2). If 3 is a factor of a, then $a = 3c$, or $a^2 = 9c^2$, where c is some natural number. Substituting for a^2 in (2) we have

$$3b^2 = 9c^2$$

or

$$b^2 = 3c^2,$$

which shows that 3 is a factor of b^2 and hence of b. But this is impossible since the numbers a and b are assumed relatively prime. Thus our assumption that $\sqrt{3}$ is a rational number must be false and we conclude that $\sqrt{3}$ is not a rational number.

Definition 2.7. *A real number is a number that can be expressed as an infinite decimal.*

In the remaining sections of this chapter we shall discuss the characteristic properties of the real and complex number systems.

EXERCISES

1. Make a list of all the natural numbers which are primes and less than 100.
2. Express each of the given numbers as a product of primes.
   a. 24.   b. 51.   c. 286.   d. 2737.
3. Find the common factors of each given pair of numbers.
   a. 20 and 32.   b. 140 and 90.   c. 175 and 300.
4. Express each given number as an infinite decimal.
   a. $\frac{6}{5}$.   b. $\frac{1}{8}$.   c. $\frac{20}{7}$.   d. $\frac{17}{3}$.   e. $\frac{728}{25}$.
5. Determine which of the following numbers are rational. Give a reason for your answer in each case.
   a. 1.32.   e. $0.636363 \cdots$.
   b. 3.1416.   f. $0.142857142857142857 \cdots$.
   c. 0.   g. $0.2101001000100001 \cdots$.
   d. $\sqrt{4}$.
6. Every real number belongs to one or more of the following sets: natural numbers, integers, rational numbers, and irrational numbers. For example, the number 5 is a natural number, it is an integer, and it is a rational number and hence belongs to three of the four above mentioned sets. On the other hand $\sqrt{3}$ belongs only to one of these sets, namely the set of irrational

numbers. Prepare a table as illustrated below and place each of the following numbers in the set or sets to which it belongs: 4, -7, $\sqrt{5}$, $\dfrac{\pi}{2}$, -3.48, 0, $\dfrac{4}{7}$, $\sqrt{9}$, -1728, $\dfrac{6.4}{.32}$, $-\dfrac{5}{3}$, $\sqrt[3]{4}$, 74378, $\dfrac{0}{7}$, $2 + \sqrt{3}$, and $\sqrt[3]{8}$.

Natural Numbers	Integers	Rational Numbers	Irrational Numbers
5	5	5	$\sqrt{3}$

7. Use a method similar to that used in the proof of Theorem 2.3 to prove that each of the following numbers is not rational.
    a. $\sqrt{2}$.   **b.** $\sqrt{6}$.   **c.** $\sqrt{7}$.   **d.** $\sqrt[3]{2}$.

8. An integer a is an even integer if and only if $a = 2n$ where n is some integer. An integer b is an odd integer if and only if $b = 2n + 1$ where n is some integer.
    a. Prove that the square of an even integer is an even integer.
    b. Prove that the square of an odd integer is an odd integer.
    c. Prove that the sum of two odd integers is always an even integer.
    d. Prove that the product of two odd integers is always an odd integer.
    e. Prove that an integer is an even integer if its square is an even integer.
    f. Prove that an integer is an odd integer if its square is an odd integer.

9. It was proved in Theorem 2.3 that $\sqrt{3}$ is not rational. Prove that $2 + \sqrt{3}$ is not rational.

10. Show by an example that:
    a. The sum of two irrational numbers may be rational.
    b. The product of two irrational numbers may be rational.
    c. The sum of two primes may be a prime. How many such examples can you find?

11. Let the Universal set U be the set consisting of all the real numbers. Draw a Venn diagram to represent the following subsets of U: all natural numbers, all integers, all rational numbers, and all irrational numbers.

3 MATHEMATICAL SYSTEMS

In general, we think of a *mathematical system* as consisting of a set of elements, a set of definitions, one or more operations that can be performed upon the elements, a set of axioms, and some theorems which can be proved from the definitions and axioms. Thus, the expression "the system of natural numbers" means much more than just the numbers themselves; they are only the elements involved.

In the next section we shall consider a very important mathematical system, namely the system of real numbers. Its importance lies, of course, in the fact that the study of arithmetic and elementary algebra is nothing more than the study of the properties of the real number system. In fact, in the remainder of the text we shall be chiefly concerned with relations among numbers, or relations among expressions that represent numbers.

4 THE REAL NUMBER SYSTEM

As was pointed out in the last section, one of the chief ingredients of any mathematical system is a set of elements. In the case of the real number system, as you no doubt have already guessed, the set of elements involved is the set of real numbers. Let us call this set R and write $R = \{a, b, c, \cdots\}$, where it is to be understood that the small letters a, b, c, etc., represent real numbers.

One of the most important relations of arithmetic is that of *equality*. We shall assume that the following properties of equality hold.

Properties of Equality

If a, b, and c are any three real numbers, then

PROPERTY 1. $a = a$ *(reflexive property).*
PROPERTY 2.   *If* $a = b$, *then* $b = a$ *(symmetric property).*
PROPERTY 3.   *If* $a = b$ *and* $b = c$, *then* $a = c$ *(transitive property).*

Property 3 justifies the following principle, which we shall state as Property 4.

PROPERTY 4.   *If* $a = b$, *then b may be substituted for a in any expression, equality, or statement involving a without changing the value of the given expression or the truth or falsity of the given equality or statement (substitution principle).*

Property 2 states that the order in which an equality is written does not affect the equality.

Example.   If $15 = 3x$, then $3x = 15$.

Example.   If $7x - 3 = x^2 + 2x$, then $x^2 + 2x = 7x - 3$.

Property 3 may be roughly translated: "If each of two real numbers is equal to the same third real number, then the numbers are equal to each other."

The student probably remembers Property 4, the substitution principle, in the form "equals may be substituted for equals." The substitution principle is a most useful tool in simplifying or changing the form of mathematical expressions or equalities.

Example. $5 + (3 + 4) = 12$ is a true statement; $3 + 4 = 7$ is a true statement. Hence we can substitute (7) for $(3 + 4)$ in the first equality and write $5 + 7 = 12$, which is also a true statement.

In Mathematics, one frequently refers to a particular set A of elements as being *closed* under a particular operation or we may say that set A possesses the closure property with respect to a particular operation. To see what is meant by such a statement, let us consider the set $A = \{-1, 0, 1\}$ with the operation multiplication. It is obvious in this case that if we multiply any element of A by itself or by another element of A the resulting product is always one of the three elements of A. We say that A is closed under multiplication. Notice, however, if we use the operation addition instead of multiplication, set A is not closed under addition, since $1 + 1 = 2$ and 2 is not in A.

Definition 2.8. *A set A is said to be closed under an operation if the result of this operation on any two elements of A always produces an element of A, whether the two elements used are the same element or are two different elements.*

Consider the set of natural numbers $N = \{1, 2, 3, 4, 5, \cdots\}$. It is a well known fact that the sum of two natural numbers is a natural number and the product of two natural numbers is a natural number. Thus, according to the above definition we can say that the set N is closed under addition and under multiplication. It is obvious that N is not closed under subtraction or under division.

We take, as the two basic operations of our system, the well-known operations addition and multiplication and, as is common, we use the plus symbol to denote addition and the raised dot to denote multiplication. However, where no confusion can result, products such as $a \cdot b$ will be expressed as ab (confusion would, of course, result from omitting the dot in a product such as $2 \cdot 3$, which would give 23 and not 2 times 3).

The following axioms, Axioms 1 to 11, are basic in all operations involving real numbers or involving expressions that represent real numbers.

The Closure Laws

If a and b are any two real numbers, then:

AxIOM 1. $a + b$ *is a unique real number.*
AxIOM 2. $a \cdot b$ *is a unique real number.*

Axioms 1 and 2 state that if any two real numbers are added or multiplied the result will always be a unique real number. A brief way of saying this is to say "The set of real numbers is closed under the operations of addition and multiplication."

The Commutative Laws

If a and b are any two real numbers, then:

AXIOM 3. $a + b = b + a$.
AXIOM 4. $ab = ba$.

These two axioms state that the order in which two numbers are added or multiplied does not affect the result of that addition or multiplication.

Example. $3 + 5 = 5 + 3 = 8$.

Example. $(3)(5) = (5)(3) = 15$.

The Associative Laws

If a, b, and c are any three real numbers, then:

AXIOM 5. $(a + b) + c = a + (b + c)$.
AXIOM 6. $(ab)c = a(bc)$.

It should be noted that addition and multiplication are binary operations. That is, they are operations which we perform with two numbers. For example, if we wish to add three numbers, we must first add two of them and then add their sum to the third. In fact, the expression $a + b + c$ or the expression *abc has no meaning* unless we define it. So we define the expression $a + b + c$ by the relation

Definition 2.9. $a + b + c = (a + b) + c$,

and we define the expression *abc* by the relation

Definition 2.10. $abc = (ab)c$.

Now that we have given meaning to an expression involving three numbers, we can extend these definitions to an expression involving four numbers. In fact, we define $a + b + c + d$ and *abcd* by the relations

$$a + b + c + d = (a + b + c) + d \quad \text{and} \quad abcd = (abc)d.$$

This procedure obviously could be extended to define an expression involving any number of real numbers. It follows from Axiom 5 that, although to add three or more real numbers we must first add two of them and then add this sum to a third, and so on, the way to select the first two to be added, or the way to select each subsequent number to be added to the sum already obtained, does not affect the final result. A similar remark holds for Axiom 6 in relation to finding the product of three or more real numbers.

Example. $3 + 5 + 2 = (3 + 5) + 2 = 8 + 2 = 10,$
$\qquad\qquad = 3 + (5 + 2) = 3 + 7 = 10,$
$\qquad\qquad = (3 + 2) + 5 = 5 + 5 = 10.$

Example. $(3)(5)(2) = [(3)(5)](2) = (15)(2) = 30,$
$\qquad\qquad = (3)[(5)(2)] = (3)(10) = 30,$
$\qquad\qquad = [(3)(2)](5) = (6)(5) = 30.$

Example. $(a)(b)(a) = a^2b.$

The Distributive Law

If a, b, and c are any three real numbers, then:

AXIOM 7. $a(b + c) = ab + ac.$ *In words, this relation states that the operation multiplication is* distributive *with respect to addition.*

Example. $5(4 + 3) = (5)(4) + (5)(3) = 20 + 15 = 35.$

Check: $(5)(7) = 35.$

Example. $5(2a - 3b) = 10a - 15b.$

It should be noted that many operations in mathematics are not distributive with respect to addition. For instance, the operation of extracting a square root is not distributive with respect to addition; that is to say, $\sqrt{a + b} \neq \sqrt{a} + \sqrt{b}$ if $a \neq 0$ and $b \neq 0$.

Example. $\sqrt{9 + 16} \neq \sqrt{9} + \sqrt{16}$ for $\sqrt{9 + 16} = \sqrt{25} = 5.$ and
$\qquad\qquad\qquad \sqrt{9} + \sqrt{16} = 3 + 4 = 7.$

The Axioms Defining the Identity Elements

AXIOM 8.   *There is a unique real number zero, denoted by* 0, *which has the special property that, if a is any real number, then* $a + 0 = 0 + a = a.$ *Zero is the only real number having this property and, because of this property, it is said to be the* additive identity element *of the set of real numbers.*

AXIOM 9.   *There is a unique real number one, denoted by* 1, *which has the special property that if a is any real number then* $a \cdot 1 = 1 \cdot a = a.$ *Because of this property,* 1 *is called the* multiplicative identity element *of the set of real numbers.*

The Axioms Defining Inverse Elements

AXIOM 10.   *For each real number a, there exists one and only one real number, which we denote by* $(-a),$ *such that* $a + (-a) = (-a) + a = 0.$ *The real number* $(-a)$ *is called the* additive inverse *of the real number a.*

AXIOM 11. *If a is any real number other than zero, there exists one and only one real number, denoted by $1/a$, such that $a \cdot 1/a = 1/a \cdot a = 1$. The number $1/a$ is said to be the* multiplicative inverse *of a.*

Definition 2.11. *The real number b is said to be the* reciprocal *of the real number a, if and only if $a \cdot b = 1$.*

Since, by Axiom 4, $a \cdot b = b \cdot a$, it follows from Definition 2.11 that, if the real number b is the reciprocal of the real number a, then a is also the reciprocal of b. From Axiom 11 it follows that, if the real number b is the reciprocal of the real number a, then $b = 1/a$; that is, the reciprocal of a number is its multiplicative inverse, and conversely. It is important to note that zero is the only real number that does not have a reciprocal. The reciprocal of zero is not defined; in other words, division by zero is not defined.

Since the eleven axioms of the real numbers together with the four properties of the equality relation, all of which are given in this chapter, furnish the basis for all manipulations with real numbers, they should be carefully memorized.

In more advanced courses in mathematics these same eleven axioms are taken as the axioms of an *abstract* mathematical system called a field. That is, any set of objects with two operations satisfying these axioms is *by definition* a field. Thus, the real number system is a field.

EXERCISES

In the following problems the letters a, b, c, $\cdots$, represent real numbers unless otherwise specified.

1. By using Definition 2.9 and any axioms which apply, prove
$$a + b + c = c + b + a.$$

2. Prove: $(a + b + c) + d = (a + d) + (c + d)$, stating each definition or axiom used.

3. Assuming $2 + 3 = 5$, what axiom or axioms justify the statement
$$2x + 3x = 5x?$$

4. **a.** Write the additive inverse for each of the following numbers: 8, $\sqrt{2}$, -4, $-\frac{1}{2}$, $\frac{3}{8}$, 0, 42.5.
   b. Find the reciprocal of each of the following numbers which has a reciprocal: $\frac{2}{3}$, 0.4, $-\frac{7}{8}$, $-\frac{4}{5}$, $\frac{\pi}{3}$, $\frac{0}{2}$, 1.2, 7, -0.25, $\sqrt{5}$, $\frac{1.2}{4.8}$, $\frac{1}{3}$.

5. Prove: $ab + de + ac + df = a(b + c) + d(e + f)$, stating each definition or axiom used.

6. **a.** What axiom justifies the statement $(2 \cdot 3)5 = 2(3 \cdot 5)$?
   b. Prove: $abc = cba$. Justify each step with a definition or axiom.

7. Define the product *abcde* and use your definition plus any axioms needed to prove $abcde = (ab)(cde)$.

8. Prove that the set consisting of all the even natural numbers is closed under addition and also under multiplication. You may assume that the set of natural numbers is closed under addition and under multiplication.

9. Find a proper subset of R, not identical with the set of even natural numbers, that is closed under (a) addition, (b) subtraction, (c) multiplication, (d) division, (e) both addition and subtraction, (f) addition and multiplication, (g) addition, subtraction and multiplication.

10. Show that the set $S = \{5, 10, 15, \cdots, 5n, \cdots\}$ is closed under addition and multiplication.

11. Suppose we invent, just for fun, a new operation and call it "multivation." Let us denote this new operation by a small rectangle, $\square$, and define it by the relation $a \square b = ab + 2$.
    a. Find $3 \square 4$, $-2 \square 5$, $(-1) \square (-2)$, and $0 \square 7$.
    b. Is the set of natural numbers closed under the operation of "multivation"?
    c. Is the statement $a \square (b + c) = a \square b + a \square c$ true or false?

12. It follows from the distributive law that $(9 \cdot 43) + (9 \cdot 57) = 9(43 + 57) = 9 \cdot 100 = 900$. Use the distributive law to evaluate
    a. $(7 \cdot 27) + (7 \cdot 13)$.
    c. $(92 \cdot 58) + (92 \cdot 42)$.
    b. $(17 \cdot 63) + (17 \cdot 37)$.
    d. $(375 \cdot 850) + (375 \cdot 150)$.

13. Sometimes the distributive law can be used to express a sum as a product. For example, $ab + ac = a(b + c)$. In such a case we say that we have factored the sum. Use the distributive law to factor the following.
    a. $x^2 + xy$.
    c. $xy + xz + ay + az$.
    e. $56 + 88$.
    b. $xy + xz$.
    d. $42 + 54$.

14. Justify each of the following statements.
    a. $0 + 7 = 7$.
    c. $1 \cdot (a + b) + 0 = a + b$.
    b. $-x + (x + y) = y$.
    d. $-xy + x(x + y) = x^2$.

15. Is the set consisting of all the rational numbers closed under division?

5 SOME BASIC THEOREMS

We shall now state and prove several theorems we shall need later and that the student will probably recognize as something he once memorized as rules of operation for his calculations.

Theorem 2.4. *If a, b, c are real numbers and $a = b$, then $a + c = b + c$.*

Proof:
$$a + c = a + c, \quad \text{(Prop. 1)}$$
$$a = b, \quad \text{(given)}$$
$$a + c = b + c. \quad \text{(Prop. 4)}$$

Thus we have proved that we may add any number to both sides of an equality and the expression will remain an equality. The student perhaps will remember this in the form "if equals are added to equals the results are equal."

Theorem 2.5. (Cancellation Law for Addition). *If $a + c = b + c$, then $a = b$.*

Proof: $a + c + (-c) = b + c + (-c).$ (Th. 2.4)

Then $a + [c + (-c)] = b + [c + (-c)]$ (Def.)

But $c + (-c) = 0.$ (Ax. 10)

Hence $a + 0 = b + 0.$ (Prop. 4)

So $a = b.$ (Ax. 8)

Theorem 2.5 is very useful in the solution of equations.

Example. Solve the equation $x + 3 = 8$.

Solution: $x + 3 + (-3) = 8 + (-3) = 5 + 3 + (-3)$ (Th. 2.4)

$x + 0 = 5 + 0$ (Ax. 10)

$x = 5.$ (Ax. 8)

Theorem 2.6. $[-(-a)] = a.$

Proof: By definition, $[-(-a)]$ is the additive inverse of $(-a)$.

Hence $[-(-a)] + (-a) = 0.$ (Ax. 10)

Also $a + (-a) = 0.$ (Ax. 10)

Whence $[-(-a)] + (-a) = a + (-a).$ (Prop. 4)

So $[-(-a)] = a.$ (Th. 2.5)

For the sake of brevity and convenience, let us agree to write $-a$ for $(-a)$ when no ambiguity can result. With this agreement, Theorem 2.3 may now be stated in the simpler form $-(-a) = a$. Similarly, we agree to write a for (a) and also for $+a$. In fact, we agree that $+(+a) = +(a) = (a) = a$. We can now formulate the following definition.

Definition 2.12.   *The symbol $a - b$ is defined to mean $a + (-b)$. We call $a - b$ the difference of a and b. The process of adding $(-b)$ to a to obtain $a - b$ is called subtraction. The expression "subtract b from a" means "add $(-b)$ to a." The number $-b$ is the additive inverse of b.*

It should be noted in this connection that we are now using the minus sign in two different ways. It is being used to indicate the additive inverse of a number and also to indicate the operation of subtraction. This, however, should not lead to confusion, for the sense in which it is being used should always be apparent.

Example. Subtract 257 from 389.

Solution: $389 - 257 = 132 + 257 + (-257)$

$= 132 + 0 = 132.$

Example. Subtract 35 from 20.

Solution: $20 - 35 = 20 - (20 + 15) = 20 - 20 - 15$

$= 20 + (-20) + (-15)$

$= 0 + (-15) = -15.$

Example. Subtract 27 from -32.

Solution: $-32 - 27 = -(32 + 27) = -(59) = -59.$

Example. Subtract -45 from 30.

Solution: $30 - (-45) = 30 + [-(-45)] = 30 + (45) = 75.$

Example. Subtract -40 from -60.

Solution: $-60 - (-40) = -(20 + 40) + 40$
$$= -20 - 40 + 40$$
$$= -20 + (-40) + 40$$
$$= -20 + 0 = -20.$$

Theorem 2.7.   *If $a = b$, then $ac = bc$.*

Proof: $ac = ac,$ (Prop. 1)
$a = b;$ (given)
hence $ac = bc.$ (Prop. 4)

This theorem states that if both sides of an equality are multiplied by the same number the result also is an equality. This is a very useful tool to use when working with equations.

Theorem 2.8.   Cancellation Law for Multiplication.   *If $ac = bc$ and $c \neq 0$, then $a = b$.*

Proof: Since $c \neq 0$, there exists a unique real number $1/c$ such that

$c \cdot 1/c = 1$ (Ax. 11)
Also, $(ac)1/c = (bc)1/c,$ (Th. 2.7)
whence $a(c \cdot 1/c) = b(c \cdot 1/c).$ (Ax. 6)
So $a \cdot 1 = b \cdot 1$ (Ax. 11)
or $a = b.$ (Ax. 9)

Example.   If $3x = 15$, then $3x = 3 \cdot 5$; therefore $x = 5$.

Definition 2.13.   *The symbol a/b, if $b \neq 0$, is defined to mean $a \cdot 1/b$. We call a/b the quotient of a and b. The process of finding the product $a \cdot 1/b$ is called division. The symbol a/b is also called a fraction and, if a and b are both integers, it is called a simple fraction. The number denoted by a/b is often referred to as the value of the fraction. In the fraction a/b, a is called the numerator of the fraction and b is called the denominator of the fraction.*

Example. $3 \cdot \frac{1}{5} = \frac{3}{5}$ and $\frac{2}{3} = 2 \cdot \frac{1}{3}$. (*Note:*   Division by zero is not defined.)

The following theorem should help to guard against any attempt to divide by zero.

Theorem 2.9.   *If $b \neq 0$, then $a/b = c$, if and only if $a = bc$. This theorem is, in fact, two theorems, namely* (a) *if $a = bc$, then $a/b = c$, and* (b) *if $a/b = c$, then $a = bc$.*

We shall prove (a) first.

Proof of (a): $\qquad\qquad a = bc, \qquad b \neq 0. \qquad$ (given)

$\qquad\qquad$ Then $\quad a = cb. \qquad\qquad\qquad$ (Ax. 4)

Since $b \neq 0$, there exists a unique real number $1/b$ such that

$$b \cdot 1/b = 1. \qquad\qquad \text{(Ax. 11)}$$

$\qquad$ Hence $\qquad a \cdot 1/b = (cb)1/b \qquad$ (Th. 2.8)

$\qquad$ and $\qquad\quad a \cdot 1/b = c(b \cdot 1/b). \qquad$ (Ax. 6)

$\qquad$ So $\qquad\quad\ a \cdot 1/b = c \cdot 1 \qquad\qquad$ (Ax. 11)

$\qquad$ or $\qquad\quad\ a \cdot 1/b = c. \qquad\qquad$ (Ax. 9)

$\qquad$ Therefore $\quad a/b = c. \qquad\qquad\ $ (Div.)

Proof of (b): $\quad\ a/b = c, \qquad b \neq 0. \qquad$ (given)

$\qquad\qquad\quad a/b \cdot b = cb, \qquad\qquad\ $ (Th. 2.8)

$\qquad\qquad (a \cdot 1/b)b = cb, \qquad\qquad$ (Def. 2.13)

$\qquad\qquad a(1/b \cdot b) = cb, \qquad\qquad$ (Ax. 6)

$\qquad\qquad\qquad a \cdot 1 = bc, \qquad\qquad\ $ (Ax. 11)

$\qquad\qquad\qquad\quad a = bc. \qquad\qquad\ $ (Ax. 9)

6 SOME PRODUCTS AND QUOTIENTS INVOLVING ZERO

The number zero is a special sort of number in many ways. In Axiom 8 we learned that if we add zero to any number a the result is a; for example, $3 + 0 = 3$, $-5 + 0 = -5$, $\sqrt{2} + 0 = \sqrt{2}$, etc. In the last section we defined division for all real numbers except zero. So, according to our definition, division by zero is not a permissible operation. The fact that division by zero is undefined actually stems from Axiom 11, which provides for a reciprocal for every real number except zero. It is not surprising, therefore, that students often have trouble with operations involving zero.

We shall now state and prove some theorems which, if completely understood by the student, should help make clear to him how to handle any situation in which zero is involved.

Theorem 2.10.   *If a is any real number, then $a \cdot 0 = 0$.*

Proof: $\qquad\qquad\qquad\ a \cdot 0 = a \cdot (0 + 0) \qquad\qquad\qquad$ (Prop. 4)

$\qquad\qquad\qquad\qquad a \cdot 0 = a \cdot 0 + a \cdot 0, \qquad\qquad\quad$ (Ax. 7)

$\qquad a \cdot 0 + [-(a \cdot 0)] = a \cdot 0 + a \cdot 0 + [-(a \cdot 0)], \qquad$ (Th. 2.4)

$\qquad\qquad\qquad\qquad\qquad = a \cdot 0 + \{a \cdot 0 + [-(a \cdot 0)]\}. \quad$ (Ax. 6)

Hence $\qquad\qquad\qquad\qquad 0 = a \cdot 0 + 0.$ $\qquad\qquad\qquad$ (Ax. 10)

Therefore $\qquad\qquad\qquad 0 = a \cdot 0.$ $\qquad\qquad\qquad\quad$ (Ax. 8)

Example. $7 \cdot 0 = 0, \; -8 \cdot 0 = 0, \; \sqrt[3]{5} \cdot 0 = 0,$ etc.

Theorem 2.11. *The product of two numbers is zero if, and only if, at least one of the numbers is zero. Stated in symbols, our theorem can be written $ab = 0$ if and only if $a = 0$ or $b = 0$.*

Proof: Suppose $a = 0$; then

$$ab = 0 \cdot b = 0. \qquad \text{(Th. 2.10)}$$

Similarly, if $b = 0$, then

$$ab = a \cdot 0 = 0.$$

Next, suppose $ab = 0$ and $b \neq 0$; then

$$
\begin{aligned}
(ab)1/b &= 0 \cdot 1/b = 0, \quad \text{(Why?)} \\
a(b \cdot 1/b) &= 0, & \text{(Ax. 6)} \\
a \cdot 1 &= 0, & \text{(Ax. 11)} \\
a &= 0. & \text{(Ax. 9)}
\end{aligned}
$$

In the same manner we can show that if $ab = 0$ and $a \neq 0$, then $b = 0$. Thus our theorem is proved. We shall discover that this is a very useful theorem in solving certain types of equations.

Example. Find the set S defined as $S = \{x \mid (x - 2)(x - 3) = 0\}$.

Solution: It follows from Theorem 2.8 that

$$(x - 2)(x - 3) = 0$$

if $x - 2 = 0$, that is, if $x = 2$; hence 2 belongs to S. Similarly,

$$(x - 2)(x - 3) = 0$$

if $x - 3 = 0$ or if $x = 3$. So $x = 3$ also belongs to S. Further, if y is a real number such that $y \neq 3$ and $y \neq 2$, then $(y - 3)(y - 2) \neq 0$. Hence $S = \{2, 3\}$.

Theorem 2.12. *If $a/b = 0$ and $b \neq 0$, then $a = 0$.*

The proof of Theorem 2.12 is left to the student.

Example. If $x/3 = 0$, then $x = 0$.

We shall state without proof the following final theorem concerning zero.

Theorem 2.13. *If $a \neq 0$, then $0/a = 0$.*

Example. $0/3 = 0, \; 0/\pi = 0, \; 0/-7 = 0,$ etc.

7 MULTIPLICATION OF NONZERO NUMBERS

Theorem 2.14. *If* a *and* b *are any two nonzero real numbers, then* $(-a)b = a(-b) = -ab$.

Proof:

$$0 = a\cdot0, \qquad\qquad \text{(Th. 2.10)}$$
$$b + (-b) = 0, \qquad\qquad \text{(Ax. 10)}$$
$$0 = a[b + (-b)], \qquad\qquad \text{(Prop. 4)}$$
$$0 = ab + a(-b), \qquad\qquad \text{(Ax. 7)}$$
$$0 = ab + (-ab), \qquad\qquad \text{(Ax. 10)}$$
$$ab + a(-b) = ab + (-ab), \qquad\qquad \text{(Prop. 3)}$$
$$a(-b) + ab = (-ab) + ab, \qquad\qquad \text{(Ax. 3)}$$
$$a(-b) = (-ab) = -ab. \qquad\qquad \text{(Th. 2.5)}$$

Similarly, by interchanging the roles of a and b we have

$$0 = b\cdot0,$$
$$= b[a + (-a)],$$
$$= ba + b(-a),$$
$$= ab + (-a)b.$$

Also,
$$0 = ab + (-ab).$$
Hence
$$ab + (-a)b = ab + (-ab),$$
$$(-a)b = (-ab) = -ab.$$

But, if $(-a)b = -ab$ and $-ab = a(-b)$, then

$$(-a)b = a(-b) = -ab. \qquad\qquad \text{(Prop. 4)}$$

By setting $a = 1$, we obtain an important special case, a corollary to Theorem 2.14.

Corollary 1. $(-1)b = -b$.

Now we can use Corollary 1 and Ax. 7 to obtain another corollary.

Corollary 2. $-(a + b) = -a - b$.

Theorem 2.15. *If* a *and* b *are any two nonzero real numbers, then* $(-a)(-b) = ab$.

Proof:
$$(-a)(-b) = -[a(-b)], \qquad \text{(Th. 2.14)}$$
$$= -(-ab) \qquad \text{(Th. 2.14)}$$
$$= ab. \qquad \text{(Th. 2.6)}$$

Corollary. $(-1)(-1) = 1$.

It should be emphasized that in Theorems 2.14 and 2.15 we have proved (a) that the product of the additive inverse of one number and a second number is the additive inverse of the product of the two numbers and (b) that the product of the additive inverses of two numbers is equivalent to the product of the two numbers.

Example. $(-3)4 = -(3 \cdot 4) = -12.$

Example. $(-3)(-4) = 3 \cdot 4 = 12.$

EXERCISES

1. Prove: If $a = b$ and $c = d$, then $a + c = b + d$.
2. Perform the indicated subtraction
a. 327 from 450.	**d.** 35 from -50.	**g.** -3.7 from 0.
b. 289 from 146.	**e.** -150 from -75.	**h.** 0.6475 from 0.0268.
c. -70 from 110.	**f.** 27 from 0.	**i.** -4.66 from 7.382.
3. Prove: $-(a - b) = -a + b$.
4. Prove: $(a + b)(c + d) = ac + bc + ad + bd$, and justify each step in your proof.
5. In each of the following statements replace the "question mark," where possible, by a real number which will make the statement true.

    a. $\dfrac{12}{3} = ?$ **e.** $\dfrac{72.9}{2.43} = ?$ **i.** $\dfrac{?}{10} = 0.$

    b. $\dfrac{57}{?} = 3.$ **f.** $\dfrac{17}{0} = ?$ **j.** $\dfrac{439856}{743} = ?$

    c. $\dfrac{?}{21} = -11.$ **g.** $\dfrac{35}{?} = 0.$ **k.** $(5)(?) = (10)(8).$

    d. $\dfrac{0}{7} = ?$ **h.** $(2.73)(0) = (?)(8.4).$

6. Prove: If a is a real number and $a + a = a$, then $a = 0$.
7. Simplify each given expression by writing it as a single number with the proper sign.
a. $(-3)(5).$	**d.** $-(-5)(4).$	**g.** $(-1)(-2)(-3)(-4)(-0.5).$
b. $(-7)(-4).$	**e.** $-[-(-3)(-7)].$	**h.** $(7 - 4)(3 - 8).$
c. $-(6 + 10).$	**f.** $-(3 - 5).$	**i.** $(3 - 5)(4 - 9).$
8. The symbols 2, 3, 4, 5, $\cdots$, used to represent the natural numbers in regular order may be defined as follows: $2 = 1 + 1$, $3 = 2 + 1$, $4 = 3 + 1$, $5 = 4 + 1$, and so, using these definitions prove
a. $3 + 2 = 5.$	**c.** $4 - 2 = 2.$	**e.** $2 - 5 = -3.$
b. $4 + 3 = 7.$	**d.** $7 - 3 = 4.$	
9. Prove: $-0 = 0$.
10. Prove the corollary to Theorem 2.15.
11. Prove: If a is any real number, then $0 - a = -a$.
12. Is subtraction commutative? That is, is $a - b = b - a$ for any two real numbers a and b?
13. Is subtraction associative? That is, is $(a - b) - c = a - (b - c)$ for all a and b?

14. Is multiplication distributive with respect to subtraction? That is, $a(b - c) = ab - ac$ for all a, b, and c?
15. If each lot in a certain residential section measures 66 feet across the front and if there are 14 lots in a certain block, how long is that block? How many such lots would there be in a distance of 1 mile (5280 feet)?
16. A certain airplane weighs 216,000 pounds at take-off. One-sixth of this weight is fuel. If the fuel weighs 7 pounds per gallon, how many gallons of fuel does the plane carry?

8 MULTIPLICATION AND DIVISION OF FRACTIONS

A clear understanding of the following theorems should be a great aid in any manipulation involving fractions.

Theorem 2.16. *If a and b are any two nonzero real numbers, then $1/a \cdot 1/b = 1/ab$.*

Proof is left to the student.

Theorem 2.17. *If a/b and c/d are any two fractions, then $a/b \cdot c/d = ac/bd$.*

Proof: The statement that a/b and c/d are fractions implies that $b \neq 0$ and $d \neq 0$:

$$a/b \cdot c/d = (a \cdot 1/b)(c \cdot 1/d),$$
$$= ac(1/b \cdot 1/d),$$
$$= ac \cdot 1/bd,$$
$$= ac/bd.$$

The justification of each step in the above proof is left to the student.

Note that Theorem 2.17 states that the product of two fractions is a fraction whose numerator is the product of the numerators of the given fractions and whose denominator is the product of the denominators of the given fractions.

If we let $c = d$ and assume $d \neq 0$, we obtain a very important result as a special case of Theorem 2.17:

$$c/c = c \cdot 1/c = 1$$

and hence $a/b = a/b \cdot 1 = a/b \cdot c/c = ac/bc$. Conversely, $ac/bc = a/b \cdot c/c = a/b \cdot 1 = a/b$. This result is the following fundamental principle.

Fundamental Principle of Fractions

The value of a fraction is not changed when the numerator and denominator are both multiplied or divided by the same number, provided they are not multiplied or divided by zero. (Memorize this.)

The importance of the fundamental principle of fractions cannot be overemphasized, for it is an invaluable tool in all manipulations involving fractions. It also should be pointed out that these are the only operations which can in general be performed upon a fraction without changing its value. For example, take the fraction $\frac{3}{4}$ and add 2 to both numerator and denominator and obtain $(3 + 2)/(4 + 2) = \frac{5}{6}$. But $\frac{5}{6} \neq \frac{3}{4}$. Next, subtract 2 from both the numerator and denominator of the fraction $\frac{3}{4}$. This gives $(3 - 2)/(4 - 2) = \frac{1}{2}$. Again, $\frac{1}{2} \neq \frac{3}{4}$. This last example is sufficient evidence for the statement that $(a + b)/(a + c) \neq b/c$ if $a \neq 0$ and $b \neq c$.

Example. $\frac{6}{8} = 3 \cdot 2/4 \cdot 2 = \frac{3}{4}$.

Theorem 2.18. *Suppose a/b and c/d are any two fractions and that $c/d \neq 0$; then $(a/b)/(c/d) = ad/bc$.*

Proof: It follows from the fundamental principle of fractions that

$$\frac{a/b \cdot bd/1}{c/d \cdot bd/1} = \frac{abd/b}{cbd/d} = ad/cb = ad/bc.$$

This theorem provides us with a simple rule for finding the quotient of two fractions.

Rule: To divide one fraction by another, invert the fraction in the denominator and multiply this inverted fraction by the fraction in the numerator.

Example. Divide $\frac{2}{3}$ by $\frac{7}{5}$.

Solution: $\dfrac{2}{3} \div \dfrac{7}{5} = \dfrac{2/3}{7/5} = \dfrac{2}{3} \cdot \dfrac{5}{7} = \dfrac{10}{21}.$

Two fractions are said to be *equivalent* if it is possible, by using the fundamental principle of fractions, to change either of the fractions into the other.

Theorem 2.19. *Given any two fractions, it is possible to write two new fractions that are respectively equivalent to the two given fractions such that the two new fractions have a common denominator, that is, that the two fractions have the same number in their denominators.*

Proof: Let a/b and c/d be any two fractions. By the fundamental principle of fractions, $a/b = ad/bd$ and $c/d = bc/bd$. But ad/bd and bc/bd have a common denominator, and hence our theorem is proved.

Note that in the proof of the last theorem a method is given of finding a common denominator for any two fractions and hence for any number of fractions; namely, a common denominator of two or more fractions is the product of the denominators of each fraction involved. Such a common denominator is not always the most desirable denominator, as will be seen in the following example.

Example.   Given the fractions $\frac{2}{3}$, $\frac{4}{5}$, and $\frac{7}{10}$, express them as equivalent fractions whose denominators are each a product of the denominators of the three given fractions.

Solution: Since $3 \cdot 5 \cdot 10$ is 150, each new fraction is to have 150 as denominator. Thus

$$\frac{2}{3} = \frac{2 \cdot 50}{3 \cdot 50} = \frac{100}{150}, \quad \frac{4}{5} = \frac{4 \cdot 30}{5 \cdot 30} = \frac{120}{150}, \quad \text{and} \quad \frac{7}{10} = \frac{7 \cdot 15}{10 \cdot 15} = \frac{105}{150}$$

are respectively equivalent to the original fractions $\frac{2}{3}$, $\frac{4}{5}$, and $\frac{7}{10}$, but the new fractions have identical denominators. In other words, they have a common denominator.

It is obvious that many other numbers would have served as common denominator of the three fractions, such as 30, 60, 90, 120. It should be noted that each of the numbers that could be used as common denominator of the three given fractions is a number that is exactly divisible by each denominator of the three fractions. This gives us a criterion for determining a common denominator of any group of fractions. This criterion may be stated in the following way: a common denominator of a set of fractions must contain as a factor the denominator of each fraction of the set. Obviously, for any given set of fractions many numbers meeting the conditions of the criterion can be found. In general, the preferred common denominator is the lowest common denominator, which is defined as follows:

The Lowest Common Denominator (L.C.D.)

The L.C.D. of a given set of fractions is a common denominator that is a factor of every common denominator of all the fractions in the set.

To find the lowest common denominator of two or more fractions, find the prime factors of the denominators of each given fraction, take the product of all the different factors thus found, and include in this product each different factor as many times as that factor occurs in any one of the denominators of the given fractions. This product is the required L.C.D.

Example.   Find the L.C.D. of the fractions $\frac{1}{6}$, $\frac{3}{8}$, and $\frac{7}{10}$, and express each fraction as an equivalent fraction whose denominator is this L.C.D.

Solution: Factoring each denominator gives $6 = 2 \cdot 3$, $8 = 2 \cdot 2 \cdot 2$, and $10 = 2 \cdot 5$. Thus the L.C.D. is $2 \cdot 2 \cdot 2 \cdot 3 \cdot 5 = 120$. By the method illustrated in the first example, $\frac{1}{6} = \frac{20}{120}$, $\frac{3}{8} = \frac{45}{120}$, and $\frac{7}{10} = \frac{84}{120}$, where $\frac{20}{120}$, $\frac{45}{120}$, and $\frac{84}{120}$ are the fractions equivalent, respectively, to $\frac{1}{6}$, $\frac{3}{8}$, and $\frac{7}{10}$, each having the common denominator, 120.

A fraction is said to be in *simplest form* when the numerator and denominator have no common factors other than 1.

9 ADDITION AND SUBTRACTION OF FRACTIONS

The rules for adding two or more signed fractions are embodied in the following theorems.

Theorem 2.20. *If a/b and c/d are any two fractions, then $a/b + c/d = (ad + bc)/bd$.*

$$Proof: \quad a/b + c/d = ad/bd + bc/bd = ad \cdot 1/bd + bc \cdot 1/bd,$$
$$= 1/bd(ad + bc),$$
$$= \frac{ad + bc}{bd}.$$

Example. $\dfrac{2}{3} + \dfrac{5}{7} = \dfrac{(14 + 15)}{21} = \dfrac{29}{21}.$

The *sign of a fraction* is the sign, actual or implied, that precedes the fraction. This sign should be placed on the same level as the line of division, for example $+\dfrac{3}{4}, -\dfrac{2}{3}, \dfrac{-4}{-7}$, etc. In the case of a fraction standing alone or one that is the first term of an expression, the sign of the fraction is usually omitted if it is a plus sign, for example $\dfrac{7}{8}$, or $\dfrac{1}{2} + \dfrac{3}{5} - \dfrac{2}{7}$. It is convenient to consider the numerator of a fraction as one term and the denominator of the fraction as one term. In this way we can associate with each fraction three signs, namely the sign of the numerator, the sign of the denominator, and the sign of the fraction. To do this we need a theorem.

Theorem 2.21. $-\dfrac{a}{b} = \dfrac{-a}{b}.$

$$Proof: \quad -\frac{a}{b} = (-1) \cdot \frac{a}{b} = [(-1)a] \cdot \frac{1}{b} = (-a) \cdot \frac{1}{b} = \frac{-a}{b}.$$

Now, by the fundamental principle of fractions, $\dfrac{-a}{b} = \dfrac{a}{-b}$ and $\dfrac{-a}{-b} = \dfrac{a}{b}.$ Therefore,

$$\frac{a}{b} = +\frac{a}{b} = \frac{-a}{-b} = -\frac{-a}{b} = -\frac{a}{-b}.$$

The following corollary follows immediately from Theorem 2.21.

Corollary. *Any two of the three signs associated with a fraction may be changed without changing the value of the fraction.*

Example. $-\dfrac{3+2}{5-7} = \dfrac{-(3+2)}{5-7} = \dfrac{-3-2}{5-7} = \dfrac{3+2}{7-5}.$

Example. $\dfrac{1}{2} - \dfrac{4}{5} = \dfrac{5}{10} - \dfrac{8}{10} = \dfrac{5-8}{10} = \dfrac{-3}{10} = -\dfrac{3}{10}.$

Example.   Combine into a single fraction and reduce to simplest form the expression $\frac{3}{12} - \frac{2}{15} + \frac{7}{20}$.

Solution: $\dfrac{3}{12} - \dfrac{2}{15} + \dfrac{7}{20} = \dfrac{15}{60} - \dfrac{8}{60} + \dfrac{21}{60} = \dfrac{15-8+21}{60}$

$$= \dfrac{28}{60} = \dfrac{7}{15}.$$

10   SYMBOLS OF GROUPING

It is often desirable to indicate that certain terms of an algebraic expression are to be grouped together and considered as a single number. Symbols of grouping in common use are *parentheses* ( ), *brackets* [ ], and *braces* { }. Since by the distributive law,

$$k(a + b - c) = ka + kb - kc,$$

it follows that for $k = +1$,

$$(+1)(a + b - c) = (+1)(a) + (+1)(b) + (+1)(-c)$$
$$= a + b - c.$$

But $(+1)(a + b - c) = +(a + b - c)$
$$= (a + b - c).$$

Hence $(a + b - c) = a + b - c.$

Similarly for $k = -1$, it follows that

$$(-1)(a + b - c) = (-1)(a) + (-1)(b) + (-1)(-c)$$
$$= -a - b + c.$$

Also $(-1)(a + b - c) = -(a + b - c).$

Therefore $-(a + b - c) = -a - b + c.$

This shows that to remove parentheses preceded by a plus sign, actual or implied, the terms involved are not changed. But to remove parentheses preceded by a minus sign, the sign of each term inside the parentheses must be changed. Hence, to insert parentheses preceded by a plus sign, no changes in the terms are to be made, while to insert parentheses preceded by a minus sign, it is necessary to change the sign of each term placed within the parentheses.

Example 1.
$$3x + 2ab + a - b = 3x + (2ab + a) - b$$
$$= 3x + 2ab + (a - b)$$
$$= (3x + 2ab) + (a - b).$$

Example 2. $6x - 5a + 3b + 7x - 3y = 6x - (5a - 3b) - (-7x + 3y).$

When removing symbols of grouping where one set of symbols is contained within another the following rule is suggested: first remove the innermost set of symbols and collect like terms; then continue this process until all symbols of grouping have been removed.

Example 3.
$$8x - \{6x - [3 - (x - 3)]\} = 8x - \{6x - [3 - x + 3]\}$$
$$= 8x - \{6x - [6 - x]\}$$
$$= 8x - \{6x - 6 + x\}$$
$$= 8x - \{7x - 6\}$$
$$= 8x - 7x + 6$$
$$= x + 6.$$

EXERCISES

1. Find each indicated product and reduce to simplest form

  a. $\dfrac{2}{3} \cdot \dfrac{7}{8}.$ **d.** $\left(\dfrac{5}{6}\right)\left(-\dfrac{7}{2}\right)\left(\dfrac{3}{14}\right).$ **g.** $\left(-\dfrac{7}{13}\right)\left(\dfrac{-5}{-21}\right)\left(\dfrac{9}{-4}\right).$

  b. $\left(-\dfrac{1}{2}\right)\left(\dfrac{4}{3}\right).$ **e.** $\left(\dfrac{3}{10}\right)\left(-\dfrac{5}{6}\right)\left(-\dfrac{2}{3}\right).$ **h.** $3\left(\dfrac{2}{3}\right)\left(\dfrac{1}{4}\right).$

  c. $\left(-\dfrac{3}{5}\right)\left(-\dfrac{15}{21}\right).$ **f.** $\left(-\dfrac{4}{9}\right)\left(-\dfrac{3}{8}\right)\left(\dfrac{7}{-2}\right).$

2. Perform each indicated division

  a. $\dfrac{2}{3} \div \dfrac{5}{6}.$ **d.** $\dfrac{7}{-5} \div \dfrac{28}{15}.$ **g.** $\dfrac{-\frac{3}{4}}{\frac{8}{9}}.$

  b. $-\dfrac{4}{7} \div \dfrac{3}{14}.$ **e.** $0 \div \dfrac{3}{4}.$ **h.** $\dfrac{\frac{3}{-7}}{\frac{-1}{4}}.$

  c. $-\dfrac{6}{11} \div \dfrac{3}{-22}.$ **f.** $\dfrac{4}{-9} \div \dfrac{-3}{-2}.$ **i.** $\dfrac{\frac{2}{3}}{5}.$

3. Combine each given expression into a single fraction reduced to simplest form

  a. $\frac{3}{7} + \frac{5}{14}.$ **d.** $\frac{1}{2} + \frac{5}{6} + \frac{3}{8}.$ **g.** $\frac{11}{15} - \frac{17}{35} + \frac{19}{21}.$
  b. $\frac{2}{5} + \frac{4}{3}.$ **e.** $\frac{1}{3} + \frac{7}{12} - \frac{1}{2}.$ **h.** $\frac{7}{18} + \frac{3}{4} - \frac{5}{8}.$
  c. $\frac{11}{12} - \frac{3}{4}.$ **f.** $-\frac{1}{6} - \frac{3}{8} + \frac{1}{2}.$

4. Simplify each given expression

a. $-\dfrac{4+2}{3-5}.$ c. $-\dfrac{5+3}{-2-4}.$ e. $\dfrac{7+3}{2+3}.$

b. $-\dfrac{-8-10}{6+3}.$ d. $\dfrac{-6-8}{3-7}.$ f. $\dfrac{ax-ay}{ax+ay}.$

5. Simplify each of the following complex fractions

a. $\dfrac{\frac{1}{2}+\frac{1}{3}}{1-\frac{1}{6}}.$ c. $\dfrac{\frac{3}{4}\cdot\frac{8}{5}}{\frac{8}{15}\div\frac{4}{5}}.$ e. $\dfrac{\frac{7}{8}+\frac{3}{5}-\frac{9}{20}}{\frac{3}{4}-\frac{7}{20}+\frac{5}{8}}.$

b. $\dfrac{\frac{2}{5}-\frac{1}{4}}{\frac{3}{2}+\frac{7}{20}}.$ d. $\dfrac{\frac{5}{7}\div\frac{3}{14}}{\frac{2}{3}\div\frac{5}{9}}.$ f. $\dfrac{\frac{-1}{2}\div\frac{3}{-4}}{\frac{2}{3}-(-\frac{1}{6})}.$

6. In each of the following expressions remove all symbols of grouping and combine terms.
   a. $(7-2)-(3-8+2).$ d. $-2(-7)+5(-3).$
   b. $(-7)(3)+(-5)(-2).$ e. $\{-[4-(3-6)+(4-1)]-(8-6)\}.$
   c. $(-6)(-4)-(-3)(-5).$
7. Write each given expression as an equivalent expression with the last two terms enclosed in parentheses preceded by a plus sign.
   a. $a+b-c.$ c. $a+b-c-d.$
   b. $a-b+c-d.$ d. $a-b-c+d.$
8. Write each given expression as an equivalent expression with the last two terms enclosed in parentheses preceded by a minus sign.
   a. $a-b-c.$ c. $a+b+c-d.$
   b. $a-b+c.$ d. $a-b-c+d.$
9. Write each given expression as an equivalent expression with no minus signs where possible and in any event with as few minus signs as possible.

a. $-\dfrac{-7}{-3}.$ c. $\dfrac{-3(-2)}{4-7}.$ e. $-\dfrac{a-b}{-a-b}.$

b. $\dfrac{-10}{-2}.$ d. $-\dfrac{8}{-4}.$ f. $\dfrac{-a-c}{a-b}.$

11 THE ORDER RELATIONS

It is often necessary to compare two real numbers. Unfortunately, their ability to be compared does not follow from the axioms and theorems already stated. To compare real numbers we need the following order axioms. The relation "is less than," $<$, is defined for the real numbers by these axioms.

The Order Axioms

Axiom 12. *If a and b are any two real numbers, then one and only one of the following statements is true: $a < b$, $a = b$, $b < a$.*

Axiom 13. *If a, b, and c are real numbers such that $a < b$ and $b < c$, then $a < c$.*

AXIOM 14.   *If a, b, and c are real numbers such that a < b, then a + c < b + c.*

AXIOM 15.   *If a, b, and c are real numbers such that a < b and 0 < c, then ac < bc.*

AXIOM 16.   *If a, b, and c are real numbers such that a < b and c < 0, then bc < ac.*

We often find it desirable to say that one number "is greater than" another number. To make this possible, we define the statement $a > b$, which is read "*a* is greater than *b*," as meaning $b < a$. Hence $a > b$ and $b < a$ are equivalent statements. Statements such as $a > b$ or $a < b$, involving "greater than" or "less than" symbols, are called *inequalities*.

In our discussion of the additive inverse of a real number we noted that the additive inverse $-a$ of the real number a is often referred to as the negative of *a*. The point was there made that $-a$ is not necessarily a negative number. The reader may have been a bit disturbed by such a statement, since positive and negative numbers had not yet been defined. We now define such numbers.

Definition 2.14.   *A real number a is said to be positive if a > 0, and it is said to be negative if a < 0.*

It follows from Axiom 12 that the real number 0 is neither positive nor negative. Also, Axiom 15 can now be stated: If $a < b$ and *c* is positive, then $ac < bc$. Similarly, Axiom 16 can be stated: If $a < b$ and *c* is negative, then $bc < ac$.

Example.   Let $a = -5$, $b = -2$, and $c = 4$; then $-5 < -2$ and $(-5)(4) < (-2)(4)$, or $-20 < -8$.

Example.   Let $a = -5$, $b = -2$, and $c = -4$; then $-5 < -2$ but $(-5)(-4) > (-2)(-4)$, or $20 > 8$.

Let us now state and prove some useful theorems concerning inequalities.

Theorem 2.22.   *If a and b are real numbers such that a < b, then b − a > 0.*

Proof:

$$a < b, \qquad \text{(given)}$$
$$a + (-a) < b + (-a), \qquad \text{(Ax. 15)}$$

Therefore
$$0 < b - a. \qquad \text{(Ax. 10)}$$

Theorem 2.22 states that if *a* is less than *b*, then $b - a$ is positive. The converse of this theorem is also true, namely: if $b - a$ is positive, then *a* is less than *b*. Stated more formally:

Theorem 2.23. *If $b - a > 0$, then $a < b$.*

We get as a special case of Theorem 2.22 for $b = 0$ the following theorem.

Theorem 2.24. *If $a < 0$, then $-a > 0$.*

Theorem 2.25. *If $ab > 0$, then either $a > 0$ and $b > 0$ or $a < 0$ and $b < 0$.*

Proof: Suppose that $a > 0$ and $b < 0$; then, by Axiom 16, $ab < 0$. This is a contradiction, because by Axiom 12 the number ab can satisfy only one of the relations $ab > 0$ and $ab < 0$. A similar argument shows that when $a < 0$ and $b > 0$ there is also a contradiction.

This theorem will be most useful, in the next chapter, for finding the solution sets of certain inequalities.

Theorem 2.26. *If $a \neq 0$, then $a^2 > 0$.*

Proof: Suppose $a > 0$.

Then	$a \cdot a > 0 \cdot a,$	(Ax. 15)
or	$a^2 > 0.$	
Next, suppose	$a < 0.$	
Then	$a \cdot a > 0 \cdot a$	(Ax. 16)
That is	$a^2 > 0.$	

By letting $a = 1$ and noting that $1^2 = 1$ we obtain the following corollary to Theorem 2.26.

Corollary. $1 > 0$.

The proofs of the following theorems are left to the student; it is understood that the letters a, b, c, etc., represent real numbers.

Theorem 2.27. *If $a + c < b + c$, then $a < b$.*

Theorem 2.28. *If $ac < bc$ and $c > 0$, then $a < b$.*

Theorem 2.29. *If $ac < bc$ and $c < 0$, then $a > b$.*

Theorem 2.30. *If $a > 0$, then $1/a > 0$ and if $a < 0$, then $1/a < 0$.*

Theorem 2.31. *If $a < b$ and $ab > 0$ then $1/a > 1/b$.*

Theorem 2.32. *For all fractions a/b and c/d, where b and d are positive, $a/b < c/d$ if and only if $ad < bc$.*

12   THE ABSOLUTE VALUE OF A REAL NUMBER

In operating with positive and negative numbers it is convenient to introduce what is called the *absolute value* of a real number a, denoted by the symbol $|a|$ and defined as follows:

Definition 2.15. $|a| = a$, *if a is positive or zero.*
$|a| = -a$, *if a is negative.*

Thus the absolute value of a non-zero number is always positive.

   Example. $|0| = 0, |6| = 6, |-7| = -(-7) = 7$. In the last case $a = -7$ and hence $-a = -(-7) = 7$.

   Let us now use the concept of absolute value to summarize the rules for adding, subtracting, multiplying, and dividing positive and negative numbers.

   Addition: To add two real numbers having like signs, add their absolute values and prefix their common sign. To add two real numbers having unlike signs, find the difference of their absolute values and prefix to it the sign of the number having the larger absolute value. (In either case, the result of adding is called the *algebraic sum* of the two numbers.)

   Subtraction: To subtract a real number a from a real number b is to find a real number c such that $a + c = b$. This operation can be accomplished by changing the sign of a and adding the result to b in accordance with the rules for addition.

   Multiplication: To multiply two real numbers, neither of which is zero, multiply their absolute values; prefix the plus sign to the product if the two numbers have like signs and prefix the minus sign if they have unlike signs.

   Division: To divide a real number a by a nonzero real number b is to find a number c such that $a = bc$. In carrying out this operation, find the quotient of the absolute value of a divided by the absolute value of b; prefix to it the plus sign if a and b have like signs and prefix the minus sign if a and b have unlike signs. (Remember: division by zero is not defined. To understand this fact better one may consider that, if a is not zero and b is zero, it is impossible to find a number c such that $a = bc$, but that, on the other hand, if $a = 0$ and $b = 0$, any real number c will satisfy the relation $a = bc$.)

   It should be observed that the set of all numbers x for which $|x| < 3$ consists of all numbers between -3 and 3.

13 THE NUMBER LINE

In working with real numbers it is often helpful to be able to think of them as being placed on a *number line;* that is, each number of the set of real numbers corresponds to a point on a line. Such a correspondence can be established in the following way.

Consider, for convenience, a horizontal line L extending indefinitely in both directions (Fig. 2.1). Choose a point O on L and let this point correspond

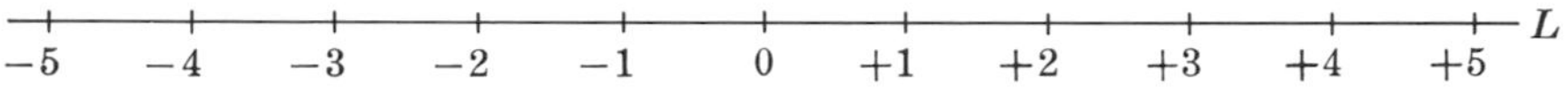

FIGURE 2.1

to the number zero. We shall call this point the *zero point*, or the *origin*. Choose a second point A, distinct from O and to the right of it; let the point correspond to the number $+1$. Taking the distance OA as the unit of distance; the number scale is now fixed, if we consider distances measured to the right as positive and those to the left as negative. If x is any positive real number, the point on the number line at a distance x units to the right of the origin shall be taken as the point which corresponds to the number x. If x is a negative real number, the point on the number line at a distance $|x|$ units to the left of the origin shall be taken as the point corresponding to the negative number x. Thus, the point that corresponds to 5 is the point on the number line five units to the right of the origin, while the point that corresponds to -4 is the point four units to the left of the origin. Conversely, a point P to the right of the origin, whose distance from the origin is d units, shall have as its corresponding real number the positive real number d and, similarly, if d is any positive real number and Q is a point d units to the left of the origin, then the real number $-d$ shall correspond to the point Q. This device provides a correspondence such that to each real number there is one and only one corresponding point on the number line. We shall assume that, conversely, to each point on the number line there corresponds one and only one real number.

It follows, from the method used in setting up the correspondence between the set of real numbers and the points on the number line and from our definition of "less than," that the real number a is less than the real number b if and only if the point on the number line that corresponds to a lies to the left of the point that corresponds to b.

Example. Draw a number line and indicate on this line the points which correspond to the real numbers $-3, -2, -1, 0, 1, 2$, and 3. Also indicate the points which correspond to $2\frac{1}{2}$ and to $\sqrt{2}$.

Solution: See Fig. 2.2.

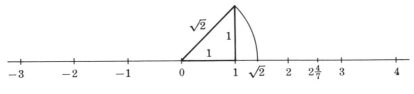

FIGURE 2.2

EXERCISES

1. Indicate the order relation between the numbers in each of the following pairs (for example in **a.** 3 < 4):
    a.   3, 4.   **d.**   −2, 1.   **g.** $\pi \frac{2 \cdot 2}{7}$.
    b.   5, −2.   **e.**   −4, −5.   **h.**   −8, 0.
    c.   0, 3.   **f.**   12.3, 12$\frac{1}{3}$.   **i.**   −423, 1.
2. Arrange the following numbers in ascending order (i.e., least one first, etc.):
    $-1, 3, 2, 0, \sqrt{3}, -4, -6, -\frac{1}{2}, \sqrt{7}, 13, \sqrt{100}, -6\frac{1}{4}, 21$.
3. Indicate the order relation between ac and bc in each of the following cases.
    a. $a = 2, b = 5, c = 4$.   **d.** $a = 2, b = 5, c = -4$.
    b. $a = 2, b = -5, c = 4$.   **e.** $a = 2, b = -5, c = -4$.
    c. $a = -2, b = -5, c = 4$.   **f.** $a = -2, b = -5, c = -4$.
4. Use Theorem 2.31 to select the larger of the two fractions in each of the following pairs of fractions.

    a. $\dfrac{2}{3}, \dfrac{4}{7}$.   **c.** $\dfrac{371}{586}, \dfrac{728}{1107}$.

    b. $\dfrac{11}{17}, \dfrac{20}{31}$.   **d.** $\dfrac{40783}{31426}, \dfrac{81565}{62752}$.

5. Prove Theorem 2.27.
6. Draw a number line and label the points corresponding to 0, 1, 3, −2, $\frac{3}{2}$, 2.4, $-\frac{5}{6}$, $\sqrt{5}$, $\sqrt{8}$.
7. How could one use the number line to define addition and subtraction of real numbers?
8. Prove Theorem 2.28 [*Hint:*   If $ac < bc$, then $c(b − a) > 0$. But $c > 0$ therefore $(b − a) > 0$, etc.].
9. Prove Theorem 2.29. [see *hint* in Exercise 8].
10. Prove Theorem 2.30. [*Hint:* $a \cdot 1/a = 1 > 0$].
11. Prove Theorem 2.31. [*Hint:*   Use Theorem 2.30].
12. Find the absolute value of each of the following numbers: 5, −8, $-\frac{3}{4}$, π, −189, 17, −2.5.
13. If $2 = 1 + 1, 3 = 2 + 1, 4 = 3 + 1$, prove
    a.   2 > 1.   **d.**   3 > 1.   **g.** $\frac{1}{2} > 0$.
    b.   2 > 0.   **e.**   4 > 0.   **h.** $-\frac{1}{3} < 0$.
    c.   3 > 2.   **f.**   −3 < −2.
14. Prove: If $a < b$ then $a < \dfrac{a + b}{2} < b$.

15. Prove: **a.** If $a > 0$ and $b > 0$, then $a + b > 0$.
    b. If $a < 0$ and $b < 0$, then $a + b < 0$.

16. Find the value of each of the following expressions; write in simplest form free of absolute value symbols.

   a. $|7 - 5|$.

   c. $\dfrac{|5 - 9|}{|6 - 4|}$.

   e. $\dfrac{4 - 8}{|-2|}$.

   b. $|3 - 8|$.

   d. $|-3| \cdot |8|$.

   f. $\dfrac{|5 - 5|}{|-7|}$.

17. By examining the four cases (1) a and b both positive; (2) a and b both negative; (3) one positive and the other negative; (4) one is zero, prove that $|a| \cdot |b| = |ab|$.

18. Label each of the following statements as T (true) or F (false):
   a. $|4| = 4$.
   b. $|-5| = -5$.
   c. $|2 + 3| = |2| + |3|$.
   d. $|-7| > 1$.
   e. If $|a| < 5$, then $-5 < a < 5$.
   f. $|3 - \pi| = \pi - 3$.
   g. $|2 - 7| = |7 - 2|$.
   h. $|5 - 8| < |5| - |8|$.

19. By examining cases similar to those used in Exercise 17, prove that if a and b are real numbers, then $|a + b| < |a| + |b|$ or $|a + b| = |a| + |b|$ and state when the equality sign holds.

20. **a.** Find four different numbers each of which lies between $\dfrac{17}{29}$ and $\dfrac{18}{29}$.

   b. Which is the larger $\dfrac{7}{-11}$ or $\dfrac{10}{-17}$?

   c. Is the following statement true or false? $\dfrac{a}{a} > 0$ for all real numbers a.

14   RECTANGULAR COORDINATE SYSTEM

In the last section we were able to set up a one-to-one correspondence between the points on a line and the real numbers. We shall now use the same general idea to set up a one-to-one correspondence between the points in a plane and ordered pairs of real numbers. Ordered pairs were briefly described in Chapter I in preparation for the definition of the Cartesian product of two sets but were not formally defined at that time. Since the concept of ordered pairs of real numbers is of great importance in this and later sections, we state the following definitions.

Definition 2.16.   *An ordered pair of real numbers is a pair of real numbers, denoted symbolically as* (a, b), *where* a *is designated as the first element or component of the pair and* b *is designated as the second element or component of the pair. The first element is always listed first in the parenthesis. Further, two ordered pairs* (a, b) *and* (c, d) *are equal if and only if* $a = c$ *and* $b = d$. *In particular,* $(a, b) = (b, a)$ *if and only if* $a = b$.

Suppose that X is some set of real numbers and that Y is also a set of real numbers. It will be recalled that the Cartesian product $X \times Y$ is the set of all possible ordered pairs (x, y) whose first element, x, belongs to X and whose second element, y, belongs to Y, x and y may or may not be identical. Stated in symbols

$$X \times Y = \{(x, y) \mid \times \in X \quad \text{and} \quad y \in Y\}.$$

Example. If $X = \{1, 2, 3\}$ and $Y = \{5, 7\}$, then

$$X \times Y = \{(1, 5), (1, 7), (2, 5), (2, 7), (3, 5), (3, 7)\}.$$

Example. If $X = \{1, 2, 3\}$ and $Y = \{1, 2, 3\}$, then

$$X \times Y = \{(1\ 1), (1, 2), (1, 3), (2, 1), (2, 2), (2, 3), (3, 1), (3, 2), (3, 3)\}.$$

Referring again to the last section, we established a one-to-one correspondence between the real numbers and the points on a line which gave what we called a number line. It is conventional to call the real number associated with a particular point on a number line the coordinate of that point and hence to refer to a number line as a *one-dimensional-coordinate system*. We have already observed that such a coordinate system gives us a graphical interpretation of the relative magnitudes of numbers. For example, the algebraic fact $4 < 7$ corresponds to the geometric fact that the point with coordinate 4 lies to the left of the point with coordinate 7. We say that a number line is the graph of the set of all real numbers. The graph of a set S of real numbers consists of the set of all the points on a number line whose coordinates are the elements of S. Thus, if S contains only one number, then the graph of S consists of just one point; or in general if S contains n distinct numbers, then the graph of S consists of the n points on a number line whose coordinates are the n numbers in S. It may happen that a set S consists of the numbers a and b and all the numbers between a and b or perhaps the set contains the numbers between a and b but not a or b. Other possibilities are that S contains all numbers between a and b and contains a but not b, or contains b but not a. In each of these cases the graph consists of a segment of a number line which may contain both, one, or neither of its end points. In discussing such cases the following notation will be helpful.

Notation: Let a and b be any two real numbers such that $a < b$. Now consider a number line and the two fixed points on this line which represent the numbers a and b respectively. For convenience we shall refer to the point corresponding to a as the point a and the point corresponding to b as the point b. The set of points on the number line consisting of the point a, the point b, and all the points between a and b is called a *closed interval* and is denoted by the symbol $[a, b]$. The graph of this set of points is shown in Fig. 2.3 (a). Note that we indicate that a and b are included in the set by the black dots at their points.

The set of points consisting only of the points between a and b, not including either a or b, is called an *open interval* and is denoted by the symbol

(a, b). The graph of (a, b) is shown in Fig. 2.3 (b). Note the small open circles at points a and b, indicating that they do not belong to the set.

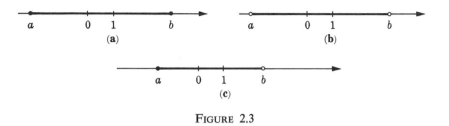

FIGURE 2.3

If we wish to include in our set the point a but not the point b, we denote such a set by the symbol [a, b) and represent it graphically as in Fig. 2.3 (c). Similarly, the symbol (a, b] denotes all the points on the number line between a and b together with the point b but not including the point a. Such a point set is often referred to as a *half-open* interval. For the sake of completeness we shall denote the set of all numbers greater than b by the symbol (b, ∞); similarly, we shall denote the set of all numbers less than a by the symbol ($-\infty$, a).

In mathematics we are often concerned with sets whose elements are ordered pairs of real numbers and thus have a need for some method of representing such a set graphically. That is, we need a system which produces an association between a point in the plane and an ordered pair of real numbers. The system we are about to describe does just that. In fact, this system establishes a one-to-one correspondence between the points in a plane and the ordered pairs (x, y) of the set $X \times Y$ of ordered pairs of real numbers, where $X = Y = R$, R being the set of all real numbers. The set $X \times Y$ is thus the set of all possible ordered pairs of real numbers.

To establish a one-to-one correspondence between the points in the plane and the ordered pairs of the set $X \times Y$, we first construct in the plane two perpendicular lines $X'X$ and $Y'Y$, which we shall call the x axis and the y axis, respectively. For purposes of discussion it is convenient to think of the x axis as being horizontal and the y axis as being vertical. Their point of intersection, we shall call the *origin*. We next set up a one-dimensional-coordinate system on each of the two axes. On each axis, we make the origin correspond to the real number 0. On the x axis the points to the right of the origin are made to correspond to the positive real numbers, and the points to the left of the origin are made to correspond to the negative real numbers. The unit of distance used on each axis is arbitrary and may be different for the two axes. In fact, it is often desirable to use different units of measurement, particularly when the units on the two are to be interpreted as representing different physical units of measurement which are not comparable (temperature, distance, speed, etc.).

The framework just described, the x and y axes together with their respective arbitrary scales, is called a *rectangular coordinate system*. The word "rectangular" here refers to the fact that the axes are mutually perpendicular.

We can now use this system to associate with each point P in the plane an ordered pair of real numbers. First, suppose that P is a point on the x axis. Since a one-to-one correspondence between the points on the x axis and the real numbers has already been established, each point on the x axis has one and only one coordinate in this one-dimensional system. Thus P corresponds to some real number a; we associate with P the ordered pair $(a, 0)$, which signifies a on the x axis and 0 on the y axis. Similarly, if P is on the y axis it has a coordinate, b, in the one-dimensional-coordinate system already established on that axis. In this case associate with the point P, the ordered pair $(0, b)$. Finally, let P be a point that is not on either of the axes. Through it draw a line parallel to the y axis and intersecting the x axis in some point M. Draw also a line through P, parallel to the x axis and intersecting the y axis in some point N (see Fig. 2.4). The point M, being on the x axis, will

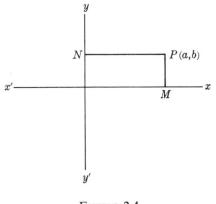

FIGURE 2.4

correspond to some real number a, and the point N, being on the y axis, will correspond to some real number b. We shall associate with the point P the ordered pair (a, b) of real numbers (Fig. 2.4).

Thus, by means of a rectangular coordinate system we have made correspond to each point P in the plane an ordered pair (a, b) of real numbers. To make the correspondence one to one, we simply agree to associate with each ordered pair of real numbers the point determined by it. For example, suppose we are given the ordered pair (a, b). The real number a corresponds to a point M on the x axis and the number b corresponds to a point N on the y axis. The line drawn through M parallel to the y axis and the line drawn through N parallel to the x axis will intersect in the desired point P.

We have now established a one-to-one correspondence between the points of a plane and the ordered pairs (a, b) of real numbers. When a rectangular coordinate system of x and y axes has been established in a plane, we often call the plane the x-y plane.

Definition 2.17.   *The real numbers a and b in the ordered pair (a, b) associated with the point P are called the* coordinates *of the point P. The first number, a, of the pair is called the* x coordinate *of P and the second number, b, is called the* y coordinate *of P.*

We often refer to a point with coordinates (a, b) as the point (a, b). We shall also say "$P(a, b)$," which is read "the point P with coordinates (a, b)." The x coordinate of a point is also known as the *abscissa* of the point and the y coordinate as the *ordinate* of the point. If a point lies to the right of the y axis its abscissa is a positive number; and if it lies to the left, the abscissa is negative. Similarly, the ordinate of a point is positive if the point lies above the x axis and it is negative if it lies below. We therefore interpret the abscissa and ordinate of a point as being the directed distances of the point from the x and y axes, respectively. That is, the abscissa and ordinate of a point each exhibit two kinds of information about the point, namely direction and distance. For example, if the abscissa of a point P is -3, the minus sign gives the direction of the point from the y axis and $|-3|$ gives the distance of the point from the y axis in terms of the units used in the scale on the x axis. So the point P is on a line parallel to the y axis and 3 units to the left.

Example.   The point $(3, -2)$ is a point that is on a line parallel to the y axis and 3 units to the right. It is also on a line parallel to the x axis and 2 units below it. Hence it is the point of intersection of these two lines. See Fig. 2.5.

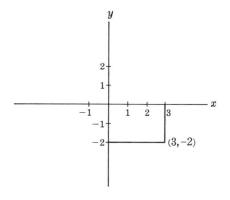

FIGURE 2.5

Let us now point out some rather obvious but yet very important details in connection with a rectangular coordinate system. The coordinates of the origin are obviously $(0, 0)$. The x and y axes divide the plane into four portions called *quadrants*. These quadrants are numbered I, II, III, IV, beginning with the one in the upper right-hand corner and going counterclockwise. See Fig. 2.6. If a point lies in quadrant I, its coordinates both are positive, and

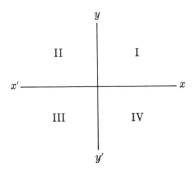

FIGURE 2.6

conversely. In quadrant II the abscissa is negative and the ordinate is positive. In quadrant III both abscissa and ordinate are negative. In quadrant IV the abscissa is positive and the ordinate is negative. The abscissa of every point on the y axis is zero and the ordinate of every point on the x axis is zero. Locating a point in the plane having a given pair of real numbers as its coordinates is called *plotting the point*. In Fig. 2.5 we plotted the point whose coordinates were $(3, -2)$.

We shall represent the coordinates of a general point in the plane as (x, y), but if we want to talk about a specified fixed point in the plane without using its actual numerical coordinates, we will either use subscripts, as (x_1, y_1), or (x_2, y_2), or we will use letters at the beginning of the alphabet, as (a, b) or (c, d). Two points whose ordinates are the same lie on a line parallel to the x axis, and two points whose abscissas are the same lie on a line parallel to the y axis. We may define *distance* between two such points as follows.

Definition 2.18. *The distance between the points $P_1(x_1, y_1)$ and $P_2(x_2, y_1)$, denoted by $d(P_1, P_2)$ is defined as $d(P_1, P_2) = |x_2 - x_1|$. The distance between the points $Q_1(x_1, y_1)$ and $Q_2(x_1, y_2)$ is defined as $d(Q_1, Q_2) = |y_2 - y_1|$.*

It is obvious that the distance between two points not on a line parallel to one of the coordinate axes is meaningless except when the same scale is used on both axes.

EXERCISES

1. Draw the graph of each given interval.
    a. $[1, 5]$.
    b. $[-3, 2]$.
    c. $[-5, 5]$.
    d. $(1, 4)$.
    e. $(-1, 3)$.
    f. $(-2, 1]$.
    g. $[3, 5)$.
    h. $(-\infty, 2)$.
    i. $(-3, \infty)$.

2. Plot the following points:
   a. $P_1(5, 3)$. c. $P_3(4, -7)$. e. $P_5(0, 4)$.
   b. $P_2(-2, 1)$. d. $P_4(-6, -3)$. f. $P_6(-5, 0)$.
3. Find the distance between the given pairs of points.
   a. $P_1(3, 2)$ and $P_2(10, 2)$. c. $P_3(-4, 3)$ and $P_4(2, 3)$.
   b. $Q_1(5, -2)$ and $Q_2(5, -9)$. d. $Q_3(-1, 7)$ and $Q_4(-1, 5)$.
4. Where must a point lie if its abscissa is 3? If -3? Where must a point lie if its ordinate is 5? If -5?
5. Using the same scale on both the x and y axes, plot the following points: $(-5, 7)$, $(-3, 5)$, $(0, 2)$, $(5, -3)$, $(8, -6)$. Do these points seem to have any property in common?
6. Using the same scale on each of the axes plot the following points: $(3, 4)$, $(0, 5)$, $(-3, 4)$, $(-4, 3)$, $(-5, 0)$, $(-4, -3)$, $(-3, -4)$, $(0, -5)$, $(3, -4)$, $(4, -3)$. Connect these points by a smooth curve. What conclusion do you come to?
7. Assuming that the same scale is used on both axes, where would all the points lie whose abscissas and ordinates were equal? Where would they lie if the units were different?

15 COMPLEX NUMBERS

Although our concern in this course will be chiefly with real numbers, problems will arise in which the real number is not adequate for their solutions. For example, the equation $x^2 + 1 = 0$ has no solution in the system of real numbers. To handle such situations we now introduce a more inclusive number system, called the *complex number system* which contains the set of real numbers as a subset.

Definition 2.19. *A complex number is an ordered pair, (a, b), of real numbers, usually represented symbolically in the form $a + bi$ or $a + ib$ which are assumed to be equivalent. If $b = 0$ the complex number is the real number a; if $a = 0$ the complex number $0 + bi = bi$ is called a pure imaginary number, i being the imaginary unit.*

When a new class of numbers is defined it is necessary at the same time to define laws of operation for them. Since, as was noted above, a complex number may be a real number, any law of operation for complex numbers must reduce to a known law for real numbers when the complex numbers being operated upon are real numbers. The following rules of operation for complex numbers will be sufficient for our purposes.

Equality: Two complex numbers $a + bi$ and $c + di$ are equal if and only if $a = c$ and $b = d$. In particular $a + bi = 0 + 0i = 0$ if and only if $a = 0$ and $b = 0$.

Example. $x + yi = 3 - 7i$ if and only if $x = 3$ and $y = -7$.

Example.   For what real values of x and y is the equation $5x - 3yi = 20 + 15i$ a true statement?

Solution: If $5x - 3yi = 20 + 15i$, then $5x = 20$ and $-3y = 15$. That is, $x = 4$ and $y = -5$.

Addition: Addition is defined by the relation

$$(a + bi) + (c + di) = (a + c) + (b + d)i.$$

Example. $(3 + 2i) + (5 + 4i) = (3 + 5) + (2 + 4)i = 8 + 6i.$
$(7 + 3i) + (-2 - 5i) = (7 - 2) + (3 - 5)i = 5 - 2i.$

In the complex number $a + bi$, a is called the *real* part of the number and b is called the *imaginary* part. Thus, to add two complex numbers, add the real parts and add the imaginary parts.

Subtraction: Subtraction is defined by the relation

$$(a + bi) - (c + di) = (a - c) + (b - d)i.$$

Multiplication: The product of two complex numbers $(a + bi)$ and $(c + di)$ is defined by the relation

$$(a + bi)(c + di) = (ac - bd) + (ad + bc)i.$$

Now if $a = 0$, $b = 1$, $c = 0$, and $d = 1$, we get the interesting relation

$$(i)(i) = i^2 = (0 - 1) + (0 + 0)i = -1.$$

Hence it is common practice to consider i as used in the form $a + bi$ to be a symbol which represents a number whose square is -1. For convenience we may write $i = \sqrt{-1}$, or in general, if a is a positive real number then $\sqrt{-a} = i\sqrt{a}$. This convention enables us to find the product $(a + bi)(c + di)$ by ordinary algebra and replacing i^2 by -1. Thus:

$$\begin{aligned}
(a + bi)(c + di) &= ac + adi + bci + bdi^2 \\
&= ac + (ad + bc)i - bd \\
&= (ac - bd) + (ad + bc)i.
\end{aligned}$$

It is therefore unnecessary to memorize the definition for the product of two complex numbers, we only need to use ordinary algebra and the relation $i^2 = -1$.

The numbers $a + bi$ and $a - bi$ are called *conjugate complex numbers.* Each is said to be the conjugate of the other. The following Table exhibits some examples of numbers and their conjugates.

Number	Conjugate
$2 + 5i$	$2 - 5i$
$-3 - 7i$	$-3 + 7i$
$-2i$	$2i$
$4 \qquad [4 = 4 + 0i]$	4

Since $(a + bi)(a - bi) = a^2 - b^2i^2 = a^2 + b^2$, it follows that the product of any complex number and its conjugate is a real number.

Division: Division is defined as the inverse of multiplication, that is

$$\frac{a + bi}{c + di} = x + yi, \qquad c + di \neq 0,$$

if and only if real numbers x and y exist such that

$$a + bi = (x + yi)(c + di).$$

Obviously, if $c + di \neq 0$, then

$$(c + di)\left(\frac{c - di}{c^2 + d^2}\right) = \frac{c^2 + d^2}{c^2 + d^2} = 1.$$

It follows from this product and the definition of division that

$$\frac{1}{c + di} = \frac{c}{c^2 + d^2} - \frac{d}{c^2 + d^2}i, \qquad c + di \neq 0.$$

That is, every non-zero complex number has a reciprocal which is also a complex number. We may generalize this result as follows.

$$\frac{a + bi}{c + di} = (a + bi)\left(\frac{1}{c + di}\right) = (a + bi)\left(\frac{c - di}{c^2 + d^2}\right) = \frac{(ac + bd) + (bc - ad)i}{c^2 + d^2}$$

or

$$\frac{a + bi}{c + di} = \frac{ac + bd}{c^2 + d^2} + \frac{bc - ad}{c^2 + d^2}i, \qquad c + di \neq 0.$$

It is important to observe that this result could have been obtained by multiplying the numerator and denominator of the given fraction by the conjugate of the denominator and replacing i^2 by -1, thus:

$$\frac{a + bi}{c + di} = \frac{(a + bi)(c - di)}{(c + di)(c - di)} = \frac{(ac - bdi^2) + bci - adi}{c^2 + d^2}$$

$$= \frac{(ac + bd)}{c^2 + d^2} + \frac{(bc - ad)i}{c^2 + d^2}.$$

In fact, this is the procedure most commonly used in expressing the quotient of two complex numbers in the form $x + yi$.

Example. Express the fraction $(5 + 4i)/(3 + 2i)$ in the form $x + yi$.

Solution: $\dfrac{5 + 4i}{3 + 2i} = \dfrac{(5 + 4i)(3 - 2i)}{(3 + 2i)(3 - 2i)} = \dfrac{15 + 2i - 8i^2}{9 - 4i^2} = \dfrac{15 + 2i + 8}{9 + 4}$

$$= \frac{23}{13} + \frac{2}{13}i.$$

It is easy to verify that the set of complex numbers, $C = \{a + bi \mid a \in R\}$ and $b \in R\}$ with the operations of addition and multiplication defined above as the two operations involved, do satisfy the eleven field axioms of Section 4. Hence the complex numbers form a field.

EXERCISES

1. Find each indicated sum.
   a. $(2 + 3i) + (7 + 11i)$.
   b. $(5 - 4i) + (-3 + 6i)$.
   c. $(-1 + i) + (-2 + 5i)$.
   d. $(-6 - 11i) + (-8 - 12i)$.
   e. $(4 + 5i) + (4 - 5i)$.
   f. $8 + (3 - 7i)$.
   g. $(-4 - 8i) + 11$.
   h. $(43 - 17i) + 85 + 49i)$.

2. Find each indicated difference.
   a. $(5 + 8i) - (3 + 4i)$.
   b. $(13 - 2i) - (8 + 5i)$.
   c. $(-4 - 5i) - (2 - 3i)$.
   d. $(6 - i) - (7 + 3i)$.
   e. $(10 - 5i) - (6 - 8i)$.
   f. $(-6 - 10i) - (-13 - 21i)$.

3. Find each indicated product.
   a. $(2 + 5i)(4 + 3i)$.
   b. $(7 - 3i)(-1 - i)$.
   c. $(1 + i)(1 - i)$.
   d. $(1 + 2i)(3 - i)$.
   e. $(3 - 2i)(6 - 5i)$.
   f. $(4i)(3i - 7)$.
   g. $(1 + i)(1 + i)$.
   h. $(1 - i)(1 - i)$.

4. Express each given quotient in the form $x + yi$.

   a. $\dfrac{1 - i}{1 + i}$.

   b. $\dfrac{2}{3 - i}$.

   c. $\dfrac{3 + 4i}{5 + 2i}$.

   d. $\dfrac{7 - 3i}{i}$.

   e. $\dfrac{25i}{3 - 4i}$.

   f. $\dfrac{-4 + 2i}{-2 - 3i}$.

5. Verify that each given equation is a true statement.
   a. $(2 + 3i)^2 - 4(2 + 3i) + 13 = 0$.
   b. $(2 - 3i)^2 - 4(2 - 3i) + 13 = 0$.
   c. $i^4 + 5i^2 + 4 = 0$.
   d. $(-1 + 2i)^2 + 2(-1 + 2i) + 5 = 0$.
   e. $(-1 - 2i)^2 + 2(-1 - 2i) + 5 = 0$.

   f. $4\left(\dfrac{3 + 5i}{2}\right)^2 - 12\left(\dfrac{3 + 5i}{2}\right) + 34 = 0$.

6. Use the definition of equality of two complex numbers to determine real values of x and y for which each given equation is a true statement.
   a. $2x + 5yi = 4 - 10i$.
   b. $3x - 2i = 9 - yi$.
   c. $i(y + xi) + 4 - 7i = 0$.
   d. $(x + y + 2) + (x - y - 4)i = 0$.

7. Suppose $Z_1 = a + bi$, $Z_2 = c + di$, and $Z_3 = e + fi$, where a, b, c, d, e, and f are real numbers. Show that
   a. $Z_1 + Z_2 = Z_2 + Z_1$.
   b. $Z_1 Z_2 = Z_2 Z_1$.
   c. $(Z_1 + Z_2) + Z_3 = Z_1 + (Z_2 + Z_3)$.
   d. $(Z_1 Z_2) Z_2 = Z_1(Z_2 Z_3)$.
   e. $Z_1(Z_2 + Z_3) = Z_1 Z_2 + Z_1 Z_3$.

8. Let $C = \{(x + yi) \mid x \in R \text{ and } y \in R\}$. Show that C is closed under the operations addition and multiplication of complex numbers.

9. The complex number Z_2 is the additive inverse of the complex number Z_1

if and only if $Z_1 + Z_2 = 0$. Find the additive inverse of each of the following complex numbers. Also find the conjugate.

a. $2 + 3i$.   **c.** $-4 - 2i$.   **e.** $\dfrac{2 + i}{1 - i}$.

b. $5 - 7i$.   **d.** $1/i$.

10. Find the multiplicative inverse of each of the numbers in Exercise 9.

11. Prove: If $Z_1 = a + bi$, $Z_2 = c + di$, and $Z_1Z_2 = 0$, then $Z_1 = 0$ or $Z_2 = 0$.

III

ELEMENTARY ALGEBRAIC PROCESSES

1 THE TERMINOLOGY OF ALGEBRA

Elementary algebra may be described as a generalized arithmetic in which letters are used to represent numbers. For example, the arithmetic facts that $5 + 5 + 5 = (3)(5)$, $6 + 6 + 6 = (3)(6)$, $(-4) + (-4) + (-4) = (3)(-4)$, etc., are all special cases of the more general statement that $x + x + x = 3x$, where the letter x represents an arbitrary number. In the study of algebra it is essential to acquaint ourselves with certain terminology. As was pointed out in Section 3 of Chapter 1, letters such as x, when used to represent numbers, are called *variables*. The four fundamental operations involving variables are precisely the same as those for real numbers; for example, if x and y represent arbitrary real numbers, we denote their sum by $x + y$, their difference by $x - y$, their product by xy, and their quotient by x/y. An *algebraic expression* is an expression formed by using specific numbers or letters which represent arbitrary numbers, or both, and symbols of operations, such as 2, x, $3x^2y - 2y^3 + 5$, $a + b$, etc. The parts of an expression that are separated by plus and minus signs are called *terms;* in the preceding examples they are $3x^2y$, $-2y^3$, and 5. An algebraic expression of one term is a *monomial*, one of two terms is a *binomial*, and one of three terms is a *trinomial*. Any expression of two or more terms may be called a *multinomial:* the monomial $6xy$, the binomial $2x + 3y$, and the trinomial $3x^2 - 5x + 4$ are multinomials. Each number, letter, or algebraic expression in an indicated product is called a *factor;* for instance, 2, x, and y are factors of $2xy$, and $(x - y)$ and $(x + y)$ are factors of $(x - y)(x + y)$. In the term $2xy$, the number 2 is the *numerical coefficient* of xy, and xy is the *variable coefficient* of 2, x is the variable coefficient of $2y$, and y is the variable coefficient of $2x$. The product of two or more identical factors is called a *power* of that factor; thus, $x \cdot x \cdot x$ is denoted by x^3, where the *exponent* 3 indicates the number of factors x in the product. A second-power number, such as x^2, is called a *square;* a third-power number, such as x^3, is called a *cube*. One of the identical factors involved in a power is called a *root* of that power. Thus x is a *square root* of x^2 and y is a *cube root* of y^3.

2 ADDITION AND SUBTRACTION OF ALGEBRAIC EXPRESSIONS

Two algebraic terms are said to be alike if their variable parts or variable coefficients are identical. For example, $3ab^2$, $-7ab^2$, and $10ab^2$ are like terms. To add two or more like terms, add their numerical coefficients and multiply this result by the common variable coefficient.

Example. Add $5xy^2$, $-3xy^2$, and $2xy^2$.
Adding numerical coefficients, $5 - 3 + 2 = 4$.
Therefore, $5xy^2 + (-3xy^2) + 2xy^2 = 4xy^2$.

This process is equivalent to indicating the algebraic sum and then collecting terms, as in $5xy^2 - 3xy^2 + 2xy^2 = (5 - 3 + 2)xy^2 = 4xy^2$. However, to add two or more terms that are unlike, such as x and y, we can only indicate their sum in the form $x + y$.

Example. Add $2x$, $(-3y)$, and $4a$. We indicate the sum thus: $2x - 3y + 4a$.

Example. Add $2x$, $(-3y)$, $5x$, $2y$, $4a$, and 3.

$$2x + (-3y) + (5x) + (2y) + (4a) + 3 = 2x - 3y + 5x + 2y + 4a + 3,$$
$$= 7x - y + 4a + 3$$
(by collecting like terms).

To subtract one like term from another like term, subtract the numerical coefficient of the former from the numerical coefficient of the latter and multiply the difference by the common variable coefficient.

Example. Subtract $4ax$ from $10ax$.

$$10ax - 4ax = (10 - 4)ax = 6ax.$$

Example. Subtract $10ax$ from $4ax$.

$$4ax - 10ax = (4 - 10)ax = -6ax.$$

Example. Subtract $(-4ax)$ from $10ax$.

$$10ax - (-4ax) = [10 - (-4)]ax = (10 + 4)ax = 14ax.$$

If the terms are unlike, the only thing that can be done is to indicate the subtraction. Thus, $3y$ subtracted from $2x$ is written $2x - 3y$ and cannot be simplified further.

To add two or more algebraic expressions, enclose each in parentheses and indicate the sum of the terms represented by each set of parentheses. Next, remove the parentheses and collect terms where possible.

Example. Add $3x + 2y$, $x - 4y$, and $-2x + 7y$.

$$(3x + 2y) + (x - 4y) + (-2x + 7y) = 3x + 2y + x - 4y - 2x + 7y,$$
$$= 2x + 5y.$$

To subtract one algebraic expression from another, enclose each in a set of parentheses and indicate the result of subtracting the term represented by the first set of parentheses from that represented by the second set of parentheses. Next, remove all parentheses and collect terms where possible.

Example. Subtract $3x - 2y + 5$ from $8x - 7y + 2$.

$$(8x - 7y + 2) - (3x - 2y + 5) = 8x - 7y + 2 - 3x + 2y - 5,$$
$$= 5x - 5y - 3.$$

EXERCISES

In each of the problems 1 through 6 find the sum of the given expressions.

1. $4xy$; $10xy$; $-6xy$; $-3xy$; xy.
2. $x + 2y$; $3x - y$; $-4x + 7y$; $5x - 6y$.
3. $6x - 4y - 3z$; $-2x - y + 5z$; $-4x - 2y + z$.
4. $3xy - 5x$; $2x + 3xy$; $-4x + 7xy$; $3x - 6xy$.
5. $8a^2 + 7a - 3$; $-5a^2 - 4a + 7$; $a^2 + 2a - 5$.
6. $x + 3y - 2$; $2x + y - 4$; $3x - 3y + 7$; $-5x - y + 2$.
7. Subtract $2x^2 - 5x$ from $5x^2 - 2x + 7$.
8. Subtract $4x - 8$ from $2x - 3$.
9. Subtract $9x - 4y$ from $-5x + 2y$.
10. Add $2x^3$, $-7x^2$, $3x$, and -8.
11. Add $x^2 - 5xy$, $-3x^2 + y^2$, $4xy - 3y^2$, and $4x^2 - 8xy$.
12. Subtract $x^2 + 3x - 4$ from $x^2 - 2x + 1$.
13. Find the value of Q if $Q = 4x - 3y + 2xy - y^2$ and
   a. $x = -3$ and $y = -4$.   c. $x = 0$ and $y = -4$.
   b. $x = 2$ and $y = 0$.   d. $x = 2$ and $y = -4$.
14. If $P = 2x^3 - 2x^2 - x + 5$, find the value of P for each of the following values of x: $x = 3$, $x = -1$, $x = 0$, $x = -3$, and $x = a$.

In each of the following exercises remove all symbols of grouping and collect terms where possible.

15. $(2x^2 - 5x + 3) + (4x^2 - 7x - 8) - (5x^2 + 4x + 3)$.
16. $[(5x - 3y) + 2y] - [(4x - 3) - (2y - x)] + (x - y - 3)$.
17. $\{[2x^2 - (3xy - 5y^2) + xy] - (x + 3y^2)]\} - (6xy - y^2)$.
18. $[3a^2 - (4a + 7) - (2a^2 - 5a + 2)] - (-2a^2 - 3a + 1)$.
19. $(2x - 5y) - [(3x + 2y) - (7x - 4y)]$.
20. $2a - \{4a - [a - (5a + 2b)]\}$.
21. $(3x - 2) - \{4x - [(2x + 8) - (5x - 3)]\}$.
22. $\{[(x + y) - 3y] - (-2x - 7y)\}$.
23. Find the value of each of the following: 2^3, $(-3)^2$, 3^4, $(-2)^3$, 0^5, $(-1)^{19}$, 2^{10}.

3 EXPONENTS AND RADICALS

Definition 3.1.   *If m is a positive integer and x is any real number, the expression x^m is defined as the product of m factors, each of which is equal to x. Thus*

Examples. $x^m = x \cdot x \cdot x \cdots x$ (*m* factors of *x*)
$$x^1 = x$$
$$x^3 = x \cdot x \cdot x$$
$$x^7 = x \cdot x \cdot x \cdot x \cdot x \cdot x \cdot x.$$

We refer to the symbol x^m as the *m*th power of *x*, *x* is called the *base* and *m* the *exponent* of the power.

Laws of Exponents

We shall prove that if *m* and *n* are positive integers the following laws hold.

LAW 1: $x^m \cdot x^n = x^{m+n}$.

LAW 2: $\dfrac{x^m}{x^n} = x^{m-n}$ for $m > n$ and $x \neq 0$,

$\qquad\qquad = \dfrac{1}{x^{n-m}}$ for $n > m$ and $x \neq 0$,

$\qquad\qquad = 1$ for $m = n$ and $x \neq 0$.

LAW 3: $(x^m)^n = x^{mn}$.

LAW 4: $(xy)^m = x^m y^m$.

LAW 5· $\dfrac{x^m}{y^m} = \left(\dfrac{x}{y}\right)^m$ for $y \neq 0$.

Proof of Law 1. $x^m \cdot x^n = (x \cdot x \cdot x \cdots$ to *m* factors$)(x \cdot x \cdot x \cdots$ to *n* factors$)$
$$= x \cdot x \cdot x \cdots \text{ to } (m + n) \text{ factors}$$
$$= x^{m+n} \qquad \text{(Def. 3.1)}$$

Example. $x^4 \cdot x^7 = x^{11}$.

Proof of Law 2.   Case $m > n$ and $x \neq 0$

$$\frac{x^m}{x^n} = \frac{x^{m-n}x^n}{x^n} \qquad \text{(Law 1)}$$

$$= x^{m-n}. \qquad \text{(Fundamental Principle of Fractions)}$$

Example. $\dfrac{x^5}{x^2} = x^{5-2} = x^3.$

Case $n > m$ and $x \neq 0$

Proof of Law 2.

$$\frac{x^m}{x^n} = \frac{x^m}{x^{n-m}x^m} \qquad \text{(Law 1)}$$

$$= \frac{1}{x^{n-m}}. \qquad \text{(Fundamental Principle of Fractions)}$$

Example. $\dfrac{x^4}{x^7} = \dfrac{1}{x^3}.$

Case $m = n$ and $x \neq 0$

$$\frac{x^m}{x^n} = \frac{x^m}{x^m} \qquad \text{(Prop. 4)}$$

$$= 1. \qquad \left(\text{If } a \neq 0, \frac{a}{a} = a \cdot \frac{1}{a} = 1.\right)$$

Proof of Law 3.
$$
\begin{aligned}
(x^m)^n &= x^m \cdot x^m \cdot x^m \cdots \text{ to } n \text{ factors} \\
&= x^{m+m+m+\cdots} \text{ to } n \text{ terms} \qquad \text{(Law 1)} \\
&= x^{mn}. \qquad\qquad\qquad\qquad\quad \text{(Addition)}
\end{aligned}
$$

Example. $(x^3)^4 = x^{12}.$

Proof of Law 4.
$$
\begin{aligned}
(xy)^m &= (xy) \cdot (xy) \cdot (xy) \cdots \text{ to } m \text{ factors} \\
&= (x \cdot x \cdot x \cdots \text{ to } m \text{ factors})(y \cdot y \cdot y \cdots \text{ to } m \text{ factors}) \\
&\qquad\qquad\qquad\qquad\qquad\qquad\qquad\qquad \text{(Why?)} \\
&= x^m \cdot y^m \qquad \text{(Why?).}
\end{aligned}
$$

Proof of Law 5.
$$
\begin{aligned}
\frac{x^m}{y^m} &= \frac{x \cdot x \cdot x \cdots \text{ to } m \text{ factors}}{y \cdot y \cdot y \cdots \text{ to } m \text{ factors}} \\
&= \left(\frac{x}{y}\right) \cdot \left(\frac{x}{y}\right) \cdot \left(\frac{x}{y}\right) \cdots \text{ to } m \text{ factors} \\
&= \left(\frac{x}{y}\right)^m.
\end{aligned}
$$

Example. $\dfrac{x^4}{y^4} = \left(\dfrac{x}{y}\right)^4.$

Example. $\dfrac{24^4}{8^4} = \left(\dfrac{24}{8}\right)^4 = 3^4 = 81.$

In defining any new type of exponent it is highly desirable that the new exponents be defined in such a way that they obey the above laws. In fact, Law 2 suggests a need for a negative exponent and a zero exponent. Better still, it even suggests their definitions as given below. Law 2 consists of three statements to cover each of the three cases $m > n$, $m < n$, and $m = n$. We can reduce Law 2 to a single statement with the following two definitions.

Definition 3.2. *If n is a positive integer and $x \neq 0$ then x^{-n} is defined by the relation $x^{-n} = \dfrac{1}{x^n}.$*

Definition 3.3. *If $x \neq 0$, x^0 is defined by the relation $x^0 = 1$. 0^0 is not defined.*

Examples. $5^0 = 1; (-17)^0 = 1; (1000)^0 = 1.$

In the light of Definition 3.2 and Definition 3.3, Law 2 now becomes one statement, namely:

$$\dfrac{x^m}{x^n} = x^{m-n}, \qquad x \neq 0.$$

Example. $\dfrac{x^2}{x^5} = x^{2-5} = x^{-3} = \dfrac{1}{x^3}, \qquad x \neq 0.$

Example. $\dfrac{x^3}{x^3} = x^{3-3} = x^0 = 1, \qquad x \neq 0.$

Definition 3.4. *If a and x are real numbers and a > 0, x is said to be a square root of a if and only if $x^2 = a$.*

Since, for any real number x, $(-x)^2 = x^2$, it follows that every positive real number has two square roots, one positive and the other negative. We employ a symbol, $\sqrt{}$, called a square root radical, to indicate a square root and define it as follows.

Definition 3.5. *If a is a positive real number, then $\sqrt{a}$ = the positive number whose square is a and $-\sqrt{a}$ = the negative number whose square is a. The square root of zero is defined as zero: $\sqrt{0} = 0$.*

Examples. $\sqrt{4} = 2;\ -\sqrt{4} = -2;\ \sqrt{81} = 9;\ -\sqrt{81} = -9.$

It follows from the above definitions and the definition of $|a|$ that if a is any real number then

$$\sqrt{a^2} = |a|.$$

Examples. $\sqrt{3^2} = 3,\ \sqrt{(-3)^2} = |-3| = 3,\ \sqrt{(3 - \pi)^2} = |3 - \pi| = \pi - 3.$

To generalize this notion of a root, we say that x is an nth *root* of a if $x^n = a$ and n is a positive integer. It can be shown that every number except zero has exactly n distinct nth roots, some or all of which may be imaginary. If n is a positive even integer, every positive number a has exactly two real nth roots, numerically equal but opposite in sign, and every negative number a has all its nth roots imaginary. If n is a positive odd integer, every real number a has just one real nth root, which is positive if a is positive and negative if a is negative.

If n is a positive even integer and a is a positive real number, the positive nth root of a is called the *principal nth root of a.* If n is even and a is negative, none of the nth roots is referred to as the principal nth root. If n is an odd integer and a is a real number, the real nth root of a is called its principal nth root. In any case, where it exists we denote the principal nth root of a by the symbol $\sqrt[n]{a}$. The symbol $\sqrt[n]{a}$ is called a *radical; n* is called the *index* of the radical and a is called the *radicand.*

What meaning could be given to a fractional exponent such as say $x^{1/2}$? If such an exponent is to obey Law 1, then

$$x^{1/2} \cdot x^{1/2} = x^{1/2+1/2} = x^1 = x, \qquad x > 0$$

and $\qquad x^{1/2} \cdot x^{1/2} = (x^{1/2})^2.$

Hence, if $\frac{1}{2}$, as an exponent, is to obey Laws 1 and 3, it is necessary that

$$(x^{1/2})^2 = x^{2(1/2)} = x^1 = x.$$

This last statement says that $x^{1/2}$ is a number whose square is x. But $\sqrt{x}$ is a positive number whose square is x. This suggests the definition

$$x^{1/2} = \sqrt{x}, \qquad x \text{ a positive real number.}$$

In general, if $1/n$, as an exponent, is to obey Law 1, it is necessary that

$$(x^{1/n} \cdot x^{1/n} \cdots \text{to } n \text{ factors}) = x^{n(1/n)} = x.$$

We thus define $x^{1/n}$ by the relation

$$(x^{1/n}) = \sqrt[n]{x}, \qquad n \text{ a positive integer.}$$

Let us now extend this definition to include all positive rational fractions m/n, where m and n are positive integers. If $1/n$ and m/n, as exponents, are to obey Law 3, it is necessary that

$$x^{m/n} = (x^{1/n})^m = (x^m)^{1/n}.$$

It follows from the definition of $x^{1/n}$ that

$$(x^{1/n})^m = (\sqrt[n]{x})^m \qquad \text{and} \qquad (x^m)^{1/n} = \sqrt[n]{x^m}.$$

Hence we define $x^{m/n}$, $(\sqrt[n]{x})^m$, and $\sqrt[n]{x^m}$ as the same number; that is,

$$x^{m/n} = (\sqrt[n]{x})^m = \sqrt[n]{x^m}.$$

We define $x^{-m/n}$ to mean $\dfrac{1}{x^{m/n}}$.

Examples. $4^{1/2} = \sqrt{4} = 2.$

$81^{1/4} = \sqrt[4]{81} = 3.$

$27^{2/3} = (\sqrt[3]{27})^2 = 3^2 = 9.$

$16^{-3/2} = \dfrac{1}{16^{3/2}} = \dfrac{1}{(\sqrt{16})^3} = \dfrac{1}{4^3} = \dfrac{1}{64}.$

$(-8)^{1/3} = \sqrt[3]{-8} = -\sqrt[3]{8} = -2.$

The following laws of radicals are direct consequences of the above definitions of roots and the laws of exponents.

If n is a positive integer and if a and b are positive when n is even, then

1. $(\sqrt[n]{a})^n = \left(a^{\frac{1}{n}}\right)^n = a.$

3. $\sqrt[n]{\dfrac{a}{b}} = \left(\dfrac{a}{b}\right)^{\frac{1}{n}} = \dfrac{a^{\frac{1}{n}}}{b^{\frac{1}{n}}} = \dfrac{\sqrt[n]{a}}{\sqrt[n]{b}}.$

2. $\sqrt[n]{ab} = (ab)^{\frac{1}{n}} = a^{\frac{1}{n}}b^{\frac{1}{n}} = \sqrt[n]{a}\,\sqrt[n]{b}.$

Example. $(\sqrt{3})^2 = 3.$

Example. $\sqrt{32} = \sqrt{16\cdot 2} = \sqrt{16}\,\sqrt{2} = 4\sqrt{2}.$

Example. $\sqrt[3]{\dfrac{5}{8}} = \dfrac{\sqrt[3]{5}}{\sqrt[3]{8}} = \dfrac{\sqrt[3]{5}}{2}.$

EXERCISES

1. Find the value of each of the following:

a. $2^8.$ d. $(\frac{2}{3})^{-1}.$ g. $-4^2.$ j. $(27)^{2/3}.$

b. $9^{1/2}.$ e. $(-27)^{-1/3}.$ h. $(25)^0.$ k. $(16)^{3/2}.$

c. $5^{-2}.$ f. $(-4)^2.$ i. $3\cdot 8^0.$ l. $(3\cdot 5)^2.$

2. Find each of the following indicated roots.

a. $\sqrt{49}.$ d. $\sqrt[3]{-8}.$ g. $\sqrt{1/4}.$ j. $\sqrt{(-2)^2}.$

b. $\sqrt[5]{32}.$ e. $-\sqrt{169}.$ h. $\sqrt[3]{64}.$ k. $\sqrt{(a+b)^2}.$

c. $\sqrt{121}.$ f. $\sqrt[4]{81}.$ i. $\sqrt{289}.$ l. $\sqrt{x^4}.$

3. Perform the indicated operations using the laws of exponents and definitions. Leave answers free of negative exponents.

a. $x^3 \cdot x^7$.

d. $\dfrac{x^5 \cdot x^{-2}}{x^{-3}}$.

g. $(x^2)^5$.

b. $2^2 \cdot 2^3 \cdot 2^4$.

e. $5^4 \cdot 5^{-4}$.

h. $(x^2 y)^3$.

c. $x^2 \cdot x^5 \cdot x^{-4}$.

f. $(a+b)^2 (a+b)^{-2}$.

i. $(a^{-1/2} b^2)^{-2}$.

4. Express each of the following in simplest form and free of negative exponents.

a. $x^2 y^{-3}$.

d. $\dfrac{x}{y^{-1}} + \dfrac{y}{x^{-1}}$.

g. $\left(\dfrac{8}{x^3}\right)^{-2/3}$.

b. $\dfrac{1}{5x^{-2}}$.

e. $\dfrac{3x^2 y^{-1}}{2x^{-1} y}$.

h. $(16x^4 y^{-2})^{1/2}$.

c. $3a^{-2}$.

f. $(x^{-1} + y^{-1})^{-1}$.

i. $\dfrac{2x^{-1}}{3y^{-2}}$.

5. By writing each number under a radical as the product of two factors and then applying the law $\sqrt[n]{ab} = \sqrt[n]{a}\,\sqrt[n]{b}$, simplify the following.

a. $\sqrt{20}$.

d. $\sqrt{160}$.

g. $\sqrt{162}$.

j. $\sqrt[3]{-125}$.

b. $\sqrt{50}$.

e. $\sqrt[3]{-54}$.

h. $\sqrt[3]{128}$.

k. $\sqrt{68}$.

c. $\sqrt[3]{24}$.

f. $\sqrt{300}$.

i. $\sqrt{800}$.

l. $\sqrt{45a^4}$.

6. Perform each indicated operation and simplify.

a. $\sqrt{3} \cdot \sqrt{12}$.

f. $\sqrt{2} + \sqrt{8}$.

b. $\sqrt{2} \cdot \sqrt{6} \cdot \sqrt{12}$.

g. $\sqrt{28} + \sqrt{63}$.

c. $\sqrt{3} \cdot \sqrt{21} \cdot \sqrt{7}$.

h. $\sqrt{12} + \sqrt{75} - \sqrt{27}$.

d. $\sqrt{5} \cdot \sqrt{20}$.

i. $\sqrt{32} - \sqrt{128} + \sqrt{200}$.

e. $\sqrt{6} \cdot \sqrt{18}$.

7. Simplify each of the following.

a. $\dfrac{\sqrt{20}}{\sqrt{5}}$.

d. $\sqrt{\dfrac{3}{4}}$.

g. $\dfrac{\sqrt{x^5}}{\sqrt{x^3}}$.

b. $\dfrac{\sqrt{75}}{\sqrt{8}}$.

e. $\sqrt{\dfrac{32}{49}}$.

h. $\dfrac{\sqrt[3]{16}}{\sqrt[3]{2}}$.

c. $\dfrac{\sqrt{18}}{\sqrt{72}}$.

f. $\dfrac{\sqrt{50}}{\sqrt{28}}$.

i. $\dfrac{\sqrt{6} + \sqrt{24}}{\sqrt{2}}$.

8. **a.** Show that $\sqrt{\dfrac{1}{2}} = \dfrac{\sqrt{2}}{2}$. $\left[Hint: \sqrt{\dfrac{1}{2}} = \sqrt{\dfrac{1 \cdot 2}{2 \cdot 2}} = \sqrt{\dfrac{2}{4}} \right]$.

b. By multiplying numerator and denominator by $\sqrt{2} + 1$ show that

$$\dfrac{1}{\sqrt{2} - 1} = \sqrt{2} + 1.$$

c. Show that $\dfrac{4}{3 - \sqrt{5}} = 3 + \sqrt{5}$.

4 MULTIPLICATION OF ALGEBRAIC EXPRESSIONS

The *product* of two or more monomials is equal to the product of their numerical coefficients multiplied by the product of their variable factors.

Example. Multiply $3xy$ by $5x^2z$.

$$(3xy)(5x^2z) = 15x^3yz.$$

To multiply any algebraic expression by a monomial, multiply each term of the algebraic expression by the monomial and add the resulting terms (see the distributive law, in Section 4 of Chapter II).

Example. Multiply $3ax - 5y + 7$ by $2xy$.

$$2xy(3ax - 5y + 7) = 6ax^2y - 10xy^2 + 14xy.$$

In general, to multiply two algebraic expressions, multiply each term of one of the expressions by each term of the other and add the resulting terms.

Example. Multiply $x^3 + 2x - 5$ by $3x^2 - 7x + 4$.

Solution:
$$
\begin{aligned}
& x^3 + 2x - 5 \\
& 3x^2 - 7x + 4 \\
\hline
& 3x^5 \qquad\quad + 6x^3 - 15x^2 \\
& \qquad - 7x^4 \qquad\quad - 14x^2 + 35x \\
& \qquad\qquad\quad + 4x^3 \qquad\quad + 8x - 20 \\
\hline
& 3x^5 - 7x^4 + 10x^3 - 29x^2 + 43x - 20.
\end{aligned}
$$

Check: When $x = 2$, $x^3 + 2x - 5 = 8 + 4 - 5 = 7$,
$$3x^2 - 7x + 4 = 12 - 14 + 4 = 2,$$
$$(x^3 + 2x - 5)(3x^2 - 7x + 4) = (7)(2) = 14.$$

Also, $3(2)^5 - 7(2)^4 + 10(2)^3 - 29(2)^2 + 43(2) - 20$
$$= 96 - 112 + 80 - 116 + 86 - 20,$$
$$= 262 - 248 = 14.$$

Therefore the answer is probably correct.

EXERCISES

Perform each indicated multiplication and simplify the results where possible.

1. $(2a^2)(3a)^2(4)(a^3)$.
2. $(-2x^2yz)^2(xy^2)(-yz^2)$.
3. $(3ab)(a^2b)(b^3)(4a)$.
4. $2ax(x - a + 3a^2)$.
5. $3x^2y(x - y^2 + 1)$.
6. $(x + y)(x^2 - xy + y^2)$.
7. $(x - y)(2x^3 - 5x^2y - 3y^3)$.
8. $(2x - 3y)(5x + 4y)$.

9. $(x + 6y)(7x - 3y)$.
10. $(x + 2y)(x - 2y)$.
11. $(2x - 3y)(4x^2 + 6xy + 9y^2)$.
12. $[(x + y) - 1][(x + y) + 1]$.
13. $(a - b - 2)(a - b + 2)$.
14. $(a + b)^3$.
15. $(3x + 5y)(3x - 5y)$.
16. $(x^{1/2} + y^{1/2})(x^{1/2} - y^{1/2})$.

17. $(12x - 8y)(5x + 7y)$.

18. $[\sqrt{x + h + 1} + \sqrt{x + 1}][\sqrt{x + h + 1} - \sqrt{x + 1}]$.

19. $[\sqrt{7 - x} - 2][\sqrt{7 - x} + 2]$.   **26.** $(x^2 - x + 2)(x^2 + 3x + 7)$.

20. $(a + b + c)^2$.   **27.** $(2x^2 - 10y^2)(2x^2 + 10y^2)$.

21. $(x^2 - 5x + 7)(x^2 - 4)$.   **28.** $(13x - 17y)(13x + 17y)$.

22. $(x^4 + x^2 + 1)(x^2 - 1)$.   **29.** $3x^{1/2}y^{3/2}(2x^{1/2}y^{-1/2} + 5x^{3/2}y^{5/2})$.

23. $(2x - 5y)^2$.   **30.** $(3x + y - 2)(x - 2y + 3)$.

24. $(x + y)(x - 2y)(2x + y)$.   **31.** $(x^{1/3} - y^{1/3})(x^{2/3} + x^{1/3}y^{1/3} + y^{2/3})$.

25. $(3x + 4)^2$.   **32.** $(ax + by + cz)^2$.

5   SPECIAL PRODUCTS AND FACTORING

For facility in multiplication, it is important that certain special types of products be memorized. By actual multiplication the following can be verified.

Special Products:

1. $k(a + b) = ka + kb$.
2. $(a + b)^2 = a^2 + 2ab + b^2$.
3. $(a - b)^2 = a^2 - 2ab + b^2$.
4. $(a + b)(a - b) = a^2 - b^2$.
5. $(ax + by)(cx + dy) = acx^2 + (ad + bc)xy + bdy^2$.
6. $(a + b)(a^2 - ab + b^2) = a^3 + b^3$.
7. $(a - b)(a^2 + ab + b^2) = a^3 - b^3$.
8. $(a + b)^3 = a^3 + 3a^2b + 3ab^2 + b^3$.

Special Products 2, 3, and 4 can be stated as follows:

Product 2′:   The square of the sum of two terms is equal to the square of the first term plus twice the product of the two terms plus the square of the second term.

Product 3′:   The square of the difference of two terms is equal to the square of the first term minus twice the product of the two terms plus the square of the second term.

Product 4′:   The product of the sum and difference of the same two terms is equal to the square of the first term minus the square of the second term.

Products 2′, 3′, and 4′ should be carefully memorized and used each time it is necessary to find products of these types.

In each of the product types listed above, the right member is the expanded form of the product and the left member is the factored form. It is often important to be able to transform an algebraic expression from the expanded form into the factored form. The process of writing an algebraic expression as the product of its simple factors is called *factoring*.

To find the simple factors, if any, of an algebraic expression is more or less a trial-and-error process. The following suggestions will often prove helpful.

Step 1: Look for the monomial factors common to each term. The product of all the monomial factors common to each term of an algebraic expression is called the *greatest common monomial factor* of the expression.

Step 2: Write the given expression as the product of the greatest common monomial factor and a second factor. This second factor is the original expression from each term of which the greatest common monomial factor has been removed.

Step 3: Next, express this second factor as the product of its simple factors, if any, according to the type forms of Products 2 to 5.

Example. Factor $2ax^2 - 2ay^2$.

Solution: The greatest monomial factor common to both terms of this expression is $2a$. Hence, $2ax^2 - 2ay^2 = 2a(x^2 - y^2) = 2a(x - y)(x + y)$, (Product 4).

If the second factor referred to above is a trinomial with two of its terms each a perfect square of some expression and the third term twice the product of these two expressions, the trinomial is a perfect square trinomial of type (2) or (3).

Example. Factor $8ax^3 + 24ax^2y + 18axy^2$.

Solution: $8ax^3 + 24ax^2y + 18axy^2 = 2ax(4x^2 + 12xy + 9y^2)$
$$= 2ax(2x + 3y)^2, \quad \text{(Product 2)}$$

If the second factor is a trinomial, but not a perfect square trinomial, we are sometimes able to find the factors, if any, by a method of trial. Before illustrating this method, let us first examine carefully the product of two binomials, Product 5 of the special products listed above, rewritten here for convenience:

$$(ax + by)(cx + dy) = acx^2 + (ad + bc)xy + bdy^2.$$

Inspection of the right member in this expansion reveals the following facts.

1.   The product of two binomials (Product 5) gives rise to a trinomial.
2.   The first term of this trinomial is the product of the first terms of the two binomials.
3.   The second term of the trinomial is the algebraic sum of two products, namely, the product of the two outer terms plus the product of the two inner terms.
4.   The third term of the trinomial is the product of the second terms of the two binomials.

Now, if we reverse the process and consider the binomial factors of a trinomial, the above results show that:

1.   The first terms of the binomials must be factors of the first term of the trinomial.

2.   The second terms of the binomials must be factors of the third term of the trinomial.

3.   These factors must be so chosen that when the product of the outer terms of the binomials is added to the product of the inner terms the result will be the middle term of the trinomial.

Example.   Factor $3x^2 + 5xy + 2y^2$.

Solution: The factors of $3x^2$ are $3x$ and x, and of $2y^2$ they are $2y$ and y. We must now combine these factors so as to get $5xy$ as the middle term. Let us try first $(3x + y)(x + 2y)$. This gives $6xy + xy = 7xy$, which is not the correct combination. As a second trial we interchange the second terms, obtaining $(3x + 2y)(x + y)$, and this combination yields the correct middle term. Hence

$$3x^2 + 5xy + 2y^2 = (3x + 2y)(x + y).$$

Example.   Factor $6s^2 - st - 12t^2$.

Solution: Since the third term here is negative, the second terms of the binomial factors must be opposite in sign. Some possible factors of $6s^2$ are $2s$ and $3s$, and $6s$ and s. Some possible factors of $-12t^2$ are $2t$ and $-6t$, $-2t$ and $6t$, $3t$ and $-4t$, $-3t$ and $4t$, $12t$ and $-t$, and $-12t$ and t. A few trials reveal that the correct combination is

$$(2s - 3t)(3s + 4t) = 6s^2 - st - 12t^2.$$

It should be pointed out that it is not always possible to factor a trinomial of the type $ax^2 + bxy + cy^2$, where a, b, and c are rational numerical coefficients, into the product of two binomials with rational numerical coefficients. For example, $x^2 + xy + y^2$ cannot be so factored.

Factoring the Sum or Difference of Two Cubes

Products 6 and 7 give us a method of factoring the sum or difference of any two perfect cubes.

Example.   Factor $8x^3 + 27y^3$.

Solution: Since $a^3 + b^3 = (a + b)(a^2 - ab + b^2)$:

$$8x^3 + 27y^3 = (2x)^3 + (3y)^3 = (2x + 3y)(4x^2 - 6xy + 9y^2).$$

Example.   Factor $m^3 - 8n^3$.

Solution: Comparing with Product 7, we find:

$$m^3 - 8n^3 = m^3 - (2n)^3$$
$$= (m - 2n)(m^2 + 2mn + 4n^2).$$

Factoring by Grouping

Sometimes it is possible to factor an algebraic expression by a proper grouping of terms.

Example. Factor $ax - by - bx + ay$.

Solution: $ax - by - bx + ay = a(x + y) - b(x + y)$,   by grouping;
$$= (a - b)(x + y),\qquad \text{by factoring.}$$

Example. Factor $y^3 + 4y^2 - y - 4$.

Solution: $y^3 + 4y^2 - y - 4 = y^2(y + 4) - (y + 4)$
$$= (y + 4)(y^2 - 1)$$
$$= (y + 4)(y + 1)(y - 1).$$

An algebraic expression has been factored correctly if and only if the product of the factors is exactly the original expression. This should be used always as a check.

EXERCISES

1. By actual multiplication verify each of the following products.
   a. $(a + b)^2 = a^2 + 2ab + b^2$.
   b. $(a + b)(a - b) = (a^2 - b^2)$.
   c. $(ax + by)(cx + dy) = acx^2 + (ad + bc)xy + bdy^2$.
   d. $(a + b)(a^2 - ab + b^2) = a^3 + b^3$.
   e. $(a - b)(a^2 + ab + b^2) = a^3 - b^3$.
2. Memorize Special Products 2′, 3′ and 4′ and then use them to write the following products by inspection.
   a. $(2x - 3y)^2$.
   b. $(5x - 2y)^2$.
   c. $(x + 6y)^2$.
   d. $(2x + y)(2x - y)$.
   e. $(8x - 3y)^2$.
   f. $(7x + 5y)^2$.
   g. $(15x - 6y)^2$.
   h. $(7x + 4y)(7x - 4y)$.
   i. $(3xy^2 + 4)^2$.
   j. $(\sqrt{x} + \sqrt{y})(\sqrt{x} - \sqrt{y})$.
   k. $(15x + 10y)(15x - 10y)$.
   l. $[(x + y) - 2]^2$.

Factor each of the following expressions.

3. $3ax - 9a^2x^2$.
4. $4x^2 - y^2$.
5. $45x^2 - 80y^2$.
6. $9a^2 + 6ab + b^2$.
7. $4x^2 - 20xy + 25y^2$.
8. $49a^2 - 36b^2$.
9. $x^3 - y^3$.
10. $x^3 + y^3$.
11. $x^2 - x - 2$.
12. $x^2y^2 - y^4$.
13. $x^4 - 16$.

14. $8a^3 - 27b^3$.
15. $(x + y)^2 - 4$.
16. $10x^2 - 11x - 6$.
17. $x^2 - 5x + 6$.
18. $x^2 - 7x + 6$.
19. $x^2 - 5x - 6$.
20. $15x^2 - x - 2$.
21. $100x^2 - 140x + 49$.
22. $4x^2 - 16x - 9$.
23. $x^6 - y^6$.
24. $2x^2 - 5x + 2$.

25. $x^4 - 2x^3 - 3x^2$.
26. $(x - y)^2 - 5(x - y) + 4$.
27. $x^4 - 10x^2 + 9$.
28. $x^2 - 5x - 150$.
29. $6x^2 + 13xy - 28y^2$.
30. $-y^2 - 5y + 24$.
31. $(a + b)^2 - (c - d)^2$.
32. $6x^2 - 19x + 10$.
33. $6x^2 - 6x - 12$.
34. $x^3 - 9x$.
35. $16m^4 + 2m$.
36. $3x^2 - 3y^2 + x - y$.
37. $x^3 - 2x^2 - 4x + 8$.

38. $(2 - x)^2 + 5(2 - x) + 4$.
39. $.04x^2 - 1.69y^2$.
40. $81x^4 - 256$.
41. $2x^2 - 36x + 162$.
42. $21x^2 - 27x + 6$.
43. $3x^3 - 12x^2 - 2x + 8$.
44. $x^2 - 4x + 4 - y^2 + 6y - 9$.
45. $6x^2 + 7x - 20$.
46. $ax - by - bx + ay$.
47. $64a^3 - 1$.
48. $12x^2 - 5x - 72$.
49. $x^3 - 2x^2 + 5x - 10$.
50. $35x^2 + 104xy + 36y^2$.

6   DIVISION OF ALGEBRAIC EXPRESSIONS

To divide one monomial by another monomial find the quotient of their numerical coefficients and then use Law 2 of exponents (Section 3) to find the quotient of their variable coefficients.

Example.   Divide $15x^3y^2z^5$ by $3x^2yz^3$.

Solution: $15x^3y^2z^5/3x^2yz^3 = 5x^{3-2}y^{2-1}z^{5-3} = 5xyz^2$.

To divide any algebraic expression by a monomial, divide each term of the expression by the monomial and add the terms thus obtained.

Example.   Divide $24x^7y^3 - 12x^4y^5 - 6x^3y^3 + 8x^2y^6$ by $(-2xy^2)$.

Solution: $(24x^7y^3 - 12x^4y^5 - 6x^3y^3 + 8x^2y^6)/(-2xy^2)$
$$= -12x^6y + 6x^3y^3 + 3x^2y - 4xy^4.$$

Division of an Algebraic Expression by an Algebraic Expression

According to our definition of division,

if
$$\frac{10x^2 + 29x - 21}{2x + 7} = 5x - 3$$

$$10x^2 + 29x - 21 = (5x - 3)(2x + 7),$$

where $10x^2 + 29x - 21$ is the dividend, $2x + 7$ is the divisor, and $5x - 3$ is the quotient. It is desirable to have a method of finding this quotient directly from the dividend and the divisor. Such a method, suggested by the method of long division in arithmetic, is illustrated in the following example.

Example.   Divide $10x^2 + 29x - 21$ by $2x + 7$.

Solution: The dividend and divisor, having been written in the order of descending powers of x, are arranged in a manner similar to that used in long division in arithmetic:

$$\begin{array}{r} 5x - 3 \\ 2x + 7\overline{\smash{)}10x^2 + 29x - 21} \\ 10x^2 + 35x \\ \hline - 6x - 21 \\ - 6x - 21 \\ \hline 0x + 0. \end{array}$$

The first term of the quotient is obtained by dividing the first term of the dividend by the first term of the divisor: $10x^2/2x = 5x$. Next, multiply the entire divisor by this first term of the quotient, placing the resulting terms under the like terms of the dividend, and subtract to obtain the new dividend. The second term of the quotient is now obtained by dividing the first term of the new dividend by the first term of the divisor, as before: $(-6x)/2x = -3$. Multiply the divisor by this second term of the quotient and place it under the like terms of the new dividend. Now subtract to obtain a second new dividend. Since in our example this second new dividend is zero, our solution is complete.

A similar procedure can be used in dividing any algebraic expression by another algebraic expression. (In arranging the dividend in the order of descending powers of some letter it may be helpful to supply any missing powers by using zero coefficients for them.) In performing divisions in arithmetic we often have a remainder. Thus $\frac{17}{7} = 2 + \frac{3}{7}$. Here the quotient is 2 and the remainder is 3. Similarly, in dividing algebraic expressions we often have a remainder. In fact, this is always the case unless the divisor is a factor of the dividend, in which case we say the remainder is zero.

Example.   Divide $8x^3 - 16x + 13$ by $2x - 3$.

Solution:

$$\begin{array}{r} 4x^2 + 6x + 1 \\ 2x - 3\overline{\smash{)}8x^3 + 0x^2 - 16x + 13} \\ 8x^3 - 12x^2 \\ \hline 12x^2 - 16x + 13 \\ 12x^2 - 18x \\ \hline 2x + 13 \\ 2x - 3 \\ \hline + 16. \end{array}$$

The quotient is $4x^2 + 6x + 1$ and the remainder is $+16$. This result can be expressed in the form

$$\frac{(8x^3 - 16x + 13)}{(2x - 3)} = 4x^2 + 6x + 1 + \frac{16}{(2x - 3)}.$$

We check our result by multiplying the quotient by the divisor and adding the remainder to obtain the dividend:

$$(4x^2 + 6x + 1)(2x - 3) + 16 = 8x^3 - 16x + 13.$$

EXERCISES

Divide, finding the quotient and remainder, and leave the result in the form

Dividend = Quotient·Divisor + Remainder.

1. $12ax^3$ by $4x$.
2. $15a^3b^2c$ by $5abc$.
3. $21x^2y^2$ by $-7x$.
4. $x^2 - 4x - 5$ by $x + 1$.
5. $8x^2 - 4x$ by $4x$.
6. $3x^2 + 13x - 10$ by $3x - 2$.
7. $2x^2 + 8x - 5$ by $x - 1$.
8. $2x^3 - 3x^2 - 11x + 6$ by $2x - 1$.
9. $x^4 - 16x^3 + 86x^2 - 176x + 105$ by $x - 7$.
10. $-6x^3 + 5x^2 - 4$ by $-2x^2 + 3x - 2$.
11. $2x^3 + 7x^2 + 10x + 6$ by $2x + 3$.
12. $2x^3 + 3x^2 - 2x - 3$ by $x - 2$.
13. $x^4 + 6x^3 - 16x^2 - 150x - 225$ by $x - 5$.
14. $2x^3 + 5x^2 - 3x - 4$ by $2x + 1$.
15. $3x^5 - 7x^4 + 10x^3 - 29x^2 + 43x - 20$ by $3x^2 - 7x + 4$.
16. $8x^3 - 12x^2 + 6x - 65$ by $2x - 5$.
17. $8x^3 - 12x^2y + 6xy^2 - y^3$ by $2x - y$.
18. $x^5 - 32$ by $x - 2$.
19. $3x^3 - 4x^2 + 2x - 1$ by $2x - 1$.
20. $x^2 - 2xy - 3y^2 + 3x - 13y - 4$ by $x - 3y - 1$.
21. $x^4 + 1$ by $x + 1$.
22. $2x^2 - xy - 6y^2 + x + 19y - 15$ by $2x + 3y - 5$.

7 ALGEBRAIC FRACTIONS

In algebra, just as in arithmetic, the indicated quotient of two numbers or expressions is called a fraction; for example, $2x/3y$, $(2a + 7b)/(x + y)$, and $(x^2 - 2xy + 7y^2)/(x^2 + 3xy + 2y^2)$ are fractions. The dividend in an indicated division is called the *numerator* of the fraction, and the divisor is called the *denominator*. In the fraction $(2a + 7b)/(x + y)$, the numerator is $(2a + 7b)$ and the denominator is $(x + y)$. The rules in algebra for operating with fractions are precisely the same as those in arithmetic, for the algebraic expressions with which we shall be concerned represent numbers and a fraction made up of algebraic expressions will likewise represent a number. Hence, the student would do well at this point to review the sections in Chapter II that are concerned with fractions. In particular, he should review the statement of the *fundamental principle of fractions* (Section 8, Chapter II).

Reducing a Fraction to Simplest Form

The student will recall from Chapter II that a fraction is said to be expressed in simplest form if the numerator and denominator have no common factors. Hence, to reduce a fraction to simplest form, factor the numerator into its simple factors and factor the denominator into its simple factors. Then divide both the numerator and denominator by each factor common to both. The resulting fraction is the given fraction reduced to simplest form.

Example. Reduce to simplest form $(2x^2 - 2xy - 4y^2)/(2x^2 - 8y^2)$.

Solution: $\dfrac{2x^2 - 2xy - 4y^2}{2x^2 - 8y^2} = \dfrac{2(x - 2y)(x + y)}{2(x - 2y)(x + 2y)} = \dfrac{x + y}{x + 2y}.$

Multiplication and Division of Fractions

In Chapter II it was proved that the product of two fractions is a fraction whose numerator is the product of the numerators of the given fractions and whose denominator is the product of the denominators of the given fraction. It is usually best, in practice, first to indicate the product of the numerators and the product of the denominators; it makes it easier to discover any possible common factors that may be removed by division.

Example. Multiply $(x + y)/(x - y)$ by $(x^2 + xy - 2y^2)/(x^2 + 2xy + y^2)$.

Solution: $\dfrac{x + y}{x - y} \cdot \dfrac{x^2 + xy - 2y^2}{x^2 + 2xy + y^2} = \dfrac{(x + y)(x + 2y)(x - y)}{(x - y)(x + y)(x + y)} = \dfrac{x + 2y}{x + y}.$

Example. Multiply $5/(x^2 - y^2)$ by $(x + y)$.

Solution: $\dfrac{5}{x^2 - y^2} \cdot \dfrac{x + y}{1} = \dfrac{5(x + y)}{(x - y)(x + y)} = \dfrac{5}{x - y}.$

By definition, the *quotient of two fractions* is a fraction whose numerator is the first fraction and whose denominator is the second fraction. In Chapter II we proved a theorem that provided us with a simple rule for finding the quotient of two fractions. We restate that rule here: To divide one fraction by another, invert the fraction in the denominator and multiply this inverted fraction by the fraction in the numerator.

Example. $\dfrac{y}{2x^2} \div \dfrac{x - 3}{6x} = \dfrac{y}{2x^2} \cdot \dfrac{6x}{x - 3} = \dfrac{6xy}{2x^2(x - 3)} = \dfrac{3y}{x(x - 3)}.$

Addition and Subtraction of Algebraic Fractions

Two or more fractions whose denominators are identical are said to have a common denominator. For example, the fractions $4x/(x^2 - y^2)$, $(x + 2y)/(x^2 - y^2)$, and $3x/(x^2 - y^2)$ have a common denominator. The *sum* of two or more fractions having a common denominator is a fraction whose numerator is the algebraic sum of the numerators of the given fractions and whose denominator is the common denominator of the given fractions.

Example. Find the algebraic sum of the following three fractions.

$$\frac{4x}{x^2 - y^2}, \qquad \frac{x + 2y}{x^2 - y^2}, \qquad \text{and} \qquad -\frac{3x}{x^2 - y^2}.$$

Solution:
$$\frac{4x}{x^2 - y^2} + \frac{x + 2y}{x^2 - y^2} - \frac{3x}{x^2 - y^2} = \frac{4x + x + 2y - 3x}{x^2 - y^2}$$

$$= \frac{2x + 2y}{x^2 - y^2}$$

$$= \frac{2(x + y)}{(x - y)(x + y)}$$

$$= \frac{2}{x - y}.$$

A rule was given in Chapter II for finding the *lowest common denominator* (L.C.D.) of a set of fractions. This rule as applied to algebraic fractions is: Find the simple factors of the denominators of each given fraction, take the product of all the factors that are different from each other, selecting from those that are alike the one with the highest exponent. This product is the required L.C.D.

Example. Find the L.C.D. of the fractions $3/(x^2 + 2x + 1)$, $4x/(x^2 - 1)$, and $(1 + 2x)/(x^2 - x - 2)$, and express each fraction as an equivalent fraction whose denominator is the L.C.D.

Solution: If we factor each denominator we get $(x^2 + 2x + 1) = (x + 1)^2$, $x^2 - 1 = (x + 1)(x - 1)$, $x^2 - x - 2 = (x - 2)(x + 1)$. The L.C.D. of the three given fractions is therefore:

$$(x + 1)^2(x - 1)(x - 2).$$

Our fractions can now be written:

$$\frac{3}{x^2 + 2x + 1} = \frac{3(x - 1)(x - 2)}{(x + 1)^2(x - 1)(x - 2)},$$

$$\frac{4x}{x^2 - 1} = \frac{4x(x + 1)(x - 2)}{(x + 1)^2(x - 1)(x - 2)},$$

$$\frac{1 + 2x}{x^2 - x - 2} = \frac{(1 + 2x)(x + 1)(x - 1)}{(x + 1)^2(x - 1)(x - 2)}.$$

We thus have three fractions, each equivalent to one of the given fractions and each having the L.C.D. of the three fractions as its denominator.

Algebraic Sum of Fractions. To find the algebraic sum of two or more fractions:

1. Find the L.C.D. of the fractions involved.
2. Express each fraction as an equivalent fraction with the L.C.D.
3. Sum the fractions: the algebraic sum of the given fractions is a frac-

tion whose numerator is the algebraic sum of the numerators of the fractions expressed with the L.C.D. and whose denominator is the L.C.D.

4. Simplify the resulting fraction, when possible, by dividing the numerator and denominator by the factors common to both.

To combine two or more fractions is to find their algebraic sum.

Example. Combine into a single fraction and simplify:

$$\frac{2a}{a^2 - 1} - \frac{1}{a - 1} + \frac{1}{a + 1}.$$

Solution: The L.C.D. of the three fractions is $a^2 - 1$, and

$$\frac{1}{a - 1} = \frac{a + 1}{a^2 - 1}, \qquad \frac{1}{a + 1} = \frac{a - 1}{a^2 - 1}.$$

Thus

$$\frac{2a}{a^2 - 1} - \frac{1}{a - 1} + \frac{1}{a + 1} = \frac{2a}{a^2 - 1} - \frac{a + 1}{a^2 - 1} + \frac{a - 1}{a^2 - 1},$$

$$= \frac{2a - (a + 1) + (a - 1)}{a^2 - 1},$$

$$= \frac{2a - a - 1 + a - 1}{a^2 - 1},$$

$$= \frac{2a - 2}{a^2 - 1} = \frac{2(a - 1)}{a^2 - 1} = \frac{2}{a + 1}.$$

Example. Combine into a single fraction: $\dfrac{2x}{x + 1} + \dfrac{x}{1 - x} - \dfrac{4}{x^2 - 1}.$

Solution: $\dfrac{2x}{x + 1} + \dfrac{x}{1 - x} - \dfrac{4}{x^2 - 1} = \dfrac{2x}{x + 1} - \dfrac{x}{x - 1} - \dfrac{4}{x^2 - 1},$

$$= \frac{2x(x - 1)}{x^2 - 1} - \frac{x(x + 1)}{x^2 - 1} - \frac{4}{x^2 - 1},$$

$$= \frac{2x(x - 1) - x(x + 1) - 4}{x^2 - 1},$$

$$= \frac{2x^2 - 2x - x^2 - x - 4}{x^2 - 1},$$

$$= \frac{x^2 - 3x - 4}{x^2 - 1},$$

$$= \frac{(x + 1)(x - 4)}{(x + 1)(x - 1)} = \frac{x - 4}{x - 1}.$$

Complex fractions.   A *complex fraction* is a fraction whose numerator, denominator, or both, contain fractions such as

$$\frac{\frac{2}{3}}{\frac{5}{7}}, \qquad \frac{2 + \frac{1}{3}}{\frac{3}{4} - 1}, \qquad \frac{3/(x + 2) + 1/(x - 3)}{(2x + 5)/(x^2 - x - 6)}, \quad \text{etc.}$$

A *simple fraction* is a fraction which has no fractions in either the denominator or numerator.

To reduce a complex fraction to a simple fraction, multiply the numerator and denominator of the complex fraction by the L.C.D. of all the fractions in both the numerator and denominator of the complex fraction.

Example. Write as a simple fraction:

$$\frac{\frac{1}{2} + \frac{3}{4}}{\frac{2}{3} - \frac{1}{6}}.$$

Solution: The L.C.D. of the four fractions in the numerator and denominator is 12. Multiply numerator and denominator of the complex fraction by 12:

$$\frac{(\frac{1}{2} + \frac{3}{4})12}{(\frac{2}{3} - \frac{1}{6})12} = \frac{6 + 9}{8 - 2} = \frac{15}{6} = \frac{5}{2}.$$

Example. Reduce to a simple fraction: $\dfrac{2/x - 3/y}{4/x^2 - 9/y^2}$.

Solution: The L.C.D. of the four fractions in the numerator and denominator of the given complex fraction is x^2y^2. Multiply the numerator and denominator of the complex fraction by x^2y^2 and obtain

$$\frac{\left(\dfrac{2}{x} - \dfrac{3}{y}\right)x^2y^2}{\left(\dfrac{4}{x^2} - \dfrac{9}{y^2}\right)x^2y^2} = \frac{2xy^2 - 3x^2y}{4y^2 - 9x^2} = \frac{xy(2y - 3x)}{(2y - 3x)(2y + 3x)} = \frac{xy}{3x + 2y}.$$

EXERCISES

Simplify, where possible, each of the following problems.

1. $\dfrac{44}{76}$.

2. $\dfrac{160}{256}$.

3. $\dfrac{105}{385}$.

4. $\dfrac{3 + 4}{10 + 4}$.

5. $\dfrac{\frac{2}{3} - \frac{1}{2}}{\frac{3}{2} - \frac{5}{6}}$.

6. $\dfrac{ax + ay}{x + y}$.

7. $\dfrac{x^2 - 2x}{x^2 - 4}$.

8. $\dfrac{a + b}{a}$.

9. $\dfrac{x^2 - 4xy + 4y^2}{x^2 - 2xy}$.

10. $\dfrac{4x^2 + 2x - 12}{2x^2 - 13x + 15}$.

11. $\dfrac{x^3 + y^3}{x^2 - xy + y^2}$.

12. $\dfrac{3a + 3b}{a^2 + 2ab + b^2}$.

Perform the indicated operations in each of the following and leave answer as a simple fraction reduced to simplest form.

13. $\dfrac{7}{15} + \dfrac{2}{3} - \dfrac{13}{30}.$

14. $\dfrac{3}{10} + \dfrac{11}{25} - \dfrac{7}{20}.$

15. $\dfrac{\frac{3}{4} + \frac{7}{10} - \frac{5}{8}}{\frac{7}{8} - \frac{3}{5} + \frac{9}{20}}.$

16. $\dfrac{7}{12} - \dfrac{13}{20} + \dfrac{17}{15}.$

17. $\dfrac{x+y}{6} - \dfrac{x-y}{3}.$

18. $\dfrac{2x+2}{8} - \dfrac{x-5}{4} + \dfrac{3x+4}{2}.$

19. $\dfrac{3x-1}{6} + \dfrac{2x+3}{4} - \dfrac{x+2}{3}.$

20. $\dfrac{2x-2}{3} - \dfrac{x-1}{6} - \dfrac{x-4}{4}.$

21. $\dfrac{2x}{x^2-1} + \dfrac{1}{x+1} - \dfrac{1}{x-1}.$

22. $\dfrac{2x-1}{x^2-4} + \dfrac{3}{x-2} - \dfrac{2}{x+2}.$

23. $\dfrac{3}{x^2} - \dfrac{x-y}{xy^2} + \dfrac{1}{y^2}.$

8   MATHEMATICAL INDUCTION

We digress at this point to describe a method of proof called *mathematical induction.* We do this for two reasons. First, because we wish to use the method in the next section to prove the Binomial Theorem and second, because the method is very useful in mathematics in proving that certain formulas or propositions involving an arbitrary positive integer n are true for all positive integers. A proof by mathematical induction is based upon the following axiom.

AXIOM OF MATHEMATICAL INDUCTION.   *Let N be the set consisting of all the positive integers, that is, $N = \{1, 2, 3, 4, \cdots\}$ and let S be any subset of N. If S possesses the following two properties*

   (*a*) $1 \in S$,
   (*b*)   *for each arbitrary positive integer K, $(K + 1) \in S$ whenever $K \in S$, then $S = N$.*

For our purposes it is more convenient to have the axiom expressed in a slightly different form, called *the principle of mathematical induction.* First, however, we introduce some notation that will aid us greatly in stating the principle and also in using the principle to prove propositions or theorems. The symbol $A(n)$, read "A of n" will be used to denote any proposition of the form "for all positive integers n, $A(n)$ is true." By $A(1)$ we shall mean the proposition obtained when 1 is substituted for n in $A(n)$. For example the notation

$$A(n): \quad 1 + 2 + 3 + 4 + \cdots + n = \frac{n}{2}(n + 1)$$

is read "$A(n)$ is the proposition, for all n in N,

$$1 + 2 + 3 + 4 + \cdots + n = \frac{n}{2}(n + 1)."$$

In this case, $A(1)$ would be

$$A(1): \quad 1 = \tfrac{1}{2}(1 + 1)$$

which is certainly a true statement.

We now state the

Principle of Mathematical Induction.   *Let $A(n)$ be any proposition of the form for all positive integers n, $A(n)$ is true. If $A(n)$ possesses the following two properties*

(*a*)   *$A(1)$ is true,*

(*b*)   *for every arbitrary but fixed positive integer K, $A(K + 1)$ is true whenever $A(K)$ is true, then $A(n)$ is true for all positive integers.*

Going back to the example mentioned above, namely

$$A(n): \quad 1 + 2 + 3 + 4 + \cdots + n = \frac{n}{2}(n + 1),$$

let us use the principle of mathematical induction to show that $A(n)$ is true for all positive integers. We have already verified that $A(1)$ is true. Now let K denote any positive integer for which $A(K)$ is true. That is, we assume

$$A(K): \quad 1 + 2 + 3 + 4 + \cdots + K = \frac{K}{2}(K + 1)$$

is a true statement. In Chapter II we proved the following theorem.

If a, b, and c are real numbers and $a = b$, then $a + c = b + c$. Let us apply this theorem by letting $a = (1 + 2 + 3 + 4 + \cdots + K)$, $b = \frac{K}{2}(K + 1)$ and $c = (K + 1)$. We then obtain the true statement

$$(1 + 2 + 3 + 4 + \cdots + K) + (K + 1) = \frac{K}{2}(K + 1) + (K + 1)$$

or

$$1 + 2 + 3 + 4 + \cdots + K + (K + 1)$$

$$= \frac{K^2 + 3K + 2}{2} = \frac{(K + 1)\,[(K + 1) + 1]}{2}$$

This last statement is $A(n)$ with n replaced by $(K + 1)$, and hence is $A(K + 1)$. Thus $A(K + 1)$ is true if $A(K)$ is true. But $A(1)$ has been shown to be true, therefore $A(2)$ is true. If $A(2)$ is true, then $A(3)$ is true. Likewise, if $A(3)$ is true, then $A(4)$ is true, and so on. Since $A(1)$ is true and $A(K + 1)$ is true whenever $A(K)$ is true, we conclude by the principle of mathematical induction that $A(n)$ is true for all positive integers.

A proof by use of the principle of mathematical induction involves three distinct steps.

Step 1:   Prove $A(1)$ is true. We do this by substituting 1 for n in the statement involving n and verifying that $A(1)$ is true.

Step 2:   Prove that $A(k + 1)$ must be true whenever $A(k)$ is true. This is done by assuming that $A(k)$ is true and then showing that this assumption leads to the conclusion that $A(k + 1)$ is true.

Step 3:   Complete the proof by concluding that $A(n)$ is true for all natural numbers, by the principle of mathematical induction.

The first two steps are the most important. To omit either of them may lead to a false conclusion. Step 3 is needed to make the argument complete.

We shall now illustrate by an example the use of mathematical induction in the proof of certain types of theorems concerning natural numbers.

Suppose we desire a simple formula for finding the sum of any number of consecutive positive odd integers. We define a positive odd integer as one that can be expressed in the form $2n - 1$, where n is a positive integer. The first odd integer is of course 1, since 1 can be expressed as $(2 \cdot 1) - 1$. We obtain the second odd integer by setting $n = 2$, as $(2 \cdot 2) - 1 = 4 - 1 = 3$, the third by setting $n = 3$, the fourth by setting $n = 4$, and so on. Hence the kth odd integer is given by $2k - 1$ and the $(k + 1)$th by $2k + 1$. Next we make a table as follows:

$$1 = 1^2$$
$$1 + 3 = 4 = 2^2,$$
$$1 + 3 + 5 = 9 = 3^2,$$
$$1 + 3 + 5 + 7 = 16 = 4^2.$$

Our table shows that the sum of the first two consecutive positive odd integers is 2^2, the sum of the first three consecutive positive odd integers is 3^2, and the sum of the first four consecutive positive odd integers is 4^2. This suggests that the sum of the first n consecutive positive odd integers is probably n^2. As yet, this last statement is just an "educated guess" and has to be proved before we can declare our search successful. So let us now attempt to prove that the statement $A(n)$ is true for all natural numbers, where

$$A(n): \quad 1 + 3 + 5 + 7 + \cdots + (2n - 1) = n^2.$$

In making our proof we shall use the principle of mathematical induction.

Proof: (a) For $n = 1$, $A(1)$ becomes $1 = 1^2$, which is true, hence $A(1)$ is true. (b) Let us assume that $A(k)$ is true, where

$$A(k): \quad 1 + 3 + 5 + 7 + \cdots + (2k - 1) = k^2.$$

But if $A(k)$ is true, then

$$A(k+1): \quad 1 + 3 + 5 + 7 + \cdots + (2k - 1) + (2k + 1)$$
$$= k^2 + 2k + 1 = (k + 1)^2$$

is a true statement since it was obtained by adding $(2k + 1)$, the $(k + 1)$th positive odd integer, to each member of the equation defining $A(k)$. We observe that if the sum of the first k consecutive positive odd integers is k^2, then the sum of the first $(k + 1)$ consecutive positive odd integers is $(k + 1)^2$. That is to say, $A(k + 1)$ is true whenever $A(k)$ is true.

We conclude, by the principle of mathematical induction, that $A(n)$ is true for all natural numbers.

EXERCISES

Use Mathematical Induction to prove each of the following statements, assuming n is a positive integer.

1. $2 + 4 + 6 + 8 + \cdots + 2n = n(n + 1)$.
2. $2 + 4 + 8 + 16 + \cdots + 2^n = 2^{n+1} - 2$.

3. $1^2 + 2^2 + 3^2 + \cdots + n^2 = \dfrac{n(n + 1)(2n + 1)}{6}$.

4. $(1 \cdot 2) + (2 \cdot 3) + (3 \cdot 4) + \cdots + n(n + 1) = \dfrac{n(n + 1)(n + 2)}{3}$.

5. $1 + r + r^2 + r^3 + \cdots + r^{n-1} = \dfrac{1 - r^n}{1 - r}$.

6. $\dfrac{1}{1 \cdot 2} + \dfrac{1}{2 \cdot 3} + \dfrac{1}{3 \cdot 4} + \cdots + \dfrac{1}{n(n + 1)} = \dfrac{n}{n + 1}$.

7. $1^3 + 2^3 + 3^3 + 4^3 + \cdots + n^3 = \dfrac{n^2(n + 1)^2}{4}$.

8. $(x^m)^n = x^{mn}$.
9. $2n \leq 2^n$.
10. $a^n - 1$ is divisible by $(a - 1)$. (*Hint:* $a^{n+1} - 1 = a(a^n - 1) + (a - 1)$.)
11. $x^n - y^n$ is divisible by $x - y$. [See *Hint* in Problem 10.]

12. $(a + d) + (a + 2d) + (a + 3d) + \cdots + (a + nd) = \dfrac{n}{2}[2a + (n + 1)d]$.

13. Prove that the sum of the cubes of any three successive positive integers is divisible by 9.
14. The principle of mathematical induction may be generalized as follows. Let r be a positive integer.
    If (a) $A(r)$ is true,
       (b)   for every arbitrary but fixed positive integer $K \geq r$, $A(K + 1)$ is true whenever $A(K)$ is true, then $A(n)$ is true for all positive integers n such that $n \geq r$.

Use this generalized principle to prove that the product of n positive odd integers is an odd integer.

15. Prove: If $0 < a < b$, then $a^n < b^n$.
16. Prove: $3^{2n} - 1$ is divisible by 8.

9 THE BINOMIAL THEOREM

We have already given rules for expanding binomials of the type $(x + y)^2$ and $(x + y)^3$. It is desirable to have a simple rule for expanding the general binomial $(x + y)^n$, where n is a positive integer. To find such a rule let us examine the following expansions, each of which is easily verified by direct multiplication.

$$(x + y)^1 = x + y$$
$$(x + y)^2 = x^2 + 2xy + y^2$$
$$(x + y)^3 = x^3 + 3x^2y + 3xy^2 + y^3$$
$$(x + y)^4 = x^4 + 4x^3y + 6x^2y^2 + 4xy^3 + y^4.$$

Careful inspection of the above expansions suggests these facts regarding the expansion of $(x + y)^n$:

1.   The first term is x^n, the last term is y^n, and the total number of terms is $n + 1$.

2.   The symbol x occurs in each term except the last and the exponent of x decreases by 1 in each succeeding term. The symbol y occurs in each term except the first; its exponent is 1 in the second term and increases by 1 in each succeeding term. In each term the sum of the exponents of x and y is n.

3.   The coefficient of the second term is n. From any given term, the coefficient of the succeeding term may be obtained by multiplying the coefficient of the given term by the exponent of x in that term and then dividing this product by the number of the given term.

The above observations enable us to write a general formula, called *The Binomial Theorem*, for the expansion of the general binomial $(x + y)^n$, n a positive integer.

Theorem 3.1.   The Binomial Theorem.   *For any positive integer n*

$$(x + y)^n = x^n + nx^{n-1}y + \frac{n(n-1)}{2} x^{n-2}y^2 + \frac{n(n-1)(n-2)}{2 \cdot 3} + \cdots + y^n.$$

The proof of the binomial theorem will be easier to understand if we employ the symbol $n!$ read "n factorial" and the symbol $\binom{n}{r}$, called a binomial coefficient. These symbols are defined as follows.

Definition 3.6. *The symbols* 0! *and* n!, *for n a positive integer, are defined to be*

(a) $0! = 1.$
(b) $n! = 1 \cdot 2 \cdot 3 \cdot 4 \cdot \ \cdots \ \cdot (n-1) \cdot n.$

In words, $n!$ is the product of all the positive integers from 1 to n inclusive. Thus $2! = 1 \cdot 2$, $3! = 1 \cdot 2 \cdot 3$, $4! = 1 \cdot 2 \cdot 3 \cdot 4$, and so on.

Example.   Evaluate $\dfrac{7!}{5!}$.

Solution: $\dfrac{7!}{5!} = \dfrac{7 \cdot 6 \cdot 5!}{5!} = 7 \cdot 6 = 42.$

Definition 3.7. *For all integers n and r such that* $0 \le r \le n$, *the symbol* $\dbinom{n}{r}$
is defined by the formula

$$\binom{n}{r} = \frac{n!}{(n-r)!\,r!}.$$

Examples. $\dbinom{4}{1} = \dfrac{4!}{(4-1)!1!} = \dfrac{4!}{3!1!} = \dfrac{4 \cdot 3!}{3!} = 4.$

$\dbinom{7}{4} = \dfrac{7!}{(7-4)!4!} = \dfrac{7!}{3!4!} = \dfrac{7 \cdot 6 \cdot 5 \cdot 4!}{1 \cdot 2 \cdot 3 \cdot 4!} = \dfrac{7 \cdot 6 \cdot 5}{6} = 35.$

By substituting $r = 0, 1, 2, 3, \cdots, n$ successively in the formula for $\dbinom{n}{r}$ we obtain the following set of numbers.

$$\binom{n}{0} = \frac{n!}{(n-0)!0!} = \frac{n!}{n!} = 1$$

$$\binom{n}{1} = \frac{n!}{(n-1)!1!} = \frac{n!}{(n-1)!} = \frac{n(n-1)!}{(n-1)!} = n$$

$$\binom{n}{2} = \frac{n!}{(n-2)!2!} = \frac{n(n-1)(n-2)!}{2(n-2)!} = \frac{n(n-1)}{2}$$

$$\binom{n}{3} = \frac{n!}{(n-3)!3!} = \frac{n(n-1)(n-2)(n-3)!}{1 \cdot 2 \cdot 3 \cdot (n-3)!} = \frac{n(n-1)(n-2)}{2 \cdot 3}$$

$$\cdots\cdots\cdots\cdots\cdots\cdots\cdots\cdots\cdots\cdots\cdots\cdots$$

$$\binom{n}{n} = \frac{n!}{(n-n)!n!} = \frac{n!}{0!n!} = 1.$$

We observe that the set of numbers just listed are precisely the set of coefficients in the expansion of $(x+y)^n$ stated in the binomial theorem. That is, $\dbinom{n}{0}, \dbinom{n}{1}, \dbinom{n}{2}, \dbinom{n}{3}, \cdots, \dbinom{n}{r}, \cdots \dbinom{n}{n}$ are respectively the coefficients of $x^n, x^{n-1}y, x^{n-2}y^2, \cdots, x^{n-r}y^r, \cdots$ and y^n in that expansion. This explains why these symbols are called binomial coefficients. Using these new symbols to represent the coefficients, the binomial theorem may be expressed in the following form.

$$A(n): \quad (x + y)^n = \binom{n}{0} x^n + \binom{n}{1} x^{n-1}y + \binom{n}{2} x^{n-2}y^2 + \binom{n}{3} x^{n-3}y^3 + \cdots$$

$$+ \binom{n}{n-2} x^2 y^{n-2} + \binom{n}{n-1} xy^{n-1} + \binom{n}{n} y^n.$$

We shall use the method of mathematical induction to prove that this formula is true for all positive integral values of n. It will be recalled from the previous section that such a method of proof involves three steps.

Step 1: $A(1)$: $(x + y)^1 = x + y$. Hence $A(1)$ is true.

Step 2: We need to show that for any arbitrary but fixed integer K, $A(K + 1)$ is true if $A(K)$ is true. It is easily seen from the statement above represented by $A(n)$ that for any integer r such that $0 \le r \le n$, the coefficient of $x^{n-r}y^r$ is $\binom{n}{r}$. Thus we need to show that in the special case $n = K$, and $r \le K$, if the coefficient of $x^{K-r}y^r$ in the expansion of $(x + y)^K$ is $\binom{K}{r}$, then the coefficient of $x^{K+1-r}y^r$ in the expansion of $(x + y)^{K+1}$ is $\binom{K+1}{r}$. To do this, let K be any positive integer for which the binomial theorem is true. That is, let's assume that

$$A(K): (x + y)^K = x^K + \binom{K}{1} x^{K-1}y + \cdots + \binom{K}{r-1} x^{K+1-r}y^{r-1}$$

$$+ \binom{K}{r} x^{K-r}y^r + \cdots + y^K$$

is a true statement. We may obtain the expansion for $(x + y)^{K+1}$ from the expansion for $(x + y)^K$ by using the identity $x(x + y)^K + y(x + y)^K = (x + y)^{K+1}$.

$$x(x + y)^K = x^{K+1} + \binom{K}{1} x^K y + \cdots + \binom{K}{r-1} x^{K+2-r}y^{r-1}$$

$$+ \binom{K}{r} x^{K+1-r}y^r + \cdots + xy^K$$

$$y(x + y)^K = x^K y + \binom{K}{1} x^{K-1}y^2 + \cdots + \binom{K}{r-1} x^{K+1-r}y^r$$

$$+ \binom{K}{r} x^{K+1-r}y^{r+1} + \cdots + y^{K+1}.$$

Adding and collecting terms we have

$$A(K + 1): (x + y)^{K+1} = x^{K+1} + \left[\binom{K}{1} + 1\right] x^K y + \cdots$$

$$+ \left[\binom{K}{r} + \binom{K}{r-1}\right] x^{K+1-r}y^r + \cdots + y^{K+1}.$$

The coefficient of $x^{K+1-r}y^r$ in the expansion of $(x + y)^{K+1}$ is $\binom{K}{r} + \binom{K}{r-1}$, assuming the formula for $(x + y)^K$ is true. But, since $(K + 1 - r)! = (K + 1 - r)(K - r)!$ and $r! = r(r - 1)!$

$$\binom{K}{r} + \binom{K}{r-1} = \frac{K!}{(K-r)!r!} + \frac{K!}{(K+1-r)!(r-1)!}$$

$$= \frac{K!}{(K-r)!(r-1)!}\left[\frac{1}{r} + \frac{1}{K+1-r}\right]$$

$$= \frac{K!}{(K-r)!(r-1)!}\left[\frac{K+1}{r(K+1-r)}\right]$$

$$= \frac{(K+1)!}{(K+1-r)!r!}$$

$$= \binom{K+1}{r}.$$

Therefore, the coefficient of $x^{K+1-r}y^r$ in the expansion of $(x + y)^{K+1}$ is $\binom{K+1}{r}$ if the coefficient of $x^{K-r}y^r$ in the expansion of $(x + y)^K$ is $\binom{K}{r}$.

Since $\binom{K+1}{r}$ $x^{K+1-r}y^r$ represents all terms in the expansion of $(x + y)^{K+1}$, then it follows that $A(K + 1)$ is true if $A(K)$ is true.

Finally, since $A(1)$ is true and $A(K + 1)$ is true if $A(K)$ is true, we conclude by the principle of mathematical induction that the binomial theorem is true for all positive integral values of n. Another proof of this theorem will be given in a later chapter.

To be able to use the binomial theorem effectively in expanding binomials the student should carefully memorize the rule for determining from a given term the coefficient of the succeeding term.

Example.   Expand $(x + y)^6$.

Solution: The first two terms of the expansion are obviously

$$x^6 + 6x^5y.$$

Third term of expansion is $\dfrac{6 \cdot 5}{2} x^4y^2 = 15x^4y^2.$

Fourth term of expansion is $\dfrac{15 \cdot 4}{3} x^3y^3 = 20x^3y^3.$

Fifth term of expansion is $\dfrac{20 \cdot 3}{4} x^2y^4 = 15x^2y^4.$

Sixth term of expansion is $\dfrac{15 \cdot 2}{5} xy^5 = 6xy^5$.

Seventh term of expansion is $\dfrac{6 \cdot 1}{6} x^0 y^6 = y^6$.

Therefore, $(x + y)^6 = x^6 + 6x^5y + 15x^4y^2 + 20x^3y^3 + 15x^2y^4 + 6xy^5 + y^6$.

It often happens that it is necessary to expand a binomial in which one or both of its terms contain two or more factors. In such a case it is best to enclose each term in parentheses, use the rule to expand the binomial, and then simplify by removing all parentheses. The following example will make clear how this is done.

Example. Expand $(2x - y^2)^5$.

Solution:

$(2x - y^2)^5 = [(2x) + (-y^2)]^5 = (2x)^5 + 5(2x)^4(-y^2) + 10(2x)^3(-y^2)^2$
$$+ 10(2x)^2(-y^2)^3 + 5(2x)(-y^2)^4 + (-y^2)^5.$$

Simplifying: $(2x - y^2)^5 = 32x^5 - 80x^4y^2 + 80x^3y^4 - 40x^2y^6 + 10xy^8 - y^{10}$.

EXERCISES

1. Evaluate:

   a. $\dfrac{6!}{4!}$.

   b. $\dfrac{7!}{3!4!}$.

   c. $\dfrac{10!6!}{2!5!7!}$.

2. Evaluate:

   a. $\dfrac{4! + 3!}{6! - 5!}$.

   b. $\dfrac{3!4!}{5!6!}$.

   c. $\dfrac{1}{3!} + \dfrac{1}{4!}$.

3. Simplify each given expression, if K and r are positive integers such that $r \leq K$.

   a. $\dfrac{(K - 1)!}{(K - 3)!}$.

   b. $\dfrac{(K + 1 - r)!}{(K - r)!}$.

   c. $\dfrac{(K + r + 1)!}{(K + r - 1)!}$.

4. Show that: a. if $n > 1$, then $n!$ is an even integer.
   b. if $n > 4$, then $n!$ is a multiple of 10.

5. Evaluate:

   a. $\dbinom{5}{3}$.

   b. $\dbinom{0}{0}$.

   c. $\dbinom{10}{2}$.

   d. $\dbinom{10}{8}$.

6. Show that: a. $\dbinom{n}{r} = \dbinom{n}{n - r}$.

   b. $\dbinom{n}{r} + \dbinom{n}{r - 1} = \dbinom{n + 1}{r}$.

In problems 7 through 21 expand each given binomial and simplify where possible.

7. $(a + h)^3$.

8. $(a + h)^4$.

9. $(a + h)^5$.

10. $(x + 2y)^4$.

11. $(2x - y)^5$.

12. $(2x + 3y)^3$.

13. $(a - 2b)^5$.

14. $(a + h)^6$.

15. $(a^2 + b)^4$.

16. $\left(x + \dfrac{1}{x}\right)^5$.

17. $(3x - y)^6$.

18. $(x^2 + 2y)^7$.

19. $\left(x^2 - \dfrac{1}{2x}\right)^5$.

20. $(2x^2 + \frac{1}{2}y)^6$.

21. $\left(x + \dfrac{1}{\sqrt{x}}\right)^8$.

Find and simplify the first four terms in the expansion of each of the following.

22. $(x + y)^{40}$.

23. $(a - b)^{20}$.

24. $(x^2 - 2y)^{10}$.

25. $(1 - x^2)^{12}$.

26. The $(r + 1)$st term in the expansion of $(x + y)^n$ is $\dbinom{n}{r} x^{n-r} y^r$, where $0 \le r \le n$. Use this fact to find the indicated term in the expansion of each given binomial.

    a. Sixth term of $(x + y)^{10}$.

    b. Fourth term of $(a - b)^8$.

    c. Tenth term of $(x - 2y)^{14}$.

    d. Twentieth term of $(2x - y)^{30}$.

27. By writing $(1.02)^{10}$ as $(1 + .02)^{10}$, expand and thus evaluate, rounding off your answer correct to five decimal places. [Express each term correct to six decimal places and round off sum to five decimal places.] Any term having no significant digit in the first six decimal places may be neglected.

Evaluate the following to five decimal places.

28. $(1.01)^5$.

29. $(1.06)^7$.

30. $(1.04)^{10}$.

31. $(1.03)^{20}$.

32. $(1.02)^{40}$.

33. $(1.01)^{50}$.

34. $(1.1)^{10}$.

35. $(1.2)^6$.

IV

POLYNOMIALS, EQUATIONS, AND INEQUALITIES

1 INTRODUCTION

Probably the most common problem encountered in elementary mathematics is that of solving an equation or inequality of some type. It is our purpose in this chapter to develop methods and procedures for solving

    (a)   polynomial equations in one variable
    (b)   polynomial inequalities in one variable
    (c)   equations and inequalities whose solutions may be reduced to the problem of solving a polynomial equation or inequality.

2 POLYNOMIALS IN ONE VARIABLE

By a polynomial in one variable, say x, we shall mean an algebraic expression involving only the one variable and, which can be written in descending powers of x and such that each exponent of x is either zero or a positive integer. Typical examples of such polynomials are:

    (a) $3x^2 - 7x + 5$,   (c) $x^3 + 2ix - 4$,   (e) $\frac{1}{2}x^4 - 9$,
    (b) $5x - 8$,   (d) $2x^7 + 5x^3 + 1$,   (f) $0x + 6$.

Stated in symbols our definition becomes

Definition 4.1.   *A polynomial in x is an expression which can be written in the form*

$$A_0 x^n + A_1 x^{n-1} + A_2 x^{n-2} + \cdots + A_{n-1} x + A_n,$$

where n is a positive integer or zero and the coefficients, $A_0, A_1, A_2, \cdots, A_{n-1}, A_n$, are elements of some number system.

If the number system is unspecified we shall assume it to be the complex number system. If $A_0 \neq 0$, the degree of the polynomial is said to be n. In the six examples of polynomials listed above, the degrees are respectively 2, 1, 3, 7, 4, and 0.

If all the coefficients are real numbers, the polynomial is often called a *real polynomial.* Let us use such symbols as $f(x)$, $g(x)$, $u(x)$, $v(x)$, etc., read "f of x," "g of x," "u of x," "v of x," and so on, to represent arbitrary polynomials in x.

In the restricted sense in which we have defined a polynomial in x, such expressions as the following are not polynomials:

$$3x^2 + 7\sqrt{x} + 2,$$

$$x^3 + 5x - \frac{7}{x} + 3,$$

$$\frac{x^4 - 3x^2 + 10}{x^2}.$$

We have chosen the symbols $f(x)$, $g(x)$, etc., to denote polynomials for two reasons: first, because we wish at times to consider arbitrary polynomials without specifying a particular polynomial and, second, such a notation gives us a very convenient means of denoting the value of the polynomial for a particular value of x. For example, the symbol $f(2)$ shall mean the value of $f(x)$ when x is replaced by 2; $f(a)$ shall mean the value of $f(x)$ when x is replaced by the arbitrary number a.

Example.   If $f(x) = 5x^2 - 3x + 10$, then
$$f(1) = 5 - 3 + 10 = 12,$$
$$f(0) = 10,$$
$$f(-2) = 5(-2)^2 - 3(-2) + 10 = 20 + 6 + 10 = 36,$$
$$f(a) = 5a^2 - 3a + 10.$$

3   EQUATIONS

It is common practice to call any statement involving the equality relation, that is, involving the equality symbol, "$=$", an *equation.* In fact the student is quite accustomed to seeing statements of the form

$$2 + 3 = 5,$$
$$5 + 7 = 10,$$

$$x + 2 = 7,$$
$$2x + 5x = 7x,$$
$$x^2 - 3x + 2 = 5 + 2x - x^2,$$

and has learned to refer to such statements as equations. We shall use the same terminology in the remainder of this text. A very important fact concerning equations is that an equation may be a true statement, it may be false, or it may be neither true nor false. Consider, for example, the equation $2 + 3 = 5$. This is certainly a true statement, since "2 + 3" and "5" are just different symbols for the same number. The equation $5 + 7 = 10$ is obviously false since "5 + 7" and "10" are symbols which represent two entirely different numbers. We could change this equation into a true statement by writing $5 + 7 \neq 10$, the negation of the original statement. On the other hand consider the equation $x + 2 = 7$. This equation is an open statement in the sense that until some particular number is substituted for x, it is neither true nor false. It is obvious, however, that if we substitute the number 5 for x, the equation becomes a true statement because $5 + 2 = 7$ is true. It is equally obvious that if we substitute any number other than 5 for x the equation becomes a false statement.

It is often desirable in mathematics to use a letter to represent a fixed number. In fact, letters a, b, c, etc., in the axioms and theorems of Chapter II were used in this way. A letter used in this way is called an *arbitrary constant*. Arbitrary constants enable us to represent by a single equation a set of particular equations. For example, $3x - 5 = 0$ and $2x + 7 - 0$ are particular first-degree equations in the variable x. However, if we make the statement $ax + b = 0$, we are making a statement about these equations and, in fact, we are making a statement about all possible first-degree equations in the variable x; that is, no matter what numbers are substituted for a and b in the equation $ax + b = 0$, provided $a \neq 0$, the result is always a first-degree equation in the variable x.

It is conventional to use letters at the beginning of the alphabet, a, b, c, etc., for arbitrary constants and letters at the end of the alphabet, x, y, z, and others, for variables.

It will be convenient for our purposes to think of equations as being of two kinds, numerical equations and equations involving variables. By a numerical equation we mean an equation that makes a statement about one or more specific numbers, $2 + 3 = 5$, $4 + 2 = 7 - 1$, and $5 + 3 = 8$. As has been pointed out above, a numerical equation is a true statement or a false statement, but not both. We shall call a numerical equation that makes a true statement a *numerical identity*. The equations just cited are numerical identities.

Equations involving variables include all equations that contain one or more letters representing arbitrary numbers from some set of numbers. Some typical equations of this kind are $3x + 2 = 10$, $2x + 3x = 5x$,

$x^2 + 3x + 8 = 0$, $x^2 - 5x = 3x^2 + 7$, $y = 4 - x^2$, $x^2 + y^2 - 5x + 2y = 9$, $ax + by + c = 0$, etc.

As we have seen, an equation involving a variable is neither true nor false until some specific number is substituted for the variable in the equation. If, however, this is done, the equation becomes either true or false, but not both. Equations that are true for all values of their variables, such as $2x + 3x = 5x$ or $(x + y)^2 = x^2 + 2xy + y^2$, also are called *identities*. Equations that are true for some values of their variables and false for others, such as $3x = 15$ or $x + y = 5$, are called *conditional equations*.

The expression to the left of the equality sign in an equation is often referred to as the *left member* of the equation, and the expression to the right of the equality sign as the *right member*. Since in an identity the left member has the same value as the right member for all possible values of their variables, either member may be substituted for the other in any expression, statement, or equation, wherever one member may occur, without changing the possible values of the expression or the truth or falsity of the statement or equation. This application, of substituting one member of an identity for the other, is one of the most important uses of identities and is certainly the one that occurs most often. In fact, each time we change from the expanded form of an expression to the factored form or combine terms in an expression or, in general, substitute equals for equals, we are making use of one or more identities.

Definition 4.2.   *An equation involving one or more variables is said to be an identity if the equation is true for all values of its variables for which both the left member and the right member are defined.*

4   SOLUTIONS AND SOLUTION SETS

One of the basic problems in elementary mathematics is that of "solving conditional equations." In this chapter we shall be concerned with discussing methods and procedures for solving a particular type of conditional equation called a *polynomial equation in one variable* which is defined as follows:

Definition 4.3.   *A polynomial equation in one variable is an equation of the form*

$$f(x) = g(x)$$

where $f(x)$ and $g(x)$ are polynomials.

Let us begin our discussion by familiarizing ourselves with some terminology that may or may not be new to you. First we want to state precisely what is meant by a solution of a polynomial equation in one variable. As was pointed out in the previous section, an equation involving a variable is an open statement and as such is neither true nor false. However, when a specific number is substituted for the variable our equation becomes a proposition and is either true or false but not both. If a specific number substituted for the variable reduces the equation to a true statement, that is, to a numerical identity, then this specific number is called a *solution*, or a *root* of the equation. For example, the number 2 is a root of the equation $x + 3 = 5$ because $2 + 3 = 5$ is a numerical identity. This leads us to the following definitions.

Definition 4.4.   *A solution, or root, of an equation in one variable is a number which when substituted for the variable reduces the equation to a numerical identity. In particular, the number a is a root of the polynomial equation $f(x) = g(x)$ if and only if $f(a) = g(a)$.*

Definition 4.5.   *A solution set of a given equation is the set consisting of all the roots of that equation. Thus, to solve an equation is to find its solution set.*

The solution set of an equation may contain no numbers, one number, two numbers, or many numbers, depending upon the degree of the equation, the coefficients involved, and any restriction which might be imposed on the universal set, U, containing the variable x. For example, the solution set, S, of the equation $2x - 3 = 0$ is the empty set if $U = N$, that is if the universal set is the set of positive integers. However, if $U = R$, then $S = \{3/2\}$.

That two or more equations may have the same solution set is easily verified. Consider the equations

$$5x - 2 = 2x + 4, \qquad 3x = 6, \qquad \text{and} \qquad x = 2.$$

Although no two of these equations are the same, a simple check will show that all of them have the same solution set, namely the set $\{2\}$. In Chapter I, two open statements having equal truth sets were called equivalent statements. This suggests the following definition.

Definition 4.6.   *Two equations, $f(x) = g(x)$ and $u(x) = v(x)$, are equivalent if and only if they have the same solution set. Such an equivalence is denoted symbolically as $f(x) = g(x) \Leftrightarrow u(x) = v(x)$, or as $\{x \mid f(x)) = g(x)\} = \{x \mid u(x) = v(x)\}$.*

The importance of the notion of equivalent equations lies in the fact that it is the basis of a procedure for solving equations. For example, suppose we wish to solve a given equation. If through one or more equivalent equations, each derived from the preceding one, we finally arrive at an equivalent equation whose solution set is obvious, we have thus found the solution set of the given equation. An equation obtained from another equation by any process whatever is called a *derived* equation. In such a case we say the second equation was derived from the *first*. Thus it is important, in solving an equation in one variable, to know what operations will produce a derived equation which is equivalent to the given equation; or as a minimum essential, what operations will produce a derived equation whose solution set contains the solution set of the given equation as a subset. We now attempt to give some answers to this basic and most important question.

The following operations will obviously always produce a derived equation equivalent to the equation from which it was derived.

1. Changing the order of the terms in a member of the equation.
2. Combining like terms in a member of the equation.
3. Using an identity to change the form of a member of the equation.

Examples.
$$5x + 8 - 2x = 9 + 2x \Leftrightarrow 3x + 8 = 2x + 9,$$
$$4(x + 2) - 2(x - 1) = x + 3 \Leftrightarrow 2x + 10 = x + 3,$$
$$2(x + 1)^2 - 5(x + 3) = 3x^2 - 7x \Leftrightarrow 2x^2 - x - 13 = 3x^2 - 7.$$

In addition to the operations mentioned the following theorems will be most helpful in solving equations.

Theorem 4.1.   *If $f(x)$, $g(x)$, and $u(x)$ are polynomials, then the equations $f(x) = g(x)$ and $f(x) + u(x) = g(x) + u(x)$ are equivalent, or stated symbolically*

$$f(x) = g(x) \leftrightarrow f(x) + u(x) = g(x) + u(x).$$

Proof: Let S be the solution set of $f(x) = g(x)$ and let T be the solution set of $f(x) + u(x) = g(x) + u(x)$. Our proof will consist of showing that $S \subseteq T$, that $T \subseteq S$, and hence $S = T$. Suppose the complex number a is a root of $f(x) = g(x)$. This means that $a \in S$ and also that $f(a) = g(a)$ is a numerical identity. $u(x)$ is a polynomial and hence $u(a)$ is a complex number. It follows by adding equals to equals that $f(a) + u(a) = g(a) + u(a)$ is likewise a numerical identity and therefore $a \in T$. In other words, this shows that every element of S is also an element of T, or simply that $S \subseteq T$. Next, suppose that $b \in T$, that is to say $f(b) + u(b) = g(b) + u(b)$ is a numerical identity. Now by subtracting $u(b)$ from both sides, subtracting equals from equals, we obtain the numerical identity $f(b) = g(b)$. This shows that $b \in S$ and hence that every element of T is an element of S, that is, $T \subseteq S$. But if $S \subseteq T$ and $T \subseteq S$, then $S = T$. This proves our theorem.

Example.   Find the solution set, S, of the equation $3x + 5 = 2x + 8$.

Solution: Here $f(x) = 3x + 5$, $g(x) = 2x + 8$. Our solution will consist of developing from the given equation, by use of Theorem 4.1 and any of the three operations listed above which apply, a successive chain of equivalent equations the last link of which is an equation whose solution set is obvious. In this case we start by applying Theorem 4.1 with $u(x) = -2x - 5$ and record the various steps in the solution as follows:

$$3x + 5 = 2x + 8 \leftrightarrow 3x + 5 + (-2x - 5) = 2x + 8 + (-2x - 5),$$
$$\leftrightarrow 3x - 2x = 8 - 5,$$
$$\leftrightarrow x = 3.$$

The solution set of the equation $x = 3$ is obviously $\{3\}$. Hence the solution set S of the given equation must be $S = \{3\}$.

Theorem 4.2. *Let $f(x)$ and $g(x)$ be polynomials and let K be a complex number such that $K \neq 0$. Then the equations $f(x) = g(x)$ and $Kf(x) = Kg(x)$ are equivalent. That is*

$$f(x) = g(x) \leftrightarrow Kf(x) = Kg(x).$$

Proof: Let S be the solution set of $f(x) = g(x)$ and let T be the solution set of $Kf(x) = Kg(x)$. Suppose the complex number a is an element of S, then $f(a) = g(a)$ is a numerical identity. Since $Kf(a)$ and $Kg(a)$ are just different names for the same number, then $Kf(a) = Kg(a)$. Thus, a is a solution of $Kf(x) = Kg(x)$, that is $a \in T$, and hence every element of S is in T. Therefore, $S \subseteq T$. Next, suppose $b \in T$. If so, $Kf(b) = Kg(b)$. But $K \neq 0$, so $\dfrac{1}{K} \neq 0$, from which it follows that $\dfrac{1}{K}[Kf(b)] = \dfrac{1}{K}[Kg(b)]$, or $f(b) = g(b)$. This implies $b \in S$. Thus every element of T is in S, or stated in symbols $T \subseteq S$. Since $S \subseteq T$ and $T \subseteq S$, then $S = T$ and our theorem is proved.

Example.   Find the solution set S of the equation

$$\frac{x + 1}{4} - \frac{2x - 9}{10} = \frac{3}{2}.$$

Solution: We use Theorem 4.2 with $K = 20$ and obtain the following chain of equivalent equations

$$\frac{x + 1}{4} - \frac{2x - 9}{10} = \frac{3}{2} \leftrightarrow 20\left(\frac{x - 1}{4} - \frac{2x - 9}{10}\right) = 20\left(\frac{3}{2}\right),$$
$$\leftrightarrow 5(x + 1) - 2(2x - 9) = 30,$$
$$\leftrightarrow 5x + 5 - 4x + 18 = 30,$$
$$\leftrightarrow x + 23 = 30,$$
$$\leftrightarrow x = 7.$$
$$\therefore S = \{7\}.$$

Theorem 4.3.   *Suppose $f(x)$ and $g(x)$ are polynomials. Suppose further $T_1, T_2,$ and S are respectively the solution sets of $f(x) = 0, g(x) = 0,$ and $f(x)g(x) = 0,$ then $S = T_1 \cup T_2$.*

Proof: Let a denote any element of S, then $f(a)g(a) = 0$. But $f(x)$ and $g(x)$ are polynomials and hence $f(a)$ and $g(a)$ are complex numbers. Thus $f(a) = 0$ or $g(a) = 0$ (see Problem 11 of Exercises at end of Section 15, Ch. II).

It follows that $a \in T_1$ or $a \in T_2$, that is, $a \in T_1 \cup T_2$, which implies that $S \subseteq T_1 \cup T_2$. Next suppose $b \in T_1 \cup T_2$; then either $f(b) = 0$ or $g(b) = 0$ and therefore $f(b) \cdot g(b) = 0$. Consequently, $b \in S$. That is, $T_1 \cup T_2 \subseteq S$. But if $S \subseteq T_1 \cup T_2$ and $T_1 \cup T_2 \subseteq S$, then $S = T_1 \cup T_2$, and our theorem is proved.

Example.   Find the solution set, S, of the equation

$$x^2 - 3x + 2 = 0.$$

Solution: Since $x^2 - 3x + 2 = (x - 1)(x - 2)$ is an identity

$$x^2 - 3x + 2 = 0 \leftrightarrow (x - 1)(x - 2) = 0.$$

Let T_1 be the solution set of $x - 1 = 0$ and let T_2 be the solution set of $x - 2 = 0$. Then

$$x - 1 = 0 \leftrightarrow x = 1 \qquad \text{and} \qquad x - 2 = 0 \leftrightarrow x = 2.$$

It follows that $T_1 = \{1\}$ and $T_2 = \{2\}$. Therefore

$$S = T_1 \cup T_2 = \{1, 2\}.$$

In Chapter III rules were given for finding the sum, the difference, and the product of two algebraic expressions. It follows from these rules and the definition of a polynomial in x that, if K is any number, and if $f(x)$ and $g(x)$ are any two polynomials in x, then $Kf(x)$, $f(x) + g(x)$, $f(x) - g(x)$, and $f(x) \cdot g(x)$ are also polynomials in x.

One important consequence of the above facts is the following theorem.

Theorem 4.4.   *If $f(x)$ and $g(x)$ are polynomials in x and $F(x) = f(x) - g(x)$ then $f(x) = g(x) \leftrightarrow F(x) = 0$. That is, every polynomial equation in x can be reduced to the standard form $F(x) = 0$.*

Definition 4.7.   *The degree of a polynomial equation in one variable, $F(x) = 0$, is the same as the degree of the polynomial $F(x)$.*

To determine the degree of a polynomial equation in one variable, reduce it to the form $F(x) = 0$ and then apply Definition 4.7. The simplest such polynomial equation is one of degree 1. Since every polynomial of degree 1 can be written in the form $ax + b$, $a \neq 0$, it follows that every polynomial equation in x of degree 1 can be written in the form $ax + b = 0$, $a \neq 0$. Such an equation is called a *linear equation* in x. The most important fact concerning linear equations of this kind is covered by the following theorem.

Theorem 4.5.   *Every linear polynomial equation in one variable has one and only one root.*

Proof: By definition every linear equation in x can be written in the form $ax + b = 0$, where $a \neq 0$. Thus to prove our theorem we only need to find the solution set S of this equation. This we do as follows.

$$ax + b = 0 \leftrightarrow ax = -b \qquad \text{(Theorem 4.1 with } u(x) = -b)$$

$$\leftrightarrow x = -\frac{b}{a} \qquad \left(\text{Theorem 4.2 with } K = \frac{1}{a}\right)$$

$$S = \left\{-\frac{b}{a}\right\}$$

Since S contains one and only one number, our theorem is proved.

EXERCISES

For each problem, 1–8, write an identity using the given expression as the left member.

1. $(x + 2)^2$.

2. $\dfrac{x^2 - 5x + 6}{x - 3}$.

3. $\dfrac{x}{3} - \dfrac{x}{5}$.

4. $\dfrac{x}{y} - \dfrac{y}{x}$.

5. $x^2 - x - 6$.

6. $(a + b)(a - b)$.

7. $2a^2 - 3ab - 5b^2$.

8. $\dfrac{x^3 + y^3}{x^2 - xy + y^2}$.

Solve each of the following equations.

9. $5x = 3x + 10$.
10. $4x - 7 = 3x - 9$.
11. $2y + 3 = 7y - 12$.
12. $6x - 5 = 8x - 10$.
13. $3(x - 2) = 5(x + 1) + 7$.
14. $5(2x - 1) - 7(x + 1) = 6$.
15. $2(3x + 4) - 2x = 5(2 - x) + 7$.
16. $y(y - 3) = (y - 1)(y + 2) - 6$.
17. $2x^2 - x(x - 3) = x^2 - 2x - 10$.

18. $\dfrac{x}{2} + \dfrac{x}{3} = 10$.

19. $\dfrac{2x}{3} - \dfrac{x}{6} = \dfrac{1}{2}$.

20. $\dfrac{3x}{4} + \dfrac{5x}{8} = \dfrac{x}{2} + \dfrac{7}{4}$.

21. $\frac{1}{2}(\frac{3}{4}x - 4) = \frac{5}{6}(4 - \frac{2}{3}x)$.
22. $\frac{2}{3}(\frac{4}{5}x - \frac{1}{2}) = \frac{1}{4}(\frac{5}{3}x + \frac{1}{15})$.

5 QUADRATIC EQUATIONS IN ONE VARIABLE

Every polynomial, $F(x)$, of degree 2 can be expressed in the form $ax^2 + bx + c$, $a \neq 0$. Hence every polynomial equation, in one variable, of degree 2 can be written as $ax^2 + bx + c = 0$, where $a \neq 0$. An equation of degree 2 in one variable is called a quadratic equation in that variable. Thus $2x^2 + 7x = 5$ is a quadratic equation in x, $y^2 - 3y + 2 = 0$ is a quadratic equation in y, $t^2 + 1 = 3t - 4$ is a quadratic equation in t, etc.

Since every quadratic equation can be written in the form $ax^2 + bx + c = 0$, we shall call this form the standard form of a quadratic equation. Unless otherwise noted, we shall assume that a, b, and c are real numbers, except a must not be zero. If $a = 0$, the degree of the equation is not 2 and hence the equation is not a quadratic. We shall consider three methods for solving a quadratic equation.

6   THE METHOD OF FACTORING

The method of factoring is a simple application of Theorem 3.3, which states in effect that if S is the solution set of the equation $f(x) \cdot g(x) = 0$ and if T_1 and T_2 are the solution sets of $f(x) = 0$ and $g(x) = 0$, respectively, then $S = T_1 \cup T_2$. The method consists of the following steps.

Step 1:   Write the quadratic in standard form.
Step 2:   Factor the left member into two factors, each of which contains the variable to the first power.
Step 3:   Set each factor equal to zero.
Step 4:   Find the solution set of each resulting equation.
Step 5:   Form union of the two solution sets found in Step 4; this is the solution set of the given quadratic equation.

It is advisable to check the solution by substituting each number of the solution set found in Step 5 into the original equation.

Example.   Solve the equation $x^2 - 3x = 2x - 6$.

Solution: Write the equation in standard form:

$$x^2 - 5x + 6 = 0. \qquad \text{(Step 1)}$$

Factor the left member:

$$(x - 2)(x - 3) = 0. \qquad \text{(Step 2)}$$

Equate each of the linear factors to zero:

$$x - 2 = 0 \quad \text{or} \quad x - 3 = 0. \qquad \text{(Step 3)}$$

Find the solution sets T_1 and T_2 of the two linear equations:

$$x - 2 = 0 \leftrightarrow x = 2 \quad \text{and} \quad x - 3 = 0 \leftrightarrow x - 3.$$

Thus $T_1 = \{2\}$ and $T_2 = \{3\}$. $\qquad \text{(Step 4)}$
Form the union of the two sets found in Step 4:

$$S = T_1 \cup T_2 = \{2, 3\}. \qquad \text{(Step 5)}$$

Check: $(2)^2 - 3(2) = 2(2) - 6$ or $(3)^2 - 3(3) = 2(3) - 6,$
$\qquad\qquad 4 - 6 = 4 - 6$ or $9 - 9 = 6 - 6,$
$\qquad\qquad\qquad -2 = -2$ or $0 = 0.$

Hence we have made no errors in our computation.

Example.   Solve the equation $(5x - 1)(2x - 1) = 13$.

Solution: Write the equation in standard form: $10x^2 - 7x - 12 = 0$.
Factor the left member: $(5x + 4)(2x - 3) = 0$.
Equate each linear factor to zero: $5x + 4 = 0$ or $2x - 3 = 0$.
Solve the linear equations: $T_1 = \{-\frac{4}{5}\}$, $T_2 = \{\frac{3}{2}\}$.
Therefore the solution set S is $S = \{-\frac{4}{5}, \frac{3}{2}\}$.

$Check:$ $[5(-\frac{4}{5}) - 1][2(-\frac{4}{5}) - 1] = 13$ or $[5(\frac{3}{2}) - 1][2(\frac{3}{2}) - 1] = 13$,
$\qquad\quad (-4 - 1)(-\frac{8}{5} - 1) = 13$ or $(\frac{15}{2} - 1)(3 - 1) = 13$,
$\qquad\quad (-5)(-\frac{13}{5}) = 13$ or $(\frac{13}{2})(2) = 13$,
$\qquad\quad\qquad\qquad 13 = 13$ or $13 = 13$.

The success of the method of factoring depends, in general, upon the ability to factor a trinomial by inspection, and hence is suitable only in cases in which the factors are readily apparent. It is therefore desirable to have a general method that will work for any quadratic equation. The method of completing the square is such a method.

We state without proof the following theorem.

Theorem 4.6.   *If S is the solution set of $[f(x)]^2 = k^2$, where k is a constant, and T_1 and T_2 are the solution sets respectively of $f(x) = k$ and $f(x) = -k$, then $S = T_1 \cup T_2$.*

EXERCISES

Solve each of the following equations by factoring and check.

1. $x^2 - x - 6 = 0$.
2. $x^2 + 3x - 10 = 0$.
3. $3x^2 = 5x$.
4. $x^2 = 0$.
5. $x^2 - 49 = 0$.
6. $x^2 - 7 = 0$.
7. $4x^2 + 12x + 9 = 0$.
8. $2x^2 + 7x - 4 = 0$.
9. $3x^2 - 5x + 2 = 0$.
10. $2x - x^2 = 0$.
11. $(x + 3)(x + 4) = 2$.
12. $(x + 1)(x + 2) = 6$.
13. $(2x - 3)(x - 2) = 1$.
14. $x(x + 3) = 4$.
15. $x^2 + bx = ax + ab$.
16. $4x^2 - x + 2 = x^2 + 7x + 5$.

17. $2n^2 - 3n = 2n - 2$.
18. $(x - 5)(x - 2) = 2x + 10$.
19. $3x^2 - 10x = x + 4$.
20. $y^2 + 6y + 9 = 1$.
21. $y^2 | 6y + 9 = 0$.
22. $5y^2 - 2y - 24 = 0$.
23. $2(x^2 - 3x) = -5 + x$.
24. $x(x - 3) = 4$.
25. $15x^2 - 23x + 4 = 0$.
26. $14x^2 - 29x - 15 = 0$.
27. $2t^2 - 3t - 17 = -3$.
28. $3t^2 + 11t + 10 = 0$.
29. $6x^2 + 13x + 6 = 0$.
30. $(y + 3)^2 = 16$.
31. $ax^2 - a = x - a^2x$.
32. $6x^2 - 31x - 60 = 0$.

33. Find a quadratic equation whose solution set is the given set
   a. $\{3, -1\}$.
   c. $\{-2, -2\}$.
   b. $\left\{\frac{1}{2}, \frac{2}{3}\right\}$.
   d. $\left\{\frac{3}{5}, -\frac{4}{7}\right\}$.

e. $\{m, n\}$.

g. $\{3 - \sqrt{5}, 3 + \sqrt{5}\}$.

f. $\left\{\dfrac{m + n}{2}, \dfrac{m - n}{2}\right\}$.

h. $\{3 + 2i, 3 - 2i\}$.

7 THE METHOD OF COMPLETING THE SQUARE

As a background for this method, let us recall the form of certain special perfect-square trinomials:

$$(x + 1)^2 = x^2 + 2x + 1$$
$$(x + 2)^2 = x^2 + 4x + 4$$
$$(x + 3)^2 = x^2 + 6x + 9$$
$$(x + n)^2 = x^2 + 2nx + n^2$$

Each such equation is an algebraic identity, and hence either member may be substituted for the other in any expression or equation in which that member occurs. Inspection of the right-hand member in each of these identities shows, first, that the coefficient of x^2 is 1 and, second, that the last term is the square of one-half the coefficient of x in the middle term. Hence, if given two terms of the form $x^2 + ax$, one can always form a perfect-square trinomial simply by adding a third term found by squaring one-half the coefficient of x: $x^2 + ax + (a/2)^2$. This trinomial is, in fact, the square of $\left(x + \dfrac{a}{2}\right)$, for

$$\left(x + \frac{a}{2}\right)^2 = x^2 + ax + \frac{a^2}{4}.$$

The rule for solving a quadratic equation by completing the square is as follows.

Step 1: Write the given equation in standard form.

Step 2: Divide both members of the equation by the coefficient of x^2, if this coefficient is not 1.

Step 3: Remove the constant term from the left member by adding (or subtracting) the same number to (from) both members.

Step 4: Add the square of one-half the coefficient of x to both members; the left member is now a perfect square trinomial.

Step 5: Write the left member as the square of a linear factor and express the right member as a single real number.

Step 6: Now obtain two linear equations by setting the linear factor found in Step 5 equal to the positive square root of the right member and then setting it equal to the negative square root of the right member.

Step 7: Find the solution sets T_1 and T_2 of the two equations of Step 6; the solution set S of the given equation is $S = T_1 \cup T_2$.

Example.   Solve by completing the square: $x^2 - 3x = 2x - 6$.

Solution: Write the equation in standard form:

$$x^2 - 5x + 6 = 0. \tag{Step 1}$$

The coefficient of x^2 is 1, making Step 2 unnecessary. Subtract 6 from each member:

$$x^2 - 5x = -6. \tag{Step 3}$$

Add $(-\tfrac{5}{2})^2$ to both members:

$$x^2 - 5x + (-\tfrac{5}{2})^2 = -6 + (-\tfrac{5}{2})^2. \tag{Step 4}$$

Write the left member as the square of a linear factor and write the right member as one number:

$$(x - \tfrac{5}{2})^2 = \tfrac{1}{4}. \tag{Step 5}$$

Next, set $x - \tfrac{5}{2}$ equal to $\tfrac{1}{2}$ and then set it equal to $-\tfrac{1}{2}$:

$$x - \tfrac{5}{2} = \tfrac{1}{2}, \qquad x - \tfrac{5}{2} = -\tfrac{1}{2}. \tag{Step 6}$$

Since $x - \tfrac{5}{2} = \tfrac{1}{2} \leftrightarrow x = 3$ and $x - \tfrac{5}{2} = -\tfrac{1}{2} \leftrightarrow x = 2$, it follows that $T_1 = \{3\}$ and $T_2 = \{2\}$; hence $S = T_1 \cup T_2 = \{3, 2\}$. Note that this is the result obtained in our first example of the method of factoring.

Example.   Solve by completing the square: $3x^2 - 4x = 2$.

Solution: Following the steps outlined above, we have

$$3x^2 - 4x - 2 = 0, \tag{Step 1}$$
$$x^2 - \tfrac{4}{3}x - \tfrac{2}{3} = 0, \tag{Step 2}$$
$$x^2 - \tfrac{4}{3}x = \tfrac{2}{3}, \tag{Step 3}$$
$$x^2 - \tfrac{4}{3}x + (-\tfrac{2}{3})^2 = \tfrac{2}{3} + (-\tfrac{2}{3})^2 = \tfrac{2}{3} + \tfrac{4}{9}, \tag{Step 4}$$
$$(x - \tfrac{2}{3})^2 = \tfrac{10}{9}, \tag{Step 5}$$

$$x - \frac{2}{3} = \frac{\sqrt{10}}{3}, \qquad x - \frac{2}{3} = -\frac{\sqrt{10}}{3}, \tag{Step 6}$$

$$x - \frac{2}{3} = \frac{\sqrt{10}}{3} \leftrightarrow x = \frac{2 + \sqrt{10}}{3}. \tag{Step 7}$$

$$x - \frac{2}{3} = -\frac{\sqrt{10}}{3} \leftrightarrow x = \frac{2 - \sqrt{10}}{3}.$$

Hence the solutions sets are

$$T_1 = \left\{\frac{2 + \sqrt{10}}{3}\right\}, \qquad T_2 = \left\{\frac{2 - \sqrt{10}}{3}\right\}, \quad \text{and} \quad S = \left\{\frac{2 + \sqrt{10}}{3}, \frac{2 - \sqrt{10}}{3}\right\}.$$

Check: We shall check one of the roots just found. When $x = (2 + \sqrt{10})/3$,

$$3\left(\frac{2 + \sqrt{10}}{3}\right)^2 - 4\left(\frac{2 + \sqrt{10}}{3}\right) = \frac{4 + 4\sqrt{10} + 10}{3} - \frac{8 + 4\sqrt{10}}{3},$$

$$= \frac{4 + 4\sqrt{10} + 10 - 8 - 4\sqrt{10}}{3},$$

$$= \tfrac{6}{3} = 2.$$

EXERCISES

Determine the number which should be added to each given binomial to make the resulting trinomial a perfect square.

1. $x^2 + 4x.$ **3.** $y^2 - \dfrac{4}{3}y.$ **5.** $v^2 + \dfrac{5}{3}v.$ **7.** $t^2 + at.$

2. $t^2 - 12t.$ **4.** $x^2 - \dfrac{3}{2}x.$ **6.** $y^2 - \dfrac{7}{5}y.$ **8.** $x^2 + \dfrac{m}{n}x.$

Solve each of the following equations by completing the square, and check one root in each case.

9. $x^2 + 4x - 2 = 0.$ **17.** $x^2 + 2x - 1 = 0.$
10. $t^2 - 12t + 12 = 0.$ **18.** $2x^2 - 4x - 5 = 0.$
11. $3y^2 - 4y - 1 = 0.$ **19.** $t^2 + at - a^2 = 0.$
12. $2x^2 - 3x - 7 = 0.$ **20.** $nx^2 + mx + p = 0.$
13. $3v^2 + 5v - 3 = 0.$ **21.** $3x^2 - 11x + 5 = 0.$
14. $5y^2 - 7y - 4 = 0.$ **22.** $2x^2 + 5x + 2 = 0.$
15. $x^2 + 3x - 3 = 0.$ **23.** $x^2 - 2x + 5 = 0.$
16. $5x^2 + 2x = 24.$ **24.** $x^2 - 3x + 4 = 0.$

8 THE QUADRATIC-FORMULA METHOD

This method consists of using the results obtained by solving the general quadratic equation $ax^2 + bx + c = 0$ by the method of completing the square and keeping in mind that a, b, and c are any triple of real numbers except that a cannot have the value zero.

Example. Solve by completing the square, the equation $ax^2 + bx + c = 0$, where $a \neq 0$.

Solution: Follow the steps outlined above:

$$x^2 + \frac{b}{a}x + \frac{c}{a} = 0, \qquad\qquad \text{(Step 2)}$$

$$x^2 + \frac{b}{a}x = -\frac{c}{a}, \qquad\qquad \text{(Step 3)}$$

$$x^2 + \frac{b}{a}x + \left(\frac{b}{2a}\right)^2 = -\frac{c}{a} + \left(\frac{b}{2a}\right)^2, \qquad\qquad \text{(Step 4)}$$

$$\left(x + \frac{b}{2a}\right)^2 = \frac{b^2 - 4ac}{4a^2}, \qquad\qquad \text{(Step 5)}$$

$$x + \frac{b}{2a} = \frac{\sqrt{b^2 - 4ac}}{2a}, \quad x + \frac{b}{2a} = -\frac{\sqrt{b^2 - 4ac}}{2a}, \qquad \text{(Step 6)}$$

$$x + \frac{b}{2a} = \frac{\sqrt{b^2 - 4ac}}{2a} \leftrightarrow x = \frac{-b + \sqrt{b^2 - 4ac}}{2a}, \qquad \text{(Step 7)}$$

$$x + \frac{b}{2a} = -\frac{\sqrt{b^2 - 4ac}}{2a} \leftrightarrow x = \frac{-b - \sqrt{b^2 - 4ac}}{2a}. \qquad \text{(Step 7)}$$

By combining the results of the last two statements, we now have shown that

$$ax^2 + bx + c = 0 \leftrightarrow x = \frac{-b \pm \sqrt{b^2 - 4ac}}{2a}, \qquad \text{(Step 7)}$$

from which it follows that the solution set S is

$$S = \left\{ \frac{-b \pm \sqrt{b^2 - 4ac}}{2a} \right\}.$$

The compound statement

$$x = \frac{-b \pm \sqrt{b^2 - 4ac}}{2a}$$

is commonly known as the *quadratic formula*.

The quadratic formula provides a quick and convenient method of obtaining the solution set of any quadratic equation. We shall demonstrate this method with the following example.

Example. Use the quadratic formula to find the solution set of the equation $2x^2 + x = 2x + 15$.

Solution: Writing the given equation in standard form, we have

$$2x^2 - x - 15 = 0.$$

If we compare this equation with the general equation $ax^2 + bx + c = 0$, we see that $a = 2$, $b = -1$, and $c = -15$. Now substitute these values for a, b, and c in the quadratic formula. This gives

$$x = \frac{-(-1) \pm \sqrt{(-1)^2 - 4(2)(-15)}}{2(2)}$$

$$= \frac{1 \pm \sqrt{1 + 120}}{4} = \frac{1 \pm \sqrt{121}}{4}$$

$$= \frac{1 \pm 11}{4}.$$

Therefore: $x = \dfrac{1 + 11}{4}$ or $x = \dfrac{1 - 11}{4}$

$$= 3, \qquad\qquad = -\tfrac{10}{4} = -\tfrac{5}{2}.$$

Hence the solution set S is $S = \{3, -\tfrac{5}{2}\}$.

Example. Find the solution set, S, of the equation $x^2 - 4x + 13 = 0$.

Solution: Here we have $a = 1, b = -4$, and $c = 13$. Substituting these values for a, b, and c in the quadratic formula we get

$$x = \frac{4 \pm \sqrt{16 - 52}}{2} = \frac{4 \pm \sqrt{-36}}{2} = \frac{4 \pm 6i}{2} = 2 \pm 3i \quad \therefore S = \{2 + 3i, 2 - 3i\}.$$

The quadratic formula is a most important tool and should be carefully memorized. It is useful not only for solving second degree polynomials in one variable but is very effective in solving second degree polynomial equations in two variables for one of the variables as the following example will illustrate.

Example. Solve the equation

$$3x^2 - 4xy + y^2 - 6x + 2y = 0$$

for y in terms of x.

Solution: Rewrite the given equation in the form

$$y^2 - (4x - 2)y + (3x^2 - 6x) = 0.$$

Now we treat this as a quadratic equation in y with $a = 1$, $b = -(4x - 2)$, and $c = 3x^2 - 6x$. Substituting these values for a, b, and c in the quadratic formula we obtain

$$y = \frac{(4x - 2) \pm \sqrt{(4x - 2)^2 - 4(3x^2 - 6x)}}{2}$$

$$= \frac{4x - 2 \pm \sqrt{16x^2 - 16x + 4 - 12x^2 + 24x}}{2}$$

$$= \frac{4x - 2 \pm \sqrt{4x^2 + 8x + 4}}{2}$$

$$= 2x - 1 \pm \sqrt{x^2 + 2x + 1}$$
$$= 2x - 1 \pm (x + 1)$$
$$\therefore y = 3x \quad \text{or} \quad y = x - 2.$$

EXERCISES

Use the quadratic formula to solve the following equations and check one root in each case.

1. $x^2 - 3x + 1 = 0$.
2. $x^2 + 4x - 7 = 0$.
3. $x^2 - 4x + 10 = 0$.
4. $6x^2 - 29x + 35 = 0$.
5. $x^2 - 12x + 9 = 0$.
6. $7x^2 - 19x + 24 = 2x^2 - 15x + 25$.
7. $5x^2 - 11x + 2 = 0$.

8. $11x^2 - 8x + 1 = 0$.
9. $20x^2 + 14x - 3 = 0$.
10. $px^2 + qx + r = 0$.
11. $3.6x^2 - 3.27x + 0.13 = 0$.
12. $1000x^2 + 605x - 864 = 0$.
13. $3x^2 - 8x + 20 = 0$.
14. $2x^2 - 5x + 12 = 0$.

15. $12x^2 - 8ax + a^2 = 0.$
16. $6x^2 - 18x - 24 = 0.$
17. $10x^2 + 29x + 10 = 0.$
18. $3x^2 + 8x - 3 = 0.$
19. $6x^2 - 8x + 7 = 0.$

20. $5x^2 - 14mx + 9m^2 = 0.$
21. $4x^2 + 12x - 15 = 0.$
22. $x^2 - 6x + 13 = 0.$
23. $3x^2 + 5x + 8 = 0.$
24. $4x^2 + 25 = 0.$

Solve each of the following equations for y in terms of x.

25. $x^2 - 3xy + 2y^2 - 3x + 3y = 0.$
26. $x^2 - 2xy + y^2 - 25 = 0.$

27. $2x^2 + 3xy + y^2 - 2x - y = 0.$
28. $4x^2 + 4xy + y^2 + 2x + y - 2 = 0.$

29. $2x^2 - 3xy + y^2 + 11x - 8y + 15 = 0.$
30. $3x^2 - 5xy + 2y^2 + 8x - 5y - 3 = 0.$
31. $2x^2 + xy - y^2 - x + 5y - 6 = 0.$
32. $2x^2 - 2xy + y^2 + 8x - 12y + 36 = 0.$

9 FACTS ABOUT THE ROOTS OF THE QUADRATIC EQUATION $ax^2 + bx + c = 0$

Often it is desirable to have information about the nature of the roots of a certain quadratic equation. That is, we may need to know whether the roots are real, whether they are equal, whether they are imaginary, etc. A careful look at the quadratic formula will suggest a method for obtaining such information without actually solving the equation.

Let r_1 and r_2 denote the roots of the general quadratic equation $ax^2 + bx + c = 0$, then, by the quadratic formula,

$$r_1 = \frac{-b + \sqrt{b^2 - 4ac}}{2a} \quad \text{and} \quad r_2 = \frac{-b - \sqrt{b^2 - 4ac}}{2a}.$$

Obviously, the expression $(b^2 - 4ac)$, called the *discriminant*, which appears under the radical sign in the above formula determines the nature of the roots r_1 and r_2 of any given quadratic equation. Thus if a, b, and c are real numbers the following possible cases result.

Case 1. $b^2 - 4ac > 0$, then r_1 and r_2 are real and unequal.
Case 2. $b^2 - 4ac = 0$, then r_1 and r_2 are real and equal.
Case 3. $b^2 - 4ac < 0$, then r_1 and r_2 are unequal and neither is real.

If we agree to count r_1 and r_2 as two roots even though $r_1 = r_2$, then the above discussion justifies the theorem.

Theorem 4.7. *Every polynomial equation, in one variable, of degree 2 has exactly two roots.*

To aid us in proving a very useful theorem we next find the sum and product of the two roots r_1 and r_2.

$$r_1 + r_2 = \frac{-b + \sqrt{b^2 - 4ac}}{2a} + \frac{-b - \sqrt{b^2 - 4ac}}{2a} = -\frac{b}{a}$$

$$r_1 r_2 = \frac{-b + \sqrt{b^2 - 4ac}}{2a} \frac{-b - \sqrt{b^2 - 4ac}}{2a}$$

$$= \frac{(-b)^2 - (b^2 - 4ac)}{4a^2} = \frac{4ac}{4a^2} = \frac{c}{a}.$$

Theorem 4.8. *If* r_1 *and* r_2 *are the roots of the quadratic equation* $ax^2 + bx + c = 0$, *then*

$$ax^2 + bx + c = a(x - r_1)(x - r_2).$$

Proof: $a(x - r_1)(x - r_2) = a[x^2 - (r_1 + r_2)x + r_1 r_2]$

$$= a\left[x^2 - \left(-\frac{b}{a}\right)x + \frac{c}{a}\right]$$

$$= ax^2 + bx + c.$$

The importance of this theorem lies in the fact that it gives us a method for factoring any quadratic $ax^2 + bx + c$.

Example.   Factor the quadratic $3x^2 - 2x - 7$.

Solution: First we find the roots r_1 and r_2 of the equation $3x^2 - 2x - 7 = 0$. Using the quadratic formula

$$x = \frac{2 \pm \sqrt{4 + 84}}{6} = \frac{2 \pm 2\sqrt{22}}{6} = \frac{1 \pm \sqrt{22}}{3}.$$

Thus

$$r_1 = \frac{1 + \sqrt{22}}{3} \qquad \text{and} \qquad r_2 = \frac{1 - \sqrt{22}}{3}.$$

Applying Theorem 4.8 we obtain

$$3x^2 - 2x - 7 = 3\left(x - \frac{1 + \sqrt{22}}{3}\right)\left(x - \frac{1 - \sqrt{22}}{3}\right).$$

10   EQUATIONS IN QUADRATIC FORM

An equation in one variable is said to be in *quadratic form* if by a suitable substitution of a new variable it can be expressed as a quadratic equation in the new variable. The following table exhibits some equations in quadratic form and a suitable substitution that could be used in each case.

Original Equation	Suitable Substitution	Quadratic Equation in y
$x^4 - 10x^2 + 9 = 0$	$y = x^2$	$y^2 - 10y + 9 = 0$
$x - \sqrt{x} - 2 = 0$	$y = \sqrt{x}$	$y^2 - y - 2 = 0$
$(x^2 - 2x)^2 - 11(x^2 - 2x) + 24 = 0$	$y = x^2 - 2x$	$y^2 - 11y + 24 = 0$
$4y^{-4} - 5y^{-2} + 1 = 0$	$y = x^{-2}$	$4y^2 - 5y + 1 = 0$

In the following examples we illustrate methods of solving equations in quadratic form.

Example. Solve the equation $x^4 - 10x^2 + 9 = 0$.

Solution: Let $y = x^2$, then our equation becomes

$$y^2 - 10y + 9 = 0.$$

Factor: $$(y - 1)(y - 9) = 0.$$

Then

$$\begin{array}{cc} y - 1 = 0 & y - 9 = 0 \\ y = 1 & y = 9 \\ \therefore x^2 = 1 & x^2 = 9 \end{array}$$

and

$$x = \pm 1 \qquad x = \pm 3.$$

The solution set of the given equation is the set $\{\pm 1, \pm 3\}$.

Example. Solve the equation $x - \sqrt{x} - 2 = 0$.

Solution: Let $y = \sqrt{x}$. This means y cannot be a negative number. We now have

$$y^2 - y - 2 = 0.$$

Factor: $$(y + 1)(y - 2) = 0.$$

Then

$$\begin{array}{cc} y + 1 = 0 & y - 2 = 0 \\ y = -1 & y = 2 \end{array}$$

Must reject since y cannot be negative. $\qquad \therefore \sqrt{x} = 2$

or $x = 4$.

Hence $x = 4$ is the only solution of the given equation.

Example. Solve the equation

$$(x^2 - 2x)^2 - 11(x^2 - 2x) + 24 = 0.$$

Solution: Let $y = x^2 - 2x$, then

$$y^2 - 11y + 24 = 0.$$

Factor: $$(y - 8)(y - 3) = 0.$$

Then

$$y - 8 = 0 \qquad\qquad\qquad y - 3 = 0$$
$$y = 8 \qquad\qquad\qquad y = 3$$
$$\therefore\ x^2 - 2x = 8 \qquad\qquad\quad x^2 - 2x = 3$$
$$\text{or } x^2 - 2x - 8 = 0 \qquad \text{or} \qquad x^2 - 2x - 3 = 0$$

Factor: $(x - 4)(x + 2) = 0 \qquad\qquad (x - 3)(x + 1) = 0$
$$x - 4 = 0 \text{ or } x + 2 = 0 \qquad x - 3 = 0 \text{ or } x + 1 = 0$$
$$x = 4 \qquad\quad x = -2 \qquad\quad x = 3 \qquad\quad x = -1.$$

Solution set of given equation is $\{-1, -2, 3, 4\}$.

EXERCISES

Compute the value of the discriminant and thus determine the nature of the roots of each of the following equations.

1. $x^2 - 5x + 4 = 0$.
2. $3x^2 - 5x - 7 = 0$.
3. $x^2 - 6x + 9 = 0$.
4. $5x^2 - 70x + 49 = 0$.
5. $2x^2 - 3x + 8 = 0$.
6. $3x^2 + 2x + 5 = 0$.
7. $4x^2 - 5 = 3x$.
8. $5 - 4x = 2x^2$.

9. $x^2 - 2ix - 6 = 0$.
10. $y^2 - \sqrt{3}y + 1 = 0$.
11. $3ix^2 + 6x - 2i = 0$.
12. $\sqrt{2}x^2 - 5x + \sqrt{8} = 0$.
13. $x^2 - 4\sqrt{3}x + 12 = 0$.
14. $4x^2 - 12ix - 9 = 0$.
15. $9x^2 - 6x + 2 = 0$.
16. $2x^2 - 5x + 4 = 0$.

Determine the value or values of the constant K for which each of the following equations have equal roots.

17. $x^2 + Kx + 4 = 0$.
18. $x^2 + Kx + K = 0$.
19. $4x^2 + 3Kx + 9 = 0$.

20. $x^2 + 2(K + 3)x + 12K = 0$.
21. $5x^2 - 2x + 3 = K(2x^2 - 2x - 1)$.
22. $7y^2 - 2y + 1 = Ky(y - 2)$.

Using the methods illustrated in the Examples of Section 10, solve each given equation.

23. $x^4 - 5x^2 - 36 = 0$.
24. $(x^2 - 3x)^2 - 2(x^2 - 3x) - 8 = 0$.
25. $x - 5\sqrt{x} + 6 = 0$.
26. $x^4 - 5x^2 + 4 = 0$.

27. $2x + 3\sqrt{x} - 20 = 0$.
28. $100x^{-4} - 29x^{-2} + 1 = 0$.
29. $6x^{-2} - 19x^{-1} + 10 = 0$.
30. $x^6 - 7x^3 - 8 = 0$.

Without solving the equation, find the sum and product of the roots for each of the equations.

31. $2x^2 - 6x + 7 = 0$.
32. $3x^2 + 4x - 9 = 0$.
33. $17x^2 - 85x + 51 = 0$.
34. $5x^2 - 6x - 8 = 0$.

35. $4x - x^2 + 5 = 0$.
36. $8x^2 = 3x - 5$.
37. $4x^2 = 7x$.
38. $3x = 4 - 8x^2$.

11 POLYNOMIALS: TWO MAJOR PROBLEMS

In Section 2 of this chapter a polynomial in one variable, say x, was defined as an algebraic expression x that could be written in the form

$$A_0x^n + A_1x^{n-1} + A_2x^{n-2} + \cdots + A_{n-1}x + A_n,$$

where n is a positive integer or zero and the coefficients $A_0, A_1, A_2, \cdots, A_n$ are arbitrary constants. If $A_0 \neq 0$, the polynomial is of degree n. If $n = 0$ and $A_0 \neq 0$, the polynomial consists of a constant term only. The coefficients are assumed to be elements of the complex number system unless otherwise restricted. The universal set U to which the variable x belongs will also be assumed to consist of the set of complex numbers.

In the study of such polynomials two major problems are of interest: first, to find the value of the polynomial for a particular value of the variable x and second, to find the value or values of x for which the polynomial will have some given value. For convenience, the symbol $f(x)$ will be used throughout the remainder of this chapter to represent the general polynomial given above; that is

$$f(x) = A_0x^n + A_1x^{n-1} + A_2x^{n-2} + \cdots + A_{n-1}x + A_n.$$

We can now restate our two problems symbolically in the following manner.

1. Given that $f(x)$ is a polynomial and a is a number, to find $f(a)$.
2. Given that $f(x)$ is a polynomial and M is a number, to find the solution set of the polynomial equation $f(x) = M$.

The first problem is obviously easier than the second. We shall consider it next.

12 SYNTHETIC SUBSTITUTION

Problem 1 is nothing more than a problem of substitution, and as such it is more laborious than difficult. For example, suppose that

$$f(x) = 2x^5 - 3x^3 + 7x^2 - 2x + 10$$

and our problem is to find $f(7)$. By direct substitution we get

$$f(7) = 2(7)^5 - 3(7)^3 + 7(7)^2 - 2(7) + 10;$$

to simplify this expression it is necessary to evaluate $(7)^2$, $(7)^3$, and $(7)^5$, which, although not difficult, is time-consuming. Performing these operations, we finally obtain

$$f(7) = 2(16,807) - 3(343) + 7(49) - 14 + 10 = 32,924.$$

If the degree of the polynomial had been higher or the number substituted for x had been larger, the labor involved would have been even more arduous. It is our purpose in this section to give a simple scheme for performing such a substitution. This scheme is called *synthetic substitution* and will be illustrated by using the polynomial just discussed.

First Step: Write on the first line the coefficients of the polynomial in the order of descending powers of x, supplying zero coefficients for missing powers of x; see the systematic arrangement below.

Second Step: Rewrite the first coefficient, 2, on the third line, immediately below its position on the first line; see below.

Third Step: Multiply this first coefficient by the given value of x, in this case 7, and enter the product, 14, on the second line directly below the second coefficient. Now add and write the sum 14 below on the third line. Similarly, we enter the product of 14 and 7 under the third coefficient, -3, add and write the sum below; etc. The final number, 32,924, in the third line, is the value of the polynomial when $x = 7$, showing that

$$f(7) = 32,924.$$

First line:	$2 +$	$0 -$	$3 +$	$7 -$	$2 +$	$10 \mid 7$
Second line:		$14 +$	$98 +$	$665 +$	$4704 +$	$32,914$
Third line:	$2 +$	$14 +$	$95 +$	$672 +$	$4702 +$	$32,924.$

That this scheme will work for any polynomial $f(x)$ and for any value of x can be seen from the following. Starting with a number A_0, multiplying it by any value of x, and adding A_1 gives $A_0x + A_1$; multiplying this sum by x and adding the A_2 gives $A_0x^2 + A_1x + A_2$; etc. Repeating this operation n times we finally arrive at

$$A_0x^n + A_1x^{n-1} + A_2x^{n-2} + \cdots + A_{n-1}x + A_n,$$

which is the value of the polynomial.

Example.   If $f(x) = 3x^4 + 7x^3 - 6x + 8$, what is $f(-2)$?

Solution:
$$\begin{array}{l} 3 + 7 + 0 - 6 + 8 \mid -2 \\ - 6 - 2 + 4 + 4 \\ \hline 3 + 1 - 2 - 2 + 12. \end{array}$$

Hence $f(-2) = 12$. Let us now verify this by direct substitution:

$$f(-2) = 3(-2)^4 + 7(-2)^3 - 6(-2) + 8 = 48 - 56 + 12 + 8 = 12.$$

Example.   If $f(x) = 6x^4 + x^3 + 4x^2 + x - 2$, what is $f(-\tfrac{2}{3})$?

Solution:
$$\begin{array}{l} 6 + 1 + 4 + 1 - 2 \mid -\tfrac{2}{3} \\ - 4 + 2 - 4 + 2 \\ \hline 6 - 3 + 6 - 3 + 0. \end{array}$$

The value of the polynomial when $x = -\tfrac{2}{3}$ is thus seen to be zero, or $f(-\tfrac{2}{3}) = 0$.

13 THE ZEROS OF A POLYNOMIAL

Our second problem concerning polynomials is a little more difficult. The problem as stated in Section 7 is: Given that $f(x)$ is a polynomial and M is a number, find the set of numbers a for which $f(a) = M$. In other words, this is a problem of solving the equation

(Eq. 1) $f(x) = M$

where by a solution of the equation we mean, of course, a number a such that

$$f(a) = M.$$

Let $F(x) = f(x) - M;$

it follows that if $f(a) = M$

then $F(a) = M - M = 0.$

(Eq. 2)   Hence any solution of $F(x) = 0$

is also a solution of $f(x) = M$

and conversely. Therefore Equations 1 and 2 are equivalent (see Section 9 of Chapter III). The problem at hand is thus the problem of finding the zeros, or the roots, of an equation

$$F(x) = 0,$$

where $F(x)$ is a polynomial in x. We shall call such an equation a *polynomial equation*.

Polynomial equations of the first and second degree were discussed in sufficient detail earlier and hence need not be considered here except to recall the quadratic formula and to emphasize again that with the aid of this formula the roots of any polynomial equation of the second degree can be written down immediately in terms of the coefficients a, b, and c when our equation has been written in the standard form

$$ax^2 + bx + c = 0,$$

which is the most general polynomial equation of the second degree. It will be recalled that, by completing the square, we found the roots to be

$$x = \frac{-b \pm \sqrt{b^2 - 4ac}}{2a},$$

which is called the *quadratic formula*. The quadratic formula, which expresses the roots of the general polynomial equation of the second degree in terms of its coefficients, might lead one to suppose that a formula could be found for expressing the roots of a polynomial equation of any degree in terms of its coefficients. Unfortunately, however, this is not the case. In fact, a famous Norwegian mathematician, N. H. Abel, proved in the early part of the nineteenth century that polynomial equations of higher degree than the fourth cannot, in general, be solved algebraically. Although we will not be able to find general methods for solving polynomial equations, we can develop a certain technique that will aid us in finding the roots of many such equations. In particular, we shall develop a technique for finding the rational roots of any polynomial equation. To do this we shall need the help of certain theorems regarding polynomials and polynomial equations, and these we shall now consider.

14   THE REMAINDER THEOREM

If a polynomial $f(x)$ of degree n is divided by a binomial $x - a$ one obtains a quotient, say $q(x)$, which is also a polynomial, and a remainder R, which will be a constant if the division is carried to completion as described in Section 6 of Chapter III. Moreover, the relation

(Eq. 1) $$f(x) = (x - a)q(x) + R,$$

as was pointed out in Chapter III is a numerical identity for all values of x. Now, since this equation is an identity, it must hold when $x = a$; hence

$$f(a) = (a - a)q(a) + R = 0 \cdot f(a) + R = R.$$

We now state this result as a theorem.

The Remainder Theorem

If a polynomial $f(x)$ is divided by a binomial $x - a$ until a remainder R not containing x is obtained, this remainder is equal to the value of the polynomial when $x = a$; that is, $R = f(a)$.

In certain special cases, R in Equation 1 is zero, and then this equation becomes

(Eq. 2) $$f(x) = (x - a)q(x),$$

which shows that in such a case $x - a$ is a factor of $f(x)$. Now, since $f(a) = R$ and R is zero, it follows that $f(a) = 0$, which establishes the following theorem.

The Factor Theorem

A polynomial $f(x)$ contains $x - a$ as a factor if and only if $f(a) = 0$.
In other words, if a is a root of the equation $f(x) = 0$, then $x - a$ is a factor of $f(x)$ and, conversely, if $x - a$ is a factor of $f(x)$, then a is a root of $f(x) = 0$.

Example.   Find the remainder when $2x^4 - 3x^3 + 7x$ is divided by $x + 2$.

Solution: Here $f(x) = 2x^4 - 3x^3 + 7x$ and, since $x - a = x + 2$, it follows that $a = -2$. Thus,

$$R = f(-2) = 32 + 24 - 14 = 42.$$

Let us check this result by long division:

$$\begin{array}{r} 2x^3 - 7x^2 + 14x - 21 \\ \hline x + 2\,|\,2x^4 - 3x^3 + 0x^2 + 7x + 0 \\ 2x^4 + 4x^3 \\ \hline -7x^3 + 0x^2 + 7x + 0 \\ -7x^3 - 14x^2 \\ \hline 14x^2 + 7x + 0 \\ 14x^2 + 28x \\ \hline -21x + 0 \\ -21x - 42 \\ \hline +42. \end{array}$$

This division shows not only that the remainder is 42 but also that the quotient $q(x)$ is $q(x) = 2x^3 - 7x^2 + 14x - 21$.

This same information can be obtained by synthetic substitution. We now demonstrate this method, using this same example:

$$\begin{array}{r} 2 - 3 + 0 + 7 + 0\,|-2 \\ -4 + 14 - 28 + 42 \\ \hline 2 - 7 + 14 - 21 + 42. \end{array}$$

The last number in the third line, as we have already learned, gives us $f(-2)$, or the remainder. Now compare the other numbers in line three with the coefficients in $q(x)$: they are identical. The reason for this will become obvious when we notice that in the substitution at each step we multiply by -2 and add, whereas in the division we multiply by $+2$ and subtract, and these are equivalent operations. Hence synthetic substitution has provided us with both the remainder and the quotient, and so the process is also called *synthetic division*.

Example. Find the quotient and remainder when $2x^3 - 3x^2 + 4$ is divided by $(x - 2)$.

Solution: Here $x - a = x - 2$, and hence $a = 2$. Using synthetic division, we get

$$\begin{array}{r} 2 - 3 + 0 + 4\,|\underline{2} \\ +4 + 2 + 4 \\ \hline 2 + 1 + 2 + 8. \end{array}$$

This shows that $q(x) = 2x^2 + x + 2$ and $R = 8$.
The student may check this result by long division.

Example. Determine whether $x - 2$ is a factor of $x^6 - 64$.

First Solution: Here $f(x) = x^6 - 64$ and $a = 2$. Substitution of 2 for x gives $f(2) = 2^6 - 64 = 0$; therefore $x - 2$ is a factor of $x^6 - 64$.

Second Solution: Let us use synthetic division:

$$\begin{array}{r} 1 + 0 + 0 + 0 + 0 + 0 - 64\,|\underline{2} \\ +2 + 4 + 8 + 16 + 32 + 64 \\ \hline 1 + 2 + 4 + 8 + 16 + 32 + 0. \end{array}$$

Hence $x - 2$ is a factor of $x^6 - 64$ and the second factor is

$$x^5 + 2x^4 + 4x^3 + 8x^2 + 16x + 32.$$

That is, $x^6 - 64 = (x - 2)(x^5 + 2x^4 + 4x^3 + 8x^2 + 16x + 32)$.

This second solution has the obvious advantage of providing us with the second factor as well.

Example.   Determine whether $x - 1$ is a factor of $x^3 + 7x^2 - 3x - 4$.

Solution: Synthetic division gives

$$\begin{array}{r} 1 + 7 - 3 - 4 \underline{1} \\ \underline{+ 1 + 8 + 5} \\ 1 + 8 + 5 + 1. \end{array}$$

Since $f(1) \neq 0$, it follows that $x - 1$ is not a factor of the given polynomial.

EXERCISES

Use the remainder theorem to find the remainder in each of the following, given the first expression divided by the second.

1. $x^3 - 3x^2 + 2x + 5$; $x - 3$.
2. $x^4 - 5x^2 + 3x + 2$; $x + 2$.
3. $x^4 - 3$; $x + 1$.
4. $3x^2 - 2x^3 + 5x$; $x - 3$.
5. $2x^7 - 5x^4 + 8x^3 - 6x + 3$; $x + 1$.
6. $4x^{19} - 12x^{17} + 8x^5 - 4x^2 + 13$; x.

Use the factor theorem to determine whether the first expression is a factor of the second.

7. $x - 1$; $5x^3 - 8x + 3$.
8. $x + 2$; $x^7 + 128$.
9. $x - 3$; $x^4 - 18x^2 + 81$.
10. $x + 2$; $x^5 - 32$.
11. x; $x^4 + 3x^2 - 1$.
12. $x - \frac{3}{2}$; $4x^3 - 12x^2 + 9x$.
13. $2x + 3$; $2x^3 + 5x^2 + 5x + 3$. (*Hint:*   If $x + \frac{3}{2}$ is a factor, does this give any indication concerning $2x + 3$?)
14. Find all the factors of $x^3 - 7x - 6$ given that $x + 2$ is one factor.

Divide the first expression by the second in each of the following. Use synthetic division to find the quotient and the remainder, and check by means of the remainder theorem.

15. $4x^3 - 6x^2 - 3x + 2$; $x - 2$.
16. $5x^3 + 7x^2 + 9$; $x + 3$.
17. $x^4 + x^2 + 1$; $x + 2$.
18. $8x^5 - 4x^3 + 7x^2 - 2x$; $x - \frac{1}{2}$.
19. $x^8 - 6561$; $x + 3$.
20. $x^4 + x^3$; $x - 1$.
21. $x^5 + 3x^2 - 4$; x.
22. $9x^3 - 6x + 5$; $x + \frac{1}{3}$.
23. $x^6 + 1$; $x + 1$.
24. $4x^2 - x^3 + 7x$; $x + 4$.

25. If n is a positive integer show that
   a. $(x - a)$ is a factor of $(x^n - a^n)$.
   b. $(x + a)$ is a factor of $(x^n - a^n)$ if n is even.
   c. $(x + a)$ is a factor of $(x^n + a^n)$ if n is odd.
26. Find the value of k such that if $x^3 - 7x^2 + 3x + k$ is divided by $(x - 2)$ the remainder is -6.
27. Determine the value of k for which $(x - 3)$ is a factor of $x^4 - 5x^3 + Kx^2 + 7x + 6$.
28. Determine whether or not $(x + 3)$ is a factor of $x^4 + 2x^3 - 2x^2 + 2x - 3$.
29. Determine whether or not $(2x + 1)$ is a factor of $2x^3 - 9x^2 + 7x + 6 = 0$.
30. If $f(x) = A_0x^n + A_1x^{n-1} + A_2x^{n-2} + \cdots + A_{n-1}x + A_n$, show that $x - 1$ is a factor of $f(x)$ if the sum of the coefficients is zero.

15 COMPLEX ROOTS OF A POLYNOMIAL EQUATION

Two complex numbers that differ only in the sign of the imaginary part are called *conjugate complex numbers*. Each is said to be the conjugate of the other. For example, $2 + 3i$ and $2 - 3i$ are conjugates or, in more general terms, $a + bi$ and $a - bi$ are conjugates. We wish now to prove a very useful theorem regarding conjugate complex numbers as roots of polynomial equations.

Theorem 4.9. *If a polynomial equation with real coefficients has the complex number $a + bi$ as a root, where $b \neq 0$, it has also the conjugate complex number $a - bi$ as a root.*

Proof: Let $f(x) = 0$ be a polynomial equation having $a + bi$, where $b \neq 0$, as a root. We form the product

$$
\begin{aligned}
P(x) &= [x - (a + bi)][x - (a - bi)] \\
&= [(x - a) - bi][(x \quad a) \mid bi] \\
&= (x - a)^2 - (bi)^2 \\
&= (x - a)^2 + b^2 \\
&= x^2 - 2ax + a^2 + b^2.
\end{aligned}
$$

Now divide $f(x)$ by $P(x)$ and carry out the division until a remainder is reached that is not of higher degree in x than the first. This remainder can be written in the form $Rx + S$, in which R and S are real numbers since the coefficients of $f(x)$ and $P(x)$ are real. If the quotient obtained in the division just described is represented by $q(x)$, we can write the following identity:

$$f(x) = q(x) \cdot P(x) + Rx + S.$$

We wish next to show that R and S are both zero and that, hence, the product $P(x)$ is a factor of $f(x)$. Since an identity holds for all values of x, we can write a second identity:

$$f(a + bi) = q(a + bi)P(a + bi) + R \cdot (a + bi) + S.$$

By hypothesis $a + bi$ is a root of $f(x) = 0$; hence

$$f(a + bi) = 0.$$

Further, it follows from the definition of $P(x)$ that

$$P(a + bi) = 0.$$

The second identity is therefore reduced to

$$
\begin{aligned}
R \cdot (a + bi) + S &= 0 \\
(Ra + S) + Rbi &= 0 + 0i.
\end{aligned}
$$

In view of the definition of equality for complex numbers we have

$$Ra + S = 0 \quad \text{and} \quad Rb = 0.$$

But $b \neq 0$ according to the statement of our theorem; therefore $R = 0$ and, consequently, $S = 0$. This gives the identity

$$f(x) = q(x)P(x).$$

From the definition of $P(x)$ it is easily seen that

$$P(a - bi) = 0,$$
$$\text{and hence} \quad f(a - bi) = 0.$$

This establishes our theorem.

The theorem just proved is sometimes stated thus: *Imaginary roots of polynomial equations with real coefficients occur in conjugate pairs.*

16   NUMBER OF ROOTS

We have learned from previous discussions that every polynomial equation of the first degree has one and only one root and that an equation of the second degree, a quadratic equation, has two roots. From these results one might suspect that the number of roots of a polynomial equation of degree n is n. This is true provided each multiple root is counted as many times as the root occurs. For instance, the equation

$$x^3 - 3x^2 + 3x - 1 = 0$$

can be factored as follows:

$$(x - 1)(x - 1)(x - 1) = 0;$$

setting each factor equal to zero and solving for x, we get three roots,

$$x = 1, 1, 1.$$

In this case all three roots are equal, and we say that 1 is a multiple root of multiplicity 3 of the given equation. Thus, when the roots of a polynomial equation are counted, each multiple root of multiplicity k is counted k times. We shall now state two important theorems regarding the roots of a polynomial equation.

Theorem 4.10.   (Fundamental Theorem of Algebra).   *Every polynomial equation of degree n has at least one root. Moreover, this root may be a real number, a pure imaginary number, or a general complex number.*

We shall accept this theorem without proof, since any proof that could be given is beyond the scope of our work here.

Theorem 4.11.   *Every polynomial equation of degree n has exactly n roots, each root of multiplicity k being counted as k roots.*

Proof: Let $f(x) = 0$ be a polynomial equation of degree n. By the fundamental theorem of algebra, this equation has at least one root, which we shall denote by r_1. It follows from the factor theorem that $x - r_1$ is a factor of $f(x)$, and so the given equation can be written

$$f(x) = (x - r_1)q_1(x) = 0.$$

The quotient $q_1(x)$ is a polynomial and hence the equation $q_1(x) = 0$ must have at least one root, say r_2. By the factor theorem,

$$q_1(x) = (x - r_2)q_2(x),$$

and consequently

$$f(x) = (x - r_1)(x - r_2)q_2(x) = 0.$$

This same type argument can be repeated n times, to give

(Eq. 1) $f(x) = q_n(x)(x - r_1)(x - r_2) \cdots (x - r_n) = 0.$

Since $f(x)$ is of degree n, it follows that $q_1(x)$ must be of degree $n - 1$, $q_2(x)$ of degree $n - 2$, $q_3(x)$ of degree $n - 3$, etc., and $q_n(x)$ of degree $n - n$, or zero. Thus $q_n(x)$ is a constant. In particular,

if $f(x) = A_0x^n + A_1x^{n-1} + A_2x^{n-2} + \cdots + A_n = 0,$
then $q_n(x) = A_0,$
(Eq. 2)   and $f(x) = A_0(x - r_1)(x - r_2) \cdots (x - r_n) = 0.$

This last equation shows that every polynomial equation of degree n has at least n roots, namely r_1, r_2, r_3, $\cdots$, and r_n, which may or may not all be distinct. However, in the sense of our theorem all are counted whether they are distinct or not.

To prove that the given equation, $f(x) = 0$, cannot have more than n roots, let us suppose that r is any number distinct from r_1, r_2, $\cdots$, and r_n. If r be substituted for x in Equation 2, in the factored form, we obtain the relation

$$A_0(r - r_1)(r - r_2) \cdots (r - r_n) \neq 0,$$

since each factor on the left is different from zero. Hence r cannot be a root of Equation 2 and Equation 2 has exactly n roots, counting each root of multiplicity k as k roots. This completes the proof.

17 THE UPPER AND LOWER LIMITS OF THE REAL ROOTS OF A POLYNOMIAL EQUATION

A positive number L is an *upper limit* of the real roots of a polynomial equation if no root of the equation is larger than L. Similarly, $-L$ is a *lower limit* of the real roots of a polynomial equation if no root of the equation is less than $-L$.

Suppose $f(x) = A_0x^n + A_1x^{n-1} + \cdots + A_{n-1}x + A_n = 0$ and A_0 is positive. Let L be a positive number. When $f(x)$ is divided by $x - L$ by synthetic division, L is an upper limit of the real roots of $f(x) = 0$ if all the numbers in the third line are positive or zero, for

$$f(x) = q(x)(x - L) + R$$

and, if all the coefficients of $q(x)$ are positive, then $q(x)$ will be positive when x is positive. Consequently, for any value of x greater than L, the factor $x - L$ is positive, $q(x)$ is positive, and R is positive. Therefore $f(x)$ cannot be zero.

Example.   Show that $x = 3$ is an upper limit of the roots of the equation

$$f(x) = 2x^3 - 5x^2 - 3x + 7 = 0.$$

Solution: Dividing $f(x)$ by $x - 3$, we get

$$
\begin{array}{r}
2 - 5 - 3 + 7 \,\underline{|3} \\
+ 6 + 3 + 0 \\
\hline
2 + 1 + 0 + 7.
\end{array}
$$

Since all the numbers in the third line are zero or positive, 3 is an upper limit of the real roots of the given equation. Obviously, if we use a number larger than 3, all the coefficients in the third line except the first, which remains the same, will be larger positive numbers than those just found.

By a similar argument it follows that if, in substituting a negative number $-L$ by synthetic substitution, the numbers in the third line are alternately positive and negative, then $-L$ is a lower limit of the roots of $f(x) = 0$. We shall use the same equation as an example of this.

Example.   Show that -2 is a lower limit of the roots of the equation given above.

Solution: Dividing by $x + 2$, we get

$$
\begin{array}{r}
2 - 5 - 3 + 7 \,\underline{|-2} \\
- 4 + 18 - 30 \\
\hline
2 - 9 + 15 - 23.
\end{array}
$$

Since the signs of the numbers in the third line are alternately positive and negative, -2 is a lower limit, for if a negative number c, which is numerically larger than 2, is used the signs in the third line will remain the same but each number except the first will be larger numerically; hence $f(c)$ cannot be zero.

18   DESCARTES' RULE OF SIGNS

Before attempting to solve a polynomial equation of degree higher than the second it is often helpful to have as much information about the roots of the equation as can be readily obtained. In the preceding sections we have discussed methods and theorems which will be helpful in obtaining such information. Descartes' rule of signs, which we shall state but not prove, will help us to gain additional information about the real roots of an equation.

If a polynomial is arranged in descending powers of x there is said to be a variation in sign whenever two successive terms have opposite signs. Missing powers are to be ignored. For example,

$$f(x) = x^4 - 2x^2 + 3x - 5$$

has three variations in sign, one between the first and second terms, another between the second and third terms, and another between the third and fourth terms.

Let $f(-x)$ denote the polynomial obtained by replacing x by $-x$ in the polynomial $f(x)$. Since $(-x)^2 = x^2$, $(-x)^3 = -x^3$, $(-x)^4 = x^4$, etc., it is obvious that $f(-x)$ can be obtained by changing the sign of the coefficient of each odd power in $f(x)$. Thus,

if $\qquad f(x) = x^4 + 2x^3 - x^2 - 7x + 5,$

then $\qquad f(-x) = x^4 - 2x^3 - x^2 + 7x + 5.$

It is clear that if a is a root of $f(x) = 0$, then $-a$ is a root of $f(-x) = 0$; hence the number of negative roots of $f(x) = 0$ is precisely the same as the number of positive roots of $f(-x) = 0$.

Descartes' Rule of Signs

A polynomial equation $f(x) = 0$ with real coefficients has either as many positive real roots as $f(x)$ has variations in sign or less than that by an even integer; the equation $f(x) = 0$ has either as many negative real roots as $f(-x)$ has variations in sign or less than that by an even integer.

A proof of Descartes' rule can be found in any standard text on the theory of equations.

Example.   What information does Descartes' rule of signs give regarding the roots of the equation $f(x) = 2x^3 + 5x^2 - 3x + 4 = 0$?

Solution: Since $f(x)$ has two variations in sign, $f(x) = 0$ has either two positive real roots or zero positive real roots. Now consider

$$f(-x) = -2x^3 + 5x^2 + 3x + 4 = 0.$$

Since $f(-x)$ has only one variation in sign, $f(x) = 0$ must have exactly one negative real root, for the first integer which is less than 1 by an even integer is -1 and the number of roots cannot be -1. Therefore the given equation has either two positive real roots and one negative real root or it has two imaginary roots and one negative root. It must have exactly three roots.

EXERCISES

Determine the upper and lower limits of the real roots of each of the following equations.

1. $x^3 - 2x^2 - x + 2 = 0$.
2. $x^3 - 5x + 7 = 0$.
3. $x^4 + x^3 - 5x^2 - 2x + 1 = 0$.
4. $x^4 + 2x^3 + x^2 + 5x + 3 = 0$.
5. $x^5 - 12x^2 + 3x + 10 = 0$.
6. $2x^4 - 3x^3 + x^2 - 3x - 2 = 0$.
7. $2x^3 - 3x^2 - 5x + 6 = 0$.
8. $x^5 - 3x^4 - 6x^3 - 8x + 2 = 0$.

Using Descartes' rule of signs and any other pertinent material discussed thus far in this chapter, obtain as much information as you can about the roots of each of the following equations.

9. $x^3 - 2x^2 - x - 4 = 0$.
10. $2x^4 - x^3 - 5x^2 + x + 3 = 0$.
11. $x^4 - 3x^2 - 4 = 0$.
12. $x^4 + 3x^2 + 4 = 0$.
13. $3x^4 - 2x^3 + 7x^2 - 5x + 1 = 0$.
14. $3x^5 - 7 = 0$.
15. $3x^5 + 7 = 0$.
16. $x^3 + 2x^2 + 9 = 0$.

19 RATIONAL ROOTS

It will be recalled from Chapter III that a rational number is one that can be expressed in the form a/b, where a and b are integers. A root of an equation that is a rational number is called a *rational root* of the equation. We shall now show how to find the rational roots of a polynomial equation by trial. The following theorem will be helpful in minimizing the number of trials required.

Theorem 4.12. *If the coefficients A_0, A_1, A_2, . . . , A_n of a polynomial equation*

(Eq. 1) $f(x) = A_0 x^n + A_1 x^{n-1} + \cdots + A_{n-1} x + A_n = 0$

are integers, and if c/d is a rational number in lowest terms that satisfies the equation, then c is a factor of A_n and d is a factor of A_0.

Proof: Since c/d is a rational number in lowest terms, c and d are integers that have no common factor. By hypothesis, c/d is a root of $f(x) = 0$; hence

$$A_0 \left(\frac{c}{d}\right)^n + A_1 \left(\frac{c}{d}\right)^{n-1} + \cdots + A_{n-1} \left(\frac{c}{d}\right) + A_n = 0.$$

Simplifying and multiplying through by d^n, we get

(Eq. 2) $A_0 c^n + A_1 d c^{n-1} + \cdots + A_{n-1} c d^{n-1} + A_n d^n = 0.$

Now transpose the last term of the left member of this relation to the right and factor the left member thus:

$$c(A_0 c^{n-1} + A_1 d c^{n-2} + \cdots + A_{n-1} d^{n-1}) = -A_n d^n.$$

Since each letter in the last equation represents an integer and since sums and products of integers all give integers, the quantity inside the parenthesis in the left member is an integer, and so the left member is the product of two integers. That is,

$$c \cdot (\text{integer}) = -A_n d^n.$$

If two numbers are equal, a factor of one must be a factor of the other. Hence c is a factor of $A_n d^n$. But since c has no factor in common with d, it has no factor in common with d^n and therefore it is a factor of A_n.

In a similar manner we can write Equation 2 as

$$d(A_1 c^{n-1} + A_2 dc^{n-2} + \cdots + A_{n-1} cd^{n-2} + A_n d^{n-1}) = -A_0 c^n,$$

from which it follows that d is a factor of A_0, and the proof of our theorem is complete.

Corollary. *Any rational root of a polynomial equation of the form*

$$x^n + A_1 x^{n-1} + A_2 x^{n-2} + \cdots + A_{n-1} x + A_n = 0,$$

where A_1, A_2, $\cdots$, A_n are integers, is itself an integer and a factor of A_n. Note that $A_0 = 1$.

Example. Find the rational roots of the equation $f(x) = 2x^3 - 9x^2 + 7x + 6 = 0$.

Solution: By the above theorem, if c/d is a rational root of the given equation, then c is a factor of 6 and d is a factor of 2. The possible rational roots in this case then are $\pm\frac{1}{2}$, $\frac{3}{2}$, 1, 2, 3, 6.

To determine whether any of these numbers are roots we shall use synthetic division, recalling that a is a root of $f(x) = 0$ if the remainder is zero after division of $f(x)$ by $x - a$, and that if the remainder is not zero then a is not a root.

Let us first try the number $x = \frac{1}{2}$.

$$
\begin{array}{r}
2 - 9 + 7 + 6 \,\big|\tfrac{1}{2} \\
+\,1 - 4 \qquad\quad \\
\hline
2 - 8 + 3. \qquad
\end{array}
$$

The division need not be continued because $(3)(\frac{1}{2})$ is not an integer and, once a fraction, and not an integer, is introduced in the third line of our synthetic substitution process, there is no need to carry the division further, for such fractions will persist and prevent a final zero. This will be true in general if the coefficients of the given equation are integers. We next try 1, $\frac{3}{2}$, and then 2.

$$
\begin{array}{ccc}
2 - 9 + 7 + 6\,\big|1 & \quad 2 - 9 + 7 + 6\,\big|2 & \quad 2 - 9 + 7 + 6\,\big|\tfrac{3}{2} \\
+\,2 - 7 + 0 & +\,4 - 10 - 6 & +\,3 - 9 - 3 \\
\hline
2 - 7 + 0 + 6 & 2 - 5 - \;3 + 0 & 2 - 6 - 2 + 3.
\end{array}
$$

These divisions show that 1 and $\frac{3}{2}$ are not roots but that 2 is a root. By the factor theorem, $x - 2$ is a factor, and the given equation can be written

$$(x - 2)(2x^2 - 5x - 3) = 0.$$

The new equation, $2x^2 - 5x - 3 = 0$, obtained by removing the factor $x - 2$, is called the *depressed equation*. Now this equation can be solved as a quadratic, to yield the remaining two roots. Factoring the depressed equation, we have

$$(2x + 1)(x - 3) = 0.$$

Solving for x, we get $x = -\frac{1}{2}$ and $x = 3$. The roots of the given equation are

$$x = 2, 3, -\tfrac{1}{2}.$$

Check: These may be checked by direct substitution or by forming the product $(x - 2)(x - 3)(2x + 1) = 2x^3 - 9x^2 + 7x + 6$.

It should be emphasized that a given number may be a root of an equation more than once; that is, it may be a multiple root. For this reason one should work with the depressed equation at each step. There is no other way of discovering that the number is a multiple root. Furthermore, if a number has been tried and found not to be a root of the original equation it will not be a root of the depressed equation at any step and need not be tried again. It should also be noted that the above procedure will enable us to find all the roots of a polynomial equation if not more than two of the roots are irrational or imaginary. This follows from the fact that, when all the rational roots have been found, the depressed equation will be a quadratic and can thus be solved by the quadratic formula.

Example.   Find all the roots of the equation $f(x) = x^6 - 9x^4 + 16x^3 - 9x^2 + 1 = 0$.

Solution: By Descartes' rule of signs the given equation has either four, two, or no positive real roots. Since the equation

$$f(-x) = x^6 - 9x^4 - 16x^3 - 9x^2 + 1 = 0$$

has two variations in sign, the original equation has either two or no negative real roots. It must have six roots. The possible rational roots are ± 1. We try $x = 1$ as follows,

$$
\begin{array}{r}
1 + 0 - 9 + 16 - 9 + 0 + 1 \,\lfloor 1 \\
\underline{+ 1 + 1 - 8 + 8 - 1 - 1} \\
1 + 1 - 8 + 8 - 1 - 1 + 0,
\end{array}
$$

and find that 1 is a root. Let us keep trying $x = 1$ in the depressed equation at each step until it fails to give a zero remainder:

$$
\begin{array}{r}
1 + 1 - 8 + 8 - 1 - 1 \,\lfloor 1 \\
\underline{+ 1 + 2 - 6 + 2 + 1} \\
1 + 2 - 6 + 2 + 1 \\
\underline{+ 1 + 3 - 3 - 1} \\
1 + 3 - 3 - 1 \\
\underline{+ 1 + 4 + 1} \\
1 + 4 + 1 + 0.
\end{array}
$$

The final depressed equation is the quadratic $x^2 + 4x + 1 = 0$, which we can solve by the quadratic formula, getting

$$x = \frac{-4 \pm \sqrt{16 - 4}}{2} = -2 \pm \sqrt{3}.$$

The roots of the original equation are $1, 1, 1, 1, -2 \pm \sqrt{3}$.

EXERCISES

Find all the rational roots of each of the following equations. Where possible find all the roots of the equation.

1. $x^3 - 6x^2 + 11x - 6 = 0.$
2. $x^3 - 2x^2 - 5x + 6 = 0.$
3. $3x^3 - 2x^2 + 6x - 4 = 0.$
4. $x^3 - 5x^2 + 7x - 3 = 0.$
5. $x^3 + 3x^2 - 25x - 75 = 0.$
6. $x^3 - 4x^2 + 9x - 10 = 0.$
7. $x^4 - 3x^3 - 11x^2 + 3x + 10 = 0.$
8. $6x^4 - x^3 - 39x^2 - 6x + 40 = 0.$
9. $8x^4 + 30x^3 + 21x^2 - 20x - 12 = 0.$
10. $x^4 - 6x^2 + 4x = 0.$

11. $2x^3 - 3x^2 - 8x + 12 = 0.$
12. $x^4 - 18x^2 + 81 = 0.$
13. $4x^4 - 8x^3 + 39x^2 + 2x - 10 = 0.$
14. $x^4 - x^3 - 2x^2 - 4x - 24 = 0.$
15. $x^4 - x^3 - 10x^2 - 8x = 0.$
16. $4x^3 - 8x^2 + 13x + 25 = 0.$
17. $x^3 - x^2 - 8x + 12 = 0.$
18. $x^4 - 2x^3 + 2x^2 - 8x + 8 = 0.$
19. $x^4 - 9x^3 + 30x^2 - 44x + 24 = 0.$
20. $8x^3 - 36x^2 + 54x - 27 = 0.$

21. $2x^3 - 45x^2 + 2000 = 0.$
22. $x^5 - 5x^4 + 6x^3 + 11x^2 - 43x + 30 = 0.$
23. $x^5 - 5x^4 + 3x^3 + 13x^2 - 8x - 12 = 0.$
24. $8x^3 - 36x^2 + 54x - 27 = 0.$
25. $2x^4 - 3x^3 - 3x^2 + 7x - 3 = 0.$
26. $x^4 - 10x^2 + 9 = 0.$
27. $4x^3 - 36x^2 + 83x - 66 = 0.$
28. $x^4 + x^3 - 11x^2 - 9x + 18 = 0.$
29. $120x^3 - 91x^2 + 54x + 40 = 0.$
30. $2x^3 - 11x^2 + x + 35 = 0.$

Factor each of the following polynomials into the product of rational factors.

31. $x^3 - 5x^2 + 2x + 8.$
32. $x^4 + 3x^3 - 3x^2 - 7x + 6.$
33. $4x^4 + 4x^3 + 5x^2 + 8x - 6.$
34. $4x^4 + x^2 - 5x.$
35. $4x^3 + 5x^2 + 13x + 3.$

36. $x^4 + 9x^3 + 30x^2 + 44x + 24.$
37. $x^6 - 64.$
38. $x^5 + 5x^4 - 4x^3 - 46x^2 - 8x + 120.$
39. $8x^3 - 1.$
40. $12x^3 - 28x^2 - 7x + 5.$

Form equations with integral coefficients having the following solution sets.

41. $\{1, 2, 3\}.$
42. $\{-1, -1, 2\}.$
43. $\{2, \pm\sqrt{3}\}.$
44. $\{1, 1 \pm 2i\}.$

45. $\{1 \pm \sqrt{2}, 2 \pm i\}.$
46. $\{\pm 1, \pm 3\}.$
47. $\{\frac{2}{3}, -\frac{1}{2}, 4\}.$
48. $\{1, 1, 1, \frac{3}{5}\}.$

20 EQUATIONS CONTAINING FRACTIONS

In the preceding sections of this chapter, methods were given for finding all the rational roots of a polynomial equation. In fact we are now able to find the solution set of any polynomial equation provided at most two of its roots are not rational numbers. This suggests that if the problem of solving a given equation can be reduced to the problem of solving an equivalent polynomial equation then our chances for finding the solution set of the given equation should be good.

In this section we shall consider a type of equation containing fractions whose solution always leads to the solution of a polynomial equation.

Definition 4.8.   *A rational fraction in one variable is a fraction whose numerator and denominator are polynomials in that variable. In particular, a rational fraction in x is one that can be expressed in the form P(x)/Q(x), where P(x) and Q(x) are polynomials.*

Some typical examples of rational fractions are:

$$3x, \quad \frac{2}{3}, \quad \frac{x}{5}, \quad \frac{4}{x}, \quad \frac{3x+7}{2-x}, \quad \frac{x^2-7x+3}{x^3+x-1}, \quad \text{etc.}$$

In Chapter III, rules were given for finding the algebraic sum of two or more fractions. These rules apply to rational fractions and enable us to combine the sum of two or more rational fractions into a single rational fraction whose numerator and denominator have no common factors other than 1.

Definition 4.9.   *A rational fraction, P(x)/Q(x), is said to be in* lowest *terms, if and only if the polynomials P(x) and Q(x) have no common factors.*

We need at this point to recall the following properties of complex numbers.

1.   Division by zero is not a valid operation.

2.   If a is a number and $a \neq 0$, then $\dfrac{0}{a} = 0.$

3.   If c and d are numbers, then $\dfrac{c}{d} = 0$ if and only if $c = 0$ and $d \neq 0.$

We now use these properties to help us prove the following theorem.

Theorem 4.13.   *Let P(x)/Q(x) be a rational fraction in lowest terms. Then*

$$\frac{P(x)}{Q(x)} = 0 \leftrightarrow P(x) = 0.$$

Proof: Let the number a be a solution of $\dfrac{P(x)}{Q(x)} = 0$. Then $\dfrac{P(a)}{Q(a)} = 0.$
That is $P(a) = 0$ and $Q(a) \neq 0$, and hence a is also a solution of $P(x) = 0.$
Thus every solution of $\dfrac{P(x)}{Q(x)} = 0$ is also a solution of $P(x) = 0.$

Next suppose the number b is a solution of $P(x) = 0$, then $P(b) = 0.$
But if $P(b) = 0$, $(x - b)$ is a factor of $P(x)$ [Factor Theorem], and hence $Q(b) \neq 0$. For if $Q(b) = 0$, then $(x - b)$ would be a factor of $Q(x)$ which contradicts our assumption that $P(x)$ and $Q(x)$ have no common factors. This means that $\dfrac{P(b)}{Q(b)} = 0$ and therefore b is a solution of $\dfrac{P(x)}{Q(x)} = 0$. So, every

solution of $P(x) = 0$ is a solution of $\dfrac{P(x)}{Q(x)} = 0$. We have now shown that $\dfrac{P(x)}{Q(x)} = 0$ and $P(x) = 0$ have the same solution set which proves our theorem.

Example.   Find the solution set, S, of the equation

$$\frac{(x - 1)(x + 2)}{(x + 3)(x - 5)} = 0.$$

Solution:

$$\frac{(x - 1)(x + 2)}{(x + 3)(x - 5)} = 0 \leftrightarrow (x - 1)(x + 2) = 0.$$

We see by inspection that $S = \{1, -2\}$.

For convenience of discussion we shall use the symbols $F(x)$ and $G(x)$ to represent algebraic expressions such that each is either a rational fraction or an algebraic sum of two or more rational fractions, keeping in mind that such terms as $2x^2$, $7x$, 0, etc., can be regarded as rational fractions since they may be written,

$$\frac{2x^2}{1}, \quad \frac{7x}{1}, \quad \frac{0}{1}, \quad \text{etc.}$$

We wish now to consider those equations expressible in the form $F(x) = G(x)$. Since the symbols $F(x)$ and $G(x)$ represent algebraic sums of rational fractions, then $F(x) - G(x)$ is also a sum of rational fractions and hence can be combined into a single rational fraction. That is, we may write

(1) $$F(x) - G(x) = \frac{N(x)}{D(x)}$$

where $N(x)$ and $D(x)$ are polynomials having no common factors. In other words Equation (1) is an identity.

Assuming the symbols $F(x)$, $G(x)$, $N(x)$, and $D(x)$ to have the same meaning as defined above, the following theorem provides a procedure for solving equations of the type $F(x) = G(x)$.

Theorem 4.14. $F(x) = G(x) \leftrightarrow \dfrac{N(x)}{D(x)} = 0$

$$\leftrightarrow N(x) = 0.$$

Proof: Obviously $F(x) = G(x) \leftrightarrow F(x) - G(x) = 0$

$$\leftrightarrow \frac{N(x)}{G(x)} = 0 \qquad \text{[Equation (1)]}$$

$$\leftrightarrow N(x) = 0 \qquad \text{(Theorem 4.13)}$$

and our theorem is proved.

Remark: If it should happen that $N(x)$ is a constant. this means that the solution set of $F(x) = G(x)$ is the empty set. That is, the equation has no solution.

The following examples will help to make clear the procedure suggested by the last theorem for solving equations of the form $F(x) = G(x)$.

Example.   Find the solution set, S, of the equation

$$\frac{2}{(x-1)(x+1)} = \frac{1}{x-1} - 2.$$

Solution:

$$\frac{2}{(x-1)(x+1)} = \frac{1}{x-1} - 2 \leftrightarrow \frac{2}{(x-1)(x+1)} - \frac{1}{x-1} + 2 = 0$$

$$\leftrightarrow \frac{2 - (x+1) + 2(x-1)(x+1)}{(x-1)(x+1)} = 0$$

$$\leftrightarrow \frac{2x^2 - x - 1}{(x-1)(x+1)} = 0$$

$$\leftrightarrow \frac{(2x+1)(x-1)}{(x-1)(x+1)} = 0$$

$$\leftrightarrow \frac{2x+1}{x+1} = 0$$

$$\leftrightarrow 2x + 1 = 0 \leftrightarrow x = -\frac{1}{2}$$

$$S = \left\{-\frac{1}{2}\right\}.$$

Check: Substituting $-\frac{1}{2}$ for x

$$\frac{2}{(-\frac{3}{2})(\frac{1}{2})} = \frac{1}{-\frac{3}{2}} - 2 \quad \text{or} \quad -\frac{8}{3} = -\frac{2}{3} - 2 = -\frac{8}{3}.$$

Example.   Find the solution set, S, of the equation

$$\frac{2}{x-1} + \frac{5}{x+1} = \frac{4}{x^2-1}.$$

Solution:

$$\frac{2}{x-1} + \frac{5}{x+1} = \frac{4}{x^2-1} \leftrightarrow \frac{2}{x-1} + \frac{5}{x+1} - \frac{4}{x^2-1} = 0,$$

$$\leftrightarrow \frac{2(x+1) + 5(x-1) - 4}{(x-1)(x+1)} = 0$$

$$\leftrightarrow \frac{7x - 7}{(x-1)(x+1)}$$

$$\leftrightarrow \frac{7}{x+1}$$

$$N(x) = 7 \neq 0, \quad \text{therefore } S = \{\ \}.$$

EXERCISES

Solve each of the following equations.

1. $\dfrac{(x-2)(x+1)}{(x-1)(x-3)} = 0.$

2. $\dfrac{x^2 - x - 1}{x(x+1)} = 0.$

3. $\dfrac{3x-1}{x} = 1.$

4. $\dfrac{x}{x+1} - \dfrac{2}{x+2} + 1 = 0.$

5. $\dfrac{1}{x} + \dfrac{2}{x+1} = \dfrac{5}{6}.$

6. $\dfrac{5}{2x} + \dfrac{4}{3x} = \dfrac{23}{12}.$

7. $\dfrac{8}{x+3} = \dfrac{3}{x-2}.$

8. $\dfrac{y+3}{y-2} + \dfrac{5}{y-2} = 4.$

9. $\dfrac{3}{x-2} + \dfrac{5}{x+2} = \dfrac{20}{x^2-4}.$

10. $\dfrac{2x-3}{x+5} = 2.$

11. $\dfrac{3}{x-1} + \dfrac{1}{x-3} = \dfrac{4}{x-2}.$

12. $\dfrac{3x+4}{6x-5} = \dfrac{2x+5}{4x-1}.$

13. $\dfrac{y+5}{y-3} + \dfrac{4}{y-3} = 5.$

14. $\dfrac{6x+9}{x^2+x-2} + \dfrac{2x+3}{x+2} - \dfrac{2x+5}{x-1} = 0.$

15. $\dfrac{5}{x-1} - \dfrac{7}{x-2} + \dfrac{2}{x-3} = 0.$

16. $\dfrac{6x}{2x+1} + \dfrac{6}{2x-1} - \dfrac{2x+3}{2x-1} = 2.$

17. $1 + \dfrac{4}{x} = \dfrac{3}{x-1}.$

18. $\dfrac{2x}{x+1} + \dfrac{x}{1-x} - \dfrac{4}{x^2-1} = 0.$

19. $\dfrac{6}{(x-1)^2} + \dfrac{1}{x} = \dfrac{1}{1-x}.$

20. $\dfrac{x-2}{x+3} + \dfrac{x+3}{x-2} = \dfrac{7-6x}{x^2+x-6}.$

21. $\dfrac{x-4}{x^2-4} = \dfrac{x+2}{x^2} - \dfrac{1}{x^2-2x}.$

22. $\dfrac{x}{x+3} + \dfrac{5x^2}{x^2-9} = 0.$

21 EQUATIONS INVOLVING RADICALS

Certain equations in one variable where the variable occurs under one or more square root radicals can often be reduced to a polynomial equation by squaring both members of the equation until the resulting equation no longer involves radicals. Such a squaring operation may lead to a new equation that is not equivalent to the original equation. However the solution set of the given equation will always be a subset of the solution set of the new equation. To show that this is the case we state and prove the following theorem.

Theorem 4.15.   *Let $f(x)$ and $g(x)$ represent arbitrary algebraic expressions which may or may not involve radicals. If S is the solution set of $f(x) = g(x)$ and T is the solution set of $[f(x)]^2 = [g(x)]^2$, then $S \subseteq T$. We denote symbolically as*

$$f(x) = g(x) \rightarrow [f(x)]^2 = [g(x)]^2.$$

(*Note the single arrow in this case.*)

Proof: Suppose the number a belongs to S, then $f(a) = g(a)$. But this is a numerical identity and consequently $[f(a)]^2 = [g(a)]^2$, that is, $a \in T$. But a is any element of S. Hence every element of S is an element of T and thus $S \subseteq T$ which proves our theorem.

A simple example will show that in some cases $S \neq T$.

Example.   Consider the equation $x = 1$. Here $S = \{1\}$. Now square both sides and get $x^2 = 1$. Obviously in this case $T = \{1, -1\}$ and $S \neq T$. This means that if in solving an equation we square both members of the equation and ultimately arrive at a new equation with solution set T, it is absolutely necessary to check each number in T by substituting it in the given equation in order to find S, the solution set of the given equation. An example may help to make the procedure clear.

Example.   Find the solution set, S, of the equation

$$\sqrt{x + 7} - \sqrt{2x - 3} = 2.$$

Solution: $\sqrt{x + 7} - \sqrt{2x - 3} = 2 \leftrightarrow \sqrt{x + 7} = \sqrt{2x - 3} + 2$

Squaring both sides $\rightarrow (\sqrt{x + 7})^2 = (\sqrt{2x - 3} + 2)^2$

Expanding $\leftrightarrow x + 7 = 2x - 3 + 4\sqrt{2x - 3} + 4$

Simplifying $\leftrightarrow 6 - x = 4\sqrt{2x - 3}$

Square again $\rightarrow (6 - x)^2 = (4\sqrt{2x - 3})^2$

Expanding $\leftrightarrow 36 - 12x + x^2 = 16(2x - 3)$

Simplifying $\leftrightarrow x^2 - 44x + 84 = 0$

    $\leftrightarrow (x - 2)(x - 42) = 0$

Factoring $\leftrightarrow (x - 2)(x - 42) = 0$

    $\therefore T = \{2, 42\}$

Test $x = 2$ Test $x = 42$

$\sqrt{2 + 7} - \sqrt{4 - 3} = \sqrt{9} - \sqrt{1}$ $\sqrt{42 + 7} - \sqrt{84 - 3} = \sqrt{49} - \sqrt{81}$

    $= 3 - 1 = 2$ $= 7 - 9 \neq 2$

    $2 \in S.$ $42 \notin S.$

EXERCISES

Find the solution set of each of the following equations.

1. $\sqrt{x + 3} = 3.$

2. $\sqrt{2x - 3} = 9 - x.$

3. $\sqrt{3x - 5} - \sqrt{x - 6} = 3.$

4. $\sqrt{x} + \sqrt{2x - 1} = 2.$

5. $x + 2\sqrt{x-1} = 9.$

6. $x + \sqrt{x^2 - 9} = 1.$

7. $x + \sqrt{x-9} = 11.$

8. $\sqrt{7x-6} - \sqrt{2x-3} = 3.$

9. $\sqrt{3x+4} = \sqrt{2x-4} + 2.$

10. $\sqrt{2x-5} - \sqrt{x-3} = 1.$

11. $\sqrt{5x-4} - \sqrt{x-1} = 2.$

12. $\sqrt{5x-1} = \sqrt{x} + 1.$

13. $\sqrt{2x+1} - \sqrt{x-3} = \sqrt{x}.$

14. $\sqrt{2x+7} = \sqrt{2-x} + \sqrt{x+3}.$

15. $\sqrt{5x-6} + \sqrt{x+1} = \sqrt{7x+4}.$

16. $\sqrt{3x+4} - 2\sqrt{x-6} = 1.$

22   GRAPHS OF POLYNOMIALS

We have learned how a rectangular coordinate system may be used to establish a one-to-one correspondence between points of the plane and ordered pairs (x, y) of real numbers. Thus if we are given a rectangular coordinate system and an ordered pair of real numbers, we can locate, in the plane, the point having this ordered pair of numbers as its coordinates. This procedure can obviously be extended to any given set of ordered pairs of real numbers and thus obtain a corresponding set of points, called the *graph* of the given set of ordered pairs. Suppose $f(x)$ is a polynomial with real numbers as coefficients and let the universal set U for the variable x be the set of all real numbers. To each real number x there corresponds one and only one real number $f(x)$, which determines the ordered pair $(x, f(x))$. For convenience, we denote by the letter y the value of $f(x)$ at x, that is, $(x, y) = (x, f(x))$. This enables us to define the graph of the real polynomial $f(x)$ as follows.

Definition 4.10.   *The graph of the real polynomial $f(x)$ is the set of all points in the plane whose coordinates are the elements of the set of ordered pairs of real numbers $\{(x, y) \mid y = f(x)\}$.*

Since for any given real polynomial $f(x)$, there corresponds to each real number x one value of $f(x)$, the set $\{(x, y) \mid y = f(x)\}$ is an infinite set. Hence the graph of $f(x)$ consists of an infinite set of points. It turns out that such a graph always consists of all the points on some straight line or all the points on some smooth curve. In the next chapter we shall prove that if the polynomial is of degree $n = 1$, the graph is always a straight line. For the time being we shall assume this to be true and shall further assume that the graph of a polynomial of degree $n \geq 2$ is a smooth curve. At best we can only draw a portion of such a graph but usually we are able to draw a large enough portion of the graph of a particular polynomial to show its position and general shape.

To draw the graph of a real polynomial $f(x)$ we use the following procedure.

Step 1.   Construct a table of ordered pairs (x, y) by assigning convenient values to x, and substituting these values in the equation $y = f(x)$ to find the corresponding values of y.

Step 2. Plot the points whose coordinates are the ordered pairs from the table of Step 1.

Step 3. Connect the points plotted in Step 2 by a smooth curve.

The following examples may help to clarify the procedure.

Example. Sketch the graph of the polynomial $f(x) = x + 2$.

Solution: We make the following table by assigning convenient values to x in the equation $y = x + 2$ and then computing the corresponding values of y.

x	-3	-2	-1	0	1	2	3
y	-1	0	1	2	3	4	5

We next plot the points whose coordinates are the ordered pairs of numbers in the table. Since the polynomial in this case is of degree $n = 1$, the graph of the polynomial should be a straight line. Our points do appear to lie on the same straight line. We draw the line,

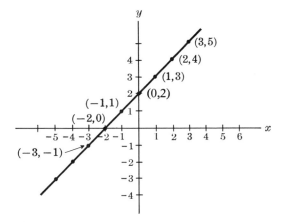

FIGURE 4.1

Example. Draw the graph of the polynomial $f(x) = x^2 - 2x - 3$.

Solution: Let $y = x^2 - 2x - 3$. We obtain the following table of ordered pairs and the corresponding graph of Fig. 4.2.

x	-2	-1	0	1	2	3	4
y	5	0	-3	-4	-3	0	5

The graph in Fig. 4.2 is called a *parabola*. It can be proved that the graph of every second degree polynomial, $f(x) = ax^2 + bx + c$, is a parabola. If $a > 0$ the

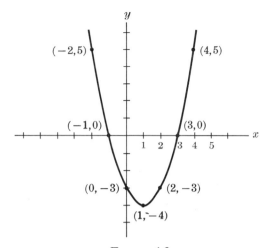

FIGURE 4.2

parabola opens upward, it has a *lowest* point at which the polynomial has its least possible value. On the other hand, if $a < 0$ the parabola opens downward, it has a *highest* point at which the polynomial has its greatest possible value. The lowest point in the case where $a > 0$, or the highest point in the case where $a < 0$, is called the vertex of the parabola and its coordinates are $\left(-\dfrac{b}{2a}, \dfrac{4ac - b^2}{4a}\right)$. The proof of this last statement is left to the student in the Exercises.

Example. Plot the graph of the polynomial $f(x) = x^3 - x^2 - 2x + 1$.

Solution: Let $y = x^3 - x^2 - 2x + 1$.

Assigning values for x, we compute the corresponding values of y. We obtain the set of ordered pairs shown in the following table and the corresponding graph of Fig. 4.3.

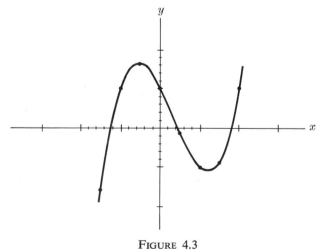

FIGURE 4.3

x	-1.5	-1	$-.5$	0	$.5$	1	1.5	2
y	-1.6	1	1.6	1	-0.1	-1	-0.9	1

Since the x-coordinates of the points where the graph of the polynomial $f(x)$ either crosses or touches the x-axis are the real roots of the polynomial equation $f(x) = 0$, then the graph of a polynomial $f(x)$ gives the roots, at least approximately, of the corresponding polynomial equation $f(x) = 0$. A close inspection of the graph in Fig. 4.3 indicates that the real roots of the equation $x^3 - x^2 - 2x + 1 = 0$ are approximately -1.2, 0.4, and 1.8. A method for approximating the real roots more accurately is discussed in the next section.

EXERCISES

1. Draw the graphs of the following polynomials, $f(x)$.
   a. $f(x) = 2x - 4$.   d. $f(x) = 7 - 2x$.
   b. $f(x) = 3x + 5$.   e. $f(x) = 4 - 5x$.
   c. $f(x) = 4$.   f. $f(x) = -x$.
2. Prove that the coordinates of the vertex of the parabola $y = ax^2 + bx + c$ are

$$\left(-\frac{b}{2a}, \frac{4ac - b^2}{4a}\right). \left[\textit{Hint:} \quad \text{Show that } y = a\left(x + \frac{b}{2a}\right)^2 + \frac{4ac - b^2}{4a}\right].$$

Find the coordinates of the vertex of each of the following parabolas and then draw its graph.

3. $y = x^2 - 2x - 3$.   7. $y = 2 + 6x - 3x^2$.
4. $y = 4x - x^2$.   8. $y = 9 - x^2$.
5. $y = x^2 - 6x + 9$.   9. $y = x^2 + 4$.
6. $y = 2x^2 + 8x + 1$.   10. $y = 1 - 10x - x^2$.

Draw the graphs of the following polynomials.

11. $f(x) = x^3$.   13. $f(x) = 2x^3 + 3x^2 - 4x - 6$.
12. $f(x) = x^3 - 2x^2 - 5x + 6$.   14. $f(x) = x^3 - 3x + 1$.

23 IRRATIONAL ROOTS OF A POLYNOMIAL EQUATION

In general, irrational roots of a polynomial equation of degree $n > 2$ cannot be found exactly, but it is always possible to approximate any such root as closely as we please. There are many well known methods for approximating the irrational roots of a polynomial equation, only the simplest of which will be considered here. Other methods such as Horner's, Graeffe's, and Newton's are discussed in most texts on the theory of equations.

The first step in the method we are considering is graphical. That is, we find the first approximations to the irrational roots of the polynomial equation $f(x) = 0$ by drawing the graph of $f(x)$ and then read the approximations from the graph as was done in the last example of the previous section.

However, before attempting to find the irrational roots of a polynomial equation one should find and remove any rational roots and then work with the depressed equation. In addition to the graph the method under consideration makes use of an important basic principle which we now state.

Location Principle.   *If $f(a)$ and $f(b)$ are opposite in sign, then $f(x) = 0$ has at least one root between a and b.*

We shall illustrate with the following example the procedure involved.

Example.   Find all the real roots of $f(x) = 2x^4 - 3x^3 - 14x^2 + 27x - 9 = 0$.

Solution: First we see that possible rational roots are $\pm 1, 3, 9, \frac{1}{2}, \frac{3}{2}, \frac{9}{2}$. Trial shows that $x = \frac{3}{2}$ is the only rational root, so by synthetic division we remove this root:

$$
\begin{array}{r}
2 - 3 - 14 + 27 - 9\ \underline{|\frac{3}{2}} \\
+3 + \ 0 - 21 + 9 \\
\hline
2 + 0 - 14 + \ \ 6.
\end{array}
$$

The depressed equation is $2x^3 + 0x^2 - 14x + 6 = 0$ or simply $x^3 - 7x + 3 = 0$. Let $F(x) = x^3 - 7x + 3 = 0$.

This equation has three roots, at least one of which must be real. By synthetic substitution we obtain the values given in the following table and find that 3 is an upper limit and -3 a lower limit:

x	-3	-2	-1	0	1	2	3
$F(x)$	-3	9	9	3	-3	-3	9

Next we plot the graph of $F(x)$ (see Fig. 4.4). The curve crosses the x axis where x has the approximate values -2.8, 0.4, and 2.4. By using synthetic division we find that $F(-2.9) = -0.933$, $F(-2.8) = 0.648$, $F(0.4) = 0.264$, $F(0.5) = -0.375$, $F(2.3) = -0.933$ and $F(2.4) = 0.024$. Thus one of the three roots lies between -2.9

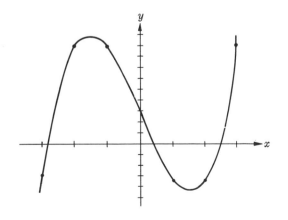

FIGURE 4.4

and -2.8, a second one lies between 0.4 and 0.5, and the third lies between 2.3 and 2.4. Also our calculations show that accurate to one decimal place the three roots are -2.8, 0.4, and 2.4. To find accuracy correct to two decimals we divide each interval into ten equal parts and successively use synthetic division for the values of x at each subdivision. For example suppose we wish the second root correct to two decimal places. We divide the interval from 0.4 to 0.5 into ten equal parts and use synthetic division for the values $x = 0.41, 0.42, 0.43, \cdots, 0.49$. We find $F(0.44) = 0.0052$ and $F(0.45) = -0.058875$, hence the root is between 0.44 and 0.45, but nearer 0.44. So, correct to two decimal places the root is 0.44. If we repeat this process for the values $0.441, 0.442, 0.443, \cdots, 0.449$, we find $F(0.441) = -0.001234$ while $F(0.440) = 0.0052$, hence this root correct to three decimal places is 0.441. Obviously this process could be continued indefinitely, thereby obtaining the root accurate to as many decimal places as desired.

The amount of work involved may be shortened by the following procedure. We found that the second root lies between 0.4 and 0.5. The graph shows that this section of the curve is approximately straight and replacing it by a straight line we get Fig. 4.5.

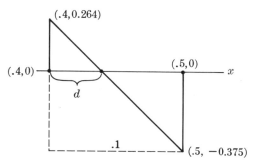

FIGURE 4.5

By similar triangles

$$\frac{d}{.264} = \frac{.1}{.639}$$

$$d = \frac{26.4}{639} = .041 \text{ approximately.}$$

This suggests that the root is $0.4 + .041 = 0.441$. We check by evaluating $F(0.440) = 0.0052$ and $F(0.441) = -0.001234$ which shows that correct to three decimal places the root actually is 0.441. We could repeat this process if greater accuracy is desired.

EXERCISES

Plot the graph of each polynomial associated with the following equations and use your graph in each case to estimate, to one decimal place, the irrational roots of the corresponding equation.

1. $2x^3 + x^2 - 10x - 4 = 0$.
2. $x^3 - 3x - 4 = 0$.
3. $x^4 - 2x^3 - 4x^2 + 4x + 4 = 0$.
4. $x^4 - x^3 - 5x^2 + 7x - 2 = 0$.
5. $x^3 + 3x - 2 = 0$.
6. $x^3 - 4x + 1 = 0$.

7. Use the method discussed in the last section to approximate to three decimal places the positive root of the equation in Problem 1.

8. Find, to three decimal places, the least positive root of the equation $x^3 - 3x + 1 = 0$.

Find accurate to three decimal places the indicated principal roots.

9. $\sqrt[3]{4}$.   10. $\sqrt[3]{10}$.   11. $\sqrt[4]{6}$.   12. $\sqrt[5]{8}$.

24 INEQUALITIES IN ONE VARIABLE

Inequalities were defined in Section II of Chapter II as being statements such as $3 < 7$, $6 - 5 < 4 - 1$, $5 > 2$, etc. We wish to extend the definition to include open statements such as $x - 3 < 0$, $x - 2 < 7$, $3x + 4 \leq x + 10$, $x^2 - 3x - 4 > 0$, or in fact any open statement of the form $f(x) < g(x)$, where $f(x)$ and $g(x)$ are polynomials with real numbers as coefficients. Just as was the case with equations, an inequality may be a true statement, or it may be a false statement or, if it involves variables it may be neither true nor false. For example, $7 > 3$ is a true statement, $8 - 2 < 4 + 1$ is a false statement, but $x + 2 < 3$ is neither true nor false until a specific number is substituted for x.

Inequalities involving one variable are of three types.

1. Conditional inequalities: Those inequalities which yield true statements for some value of the variable and false statements for other values of the variable. Example: $2x > 3$ is true if $x = 2$ and false if $x = 1$.

2. Absolute inequalities: Those which yield true statements for all values of the variable. Example: $x + 1 > x$.

3. Contradictory inequalities: Those which yield false statements for all values of the variable. Example: $x + 1 < x$.

The real number a is said to be a *solution* of a given inequality in one variable if and only if the inequality becomes a true statement when a is substituted for that variable in the inequality. For example, 2 is a solution of $3x + 1 < 10$, because $3(2) + 1 = 7$, and $7 < 10$ is a true statement. Similarly, 1 is a solution, and so is -1. In fact, any real number less than 3 is a solution. However, 4 is not a solution, since $3(4) + 1 = 13$, and $13 < 10$ is a false statement. Clearly, 3 is not a solution, nor is any number greater than 3 a solution.

The set of all the solutions of an inequality is called the *solution set* of the inequality. The solution set S of the above inequality is $S = \{x \mid x < 3\}$, which is read "S is the set of all real numbers x such that x is a number less than 3." In this case the solution set contains an infinite number of elements. This fact is rather typical of inequalities, for most inequalities commonly encountered do have infinitely many solutions. The graph of $S = \{x \mid x < 3\}$

is given in Fig. 4.6. Here we indicate that 3 is not in the graph by placing an open circle at its spot.

FIGURE 4.6

To solve an inequality is to find its solution set. The methods of solving inequalities are very similar to those of solving equations. For example, we say two inequalities are equivalent if, and only if, they have the same solution set. Also, the usual procedure in solving an inequality is to attempt to reduce the inequality to an equivalent inequality whose solution set can be found by inspection. We next state and prove some theorems that will prove helpful in this reduction process.

The definitions and theorems of Chapter II pertaining to inequalities were concerned only with order relations between two real numbers, that is, order relations between two nonreal numbers were not defined. Hence we concern ourselves here with inequalities whose solution sets are sets of real numbers.

Theorem 4.16. *If $f(x)$, $g(x)$, and $u(x)$ are polynomials with real numbers as coefficients, then*

$$f(x) < g(x) \leftrightarrow f(x) + u(x) < g(x) + u(x).$$

Proof: If a is a real number, then $f(a)$, $g(a)$, and $u(a)$ are real numbers. Thus if a is a solution of $f(x) < g(x)$, then a is also a solution set of $f(x) + u(x) < g(x) + u(x)$ and conversely if a is a solution of $f(x) + u(x) < g(x) + u(x)$ then a is a solution of $f(x) < g(x)$. For $f(a) < g(a)$ if and only if $f(a) + u(a) < g(a) + u(a)$. (See Axiom 14 and Theorem 2.27 of Chapter II.) Thus every solution of $f(x) < g(x)$ is a solution of $f(x) + u(x) < g(x) + u(x)$ and conversely. Hence the two inequalities are equivalent which proves our theorem.

Theorem 4.17. *If K is any non-zero real number then*

$$f(x) < g(x) \leftrightarrow Kf(x) < Kg(x) \qquad if \ K > 0,$$

and

$$f(x) < g(x) \leftrightarrow Kf(x) > Kg(x) \qquad if \ K < 0.$$

In particular for $K = -1$

$$f(x) < g(x) \leftrightarrow -f(x) > -g(x).$$

Proof: The proof follows immediately from Axiom 15, Axiom 16, Theorem 2.28, and Theorem 2.29 of Chapter II. For example, combining Axiom 15 and Theorem 2.28 we obtain the result

$$Kf(a) < Kg(a) \qquad \text{if and only if } f(a) < g(a) \qquad \text{and} \qquad K > 0.$$

Likewise Axiom 16 and Theorem 2.29 combine to give

$$Kf(a) > Kg(a) \qquad \text{if and only if } f(a) < g(a) \qquad \text{and} \qquad K < 0.$$

The details of the proof are left to the student.

25 LINEAR INEQUALITIES IN ONE VARIABLE

The simplest polynomial inequalities in one variable are those which have, or may be reduced to, one of the following forms: $ax + b < 0$, $ax + b \leq 0$, $ax + b > 0$, $ax + b \geq 0$. Such inequalities are called linear inequalities in one variable. To solve a linear inequality we apply one or both of the theorems from Section 24. The procedure is illustrated in the following examples.

Example. Solve the inequality $3x - 5 < 0$.

Solution: $3x - 5 < 0 \leftrightarrow 3x < 5$ (Theorem 4 with $u(x) = 5$)

$\qquad\qquad 3x < 5 \leftrightarrow x < \frac{5}{3}$ (Theorem 4 with $K = \frac{1}{3}$)

$\qquad\qquad 3x - 5 < 0 \leftrightarrow x < \frac{5}{3}.$

Thus the solution set S of $3x - 5 < 0$ is $S = \{x \mid x < \frac{5}{3}\}$. The graph of S is shown in Fig. 4.7. Observe that the solution set T of $3x - 5 \leq 0$ is identical with the

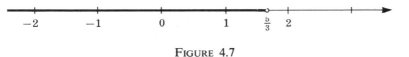

FIGURE 4.7

solution set of $3x - 5 < 0$ except T contains one more number than S, namely $\frac{5}{3}$. The graph of T is shown in Fig. 4.8.

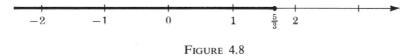

FIGURE 4.8

Example. Find the solution set S of the inequality $3x + 5 < 5x + 7$.

Solution: $3x + 5 < 5x + 7 \leftrightarrow 3x - 5x < 7 - 5$

$\qquad\qquad\qquad\qquad\quad \leftrightarrow -2x < 2$

$\qquad\qquad\qquad\qquad\quad \leftrightarrow 2x > -2$

$\qquad\qquad\qquad\qquad\quad \leftrightarrow x > -1.$

Therefore $S = \{x \mid x > -1\}$. The graph of S is shown in Fig. 4.9.

FIGURE 4.9

It is sometimes necessary to solve linear inequalities which involve absolute values. For example, inequalities such as $|x| > 3$, $|2x - 1| < 5$, $|3 - 2x| \leq 1$, etc. To solve inequalities like these we need to recall our definition of absolute value, namely, $|x| = x$ if $x \geq 0$ or $|x| = -x$ if $x < 0$, and that consequently, $|x| = |-x|$ for all values of x. We can now deduce the following equivalent inequalities.

(1) If $c > 0$, then $|x| > c \leftrightarrow (x > c$ or $x < -c)$. That is, $\{x \mid |x| > c\} = \{x \mid x > c$ or $x < -c\} = \{(-\infty, -c) \cup (c, \infty)$.
To see that this is true we observe that

$$|x| > c \leftrightarrow x > c \qquad \text{for } x \geq 0$$

or

$$|x| > c \leftrightarrow -x > c \qquad \text{for } x < 0.$$

But $-x > c \leftrightarrow x < -c$. Combining these results give (1), where $(-\infty, -c)$ and (c, ∞) are the open intervals shown in Fig. 4.10.

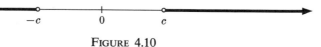

FIGURE 4.10

By a similar argument we obtain

(2) If $c > 0$, then $|x| < c \leftrightarrow (-c < x < c)$ or $\{x \mid |x| < c\} = (-c, c)$, recalling that the symbol $(-c, c)$ represents an open interval, namely, all the numbers between $-c$ and c but not $-c$ and not c. The graph of the solution set of the inequality $|x| < c$ is shown in Fig. 4.11.

FIGURE 4.11

We can generalize the results in (2) in the following way.

(3) If $a > 0$ and $c > 0$, then

$$|ax + b| < c \leftrightarrow \frac{-c - b}{a} < x < \frac{c - b}{a},$$

or

$$\{x \mid |ax + b| < c\} = \left(\frac{-c - b}{a}, \frac{c - b}{a}\right).$$

Proof: Replacing x in (2) by $ax + b$ we get

$|ax + b| < c \leftrightarrow -c < ax + b < c$

$\qquad \leftrightarrow -c - b < ax < c - b \qquad$ (add $-b$ to each member)

$\qquad \leftrightarrow \dfrac{-c - b}{a} < x < \dfrac{c - b}{a} \qquad$ (Divide each member by $a > 0$)

$\qquad = \left(\dfrac{-c - b}{a}, \dfrac{c - b}{a}\right).$

An important special case of (3) is

(4) $$|x - k| < c \leftrightarrow k - c < x < k + c.$$

Example.   Solve the inequality $|3 - 2x| < 5$.

Solution: $|3 - 2x| = |2x - 3|$, therefore

$$|3 - 2x| < 5 \leftrightarrow |2x - 3| < 5 \leftrightarrow -5 < 2x - 3 < 5$$
$$\leftrightarrow -2 < 2x < 8$$
$$\leftrightarrow -1 < x < 4.$$

Hence $\{x \mid |3 - 2x| < 5\} = (-1, 4)$. See Fig. 4.12 for graph.

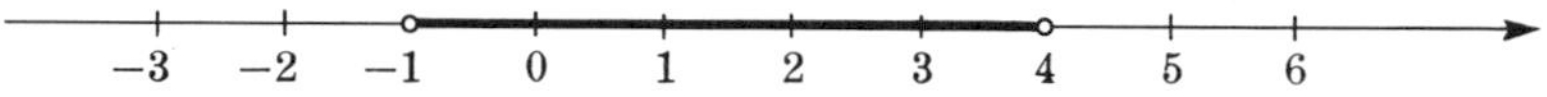

FIGURE 4.12

EXERCISES

Solve each of the following inequalities and draw the graph of the solution set in each case.

1. $x + 3 < 5$.
2. $x - 1 \geq 3$.
3. $2x - 1 \leq x + 2$.
4. $3x - 5 < 0$.
5. $7 - 2x > 11$.
6. $5x + 2 \leq 3x + 8$.
7. $5x + 4 < 7x - 2$.
8. $4x - 10 < 5x - 3$.

9. $|x| > 3$.
10. $|x| \leq 2$.
11. $|x - 1| < 4$.
12. $|x - 1| > 4$.
13. $|x + 2| < 3$.
14. $|2x - 1| \leq 5$.
15. $|3x + 8| \leq 11$.
16. $|x - 1| < 0.01$.

17. Write an equality which states that the distance from x to 3 is less than 2.
18. Write an inequality which expresses the fact that the distance from x to 2 is greater than 3.

Solve the following inequalities.

19. $|x - 1| < 2x$. [*Hint:* Check the intervals $(-\infty, 1)$ and $(1, \infty)$].
20. $|x - 3| > 2x + 1$.
21. $|x - 5| < |x + 1|$. [Check the intervals $(-\infty, -1)$, $(-1, 5)$, and $(5, \infty)$].
22. $|2x - 1| < |x - 4|$.

26   QUADRATIC INEQUALITIES

By quadratic inequalities is meant inequalities such as $ax^2 + bx + c < 0$, $ax^2 + bx + c \leq 0$, $ax^2 + bx + c > 0$, and $ax^2 + bx + c \geq 0$, where a, b, and c are real numbers and $a \neq 0$. It was shown in an earlier section of this chapter that

$$ax^2 + bx + c = a(x - x_1)(x - x_2),$$

where

$$x_1 = \frac{-b - \sqrt{b^2 - 4ac}}{2a} \quad \text{and} \quad x_2 = \frac{-b + \sqrt{b^2 - 4ac}}{2a}.$$

The numbers x_1 and x_2 are called the *zeros* of $ax^2 + bx + c$. For a full and complete discussion of quadratic inequalities we need to consider three cases.

Case 1. If $b^2 - 4ac > 0$, then x_1 and x_2 are real numbers and $x_1 < x_2$. Also, since $a \neq 0$, it follows from Theorem 4.18 that

$$a(x - x_1)(x - x_2) < 0 \leftrightarrow (x - x_1)(x - x_2) < 0, \quad \text{if } a > 0$$

or

$$a(x - x_1)(x - x_2) < 0 \leftrightarrow (x - x_1)(x - x_2) > 0, \quad \text{if } a < 0.$$

Further, to obtain the solution set of $(x - x_1)(x - x_2) \leq 0$ we need only add the two numbers x_1 and x_2 to the solution set of $(x - x_1)(x - x_2) < 0$. Similarly, to obtain the solution set of $(x - x_1)(x - x_2) \geq 0$ we add the numbers x_1 and x_2 to the solution set of $(x - x_1)(x - x_2) > 0$. Thus it will suffice to discuss a procedure for obtaining the solution sets of $(x - x_1)(x - x_2) < 0$ and $(x - x_1)(x - x_2) < 0$. The solution set of the first of these two inequalities is the set consisting of the values of x for which the product $(x - x_1)(x - x_2)$ is negative and the solution set of the second is the set consisting of all the values of x for which this same product is positive. Obviously, when we have found one of these two solution sets, this automatically determines the other one. Let us now examine the product $(x - x_1)(x - x_2)$, recalling that the product of two non-zero numbers is positive if and only if both numbers are positive or both are negative, otherwise the product is negative. The values of x for which $(x - x_1)$ is positive is just the solution set of the inequality $x > x_1$ and the values of x for which $(x - x_1)$ is negative is the solution set of $x < x_1$. Likewise the values of x for which $(x - x_2)$ is positive is the solution set of $x > x_2$ and the values of x for which $(x - x_2)$ is negative is the solution set of $x < x_2$. In other words $(x - x_1)$ is positive in the open interval (x_1, ∞) and is negative in the open interval $(-\infty, x_1)$. Similarly $(x - x_2)$ is positive in the open interval (x_2, ∞) and negative in the open interval $(-\infty, x_2)$. Having these facts it is a simple matter to determine the values of x for which the product $(x - x_1)(x - x_2)$ is positive and those for which it is negative. Perhaps the easiest method for doing this is a graphical one, illustrated in Fig. 4.13. The figure shows three parallel lines, (1), (2), and (3). Line (1) represents a number line upon which the points representing the numbers x_1 and x_2 have been located. The solid portion of Line (2) indicates the values of x for which $x > x_1$ and dotted portion of the same line shows the values of x for which $x < x_1$. Likewise the solid portion of Line (3) shows where $x > x_2$ and the dotted portion where $x < x_2$. Now we examine the segments of Lines (2) and (3) above each of the three intervals into which the points x_1 and x_2 divide the number line. In the intervals where both segments of Lines (2) and (3) are solid or are both dotted the product $(x - x_1)(x - x_2)$ is positive and the intervals where one segment is dotted and the other solid this product is negative. An inspection of Figure 4.13

FIGURE 4.13

shows that

$$(x - x_1)(x - x_2) > 0 \qquad \text{when } x > x_2 \text{ or } x < x_1$$

and

$$(x - x_1)(x - x_2) < 0 \qquad \text{when } x_1 < x < x_2.$$

We summarize the above facts in the following theorem.

Theorem 4.18. *If $ax^2 + bx + c = a(x - x_1)(x - x_2)$, where x_1 and x_2 are real numbers such that $x_1 < x_2$ and $a > 0$, then*

(1) $\{x \mid ax^2 + bx + c < 0\} = (x_1, x_2),$
(2) $\{x \mid ax^2 + bx + c \leq 0\} = [x_1, x_2],$
(3) $\{x \mid ax^2 + bx + c > 0\} = (-\infty, x_1) \cup (x_2, \infty),$
(4) $\{x \mid ax^2 + bx + c \geq 0\} = (-\infty, x_1] \cup [x_2, \infty).$

Example. Solve the inequality $15 + x - 6x^2 \geq 0$.

Solution: $15 + x - 6x^2 \geq 0 \leftrightarrow 6x^2 - x - 15 \leq 0$ (Multiply by -1)
$\leftrightarrow (2x + 3)(3x - 5) \leq 0$ (Factoring)
$\leftrightarrow (x + \frac{3}{2})(x - \frac{5}{3}) \leq 0.$ (Divide by 6)

Now applying the definition of equivalent inequalities and part (2) of Theorem 4.18, with $x_1 = -\frac{3}{2}$ and $x_2 = \frac{5}{3}$, we obtain

$$\{x \mid 15 + x - 6x^2 \geq 0\} = \{x \mid (x + \frac{3}{2})(x - \frac{5}{3}) \leq 0\} = [-\frac{3}{2}, \frac{5}{3}].$$

Example. Solve the inequality $2x^2 - 3x - 5 > 0$.

Solution: $2x^2 - 3x - 5 > 0 \leftrightarrow (x + 1)(2x - 5) > 0$ (Factoring)
$\leftrightarrow (x + 1)(x - \frac{5}{2}) > 0.$ (Divide by 2)

Here $x_1 = -1$ and $x_2 = \frac{5}{2}$. Applying part (3) of Theorem 4.18 we get

$$\{x \mid 2x^2 - 3x - 5 > 0\} = \{x \mid (x + 1)(x - \frac{5}{2}) > 0\} = (-\infty, -1) \cup (\frac{5}{2}, \infty).$$

Case 2. If $b^2 - 4ac = 0$, then x_1 and x_2 are real numbers and $x_1 = x_2$. That is, $ax^2 + bx + c = a(x - x_1)^2$. The factor $(x - x_1)^2$ is positive for all values of x except $x = x_1$. Hence, for $x \neq x_1$

$$a(x - x_1)^2 > 0 \qquad \text{when } a > 0$$

and

$$a(x - x_1)^2 < 0 \qquad \text{when } a < 0.$$

Of course when $x = x_1$, then $a(x - x_1)^2 = 0$ for all values of a. These facts justify the following theorem.

Theorem 4.19.   *If* $ax^2 + bx + c = a(x - x_1)^2$ *and* $a > 0$, *then*

(1) $\{x \mid ax^2 + bx + c < 0\} = \{x \mid (x - x_1)^2 < 0\} = \{\ \}.$ (*The empty set*)

(2) $\{x \mid ax^2 + bx + c \le 0\} = \{x \mid (x - x_1)^2 \le 0\} = \{x_1\}.$

(3) $\{x \mid ax^2 + bx + c > 0\} = \{x \mid (x - x_1)^2 > 0\} = \{$*all real numbers except* $x = x_1\}$
$$= (-\infty, x_1) \cup$$
$$(x_1, \infty).$$

(4) $\{x \mid ax^2 + bx + c \ge 0\} = \{x \mid (x - x_1)^2 \ge 0\} = \{$*all real numbers*$\}$
$$= (-\infty, \infty).$$

Example.   Solve the inequality $-x^2 + 4x - 4 < 0$.

Solution: $-x^2 + 4x - 4 = -(x^2 - 4x + 4) = -(x - 2)^2.$ Therefore
$$-x^2 + 4x - 4 < 0 \leftrightarrow -(x - 2)^2 < 0$$
$$\leftrightarrow (x - 2)^2 > 0.$$

Applying part (3) of Theorem 4.19 with $x_1 = 2$, we obtain

$$\{x \mid -x^2 + 4x - 4 < 0\} = \{x \mid (x - 2)^2 > 0\} = (-\infty, 2) \cup (2, \infty).$$

Case 3.   Here we assume that $b^2 - 4ac < 0$. By completing square in x, we may write

$$ax^2 + bx + c = a\left(x^2 + \frac{b}{a}x + \frac{b^2}{4a^2}\right) + c - \frac{b^2}{4a}$$

$$= a\left(x + \frac{b}{2a}\right)^2 + \frac{4ac - b^2}{4a}$$

$$= \frac{1}{4a}\left[a^2\left(x + \frac{b}{2a}\right)^2 + (4ac - b^2)\right].$$

Since $b^2 - 4ac < 0$, then $4ac - b^2 > 0$; hence the quantity inside the bracket is always positive. This shows that

$$ax^2 + bx + c > 0 \qquad \text{when } a > 0$$

and

$$ax^2 + bx + c < 0 \qquad \text{when } a < 0.$$

Note that $ax^2 + bx + c \ne 0$ for all values of x. So, we have

Theorem 4.20.   *If* $b^2 - 4ac < 0$,

(1) $\{x \mid ax^2 + bx + c < 0\} = \{\ \ \}, \quad$ *for* $a > 0$,

$= (-\infty, \infty), \quad$ *for* $a < 0$.

(2) $\{x \mid ax^2 + bx + c > 0\} = (-\infty, \infty), \quad$ *for* $a > 0$,

$= \{\ \ \}, \quad$ *for* $a < 0$.

Example.   Solve the inequality $2x^2 - 5x + 7 > 0$.

Solution: Here $b^2 - 4ac = 25 - 56 < 0$ and $a = 2 > 0$. It follows from part (2) of Theorem 4.20 that

$$\{x \mid 2x^2 - 5x + 7 > 0\} = (-\infty, \infty).$$

27   INEQUALITIES IN ONE VARIABLE INVOLVING POLYNOMIALS OF DEGREE $n > 2$ AND INEQUALITIES INVOLVING FRACTIONS

The procedure described in Case 1 of quadratic inequalities is easily extended to cover inequalities such as $f(x) < 0$, $f(x) \leq 0$, $f(x) > 0$, and $f(x) \geq 0$ where $f(x)$ is a real polynomial. Symbolically,

$$f(x) = A_0 x^n + A_1 x^{n-1} + A_2 x^{n-2} + \cdots + A_{n-1} x + A_n,$$

n is a positive integer, and the coefficients $A_0, A_1, A_2, \cdots, A_n$ are real numbers. It was shown in Section 16 of this chapter that

$$f(x) = A_0(x - r_1)(x - r_2) \cdots (x - r_n),$$

where $r_1, r_2, \cdots, r_n$ are complex numbers some, or all, of which may be real numbers. These numbers are called the *zeros* of the polynomial $f(x)$. They, obviously, are also the roots of the equation $f(x) = 0$. Since imaginary roots of a polynomial equation (Section 15) occur in conjugate pairs, it follows that every real polynomial of degree $n > 2$ is factorable into a product of linear and quadratic factors, each factor having real coefficients. We again need to consider three cases.

Case 1.   The polynomial $f(x)$ is factorable into a product of real linear factors and no factor is repeated. In this case we use a procedure that is an obvious extension of that described in our discussion of Case 1 for quadratic inequalities and used in arriving at the truth of Theorem 4.18. We illustrate this extended procedure by means of an example.

Example.   Solve the inequality $f(x) = (x + 2)(x - 1)(x - 3)(x - 5) < 0$.

Solution: The zeros of $f(x)$ are -2, 1, 3, and 5. We draw the parallel lines (1), (2), (3), (4), and (5) and locate on line (1) the points representing the numbers -2, 1, 3, 5. The other four lines, one for each factor, indicate where the factor is positive and where it is negative, the solid portion of a line indicates where the factor is positive and the dotted portion where it is negative. See Fig. 4.14. The zeros of

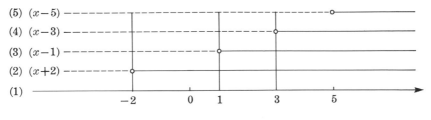

FIGURE 4.14

$f(x)$, namely, -2, 1, 3, and 5, divide Line (1), the number line, into the five open intervals $(-\infty, -2)$, $(-2, 1)$, $(1, 3)$, $(3, 5)$, and $(5, \infty)$. To determine whether $f(x)$ is positive or is negative in any one of these intervals we count the number of dotted line segments above that interval in Fig. 4.14. If the number of dotted line segments above the interval is an odd integer, then $f(x)$ is negative for all values of x in that interval; if the number of dotted line segments above the interval is an even integer of zero, $f(x)$ is positive in that interval. An inspection of Fig. 4.14 gives us the following table.

Interval	No. Dotted Segments above Interval	Sign of $f(x)$ in Interval
$(-\infty, -2)$	4	$+$
$(-2, 1)$	3	$-$
$(1, 3)$	2	$+$
$(3, 5)$	1	$-$
$(5, \infty)$	0	$+$

The solution set of $f(x) < 0$ is the set of all values of x for which $f(x)$ is negative. Therefore

$$\{x \mid (x + 2)(x - 1)(x - 3)(x - 5) < 0\} = (-2, 1) \cup (3, 5).$$

Remark: Since any non-zero number and its reciprocal always have the same sign, the solution sets of many other inequalities involving those same four factors can be obtained from the above table. As one example, consider the inequality

$$F(x) = \frac{(x + 2)(x - 3)}{(x - 1)(x - 5)} < 0.$$

Obviously the same intervals are involved and the sign of $F(x)$ in any interval is the same as the sign of $f(x) = (x + 2)(x - 1)(x - 3)(x - 5)$ in that same interval. Therefore $F(x) < 0 \leftrightarrow f(x) < 0$, that is

$$\{x \mid \frac{(x + 2)(x - 3)}{(x - 1)(x - 5)} < 0\} = \{x \mid (x + 2)(x - 1)(x - 3)(x - 5) < 0\}$$

$$= (-2, 1) \cup (3, 5).$$

Case 2. The polynomial $f(x)$ is factorable into a product of real linear factors some of which are repeated. It is helpful in this case to keep in mind that any even power of a non-zero number is positive and that any odd power of a negative number is a negative number. For example $(x - r)$ and $(x - r)^n$ have the same sign for the same value of x if n is an odd integer. We illustrate with an example a procedure for the case of repeated factors.

Example. Solve the inequality $(x + 1)(x - 2)^3(x - 4)^4 > 0$.

Solution: Since $(x - 2)^3$ and $(x - 2)$ always have the same sign for $x \neq 2$ and since $(x - 4)^2$ and $(x - 4)^4$ are both positive for $x \neq 4$, we may, if we like, simplify our problem slightly by noting that

$$(x + 1)(x - 2)^3(x - 4)^4 > 0 \leftrightarrow (x + 1)(x - 2)(x - 4)^2 > 0.$$

The next step is to draw the sketch shown in Fig. 4.15 and from it form the

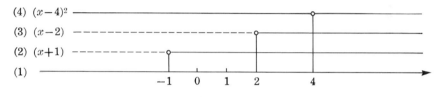

FIGURE 4.15

accompanying table. The zeros, -1, 2, 4, of the left member of the given inequality divide the number line into the open intervals $(-\infty, -1)$, $(-1, 2)$, $(2, 4)$, $(4, \infty)$. Let $f(x) = (x + 1)(x - 2)(x - 4)^2$.

Interval	No. Dotted Segments above Interval	Sign of $f(x)$ in Interval
$(-\infty, -1)$	2	$+$
$(-1, 2)$	1	$-$
$(2, 4)$	0	$+$
$(4, \infty)$	0	$+$

The table shows the solution set of $f(x) > 0$, and hence of the given inequality to be

$$\{x \mid (x + 1)(x - 2)^3(x - 4)^4 > 0\} = \{x \mid (x + 1)(x - 2)(x - 4)^2 > 0\}$$
$$= (-\infty, -1) \cup (2, 4) \cup (4, \infty).$$

Note that $x = 4$ does not belong to the solution set.

Case 3. The polynomial $f(x)$ is not factorable into a product of real linear factors. As was mentioned above, every polynomial in x can be factored into a product of real linear and real quadratic factors. This means that at least one of the real factors of $f(x)$ must be an irreducible quadratic factor, that is a factor of the form $ax^2 + bx + c$, where $b^2 - 4ac < 0$. In the discussion of Case 3 in Section 26 it was proved that such a quadratic is positive for all values of x if $a > 0$ and is negative for all values of x if $a < 0$. Thus an irreducible quadratic factor $ax^2 + bx + c$ in any polynomial inequality may be replaced by 1 if $a > 0$, or by -1 if $a < 0$, and the resulting inequality will have the same solution set as the original inequality. We can therefore always reduce the problems of Case 3 to a problem of Case 1 or of Case 2.

Example.   Solve the inequality

$$(x + 2)(x - 1)(7 + 3x - 2x^2) > 0.$$

Solution: Since $7 + 3x - 2x^2$ is negative for all values of x, it follows that

$$(x + 2)(x - 1)(7 + 3x - 2x^2) > 0 \leftrightarrow (x + 2)(x - 1)(-1) > 0$$
$$\leftrightarrow (x + 2)(x - 1) < 0.$$

It is easily shown that

$$\{x \mid (x + 2)(x - 1) < 0\} = (-2, 1),$$

hence

$$\{x \mid (x + 2)(x - 1)(7 + 3x - 2x^2) > 0\} = (-2, 1).$$

The methods already discussed for solving polynomial equations are equally valid for solving certain inequalities in one variable that involve fractions. To justify the last statement, suppose that $N(x)$ and $D(x)$ are real polynomials having no common factors and define $F(x)$ and $G(x)$ by the equations

$$F(x) = \frac{N(x)}{D(x)} \quad \text{and} \quad G(x) = N(x)D(x).$$

If a is any real number such that $N(a) \neq 0$ and $D(a) \neq 0$, then $F(a)$ and $G(a)$ are also real numbers and they have the same sign. That is, they are both positive or they are both negative. Furthermore if $N(x)$ and $D(x)$ are each factored completely into a product of real linear and real quadratic factors we see that $F(x)$ and $G(x)$ involve identical factors. Hence

$$F(x) < 0 \leftrightarrow G(x) < 0 \quad \text{and} \quad F(x) > 0 \leftrightarrow G(x) > 0.$$

In other words we can solve the inequalities $F(x) < 0$ and $F(x) > 0$ by solving a polynomial inequality. It is important to point out in this connection that the inequalities $F(x) \leq 0$ and $G(x) \leq 0$ will not be equivalent if $D(x)$ has any real zeros, however, the solution set of $F(x) \leq 0$ is always a subset of the solution set of $G(x) \leq 0$, the only difference in any event being that the real zeros of $D(x)$ belong to solution set of $G(x) \leq 0$ but not to the solution set of $F(x) \leq 0$. A similar statement can be made regarding the inequalities $F(x) \geq 0$ and $G(x) \geq 0$.

The above discussion applies to any inequality in one variable containing fractions if the inequality can, by combining two or more fractions into a single fraction in simplest form, be transformed into an inequality equivalent to $F(x) < 0$ or $F(x) > 0$ where $F(x)$ has the same meaning as in the previous paragraph.

Example. Solve the inequality

$$\frac{2x}{x+1} - \frac{x}{x-1} < \frac{4}{x^2-1}.$$

Solution:

$$\frac{2x}{x+1} - \frac{x}{x-1} < \frac{4}{x^2-1} \leftrightarrow \frac{2x}{x+1} - \frac{x}{x-1} - \frac{4}{x^2-1} < 0$$

$$\leftrightarrow \frac{x^2 - 3x - 4}{(x+1)(x-1)} < 0$$

$$\leftrightarrow \frac{(x+1)(x-4)}{(x+1)(x-1)} < 0$$

$$\leftrightarrow \frac{x-4}{x-1} < 0$$

$$\leftrightarrow (x-4)(x-1) < 0.$$

It follows from the definition of equivalent inequalities and Theorem 4.18, Part 1, that

$$\left\{ x \left| \frac{2x}{x+1} - \frac{x}{x-1} < \frac{4}{x^2-1} \right. \right\} = \{x \mid (x-4)(x-1) < 0\} = (1, 4).$$

EXERCISES

Solve each of the following inequalities.

1. $(x+3)(x-2) < 0$.
2. $(x-1)(x-5) \geq 0$.
3. $(3x+7)(2x-5) \leq 0$.
4. $x^2 - 3x - 4 < 0$.
5. $x^2 + x < 4x + 10$.
6. $5x^2 - 2x - 24 < 0$.
7. $4x^2 - x + 2 < x^2 + 7x + 5$.
8. $2x^2 - 3x > 14$.
9. $(x+1)(x+2) < 6$.
10. $3x^2 - 27 < 0$.
11. $4x^2 - 4x + 1 > 0$.
12. $x^2 - 6x + 9 \leq 0$.
13. $x^2 - 2x + 2 > 0$.
14. $x^2 - 3x + 4 < 0$.
15. $x(x-3) > 2x - 6$.
16. $x^2 - 5 \geq 0$.
17. $x^2 - 2x - 4 < 0$.
18. $3x^2 - 7x - 2 < 0$.
19. $(x+2)(x-2)(x-4) < 0$.
20. $(x-3)(x-5)(x-7) \leq 0$.

21. $(3x+1)(2x-1)(x-3) \leq 0$.
22. $(x+1)(x-1)(x-3)(x-5) < 0$.
23. $2x^3 - 9x^2 + 7x + 6 > 0$.
24. $x^3 + 11x > 6x^9 + 6$.
25. $(x+1)^3(x-2)(x-5)^2 < 0$.
26. $(x+2)^5(x-1)^3(x-3)^7 < 0$.
27. $(x+3)(x+1)(x-1)(x-2)(x-4) > 0$.
28. $2x^4 - 5x^3 < 11x^2 - 20x - 12$.

29. $\dfrac{x+2}{(x-2)(x-4)} < 0$.

30. $\dfrac{(3x+1)(x-3)}{2x-1} \leq 0$.

31. $\dfrac{(x-1)(x-5)}{(x+1)(x-3)} < 0$.

32. $\dfrac{(2x+3)(x^2 - 5x + 8)}{(3x-4)(2x^2 + 3x + 2)} > 0$.

33. $\dfrac{4}{x-3} < \dfrac{3}{2x-5}.$

34. $x - \dfrac{3}{x} < 2.$

35. $\dfrac{2x-3}{x-2} + \dfrac{x+3}{3x-2} > 0.$

36. $\dfrac{2}{x} + 1 < \dfrac{9}{x+2}.$

V

RELATIONS, FUNCTIONS AND GRAPHS

1 A PREVIEW

As we go about our daily activities we are constantly in situations in which we observe that two quantities are related to each other in such a way that a value of the one corresponds to a value of the other, and that a change in one produces a corresponding change in the other. For example, the weekly income of a wage earner, paid by the hour, varies with the number of hours per week he works. The distance you can drive your car in five hours varies with the average speed at which you drive, the cost of coffee varies with the size of the crop, if water is heated to boiling and then allowed to cool, its temperature varies with the time of cooling, the heat lost by radiation from a steam pipe varies with the thickness of the pipe.

It is easy to see how this list might be extended to any length, for the cases in nature, of quantities that are related, are unlimited. A large number are so involved and so complex that no elementary means of analyzing their modes of variation exists. On the other hand, so many cases of importance can be studied with the help of the proper mathematical tools that it is worthwhile to investigate the nature of such tools and to master the use of a few of the basic ones.

One of our chief goals will be to learn methods of solving two very basic variation problems. The first of these is to find the rate of change of one quantity with respect to a second quantity, when a relation between the quantities is known. This first problem we call "the rate problem"; the process of finding the rate is called *differentiation*. The second basic problem is the reverse of the rate problem: given the rate, to find a relation between the two quantities; in other words, given the rate at which one quantity changes with the other, to find the value of the first quantity for any given value of the second. The process of finding this relation is called *integration*. A mastery of the methods involved in solving these two basic problems will, as we shall see, enable us to solve with ease and precision a vast number of problems that would be very troublesome otherwise. A chapter will be devoted to each of these two problems and processes, but first we shall examine some aspects of the relations between two variables.

2   RELATIONS

In Section 1 we talked about two quantities being *related*, but failed to say precisely what is meant by such a statement. In this section we shall pursue the notion of related quantities a bit further; we start by stating some definitions that should help to clarify statements previously made regarding such quantities.

First, we shall understand the word *quantity*, as used above, to mean a variable whose range is some subset of R, the set of all real numbers.

Definition 5.1.   *Suppose X and Y are subsets of R. Also suppose x and y are variables such that $x \in X$ and $y \in Y$. The variable y is said to be related to the variable x, or a relation is said to exist between y and x, if there exists a rule of correspondence which assigns, or makes correspond, to each value of x belonging to X one or more values of y belonging to Y. Such a correspondence obviously pairs with each x in X one or more values of y, and hence generates a set of ordered pairs (x, y) of real numbers.*

A correspondence, or relation, between the variables y and x can be expressed by means of a verbal description, a formula, a list of pairs, or by one of many other means. But no matter how the relation is expressed, the end result is always a set of ordered pairs. It seems quite natural, therefore, to make the following definition.

Definition 5.2.   *A* relation *is a set of ordered pairs, (x, y), of real numbers. Also, a set of ordered pairs of real numbers is a relation.*

The set X consisting of all the first elements x of the ordered pairs (x, y) of a relation is called the *domain of definition of the relation*. The set Y consisting of all the second elements y of this set of ordered pairs (x, y) is called the *range of the relation*.

Example.   Consider the relation

$$A = \{(-1, 0), (1, 2), (1, -1), (2, 3), (2, -2), (3, 5)\}.$$

The domain of definition of A is the set $\{-1, 1, 2, 3\}$. The range of A is the set $\{-2, -1, 0, 2, 3, 5\}$.

Example.   Suppose $X = \{2, 3, 4\}$ and $Y = \{1, 2, 3\}$. List all the elements of the relation B if

$$B = \{(x, y) \mid y < x, x \in X, \text{ and } y \in Y\}.$$

Solution: $B = \{(2, 1), (3, 1), (3, 2), (4, 1), (4, 2), (4, 3)\}.$

3   THE FUNCTION CONCEPT

One of the most important concepts in mathematics is that of a special type of relation called a *function*.

Definition 5.3.   *A* function *is a set of ordered pairs* (x, y) *of real numbers such that to each value of the first variable,* x, *there corresponds one and only one value of the second variable,* y.

It follows from the definition of a function that every function is a relation but that not every relation is a function. In fact, a relation is a function if and only if any two of its ordered pairs with equal first elements have second elements which are also equal. For example, neither the relation A nor the relation B of the examples in the last section is a function. It should be noted, however, that a function may possess two or more ordered pairs with unequal first elements, even though their second elements are equal.

Example.   Let $C = \{(-1, 2), (1, 2), (2, 2), (3, 4)\}$. Relation C is a function.

Example.   Let $D = \{(-1, 2), (1, 2), (1, 3), (2, 2), (3, 4)\}$. Relation D is not a function, because it possesses the two pairs $(1, 2)$ and $(1, 3)$ with equal first element but unequal second elements.

As in the case of relations in general, the set X consisting of all the values of the first variable, x, in the ordered pairs (x, y) which define the function, is called the *domain of definition of the function*. The set Y consisting of all the values of the second variable, y, is called the *range of the function*. The variable x, which represents the numbers in the domain of definition of a function, is called the *independent variable;* the variable y, which represents the numbers in the range, is called the *dependent variable*. The dependent variable y is also called the *value of the function at x*.

It is important to recognize that, to determine a function, all that is really needed are the domain of the independent variable x and a rule which pairs with each number x in the domain one and only one number y in the range.

Example. Let the domain of x be the set $\{-1, 0, 1, 2, 3\}$. Now, suppose to each value of x we assign the number y and we apply the rule "square and add 3." The function thus defined is $\{(-1, 4), (0, 3), (1, 4), (2, 7), (3, 12)\}$. The range of this function is the set $\{3, 4, 7, 12\}$. The pair $(0, 3)$ is one member of the function; it is said, also, to belong to the function. The value of the function at $x = 0$ is 3 and the value of the function at $x = 2$ is 7.

4   FUNCTIONAL NOTATION

In our previous discussions of sets of elements we have used capital letters to designate the sets, being unmindful of whether the elements of the set were ordered pairs or not. However, it is conventional to use lower-case letters to designate functions and so in general we shall follow this practice and only on occasion use capital letters. A very convenient form of designating a function is represented by the symbol $f: (x, y)$, which is read "the function f whose ordered pairs are (x, y)." The phrase "y is a function of x" implies the same thing. Now, it has been mentioned in the last section that the dependent variable y is called the value of the function at x. It is customary also to represent the value of a function $f: (x, y)$ at x by the symbol $f(x)$, which is read "the value of f at x" or, more simply, "f of x." Since y and $f(x)$ are different names for the value of f at x, we can write $y = f(x)$, which is read "y equals f of x" or, more precisely, "y is the value of the function f at x." We must emphasize here that $f(x)$ does not mean f times x and is never so read.

In this connection, we must warn the student of the double usage of the symbol $f(x)$, prevalent in mathematical literature. The notation $f(x)$ is used to symbolize the function f and also to symbolize the value of the function. It is common practice to write such statements as "the function $f(x)$" or "the function $f(x) = 2x + 1$" as abbreviations of "the function f whose value at x is $f(x)$" and "the function f defined by the equation $f(x) = 2x + 1$." We shall be guilty of using such abbreviations on occasion, but it should cause no confusion if the student clearly understands that $f(x)$ is not the function but is the value of the function at x. The function is f, a set of ordered pairs. The equation $f(x) = 2x + 1$ is not the function but a rule for obtaining the value of the function f for each value of x in the domain. Hence, if $x = 2$, then $f(2) = 2(2) + 1 = 5$; that is, $f(2)$ represents the value of the function f at $x = 2$. Similarly, we would represent the value of f at $x = a$ by $f(a)$ and we would evaluate $f(a)$ by replacing x by a thus: $f(a) = 2a + 1$.

It will be recalled that the symbols $f(x)$, $g(x)$, $u(x)$, and $v(x)$ were introduced in Section 2, Chapter IV, to represent polynomials. Since each polynomial in one variable, say x, can be interpreted as the value of a function at x, we were then just using functional notation. The following two examples illustrate the force and convenience of functional notation.

Example. Suppose that $f:(x, y)$ is defined by the equation $f(x) = x^2 - 5x + 2$. Then

$$f(2) = (2)^2 - 5(2) + 2 = -4,$$
$$f(0) = (0)^2 - 5(0) + 2 = 2,$$
$$f(-3)^2 = (-3)^2 - 5(-3) + 2 = 26,$$
$$f(4 + h) = (4 + h)^2 - 5(4 + h) + 2,$$
$$- 16 + 8h + h^2 - 20 - 5h + 2,$$
$$= h^2 + 3h - 2.$$

Example. If $f(x) = x/(x - 1)$, what are $f(2), f(-1), f(x^2)$, and $f(1/x)$?

Solution: $f(2) = \dfrac{2}{2 - 1} = 2,$

$$f(-1) = \frac{-1}{-1 - 1} = \frac{1}{2},$$

$$f(x^2) = \frac{x^2}{x^2 - 1},$$

$$f\left(\frac{1}{x}\right) = \frac{1/x}{1/x - 1} = \frac{1}{1 - x}.$$

In our discussion we have used the letter f to represent the function, the letter x to represent the independent variable, and the letter y to represent the dependent variable. These are the letters customarily used to represent functions and variables in general: "a function," "the function," "any function," etc. Any other letters would have served equally well, and many others will be used at various times throughout the remainder of this text, especially when we are speaking of some particular variable or particular function.

It is quite possible for two or more quantities under discussion to be functions of the same independent variable. In such a case it would be necessary, to avoid confusion, to represent each different function and each different quantity by different letters. For example, suppose you leave a certain place at a certain time with a full tank of gas in your car. Suppose, further, that you drive at a certain rate of speed. The distance traveled, D miles, and the amount of gasoline, N gallons, remaining in your tank after t hours are each a function of t. Symbolically, this may be written

$$D = f(t) \qquad \text{and} \qquad N = g(t).$$

Here it is necessary to use different letters f, g, D, and N, because the two functions are different and the two dependent variables are different.

So far we have restricted our definition of a function to that of one independent variable. However, it is easy to see how our definition and also our notation could be generalized so as to describe functions of any number of variables. Also, it is easy to cite examples of quantities that are functions of more than one independent variable. For example, the area A of a triangle is a function of its base b and altitude h or, expressed in functional notation, $A = f(b, h)$; the volume V of a rectangular box is a function of its length l, width w, and height h or, in symbols, $V = g(l, w, h)$. In this text we shall be concerned primarily with functions of a single independent variable. We turn next to a discussion of some common methods of expressing the rules which define such functions.

5   RULES USED IN DEFINING FUNCTIONS

It has already been pointed out that a function is usually determined by the domain and a rule (last example in Section 3). A rule may be given in many ways but the following are the four most common.

A Verbal Statement: We may say that the cost p in cents, of sending a letter by first-class mail, is a function of its weight w in ounces. Here w is the independent variable and its domain is the set of all positive real numbers. The rule is: the rate of postage on first-class mail is 6 cents per ounce or a fraction thereof. Thus the postage on a letter weighing 2.3 ounces is 18 cents. Hence (2.3, 18) is a number pair belonging to our function.

A Formula or an Equation: This is usually the most desirable means of stating a rule because of its simplicity and convenience. When a rule is stated in words, we usually try to translate it into a formula or an equation for ease in using.

A Table of Values: The rule here is, "Look it up in the table."

A Graph: The rule here is "Read it from the graph." This and the last two are, for our purposes, the most important ways of giving a rule, and they will be discussed in more detail in the following sections.

6   FUNCTIONS DEFINED BY A FORMULA OR AN EQUATION

Right now we should like to emphasize one very important fact, namely, that no matter what method is used for stating the rule of correspondence, a function is not completely known until we know precisely its domain of definition and its range. The range of a function usually either is obvious or can be determined by little effort, particularly when the rule is given by means of an equation or formula. As a matter of fact, it is quite conventional to not mention either the domain or the range. This is not only legitimate but really time-saving, provided we have a definite agreement in advance on what assumptions are being made concerning the domain and range.

For our purposes in this text we shall make the following *agreement:* When only the rule is given in defining a function, the domain and range of the function are the largest subsets of the real number system for which the rule is valid.

Example. Let $f: (x, y)$ be defined by the equation $f(x) = 2x + 1$. We are assuming here that the domain of definition X is the set of all the real numbers.

Example. Suppose $f: (x, y)$ is defined by $y = \sqrt{x - 3}$. Since by agreement y must be real, it follows that $x - 3 \geq 0$. Hence the domain X obviously is the set $\{x \mid x \geq 3\}$. Recalling the definition of the symbol $\sqrt{a}$, where $a \geq 0$, we have $\sqrt{x - 3} \geq 0$ if $x \geq 3$. Therefore, the range Y is the set $\{y \mid y \geq 0\}$.

Example. If $y = f(x) = 1/(x - 1)$, what are the domain and the range of f?

Solution: The value of the function is not defined at $x = 1$, for $f(1)$ equals $1/(1 - 1)$, which is $1/0$, and division by zero is not defined. Thus, the domain is the set $X = \{x \mid x \neq 1\}$. To obtain the range we solve for x by writing

$$xy - y = 1,$$
$$xy = 1 + y,$$

$$x = \frac{1 + y}{y}.$$

This shows that y cannot be zero. Therefore the range is the set $Y = \{y \mid y \neq 0\}$.

Example. If $y = f(x) = x^2 - 2x$, what are the domain and the range of f?

Solution: The domain here is, obviously, the set of all real numbers. To find the range we solve the quadratic equation

$$x^2 - 2x - y = 0$$

for x, keeping in mind that x must be a real number. Solving for x by means of the quadratic formula we get

$$x = \frac{2 \pm \sqrt{4 + 4y}}{2} = 1 \pm \sqrt{1 + y}.$$

We see that x is real if and only if $y \geq -1$. Hence the range is the set $Y = \{y \mid y \geq -1\}$.

Example. Consider the function $f: (x, y)$ defined by the equation $y = 4$. Since the domain is not explicitly stated, it is, according to our agreement, the set consisting of all the real numbers. The range is the set $Y = \{4\}$. In other words, the function f has the same value for every x in the domain. We call such a function a *constant* function.

Definition 5.4. *A function $f: (x, y)$ is called a* constant function *if its range Y consists of a single element, that is, of one and only one real number.*

7 FUNCTIONS DEFINED BY A TABLE OF VALUES

A very simple way to show how one quantity varies with another is by means of a table of values. In fact, this is such a forceful and convenient way of conveying certain types of information that we see it in use every day. To cite just a few such examples: the daily paper may have a table showing the hourly temperature for the past 24 hours, the United States Series E Savings Bond has on it a table showing its redemption value each half-year until maturity, perhaps the local water bill has printed on it a table showing how the cost of water varies with the number of gallons used, the parcel post clerk consults a table to see how much postage to put on your package, the clerk in the store refers to a table, posted in a convenient spot near the cash register, to see how much sales tax is due on your purchase, the income tax for incomes of less than $5000 can be read from a tax table. For examples of tables of values that will be more immediately interesting to us in this course, we may turn to the tabular Appendix near the back of this book. A detailed discussion of these tables will be given later in the text. Here we point out, and wish to emphasize, that some rather complicated formulas were used to compute the entries in each table and, strictly speaking, we should think of the formula used in each case as being the rule; however since it will be unnecessary for us to concern ourselves with these formulas we shall be content to take as our rule the simple command, "Look it up in the table."

When a function is defined by means of a table of values, it is very important to know whether the table gives the complete rule or whether the domain of definition of the function actually consists of all the numbers in some interval of the real number system while the table gives only the values of the function at certain selected points of the interval. The tables in the appendix are of this type. In the latter we may find the approximate value of the function at intermediate points by a method called interpolation, which will be described.

Examples of the two types of tables are given below.

Example. The following table shows the number of hotel rooms, N, that are let at a given rate, P dollars per day.

P	6	7	8	10	12	14
N	40	80	100	200	160	120

This table defines completely the function, in the sense that intermediate values are of no significance. The domain of definition is the set $\{6, 7, 8, 10, 12, 14\}$ and the range is the set $\{40, 80, 100, 120, 160, 200\}$.

Example.   A liquid is heated to 90°C and allowed to cool to room temperature. The temperature, $T°$, of the liquid after t minutes of cooling was that shown below.

t	0	2	4	6	8	10	12	14	16	18	20
$T°$	90	74	62	54	49	44	40	37	34	32	30

Since the liquid obviously was cooling throughout the interval of time $t = 0$ to $t = 20$, it seems reasonable to assume that the domain of t consists of at least all the numbers in the closed interval $[0, 20]$. This being assumed, one may then reasonably ask such questions as "What was the temperature of the liquid when t was 3.2?" or "How many minutes after cooling started was the temperature 50°?"

Interpolation by Proportional Parts: If we can assume that the domain of an independent variable includes not only the numbers given in a table but also all possible numbers between the smallest and largest of these given numbers, we say that the independent variable varies continuously. In such case we are often able to obtain by interpolation rather good approximations of the values of the function for numbers in the domain but not in the table. The most common type of interpolation is called interpolation by proportional parts and is best explained by means of an example. We shall use the table of temperatures given above and find by interpolation the temperature at $t = 3.2$.

Write in tabular form the two entries, the interpolated entry, and the distances between them, as shown below.

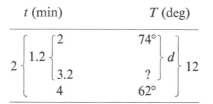

The method assumes that the ratios of the corresponding differences on the two sides of the table are equal. Thus,

$$\frac{d}{12} = \frac{1.2}{2},$$

from which it follows that $d = 7.2°$ or, rounded off to the nearest degree, $d = 7°$. The desired value of T is found by subtracting 7° from 74°, or $T = 74° - 7° = 67°$.

EXERCISES

1.   Determine which of the following relations are also functions, and for the functions give the domain and range.

    a. $A = \{(-3, 1), (-2, 0), (-1, 3), (-1, 6), (0, 5), (1, 7)\}$.
    b. $B = \{(1, 0), (1, -5), (1, 2), (1, 7), (1, 10)\}$.
    c. $C = \{(-5, 2), (-3, 2), (0, 2), (1, 2), (3, 2), (5, 2)\}$.
    d. $D = \{(5, 17), (8, 21), (10, 27), (13, 31), (15, 42), (8, 21)\}$.

2. A function $f: (x, y)$ is completely defined by the given table. Write down the elements of the function. Find $f(2)$ and $f(20)$.

x	-1	2	5	7	10	20
y	-8	1	10	16	25	55

3. If a function f is defined by the equation $y = f(x) = 2x^2 - 4$, what are $f(0)$, $f(-1)$, $f(a)$, $f(\frac{1}{2})$, and $f(-\frac{2}{3})$?

4. If $y = f(x) = x^3 - 2x^2 + 10$, what are $f(2)$, $f(-1)$, and $f(-3)$?

5. If $y = f(x) = 1 - x^2$, what are $f(0)$, $f(1)$, and $f(-1)$?

6. Assuming each of the following equations defines a function, find its domain and range in each case.

    a. $y = \sqrt{16 - x^2}$.   **b.** $y = \sqrt{5 + x}$.   **c.** $y = \dfrac{4}{x - 2}$.   **d.** $y = \dfrac{7}{x^2 - 9}$.

7. Could the given table define a function? If so, what is the domain of definition and what is the range? Which variable is the independent variable?

p	q
1	0
2	4
3	0

8. Let $g(x) = 3x^2 - 4x + 7$; find $g(t)$, $g(1/t)$, $g(t^2)$, and $g(1 - t)$.

9. Let $f(x) = x^2 + 5x - 3$; find **(a)** $f(x + h)$, **(b)** $f(x + h) - f(x)$, and **(c)** $(f(x + h) - f(x))/h$.

10. Let $F(x) = (1 - x)/(1 + x)$; find $F(x^2)$, $[F(x)]^2$, $F(2x + 3)$, $1/F(x)$, $F(1/x)$, $F[F(x)]$.

11. Let $f(t) = 4/(t + 2)$. Find:
    a. $f(3)$.   **c.** $f(3 + h) - f(3)$.

    b. $f(3 + h)$.   **d.** $\dfrac{f(3 + h) - f(3)}{h}$.

12. Which of the following equations define a function $f: (x, y)$?
    a. $y = 2x + 7$.   **e.** $y = 4$.
    b. $3x - 7y = 10$.   **f.** $x = 7$.
    c. $y = x^2$.   **g.** $x^2 + y^2 = 16$.
    d. $y^2 = 4x$.   **h.** $xy = 5$.

13. We say that the equation $A = \pi r^2$ expresses the area of a circle as a function of the radius of the circle.
    a. Express the area A of a square as a function of S, the length of one side.
    b. Express the volume V of a cube as a function of x, the length of one edge.
    c. Express the area A of an equilateral triangle as a function of S, the length of one side.
    d. A rectangle is inscribed in a circle of radius 10. Express the area A of this rectangle as a function of x, the length of one side of the rectangle.
    e. An open cylindrical can has a volume of 100π cubic inches. Express the total surface area of the can as a function of r, the radius of the base.

14. The given table shows the amount (A dollars) at the end of 20 years for a principal of $100.00 at compound interest and various rates (r percent).

r	2	3	4	5	6	7
A	148.59	180.61	219.11	265.33	320.71	386.97

Assuming r to be a continuous variable, use interpolation of proportional parts to find:

a. The value of A when $r = 3.5$ percent.
b. The value of r when $A = \$250.00$.
c. The value of A when $r = 4.6$ percent.

15. The table shows the positive square roots $(\sqrt{N})$ for several numbers N. Tell whether interpolation in this table is justified; if so, find **(a)** $\sqrt{4.64}$, **(b)** $\sqrt{4.76}$.

N	4.4	4.5	4.6	4.7	4.8
$\sqrt{N}$	2.0976	2.1213	2.1448	2.1679	2.1909

16. The temperature $T°$ in Knoxville at 12:00 noon, December 25, t years after December 25, 1935 is shown in the following table.

t	0	1	2	3	4	5	7
$T°$	29	52	59	48	43	57	51

a. Would you consider t a continuous variable in this case?
b. If this table defines the function $F: (t, T)$, what is the domain of definition of F?
c. What is $F(0)$? $F(3)$?
d. Does $F(2.5)$ have any significance?

8   GRAPHS OF RELATIONS AND FUNCTIONS

We learned in Chapter IV how a rectangular coordinate system may be used to establish a one-to-one correspondence between the points of the plane and the ordered pairs (x, y) of real numbers. In Section 22 of that chapter we defined and discussed in some detail the graphs of polynomials. We now define the graph of a relation.

Definition 5.5.   *The graph of a relation A is the set, of all the points in the plane, whose coordinates are elements of A.*

Example.   The graph of the relation

$$A = \{(-2, 1), (-1, 2), (1, 3), (1, 1), (-2, -1)\}$$

is shown in Fig. 5.1.

Since a function is a relation, the graph of a function f is the set of all points in the plane whose coordinates are elements of f. If the function is

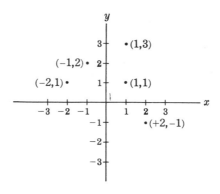

FIGURE 5.1

defined by means of a table of values we plot the points whose coordinates are the ordered pairs of numbers given in the table. It is conventional, in plotting the graphs of functions, to associate the values of the dependent variable with points on the vertical axis. It is not necessary that the scales on the two axes be the same; hence, we try to choose the scale for each axis that best fits the range of values of the variable to be represented. This is illustrated in Fig. 5.2 and Fig. 5.3, which show graphs of the function defined in the second example in Section 7.

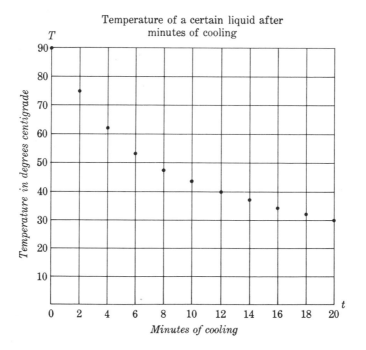

FIGURE 5.2

Figure 5.2 shows only the set of points whose coordinates are actually listed in the given table of values. If it is assumed that the table is the complete rule, then this set of *points* is the graph of the function. However, if it is assumed that the domain of the independent variable *t* includes all the numbers on the closed interval [0, 20], then we connect the plotted points by a smooth continuous curve and refer to the *curve* as the graph of the function; see Fig. 5.3.

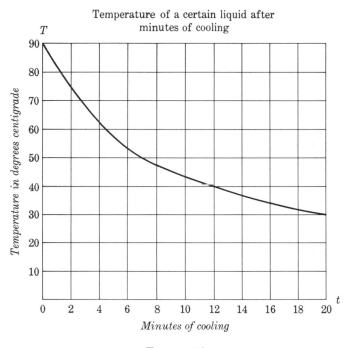

FIGURE 5.3

Graphical Interpolation: If the graph of a function is a smooth curve, we can read from it those values of the function corresponding to values of the independent variable that are not given in the table. Also, we can read the value or values of the independent variable for which the function has some particular value in its range and which are not listed in the table. Such readings are called graphical interpolation. How accurate these inter-polated values are depend, of course, on how accurately the graph is drawn and on how accurately one can read the scales. Thus, at the very best, an interpolated result is an approximation, but if care has been exercised in getting it, the accuracy is often sufficient for most purposes.

To illustrate the use of graphical interpolation, let us find from the graph of Fig. 5.3 the temperature when $t = 1$. Reading from the graph we see that $T = 82°$, approximately. When was the temperature 45°? Reading again from the graph, we see that when $T = 45°$, $t = 9$. That is, the temperature was 45° after approximately 9 minutes of cooling.

A curve which is the graph of a function is often referred to as a *function-graph*. A characteristic property of a function-graph is that if (x_1, y_1) is a point of the graph, then (x_1, y_2), $y_1 \neq y_2$, is not a point of the graph. That is to say, a vertical line cannot intersect a function-graph in more than one point, but a horizontal line can. See Fig. 5.4.

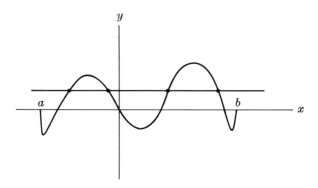

FIGURE 5.4

Just as not all relations are functions, not all graphs are function-graphs. For example the graph of Fig. 5.5 is not a function-graph.

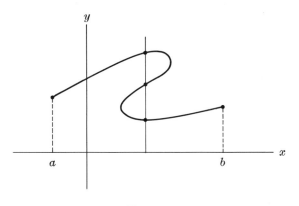

FIGURE 5.5

We shall end this section with some suggestions concerning the mechanics of constructing a graph. One of the purposes of the graph of a function is to show at a glance how one quantity varies with another. Hence it is most important that each axis be properly labeled showing what the varying quantities are and what the units on each scale represent. The first step in drawing the graph of a function is to draw and label the horizontal and vertical axes and to mark on each of them a scale suited to the table of data. Graph paper with 20 squares to the inch is probably best for most purposes. For the horizontal axis, select a scale unit of such length that the range of values of the independent variable will cover most of the page width, at least more than half. For the vertical axis, the unit should be so chosen that the total length of the axis need not be more than half the height of a sheet of regular graph paper. There are of course exceptions to this. The important thing is to spread the graph across the width of the paper as much as can be done conveniently and try to limit the height without distorting the shape of the graph. If the independent variable is not a continuous variable, then the graph of the function is just a set of isolated points. However, to make the graph easier to follow with the eye and to show the mode of variation a little better, the isolated points are usually joined by a series of segments of straight lines. This is often called a *broken-line* graph. It should be emphasized that on the broken-line graph only the plotted points have significance: the line segments connecting them serve only to aid the eye in following the series of points.

9   GRAPHS OF EQUATIONS INVOLVING TWO VARIABLES

To plot the graph of a function defined by means of a table of values, we simply plot the points whose coordinates are the ordered pairs of numbers listed in the table. If, however, we wish to plot the graph of a function defined by means of an equation, we must first make a table of ordered pairs which are elements of the function. These ordered pairs are determined from the equation defining the function; we substitute, for x in the equation, selected values from the domain of definition and then solve the resulting equation for the corresponding value of y. The ordered pair is called a *solution* of the equation. The set consisting of all the possible solutions of the equation is called the *solution set* of the equation. In this discussion we are concerned only with functions of a single independent variable, which means that any equation defining a function will involve exactly two variables, whether these are actual or implied.

In general, when a function is defined by an equation, the independent variable is a continuous variable and, hence, the solution set of the defining equation is infinite. To obtain the graph of a function in such a case, we usually find a small number of solutions of the defining equation, plot the corresponding points, and then join these points by a smooth graph.

Our discussion suggests the following general definition.

Definition 5.6.   *The graph of an equation involving two variables is the set of points consisting of all the points whose coordinates are elements of the solution set of the equation.*

Example.   Plot the graph of the equation $y = x + 120/x$, assuming $x > 0$.

Solution: We obtain the following table of ordered pairs (x, y).

x	4	6	8 ·	10	12	15	20
y	34	26	23	22	22	23	26

An examination of the table shows that, as x increases, y decreases at first and then increases. The turning point occurs between $x = 10$ and $x = 12$. Hence, it would probably be desirable to enlarge our table by finding at least the value of y for $x = 11$. With our equation we can get as many points on the graph between $x = 10$ and $x = 12$ as we need for locating the turning point fairly accurately. The graph is shown in Fig. 5.6.

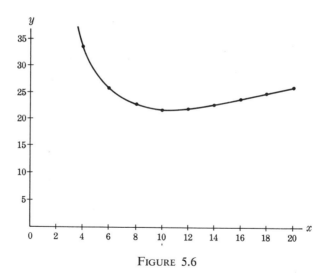

FIGURE 5.6

Example.   Plot the graph of the equation $y = 2$.

Solution: This problem may be restated as: Plot the graph of the function $f: (x, y)$ defined by the equation $y = 2$. This is a case in which the defining equation actually exhibits only the variable y; however, the second variable, x, needed to produce ordered pairs (x, y), is implied. Freely translated, our problem says "Given a rectangular coordinate system, locate all the points whose y coordinate, referred to this system, is 2." The solution set of the equation $y = 2$ obviously consists of ordered pairs, such as $(-25, 2), (-10, 2), (-3, 2), (0, 2), (5, 2), (50, 2)$, and so on. The graph of this set is a line two units above the x axis and parallel to it, as in

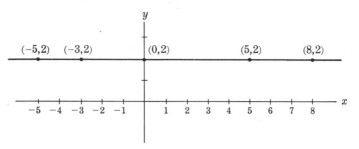

FIGURE 5.7

Fig. 5.7. This is a typical example of a constant function with the domain $X = R$ and the range $Y = \{2\}$.

Example.   Plot the graph of the equation $x = -2$.

Solution: Here the domain of the independent variable is $X = \{-2\}$, and the range is $Y = R$. Hence the graph is a line two units to the left of the y axis and

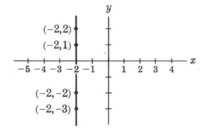

FIGURE 5.8

parallel to it, as shown in Fig. 5.8. It should be noted that the equation $x = -2$ defines a relation but does not define a function.

EXERCISES

In each of the problems 1 through 10, draw the graph of the given relation and specify which of the graphs are function-graphs.

1. $A_1 = \{(x, y) \mid y = x\}$.
2. $A_2 = \{(x, y) \mid y = |x|\}$.
3. $A_3 = \{(x, y) \mid x = 2\}$.
4. $A_4 = \{(x, y) \mid y = 5\}$.

5. $A_5 = \{(x, y) \mid |x| + |y| = 1\}$.
6. $A_6 = \{(x, y) \mid y = \sqrt{25 - x^2}\}$.
7. $A_7 = \{(x, y) \mid x = \sqrt{25 - y^2}\}$.
8. $A_8 = \{(x, y) \mid y = x + 1 \text{ and } -2 \le x \le 2\}$.

9. $A_9 = \{(x, y) \mid y^2 = x \text{ and } 0 \le x \le 3\}$.
10. $A_{10} = \{(x, y) \mid y = x - |x - 2|\}$.

11. Study the four graphs shown below and state for each whether it is or is not a function-graph.

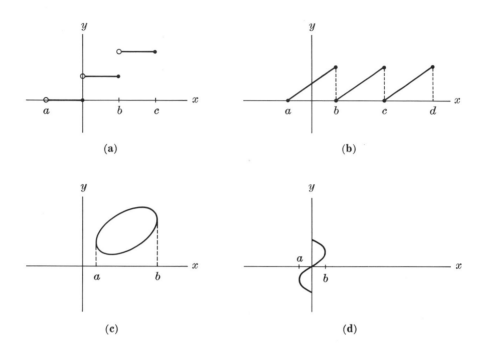

(a)   (b)

(c)   (d)

12. A manufacturing firm finds that the total cost, $C, of producing x units of a certain product is that shown in the following table. Draw the graph exhibiting the relationship between C and x. The curve thus obtained is called a *cost curve*.

x	10	20	30	40	50	60
C	127	233	343	457	575	697

About how many units could be produced for $300? Approximately what would be the cost of producing 35 units?

13. The average cost, $A per unit, for an output of x units of the product in Problem 12 is given in the following table. Plot the graph.

x	10	20	30	40	50	60
A	12.70	11.60	11.40	11.40	11.50	11.60

What output will give lowest average cost?

14. The following table shows the temperature, $T°$, at 12:00 o'clock noon, on December 25, in a certain city, t years after December 25, 1958. Plot the graph. Should the graph be a smooth curve?

t	0	1	2	3	4	5	6	7
$T°$	34	44	63	48	56	29	52	59

10 LENGTH AND MIDPOINT OF A LINE SEGMENT

We have seen how a rectangular coordinate system enables us to determine the position of points in a plane with the use of ordered pairs of numbers and how it enables us to describe lines and curves by means of equations. Since plane geometry basically is a study of points, lines, and curves in a plane, it is easy to see how a rectangular coordinate system could be a very important tool in it. In fact, geometry studied by means of algebra is a study by itself, called *analytic geometry;* in it the basic connecting link between the geometry and the algebra is a rectangular coordinate system. However, to use such a system in the study of geometry it is necessary that the unit used in marking the scale on each axis be a unit of distance. Furthermore, to use the coordinate system for calculating lengths of line segments which are not parallel to a coordinate axis, we must use the same scale on both axes.

Analytic geometry is essentially concerned with two major problems:

Problem 1.   Given an equation involving x and y, to plot its graph.

Problem 2.   Given a set of points in the plane, to find an equation having this set and only this set of points as its graph.

In the last section we gave, by means of examples, a procedure for handling the first of these. This procedure may be briefly summarized as follows.

Step 1:   Solve the equation for y in terms of x.

Step 2:   Substitute, for x, convenient positive and negative values (usually integers) from its domain and compute the corresponding values of y.

Step 3:   Make a table of values by arranging these pairs in order of magnitudes of the values of x.

Step 4:   Plot the points whose coordinates are these ordered pairs and connect them by a smooth curve in the order their coordinates appear in the table.

Remarks: In some cases it may be easier or more convenient to solve for x rather than y. If so, solve for x and then apply the rules given above interchanging the roles of x and y.

If solving for y in terms of x, or x in terms of y, involves a square-root radical, the double sign $\pm$ must be used with the radical. This usually results in giving two values of y for each value of x.

Although this procedure may be quite laborious, it should always work.

We shall, however, as we proceed, learn ways of obtaining the graphs of certain types of equations with a minimum amount of point-by-point plotting.

Distance Between Two Points

Before turning our attention to Problem 2 mentioned above we shall derive some formulas which we shall need. The first, and most important, of these formulas is called the *distance formula*. It is a formula for finding the distance between two points whose coordinates are known. To derive this formula we shall need to recall a very important theorem from plane geometry regarding right triangles, which we shall state without proof.

Theorem 5.1. (Pythagorean Theorem). *The sum of the squares of the lengths of the legs of a right triangle is equal to the square of the length of the hypotenuse.*

See Fig. 5.9. Our theorem may be stated in the simple form

$$a^2 + b^2 = c^2.$$

The converse of this theorem is also true: If the sum of the squares of the lengths of two sides of a triangle is equal to the square of the length of the third side, then the triangle is a right triangle.

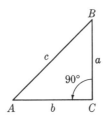

FIGURE 5.9

We are now ready to derive the distance formula. Let the points $P_1(x_1, y_1)$ and $P_2(x_2, y_2)$ be any two points in the plane and let $d(P_1, P_2)$ be the distance between P_1 and P_2. Draw a line through P_1 parallel to the x axis and a line through P_2 parallel to the y axis. These two lines meet in some point M (see Fig. 4.13) whose coordinates are easily found to be (x_2, y_1). The distance $d(P_1, M)$ between two points $P_1(x_1, y_1)$ and $M(x_2, y_1)$ on a line parallel to the x axis was defined, in Section 3, as $d(P_2, M) = |x_2 - x_1|$. Similarly, the distance $d(P_2, M)$ between two points $P_2(x_2, y_2)$ and $M(x_2, y_1)$ on a line parallel to the y axis was defined as $d(P_2, M) = |y_2 - y_1|$. The triangle P_1P_2M is a right triangle, the vertex of whose right angle is at M. Hence, by the Pythagorean theorem,

$$[d(P_1, P_2)]^2 = |x_2 - x_1|^2 + |y_2 - y_1|^2,$$
$$= (x_2 - x_1)^2 + (y_2 - y_1)^2,$$

or $d(P_1, P_2) = \sqrt{(x_2 - x_1)^2 + (y_2 - y_1)^2}.$

The last equation is known as the distance formula. It should be observed from the distance formula that, first, $d(P_1, P_2)$ is always positive or zero and that, second, since $(x_2 - x_1)^2 = (x_1 - x_2)^2$ and $(y_2 - y_1)^2 = (y_1 - y_2)^2$, the relation $d(P_1, P_2) = d(P_2, P_1)$ obtains. In other words, when the distance formula is used to find the distance between two given points, it makes no difference which of the two points is denoted by P_1 and which by P_2.

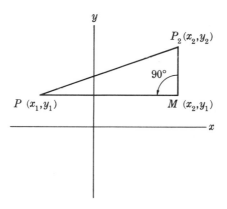

FIGURE 5.10

Example.   Use the distance formula to calculate the distance between the two points $A(-2, 1)$ and $B(4, 3)$.

Solution: Let $(x_1, y_1) = (-2, 1)$ and $(x_2, y_2) = (4, 3)$. Then $x_1 = -2$, $y_1 = 1$, $x_2 = 4$, and $y_2 = 3$. Substituting in the distance formula, we get

$$d(A, B) = \sqrt{[4 - (-2)]^2 + (3 - 1)^2} = \sqrt{6^2 + 2^2} = \sqrt{40}.$$

Remark: Since the pair of coordinates of a point completely specifies the point, it is common practice to designate the point $P_1(x_1, y_1)$ simply as the point (x_1, y_1), the point $P_2(x_2, y_2)$ as (x_2, y_2), and the distance between two points by the single letter d. Then the distance formula is written

$$d = \sqrt{(x_2 - x_1)^2 + (y_2 - y_1)^2}.$$

The Midpoint Formulas

By means of similar triangles, it is easy to show that the coordinates $(\bar{x}, \bar{y})$ of the midpoint of the line segment joining the points $P_1(x_1, y_1)$ and $P_2(x_2, y_2)$ are given by the formulas: $\bar{x} = (x_1 + x_2)/2$ and $\bar{y} = (y_1 + y_2)/2$. The derivation is left to the student. These formulas are called the *midpoint formulas*.

Example.   Find the coordinates of the midpoint of the line segment joining the two points $(-3, 2)$ and $(5, 5)$.

Solution: Let $(x_1, y_1) = (-3, 2)$ and $(x_2, y_2) = (5, 5)$. Applying the midpoint theorem, we have

$$\bar{x} = \frac{-3 + 5}{2} = 1 \quad \text{and} \quad \bar{y} = \frac{2 + 5}{2} = \frac{7}{2}.$$

The coordinates of the midpoint of the given line segment are therefore $(1, 7/2)$.

Example.   Using the distance formula only, show that the points $A(3, -3)$, $B(4, 0)$, $C(7, 3)$, and $D(6, 0)$ are the vertices of a parallelogram.

Solution: We need to recall a theorem from plane geometry, namely "If the opposite sides of a quadrilateral are equal, the quadrilateral is a parallelogram." Our problem now is simply one of showing that the opposite sides of our parallelo-

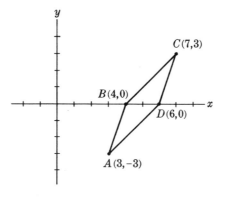

FIGURE 5.11

gram are equal. First let us plot the given points, Fig. 5.11. Now we use the distance formula to calculate the length of each side:

$$d(A, B) = \sqrt{(3 - 4)^2 + (-3 - 0)^2} = \sqrt{1 + 9} = \sqrt{10},$$
$$d(B, C) = \sqrt{(7 - 4)^2 + (3 - 0)^2} = \sqrt{9 + 9} = \sqrt{18},$$
$$d(C, D) = \sqrt{(7 - 6)^2 + (3 - 0)^2} = \sqrt{1 + 9} = \sqrt{10},$$
$$d(A, D) = \sqrt{(6 - 3)^2 + [0 - (-3)]^2} = \sqrt{9 + 9} = \sqrt{18}.$$

Our calculations show that

$$d(A, B) = d(C, D) \quad \text{and} \quad d(B, C) = d(A, D),$$

and that, hence, the quadrilateral $ABCD$ is a parallelogram.

EXERCISES

1.   Find $d(A, B)$ for each given pair of points.
   a. $A(5, 3)$, $B(-2, 1)$.   **b.** $A(5, 3)$, $B(-6, -3)$.

c. $A(4, -7), B(-6, -3).$ **e.** $A(0, 4), B(-5, 0).$

d. $A(-6, -3), B(0, 4).$ **f.** $A(-2, 1), B(0, 4).$

2. Find the coordinates of the midpoint of the line segment joining each of the pairs of points in Exercise 1.
3. Show that the points $(-3, 0)$, $(1, -2)$, and $(5, 6)$ are the vertices of a right triangle.
4. Show that the quadrilateral whose vertices are $(8, 0)$, $(6, 6)$, $(-3, 3)$, and $(-1, -3)$ is a parallelogram. Is it a rectangle? (*Hint:* Show that the diagonals are equal.)
5. Plot the graph of each given equation.

     a. $y - 2x.$ **c.** $y = x^3.$ **e.** $2x - 3y = 6.$

     b. $y = x^2.$ **d.** $y = \sqrt{25 - x^2}.$ **f.** $x^2 + y^2 = 4.$

6. If the lengths of two sides of a triangle are equal, the triangle is isosceles. Show that the points $(2, 4)$, $(5, 1)$, and $(6, 5)$ are the vertices of an isosceles triangle.
7. Three points $P_1(x_1, y_1)$, $P_2(x_2, y_2)$, and $P_3(x_3, y_3)$, such that $x_1 < x_2 < x_3$, lie on the same straight line if and only if $d(P_1, P_2) + d(P_2, P_3) = d(P_1, P_3)$. Show that the points $(-2, 4)$, $(1, 1)$ and $(3, -1)$ all lie on the same straight line.
8. A median of a triangle is a line segment joining a vertex to the midpoint of the side opposite that vertex. Find the lengths of the medians of the triangle whose vertices are the points $A(1, -2)$, $B(5, 4)$, and $C(9, 8)$.
9. The point P is the midpoint of the line segment joining the points P_1 and P_2. Find the coordinates of **(a)** P_1 if given $P(2, 3)$ and $P_2(7, 5)$ and **(b)** P_2 if given $P_1(-4, -7)$ and $P(2, -1)$.
10. Plot the graph of each of the following equations.

     a. $x^2 + 4y^2 = 16.$ **c.** $y = \dfrac{x}{1 + x}.$

     b. $x^2 - 2x = 4y - 9.$ **d.** $y^2 = 4x.$

11. Determine the value of c so that the graph of the equation $3x + 5y + c = 0$ will pass **(a)** through the point $(3, -2)$ and **(b)** through the point $(-4, 1)$.
12. Which of the given points are on the graph of the equation $y^2 = 12x$: $(3, 6)$, $(0, 0)$, $(-3, 6)$, $(12, -12)$, $(\frac{4}{3}, 4)$, $(48, 24)$?
13. How far is $(7, 4)$ from the midpoint of the line segment joining $(3, 2)$ and $(5, 14)$?
14. Express by an equation free from radicals the fact that the point (x, y) is equidistant from the two points $(1, 0)$ and $(6, 4)$.
15. Find the coordinates of a point 10 units' distance from the point $(-3, 6)$ and having 3 as its abscissa (two solutions).

11 THE SLOPE OF A LINE

Let L be any line in the x-y plane not parallel to the y axis, and let $P_1(x_1, y_1)$ and $P_2(x_2, y_2)$ be any two distinct points on L. We associate with the line L a number, m, called the slope of L, and define it as the ratio

$$m = \frac{y_2 - y_1}{x_2 - x_1}.$$

The importance of this ratio stems from the fact that the number m is independent of the two distinct points on L that are used to calculate it.

To see that this statement is true, let $P_3(x_3, y_3)$ be any third point on L distinct from P_1 and P_2 (see Fig. 5.12). Draw a line through P_1 parallel to the x axis

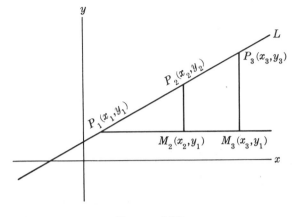

FIGURE 5.12

and draw lines through P_2 and P_3 parallel to the y axis and intersecting the first line in the points M_2 and M_3 respectively. The coordinates of M_2 are (x_2, y_1) and of M_3 they are (x_3, y_1). The triangles $P_1M_2P_2$ and $P_1M_3P_3$ are both right triangles that have an acute angle in common and are therefore similar. The ratios of the lengths of corresponding sides of similar triangles are equal. Hence,

$$\frac{y_2 - y_1}{x_2 - x_1} = \frac{y_3 - y_1}{x_3 - x_1}$$

which proves our statement. It should be emphasized that the definition of the slope of L and the statement just proved both assume that the difference of the two x coordinates and the two y coordinates are both taken with the points in the same order.

If we choose P_1 arbitrarily, then choose P_2 such that $x_2 - x_1 = 1$, our slope formula becomes $m = y_2 - y_1$. The slope of a line is therefore the algebraic change in y per unit increase in x, as the point P_1 moves along the line. Thus, if y increases as x increases, the slope is positive and the line rises to the right. On the other hand, if y decreases as x increases, the slope is negative and the line falls to the right, or rises to the left. If y remains constant as x increases, then the slope is zero and the line is parallel to the x axis.

Important.   1. *The slope of a line parallel to the x axis is zero.*
          2. *The slope of a line parallel to the y axis is not defined.*

Note that we deliberately avoided saying "a vertical line has no slope," because such a statement could lead some to the false conclusion that a vertical line has zero slope. Only lines parallel to the x axis have zero slope.

Since the slope m of a nonvertical line can be interpreted as the change in y per unit increase in x as the point (x, y) moves along the curve, we may also say that m is the rate of change of y per unit increase in x. This leads us to the following observation regarding functions: Every function whose graph is a straight line increases (or decreases) at a constant rate. Conversely, if a function increases (or decreases) at a constant rate, its graph is a straight line.

Parallel Lines

The common concept that most of us have about parallel lines is the following: Two lines in the same plane are parallel if they do not intersect. Using this as our definition of parallel lines, let us show that any two lines having the same slope are parallel. Let L be any line and let m be its slope. By the definition of a slope, the line L is rising (or falling if m is negative) m units for each horizontal unit increase. Take any point P not on L and draw a line L' through P having slope m. Now L' rises (or falls) m units for each horizontal unit increase. Hence, L and L' will never intersect. As a matter of fact, we might well define parallel lines as lines having the same slope.

Example. Find the slope of the line passing through the two points whose coordinates are $(-2, 5)$ and $(4, -1)$.

Solution: Let P_1 be the point $(-2, 5)$ and P_2 be the point $(4, -1)$; then $x_1 = -2$, $y_1 = 5$, $x_2 = 4$, and $y_2 = -1$. Hence, by definition,

$$m = \frac{y_2 - y_1}{x_2 - x_1} = \frac{(-1) - (5)}{4 - (-2)} = \frac{-1 - 5}{4 + 2} = -\frac{6}{6} = -1.$$

Example. Show that the line L_1 determined by the two points $(3, -1)$ and $(6, 8)$ is parallel to the line L_2 determined by the two points $(5, 2)$ and $(3, -4)$.

Solution: Let m_1 and m_2 be the slopes of L_1 and L_2 respectively; then

$$m_1 = \frac{8 + 1}{6 - 3} = 3 \quad \text{and} \quad m_2 = \frac{-4 - 2}{3 - 5} = 3.$$

Since $m_1 = m_2$, the lines L_1 and L_2 are parallel.

Perpendicular Lines

What is the relation between the slopes of two lines that are perpendicular? To answer this question, let us consider two lines, L and L', which intersect at $P(h, k)$ and neither of which is parallel to either of the coordinate axes. Let $A(a, b)$ be a second point on L and $B(c, d)$ a second point on L', both distinct from P. Draw the line segment joining points A and B (see Fig. 4.16). The lines L and L' are mutually perpendicular if and only if the triangle PAB is a right triangle with the segment AB as the hypotenuse. This will be true if and only if

$$[d(P, A)]^2 + [d(P, B)]^2 = [d(A, B)]^2,$$

that is, if and only if

$$(h - a)^2 + (k - b)^2 + (h - c)^2 + (k - d)^2 = (a - c)^2 + (b - d)^2.$$

When the squared terms in the last equation are expanded, this equation becomes

$$h^2 - 2ah + a^2 + k^2 - 2bk + b^2 + h^2 - 2ch + c^2 + k^2 - 2kd + d^2$$
$$= a^2 - 2ac + c^2 + b^2 - 2bd + d^2,$$

which is true if and only if

$$(h - a)(h - c) + (k - b)(k - d) = 0$$

or if and only if

$$\frac{k - b}{h - a} = -\frac{h - c}{k - d};$$

but the slope of L is

$$m = \frac{k - b}{h - a}$$

and the slope of L' is

$$m' = \frac{k - d}{h - c};$$

hence we have shown that the triangle PAB is a right triangle with AB as hypotenuse if and only if

$$m = -\frac{1}{m'}.$$

In other words, we have proved that two lines are perpendicular if and only if the slope of one of them is the negative reciprocal of the slope of the

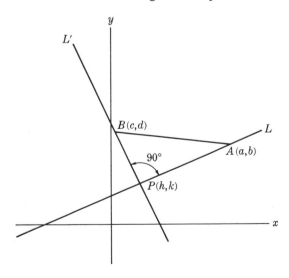

FIGURE 5.13

other. This equation gives us a simple method of testing two given lines for perpendicularity when the slopes of the lines are known or can be calculated.

Example.   Show that the line L_1 determined by $(3, -1)$ and $(9, 2)$ is perpendicular to the line L_2 passing through $(-2, 10)$ and $(5, -4)$.

Solution: Let m_1 be the slope of L_1 and m_2 the slope of L_2; then

$$m_1 = \frac{2 - (-1)}{9 - 3} = \frac{3}{6} = \frac{1}{2} \quad \text{and} \quad m_2 = \frac{10 - (-4)}{-2 - 5} = \frac{14}{-7} = -2.$$

Since $m_1 = -1/m_2$, the lines L_1 and L_2 are perpendicular.

EXERCISES

1.   In each of the following problems, plot the given points and find the slope of the line determined by them in each case.
  a. $(3, 1)$ and $(7, 4)$.   **d.** $(-3, 1)$ and $(4, 2)$.
  b. $(2, -3)$ and $(6, 5)$.   **e.** $(\frac{1}{2}, \frac{2}{3})$ and $(\frac{5}{6}, -\frac{3}{4})$.
  c. $(-2, 4)$ and $(6, -2)$.   **f.** (a, b) and (c, d).
2.   The line L passes through the point $(3, 2)$ and has slope $\frac{4}{7}$. **(a)** Find the coordinates of a second point on L. **(b)** Draw L.
3.   Find the length, slope and midpoint of the line segment joining the two points.
  a. $(-1, 1)$ and $(7, 7)$.   **b.** $(3, -2)$ and $(9, 8)$.
4.   Find the slope of the perpendicular bisector of the line segment joining $(2, 1)$ and $(6, 9)$.
5.   Draw the line having the given slope, through the given point.
  a. $(2, 0)$ with slope $\frac{1}{2}$.   **d.** $(0, 0)$ with slope 3.
  b. $(2, 0)$ with slope $-\frac{1}{2}$.   **e.** $(1, 1)$ with slope $-\frac{1}{3}$.
  c. $(0, 0)$ with slope $\frac{2}{3}$.   **f.** $(1, 2)$ with slope $-\frac{3}{2}$.
6.   By calculating slopes, show that the quadrilateral whose vertices are $(3, -3)$, $(4, 0)$, $(7, 3)$, and $(6, 0)$ is a parallelogram.
7.   Prove by means of slopes that the three points $(2, 3)$, $(6, -3)$, and $(-2, 9)$ all lie on the same straight line. Do the same for the three points $(1, -2)$, $(2, 0)$, and $(3, 2)$.
8.   Prove by means of slopes that the points $(5, 5)$, $(2, 8)$, and $(10, 10)$ are the vertices of a right triangle. Do the same for the three points $(0, 6)$, $(-3, 0)$, and $(9, -6)$.
9.   Show that $(10, 8)$, $(-3, 9)$, $(-4, -4)$, and $(9, -5)$ are the vertices of a square.
10.   Three vertices of a parallelogram are in the order $(2, 5)$, $(4, -2)$, and $(10, -1)$. Find the coordinates of the fourth vertex.
11.   If $(1, 0)$, $(3, 5)$, and $(7, 10)$ are three vertices of a parallelogram, what are three other points, each of which with the first three will form the vertices of a parallelogram?
12.   Given the triangle whose vertices are $A(2, 1)$, $B(6, -5)$, and $C(10, 3)$, show that the line segment joining the midpoints of AB and BC is parallel to AC and equal in length to $\frac{1}{2}d(A, C)$.
13.   Write an equation which states that the line joining the point (x, y) to the point $(-4, 0)$ is perpendicular to the line joining (x, y) to the point $(4, 0)$.
14.   Write an equation which expresses the fact that the point (x, y) is twice as far from the origin as it is from the point $(5, 4)$.

15. **Theorem:** *The diagonals of a rectangle are equal.* By using a rectangular coordinate system and a rectangle whose length is a units and width b units, prove the theorem. (*Hint:* Choose one vertex of your rectangle as the origin, and the axes to lie along adjacent sides of the rectangle.)

16. Use a rectangular coordinate system to prove that the diagonals of a parallelogram bisect each other.

17. Given a quadrilateral $ABCD$, show that the lines joining the midpoints of adjacent sides form a parallelogram.

18. Show that the conclusions stated in Exercise 12 are true for any triangle ABC.

12 EQUATIONS OF STRAIGHT LINES

In Section 11 we defined the graph of an equation as the set of all points in the xy plane whose coordinates satisfy the equation, that is, whose coordinates belong to the solution set of that equation. We now define the equation of a set of points in the xy plane, assuming such an equation exists.

Definition 5.7.   *The equation, if it exists, of a given set of points is the equation whose graph consists of all the points of the given set and only those points.*

In this section we wish to show that every straight line has an equation, in the sense of the above definition, and we wish to indicate a procedure for finding that equation when sufficient information about the line is known.

First we consider the lines in the xy plane that are parallel to the y axis. If a line L is parallel to the y axis, then every point on it has the same x coordinate. If this coordinate is k, it is obvious that the coordinates of every point on L satisfy the equation

(Eq. 1) $x = k.$

Furthermore, if a point is not on L, then its x coordinate is different from k and, hence, its coordinates do not satisfy Eq. (1). Thus, in accordance with Definition 4.10, Equation 1 is the equation of L.

If k is a positive number, L is a line parallel to the y axis and k units to the right; if k is negative, L is $|k|$ units to the left; if $k = 0$, L is the y axis. For example, the equation of a line parallel to the y axis and 5 units to the right is

$$x = 5,$$

while the equation of a line parallel to the y axis and 7 units to the left is

$$x = -7.$$

Thus, if a line is parallel to the y axis and its directed distance from y axis is known, we can write its equation.

Example.   Write the equation of a line parallel to the y axis and passing through the point $(-3, 2)$.

Solution: Since the line passes through $(-3, 2)$, the x coordinate of every point is -3; hence the equation of the line is $x = -3$.

Next consider a line L not parallel to the y axis, passing through the fixed point $P_1(x_1, y_1)$ and having the slope m. Let $P(x, y)$ be a variable point. The slope of a line passing through (x_1, y_1) and (x, y) is

$$\frac{y - y_1}{x - x_1}.$$

Therefore the point $P(x, y)$ is a point on L if and only if

$$\frac{y - y_1}{x - x_1} = m$$

(Eq. 2)   or $y - y_1 = m(x - x_1)$.

It is obvious from the manner in which Equation 2 was derived that the coordinates of every point on L satisfy Equation 2 and, conversely, every ordered pair (x, y) of numbers which satisfy Equation 2 represents the coordinates of a point on L. Hence L is the graph of Equation 2 and therefore Equation 2 is the equation of the line L. Since two equations are equivalent if and only if they have the same solution set, any equation equivalent to Equation 2 is also the equation of L.

Equation 2, $y - y_1 = m(x - x_1)$, is called the *point slope* form of the equation of L because it exhibits the coordinates of a fixed point (x_1, y_1) on L and also the slope m of L. Thus, if we know the coordinates of one point on a line and also the slope of the line, we may use the point slope form to write the equation of the line. Note that the three numbers x_1, y_1, and m in Equation 2 are constants while x and y are variables.

Example.   Write the equation of a line passing through the point $(5, 3)$ and having the slope -2.

Solution: Here $x_1 = 5$, $y_1 = 3$, and $m = -2$. Substituting in Equation 2 we obtain $y - 3 = -2(x - 5)$, or $2x + y = 13$.

Example.   Write the equation of the line determined by the points $(2, 3)$ and $(-1, 5)$.

Solution: We first find the slope $m = \dfrac{3 - 5}{2 - (-1)} = \dfrac{-2}{2 + 1} = -\dfrac{2}{3}$.

Now, using either of the two points, say $(2, 3)$, we substitute in Equation 2 and we get

$$y - 3 = -\tfrac{2}{3}(x - 2), \quad \text{or} \quad 3y - 9 = -2x + 4,$$

which when simplified becomes $2x + 3y = 13$.

Check: We may check our solution for errors in algebra by substituting the coordinates of each given point for x and y in our final equation: $2(2) + 3(3) = 4 + 9 = 13$ and $2(-1) + 3(5) = -2 + 15 = 13$.

Since the coordinates of each given point are a solution of our equation, the solution must be correct.

The y coordinate of the point of intersection of a line L and the y axis is called the y *intercept* of the line L. Suppose a line L with slope m intersects the y axis at the point $(0, b)$. The y intercept of L is b. The equation of L is

$$y - b = m(x - 0)$$

(Eq. 3)   or $y = mx + b.$

Equation 3 is called the *slope-intercept* form of the equation of a line. This form is of interest because it enables us to obtain by inspection the slope of a line from the equation of the line. To do this, we solve the equation of the line for y and then compare our equation with Equation 3. For example, suppose the equation of a given line is

$$3x + 5y = 20.$$

Solving for y, we write $5y = -3x + 20$, or

$$y = -\tfrac{3}{5}x + 4.$$

Comparing this last equation with Equation 3, we see that

$$m = -\tfrac{3}{5} \quad \text{and} \quad b = 4.$$

Hence $3x + 5y = 20$ is the equation of a line with slope $-\tfrac{3}{5}$ and y intercept 4.

It should be noted that if $m = 0$ then Equation 3 becomes $y = b$. That is to say, if a line is parallel to the x axis, its equation can always be written in the simple form $y = b$. Then, if b is positive, the line is b units above the x axis; if b is negative, the line is $|b|$ units below the x axis; if $b = 0$, the line is the x axis. Thus, the equation of the x axis is

$$y = 0.$$

It follows from the above discussion that the equation of every vertical line can be written in the form

$$x = k$$

and that the equation of every nonvertical line can be written in either of the equivalent forms

$$y - y_1 = m(x - x_1) \quad \text{and} \quad y = mx + b.$$

Since each of these equations is an equation of the first degree in x and y, that is, it contains only first powers of x and y, we conclude that every straight line has an equation and that the equation is of the first degree in x and y. Such an equation is said to be "linear in x and y." We wish, next, to show that every equation linear in x and y is the equation of a straight line.

Consider the general linear equation in x and y

(Eq. 4) $ax + by + c = 0,$

where a, b, and c are fixed real numbers but a and b are not both zero. If $b \neq 0$, this equation can be written in the form

(Eq. 5)
$$y = -\frac{a}{b}x - \frac{c}{b}.$$

In comparing this equation with Equation 3 we see that it is the equation of a line with slope $-a/b$ and y intercept $-c/b$. If $b = 0$ and $a \neq 0$, then Equation 4 can be written in the form

$$x = -\frac{c}{a}$$

which, according to Equation 1, is the equation of a line parallel to the y axis and $|-c/a|$ units from it. These results may be summarized in the following theorem.

Theorem 5.2. *Every straight line has an equation which is linear in x and y and, conversely, every linear equation in x and y is the equation of a straight line.*

We are now able to solve the following two problems: (a) given a straight line, find its equation; (b) given a linear equation in x and y, draw its graph.

Example. Write the equation of a line passing through the point $(2, -3)$ and parallel to the line whose equation is $5x - 2y = 7$.

Solution: To write the equation of a line we need the coordinates of a point on the line and the slope of the line if it has a slope. Since our line is parallel to the line $5x - 2y = 7$, it has the same slope as this line. We find the slope by solving for y:

$$2y = 5x - 7 \quad \text{or} \quad y = \tfrac{5}{2}x - \tfrac{7}{2}.$$

Hence the slope is $\tfrac{5}{2}$. Now, by using this slope and the given point $(2, -3)$ we can write

$$y + 3 = \tfrac{5}{2}(x - 2) \quad \text{or} \quad 2y + 6 = 5x - 10,$$

which when simplified becomes $5x - 2y = 16$.

Example. Draw the graph of the line whose equation is $3x - 5y = 10$.

Solution: Since we know the graph is a straight line, two points are sufficient to determine the line. A third point is desirable, as a check. To find the coordinates of three points on our line, we solve the given equation for y, obtaining $y = \tfrac{3}{5}x - 2$, and then substitute any three convenient values for x, preferably ones that give integers as coordinates. In this case x equals -5, 0, and 5, gives the table

x	-5	0	5
y	-5	-2	1

The graph of the line is shown in Fig. 5.14.

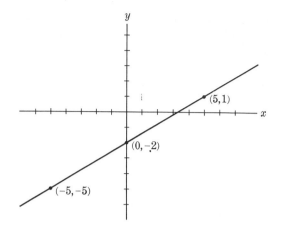

FIGURE 5.14

EXERCISES

Find the equation of each of the straight lines described in Problems 1–6.

1. Passing through (1, 1) with slope
   a. $m = 2$.   **b.** $m = -1$.   **c.** $m = \frac{3}{5}$.   **d.** $m = -\frac{2}{3}$.   **e.** $m = 0$.
2. Having y intercept 3 and slope $\frac{1}{2}$.
3. Having y intercept 3 and x intercept 4.
4. **a.** Parallel to y-axis and 4 units to left of it.
   b. Parallel to y-axis and 7 units to right of it.
5. Parallel to x-axis and 5 units below it.
6. Passing through (3, −2) and
   a. parallel to y-axis.   **d.** parallel to the line $5x + 7y = 8$.
   b. parallel to x-axis.   **e.** perpendicular to the line $4x + 5y = 10$.
   c. through (7, 4).
7. Each of the following pairs of points determines a line. Write its equation.
   a. (2, 1), (7, 4).   **c.** (−3, 2), (4, 7).   **e.** (0, 0), (4, 3).
   b. (−5, −2), (−1, −4).   **d.** ($\frac{5}{2}$, $\frac{1}{2}$), (8, 5).   **f.** (0, 0), (a, b).
8. Write the equation of the perpendicular bisector of the line segment joining the pair of points
   a. (1, 2), (5, 6).   **b.** (−2, 3), (4, −1).   **c.** (−8, −3), (2, 7).
9. Show that an equation of the line whose x-intercept is $a \neq 0$ and whose y-intercept is $b \neq 0$ is $\dfrac{x}{a} + \dfrac{y}{b} = 1$.
10. Express by an equation free from radicals the condition that the point (x, y) is equidistant from the two points (1, 8) and (9, 2).
11. Show that if $a \neq 0$ and $b \neq 0$, the lines $ax + by = c$ and $bx - ay = d$ are perpendicular. Use this fact to write the equation of a line passing through the point (1, 1) and perpendicular to the line $4x - 7y = 5$.
12. Sketch the graph of each given equation.
    a. $3x + 2y = 6$.   **d.** $x + 4 = 0$.   **g.** $7x + 4y = 15$.
    b. $3x + y = 4$.   **e.** $2x - 3y = 0$.   **h.** $y^2 - 9 = 0$.
    c. $5x - 4y = 20$.   **f.** $y - 6 = 0$.

13. Find by inspection the slope of each of the following lines.
  a. $3x - y = 7.$ **c.** $x + 5y + 8 = 0.$ **e.** $3x - 2y = 0.$
  b. $2x + 3y - 4 = 0.$ **d.** $4x + 3y = 15.$ **f.** $7x - 8y = 20.$

14. Write the equations of the medians of the triangle with vertices at $A(0, 1)$, $B(4, 5)$, and $C(6, -3)$.

15. Write the equations of the perpendicular bisectors of the sides of the triangle ABC given in Exercise 14.

16. Write the equations of the three lines, each passing through a different vertex and each perpendicular to the opposite side of the triangle ABC of Exercise 14.

17. Show that the line $3x - 2y + 5 = 0$ is:
  a. Parallel to the line $12x - 8y = 17$.
  b. Perpendicular to the line $4x + 6y - 3 = 0$.
  c. The same as the line $9x - 6y + 15 = 0$.

18. Show that the following lines form the sides of a rectangle: $x - 2y = 9$, $6x + 3y = 14$, $4x - 8y = 15$, and $2x + y + 5 = 0$.

19. The three points $(-2, -2)$, $(10, -8)$, and $(7, 1)$ determine a circle. Find the equations of two different lines, each of which passes through the center of the circle. Using your knowledge gained in high school algebra, of solutions of simultaneous equations, find the coordinates of the center of the circle.

20. a. Find the equation of a line L passing through $(1, 5)$ and perpendicular to the line L' whose equation is $x + y = 2$.
  b. Determine the coordinates of the point of intersection of lines L and L' in part **a**.
  c. Use the distance formula to find the perpendicular distance from the line L' in part **a** to the point $(1, 5)$.

13 EQUATIONS OF CIRCLES, PARABOLAS, ELLIPSES AND HYPERBOLAS

In Section 10 of this chapter we stated two major problems with which analytic geometry is concerned. The second of these problems was, given a set of points in the plane, to find an equation having this set and only this set of points as its graph. We refer to such an equation as the equation of the set of points. In the last section we learned how to write the equation of a line in the coordinate plane having given enough conditions to completely determine the line. In this section we shall define four other special sets of points and determine an equation for each.

Definition 5.8.   *The set of all points in the plane equidistant from a fixed point is called a* circle. *The fixed point is called the* center *of the circle and the common distance of each point of the circle from the center is called the* radius *of the circle.*

To find an equation for a given circle of radius r, let us choose a rectangular coordinate system in the plane such that the center of the circle is at the point (h, k), where h and k are measured in the same units as the given radius r. A point $P(x, y)$ is a point on the circle if and only if

$$\sqrt{(x - h)^2 + (y - k)^2} = r,$$

and by squaring, this equation reduces to

(1) $$(x - h)^2 + (y - k)^2 = r^2.$$

We call this the *standard form* for the equation of the circle. This form exhibits the coordinates of the center and the radius of the circle and hence is most useful as a formula for writing equations of specific circles.

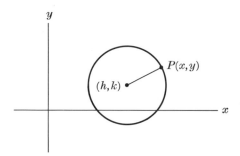

FIGURE 5.15

Example. Write an equation of the circle with center at $(2, -3)$ and radius equal 4.

Solution: Here $h = 2, k = -3$, and $r = 4$. Substituting these values in Equation (1) we obtain

$$(x - 2)^2 + (y + 3)^2 = 16.$$

Obviously any equation that can, by performing algebraic operations be reduced to the form of Equation (1) is the equation of a circle. For example, consider the equation

(2) $$Ax^2 + Ay^2 + Bx + Cy + D = 0, \qquad A \neq 0.$$

Now divide both sides by A, which gives

(3) $$x^2 + y^2 + ax + by + c = 0,$$

where $a = \dfrac{B}{A}, b = \dfrac{C}{A}$, and $c = \dfrac{D}{A}$, and then completing the square in x and in y, Equation (3) can be reduced to

(4) $$\left(x + \frac{a}{2}\right)^2 + \left(y + \frac{b}{2}\right)^2 = \frac{a^2}{4} + \frac{b^2}{4} - c.$$

Comparing this equation with Equation (1) we see that it is the equation of a circle with center at $\left(-\dfrac{a}{2}, -\dfrac{b}{2}\right)$ and radius

$$r = \sqrt{\frac{a^2}{4} + \frac{b^2}{4} - c}$$

provided, of course, that $\frac{a^2}{4} + \frac{b^2}{4} - c$ is positive. If $\frac{a^2}{4} + \frac{b^2}{4} - c$ is negative, then Equation (3), and hence Equation (2), has no graph. That is, Equation (2) is not the equation of any set of points. In other words, if Equation (2) has a graph it is a circle. Thus to find the center and radius of a circle from its equation we proceed as we did in obtaining Equation (4).

Example. Find the center and radius of the circle

$$x^2 + y^2 - 6x + 4y - 12 = 0.$$

Solution: Completing the square in x and in y we obtain

$$x^2 - 6x + 9 + y^2 + 4y + 4 = 12 + 9 + 4$$

or

$$(x - 3)^2 + (y + 2)^2 = 25,$$

and hence the center is at $(3, -2)$ and the radius is $r = 5$.

Remark: It follows from the above discussion that the distinguishing features of an equation of a circle are: (1) the equation contains an x^2 term and a y^2 term; (2) the coefficients of x^2 and y^2 are identical; (3) it may or may not contain a first degree term in x or in y.

Definition 5.9. *The set of all points in a plane which are equidistant from a fixed point and a fixed line is called a* parabola. *The fixed point is called the* focus *of the parabola and the fixed line is called the* directrix *of the parabola.*

Suppose that the point F is the focus and the line L is the directrix of a given parabola. Obviously the form of an equation of this parabola will depend upon the location of the x and y axes relative to the focus and directrix. The simplest form of such an equation is obtained if we choose the origin of our coordinate system at the midpoint of the perpendicular drawn from F to the line L, and choose the x-axis parallel to L. See Fig. 5.16.

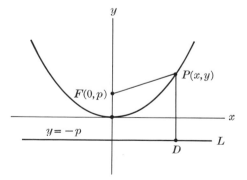

FIGURE 5.16

Denote the distance between F and L by $2p$, $p > 0$. A point $P(x, y)$ is a point on the parabola if and only if

$$FP = DP$$

or if

$$\sqrt{x^2 + (y - p)^2} = |y + p|.$$

Squaring

$$x^2 + y^2 - 2py + p^2 = y^2 + 2py + p^2$$

and simplifying we obtain

(5) $$x^2 = 4py$$

as an equation of the given parabola. The line which passes through the focus and is perpendicular to the directrix is called the *axis* of the parabola. The axis of the parabola discussed above is the y-axis. An inspection of Equation (5) reveals that the origin, $(0, 0)$, is a point of the parabola and since $p > 0$, then $y \geq 0$, and hence $(0, 0)$ is the lowest point on the parabola. This is the point on the parabola nearest the directrix. Such a point is called the vertex of the parabola. Also if (x_1, y_1) is a point on the parabola then $(-x_1, y_1)$ is also on the parabola. This shows that the axis of the parabola bisects every chord of the parabola that is perpendicular to the axis. Two points are said to be symmetric with respect to a line if the line is a perpendicular bisector of the segment joining them. Further, a set, S, of points is said to be symmetric with respect to a line L if for each point $A \in S$ there is a point $B \in S$ such that A and B are symmetric with respect to L. It follows from this definition that a parabola is symmetric with respect to its axis.

Suppose we choose a new coordinate system so that its axes are parallel to the corresponding axes in Fig. 5.16 but so that the vertex of the parabola

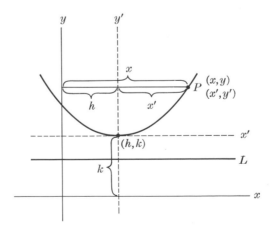

FIGURE 5.17

is at the point (h, k) referred to as the new axis. See Fig. 5.17. The equation of the parabola now becomes

(6) $$(x - h)^2 = 4p(y - k).$$

To see that this is true draw in the old coordinate axes using dotted lines and denote them by x' and y'. In terms of x' and y' the equation of the parabola, Equation (5), is

(7) $$x'^2 = 4py'.$$

Let P be a point on the parabola whose old coordinates are (x', y') and whose new coordinates are (x, y). It is obvious from the figure that

$$x = x' + h \quad \text{and} \quad y = y' + k,$$

or

$$x' = x - h \quad \text{and} \quad y' = y - k.$$

Substituting these values into Equation (7) it becomes Equation (6).

Expanding Equation (6) and solving for y we obtain

$$y = \frac{1}{4p} x^2 - \frac{h}{2p} x + \frac{h^2 + 4pk}{4p}$$

or

$$y = ax^2 + bx + c,$$

where $a = \dfrac{1}{4p}$, $b = -\dfrac{h}{2p}$, and $c = \dfrac{h^2 + 4pk}{4p}$, and since $p > 0$, then $a > 0$. This helps to verify a statement made earlier about the graph of $y = ax^2 + bx + c$.

If we interchange the positions of the focus and directrix and keep the same coordinate system the equation of the parabola will be

$$(x - h)^2 = -4p(y - k)$$

and the parabola will open downward. If we had chosen the y-axis to be parallel to the directrix and kept the vertex at (h, k) the equation of the parabola would have been

$$(y - k)^2 = 4p(x - h),$$

or

$$(y - k)^2 = -4p(x - h).$$

Definition 5.10. *The set of all the points in the plane the average of whose distances from two fixed points in the plane is a given positive number is called an* ellipse. *The two fixed points are called the* foci *and the midpoint of the segment joining them is called the* center.

To write an equation of an ellipse, let F and F' be the two fixed points, denote the distance between them by $2c$, and let $a > 0$ be the given number with $a > c$. Choose the line determined by F and F' as the x-axis and choose the midpoint of the segment joining F and F' as the origin. In this coordinate system the coordinates of F and F' are those shown in Fig. 5.18.

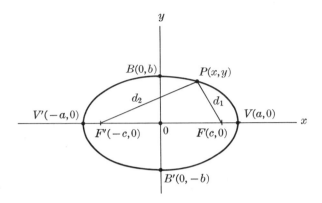

FIGURE 5.18

A point $P(x, y)$ will be a point on the ellipse if and only if

$$\tfrac{1}{2}(\overline{F'P} + \overline{FP}) = a$$

or

(8) $$\overline{F'P} + \overline{FP} = 2a.$$

$$\overline{PF'} = \sqrt{(x + c)^2 + y^2} \quad \text{and} \quad PF = \sqrt{(x - c)^2 + y^2}.$$

Substituting these values in Equation (8) we get

$$\sqrt{(x + c)^2 + y^2} + \sqrt{(x - c)^2 + y^2} = 2a.$$

To obtain an equivalent equation free from radicals we transpose the second radical to the right member and square, which produces

$$(x + c)^2 + y^2 = 4a^2 - 4a\sqrt{(x - c)^2 + y^2} + (x - c)^2 + y^2.$$

When we simplify the last equation we have

$$a\sqrt{(x - c)^2 + y^2} = a^2 - cx.$$

Squaring again gives

$$a^2[(x - c)^2 + y^2] = a^4 - 2a^2cx + c^2x^2$$

which when simplified becomes

$$(a^2 - c^2)x^2 + a^2y^2 = a^2(a^2 - c^2).$$

Since $a > c$, $a^2 - c^2 > 0$, so for convenience we let $b = \sqrt{a^2 - c^2}$ and we obtain as the equation of our ellipse

(9) $$b^2x^2 + a^2y^2 = a^2b^2.$$

Equation (9) is often written in the form

(10)
$$\frac{x^2}{a^2} + \frac{y^2}{b^2} = 1,$$

which is obtained by dividing both members of (9) by a^2b^2.

Any point whose coordinates satisfy Equation (10) is a point on the ellipse which is the graph of this equation. It is readily seen that if the coordinates of the point (x_1, y_1) satisfy Equation (10), then so do the coordinates of the points $(-x_1, y_1)$ and $(x_1, -y_1)$, hence our ellipse is symmetric with respect to both the x-axis and the y-axis. When $y = 0$, then $x = \pm a$, and when $x = 0$, $y = \pm b$. Hence the ellipse crosses the x-axis at the points $V(a, 0)$ and $V'(-a, 0)$ and it crosses the y-axis at the points $B(0, b)$ and $B'(0, -b)$. The segment VV' of length $2a$ is called the major axis of the ellipse and the segment BB' of length $2b$ is called the minor axis. The ends of the major axis, V and V', are called the vertices of the ellipse. If Equation (10) is solved in turn for x and then for y, we get

$$x = \pm \frac{a}{b} \sqrt{b^2 - y^2} \quad \text{and} \quad y = \pm \frac{b}{a} \sqrt{a^2 - x^2},$$

which shows that the permissible values of x and y are $-a \le x \le a$ and $-b \le y \le b$. Thus all the points of the ellipse lie inside or on the rectangle determined by the lines $x = -a$, $x = a$, $y = -b$, and $y = b$.

It should be noted that had we taken the line determined by the foci as the y-axis instead of the x-axis but retained the origin at the same place the equation of the ellipse would be

(11)
$$\frac{x^2}{b^2} + \frac{y^2}{a^2} = 1,$$

where a and b have the same significance as before.

Example.   Sketch the ellipse $\dfrac{x^2}{16} + \dfrac{y^2}{25} = 1$ and indicate the location of the foci.

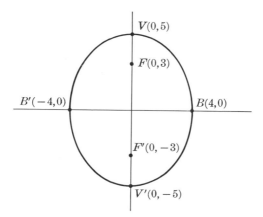

FIGURE 5.19

Solution: Remembering that $a > b$, and comparing our equation with Equation (11) we find that $a^2 = 25$, $b^2 = 16$, and $c^2 = 25 - 16 = 9$. Therefore $a = 5$, $b = 4$ and $c = 3$. The major axis is vertical and hence the coordinates of the foci are $(0, -3)$ and $(0, 3)$. See Fig. 5.19.

Suppose in Fig. 5.8 we relabel the coordinates axes shown there as x' and y' and then draw new x and y axes parallel to x'-axis and y'-axis respectively (see Fig. 5.20) and let (h, k) be the coordinates of the center of

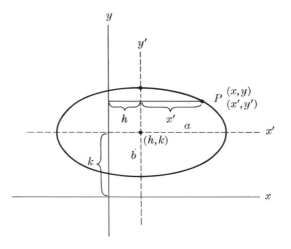

FIGURE 5.20

the ellipse referred to as the new axes. The equation of our ellipse in the x', y' coordinate system is

$$\frac{x'^2}{a^2} + \frac{y'^2}{b^2} = 1.$$

Now substituting the relations $x' = x - h$, $y' = y - k$ for x', y' we see that the equation of the ellipse referred to the x, y-system is

(12) $$\frac{(x - h)^2}{a^2} + \frac{(y - k)^2}{b^2} = 1, \qquad a > b.$$

A similar generalization of Equation (1) would give

(13) $$\frac{(x - h)^2}{b^2} + \frac{(y - k)^2}{a^2} = 1, \qquad a > b.$$

Equation (12) is called the *standard form* for the equation of an ellipse with center at (h, k) and major axis parallel to x-axis. If major axis is parallel to y-axis, then Equation (13) is the standard form.

In expanded form Equation (12) is

$$b^2x^2 + a^2y - 2b^2hx - 2a^2ky + b^2h^2 + a^2k^2 - a^2b^2 = 0$$

or

$$Ax^2 + By^2 + Cx + Dy + E = 0,$$

where $A = b^2$, $B = a^2$, $C = -2b^2h$, $D = -2a^2k$, and $E = b^2h^2 + a^2k^2 - a^2b^2$. Note that A and B are both positive but unequal.

Definition 5.11. *The set of all points in the plane, the absolute value of the difference of whose distances from two given points in the same plane is a given positive number 2a, is called an* hyperbola. *The two given points are called the* foci, *and the midpoint of the segment joining the foci is called the* center *of the hyperbola.*

Consider the hyperbola whose foci are $F(c, 0)$ and $F'(-c, 0)$. A point (x, y) is a point of the hyperbola if and only if

$$|\overline{F'P} - \overline{FP}| = 2a$$

or

$$|\sqrt{(x + c)^2 + y^2} - \sqrt{(x - c)^2 + y^2}| = 2a.$$

If we rationalize this last equation as we did in the case of the ellipse the result is

(14)
$$\frac{x^2}{a^2} - \frac{y^2}{b^2} = 1$$

where $b = \sqrt{c^2 - a^2}$. Since the points F, F', and P are the vertices of a triangle and since the difference in the lengths of any two sides of a triangle is less than the length of the third side, then we must have $a < c$. The ellipse crosses the x-axis in the points $V(a, 0)$ and $V'(-a, 0)$. It does not intersect the y-axis. The segment VV' is called the transverse axis and the points V and V' are called the vertices. If we solve Equation (14) for x and for y, we get

$$x = \pm\frac{a}{b}\sqrt{b^2 + y^2} \quad \text{and} \quad y = \pm\frac{b}{a}\sqrt{x^2 - a^2},$$

which shows that y can be any real number but x^2 cannot be less than a^2. In other words the graph extends infinitely far to the left and to the right but no point of the hyperbola lies between the lines $x = a$ and $x = -a$.

If the center of the hyperbola is at (h, k) and the x-axis is parallel to the transverse axis then an equation of the hyperbola is

(15)
$$\frac{(x - h)^2}{a^2} - \frac{(y - k)^2}{b^2} = 1,$$

but if the transverse axis is parallel to the y-axis, then the equation is

(16)
$$\frac{(y - k)^2}{a^2} - \frac{(x - h)^2}{b^2} = 1.$$

By expanding and renaming the coefficients, Equation (15) may be written in the form

$$Ax^2 + By^2 + Cx + Dy + E = 0,$$

where $A \neq 0$, $B \neq 0$, and A and B are opposite in sign.

We end this section by calling attention to two very important lines associated with an hyperbola called *asymptotes* of the hyperbola. These lines are the extended diagonals of the rectangle determined by the lines $x = a$,

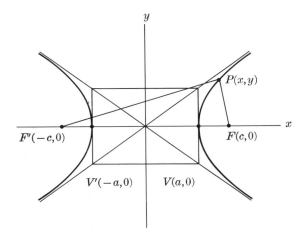

FIGURE 5.21

$x = -a$, $y = b$, and $y = -b$. See Fig. 5.21. The equations of the asymptotes are

$$y = \frac{b}{a}x \quad \text{and} \quad y = -\frac{b}{a}x.$$

To see how the asymptotes are related to the hyperbola consider the height of the asymptote and the height of the hyperbola in the first quadrant. For a given x, these heights are

$$y = \frac{b}{a}x \quad \text{and} \quad y = \frac{b}{a}\sqrt{x^2 - a^2}.$$

These two equations show that in the first quadrant the asymptote is above the hyperbola at each point for which $x \geq a$. However, as x increases the difference in the heights of the asymptote and the hyperbola decreases, and this difference in heights approaches zero as $x \to \infty$. To see that this is true, note that

$$\frac{b}{a}x - \frac{b}{a}\sqrt{x^2 - a^2} = \frac{b}{a}(x - \sqrt{x^2 - a^2})$$

$$= \frac{b}{a}\left[\frac{x^2 - (x^2 - a^2)}{x + \sqrt{x^2 - a^2}}\right] = \frac{ab}{x + \sqrt{x^2 - a^2}}.$$

But

$$\lim_{x \to \infty} \frac{ab}{x + \sqrt{x^2 - a^2}} = 0.$$

EXERCISES

Write the equation of the circle described in each of the problems 1–8.

1. center $(0, 0)$, radius 5.
2. center $(3, 1)$, radius 8.
3. center $(-5, 2)$, radius 7.

4. center $(-2, -1)$, radius 4.
5. center $(\frac{3}{2}, \frac{1}{2})$, radius 3.
6. center $(-4, \frac{2}{3})$, radius $\sqrt{8}$.

7. center at $(5, 2)$ and passing through $(1, 5)$.
8. The segment joining $(-1, 3)$ and $(3, 7)$ is a diameter.
9. Write the equation of the circle determined by the three given points.
   a. $(1, 7)$, $(8, 6)$, $(7, -1)$. b. $(-8, -3)$, $(8, 5)$, $(6, -1)$.
10. A tangent line to a circle at a point on the circle is perpendicular to the radius drawn to that point. Use this fact to find the slope of the tangent line to the circle $x^2 + y^2 = 25$ at the point $(-3, 4)$ and then find its equation.
11. Find the equation of the circle which passes through $(7, -8)$ and $(0, 9)$ and has its center on the line $x - 2y = 1$.
12. Find the center and radius of each of the following circles and sketch the graph.
    a. $x^2 + y^2 - 2x - 4y - 11 = 0$. d. $x^2 + y^2 - 4x = 0$.
    b. $x^2 + y^2 + 6x - 2y - 6 = 0$. e. $x^2 + y^2 + 6y = 0$.
    c. $4x^2 + 4y^2 - 12x - 20y + 9 = 0$. f. $x^2 + y^2 - 3x - 7y - 5 = 0$.
13. Sketch each of the following parabolas.
    a. $y = x^2$. d. $x^2 = -4y$.
    b. $x^2 = 8y$. e. $(x - 2)^2 = 12(y - 1)$.
    c. $y^2 = 4x$. f. $(x + 3)^2 = 8(y + 2)$.
14. Sketch each of the following ellipses.
    a. $\dfrac{x^2}{16} + \dfrac{y^2}{4} = 1$. d. $25x^2 + 9y^2 - 225$.

    b. $\dfrac{x^2}{16} + \dfrac{y^2}{49} = 1$. e. $\dfrac{(x - 2)^2}{25} + \dfrac{(y + 1)^2}{9} = 1$.

    c. $4x^2 + 9y^2 = 36$. f. $\dfrac{(x + 2)^2}{4} + \dfrac{(y + 1)^2}{16} = 1$.

15. Sketch each of the following hyperbolas and show its asymptotes.
    a. $x^2 - y^2 = 4$. c. $\dfrac{x^2}{4} - \dfrac{y^2}{9} = 1$.

    b. $y^2 - x^2 = 1$. d. $\dfrac{y^2}{16} - \dfrac{x^2}{9} = 1$.

16. Write each of the following equations in standard form and sketch its graph.
    a. $x^2 + y^2 = 6x - 4y$. d. $9x^2 + 4y^2 + 54x - 32y + 1 = 0$.
    b. $x^2 + 4y^2 - 2x - 24y + 21 = 0$. e. $y^2 - 4x + 4y = 4$.
    c. $x^2 + 2x = 10y + 19$. f. $4x^2 - y^2 - 8x + 4y + 4 = 0$.

14   GRAPHS OF LINEAR INEQUALITIES IN TWO VARIABLES

We conclude this chapter with a discussion of a method of plotting the graph of the solution set of a linear inequality in two variables.

An inequality of the form

$$ax + by + c > 0 \quad \text{or} \quad ax + by + c < 0,$$

where a, b, and c are arbitrary but fixed real numbers and a and b are not both zero, is called a *linear inequality in x and y*. Some examples of linear inequalities are

$$2x + 3y > 5,$$
$$x + 2y < 3x - 4,$$
$$x + 7 > 0,$$
$$y - 2 < 0,$$
$$2y < 5x.$$

A solution of a linear inequality in x and y is an ordered pair (x_1, y_1) of real numbers such that if x_1 is substituted for x and if y_1 is substituted for y in the inequality, the resulting numerical inequality is a true statement. For example, the pair $(3, 1)$ is a solution of $2x + 3y > 5$, because the inequality $6 + 3 > 5$ is a true statement. The set consisting of all the solutions of a given inequality is called the *solution set* of that inequality. The graph of a linear inequality is the set of points consisting of all the points whose coordinates are elements of the solution set of the inequality. In plotting the graphs of linear inequalities we shall find the following theorem useful.

Theorem 5.3.   *Let $f(x, y)$ denote the value of the linear form $ax + by + c$ at (x, y), that is, $f(x, y) = ax + by + c$, and let L be the graph of $ax + by + c = 0$. If P and Q are any two points, neither of which is on L, that can be joined by a straight line segment having no point in common with L, then the values of $f(x, y)$ at P and Q have the same sign.*

A rigorous proof of this theorem is beyond the scope of this text; however, the following intuitive argument may make it seem plausible. It is understood that by a straight line segment joining P and Q we mean only the points on the line determined by P and Q that lie between P and Q. Now consider the points $P(x_1, y_1)$ and $Q(x_2, y_2)$ and the straight line segment joining them. Assume that the line segment PQ has no point in common with L. Suppose that $f(x_1, y_1)$ and $f(x_2, y_2)$ are opposite in sign and, for the sake of the argument, that $f(x_1, y_1)$ is positive. If $f(x, y)$ is positive at P and negative at Q and if the point (x, y) moves from P to Q along the segment Q, then $f(x, y)$ must be zero at some point R between P and Q. But every point at which $f(x, y)$ is zero is a point on L, and hence R would be a point on L. This contradicts our assumption that the segment PQ has no point in common with L. We conclude therefore that the supposition that $f(x_1, y_1)$ and $f(x_2, y_2)$ are opposite in sign is false. We shall assume the validity of the theorem.

Every straight line L in the xy plane divides the plane into portions, called *half-planes*. It follows from Theorem 5.3 that if the point $P(x_1, y_1)$ is any point in one of the half-planes determined by the line L, where L is the graph of the linear equation $ax + by + c = 0$, and if $ax_1 + by_1 + c > 0$ at P, then $ax + by + c > 0$ at every point in the same half-plane with P, and $ax + by + c < 0$ at every point in the other half-plane. Thus if we wish to plot the graph of the inequality $ax + by + c > 0$ we first draw L, the graph of $ax + by + c = 0$, and then check the value of $ax + by + c$ at any convenient point in either half-plane determined by L. This will determine the half-plane in which $ax + by + c > 0$. The graph is this half-plane, which is

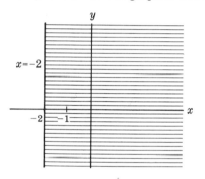

FIGURE 5.22

indicated by the shading in Fig. 5.22. Some examples will show how such a solution is arrived at.

Example.   Draw the graph of the solution set of $x > -2$.

Solution: We draw the line $x = -2$ lightly to show that it is not part of the graph. Our graph then consists of the right half-plane, which we indicate by shading.

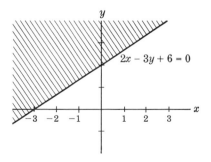

FIGURE 5.23

Example.   Draw the graph of the solution set of $2x - 3y + 6 < 0$.

Solution: We plot the graph of $2x - 3y + 6 = 0$. The point $(0, 0)$ is in the lower half-plane determined by the line $2x - 3y + 6 = 0$ and, since $0 - 0 + 6 < 0$ is false, we know that the desired graph is the upper half-plane, which we shade as shown in Fig. 5.23.

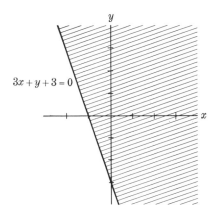

$3x + y + 3 = 0$

FIGURE 5.24

Example.   Draw the graph of the solution set of $3x + y + 3 \geq 0$. The line $3x + y + 3 = 0$ passes through the points $(-1, 0)$ and $(0, -3)$. We draw this line in heavily, to indicate that it is part of the graph. The point $(0, 0)$ is in the upper half-plane and, since $0 + 0 + 3 \geq 0$ is true $(0, 0)$ belongs to the solution set; therefore, the rest of the graph is also in the upper half-plane, as shown in Fig. 5.24.

EXERCISES

Draw the graph of the solution set of each of the following.

1. $x - 1 < 0$.
2. $y + 2 \geq 0$.
3. $x - y + 1 \leq 0$.
4. $2x + y - 4 > 0$.
5. $3x - y > 6$.

6. $5x + 4y \leq 20$.
7. $|x - 1| < 3$.
8. $|2y + 1| < 3$.
9. $5x - 3y + 10 < 0$.
10. $2x - 3y < 0$.

VI

AVERAGE RATES, INSTANTANEOUS RATES, AND LIMITS

1 AVERAGE RATES

As was pointed out in the preview at the beginning of Chapter V, one of the basic problems in mathematics is the rate problem. If one quantity is varying with a second quantity, it is often very desirable to know how fast this first quantity is increasing or decreasing per unit change in the second quantity. To give a precise meaning to this last statement it is first necessary to define what we call the "average rate" of change of one quantity per unit change of another over some fixed interval of given values of the latter. This idea of average rate is not completely new to us, for everyone is familiar with the notion that a distance, divided by the time required to travel that distance, is equal to the average speed, that is, the average rate. If one travels 200 miles in 5 hours, we say that his average speed is 40 miles per hour. It is important to notice here that this "40 miles per hour" refers only to the average and gives no information about the speed at any specific instant during the 5 hours. Of course, it could well have been that the person traveled at 40 miles per hour for very little of the 5 hours, and he could even have stopped for several minutes. Another familiar example of this type of rate is the following. A water tank has a slight leak and during a two-hour period 10 gallons of water leaked out. We say that the volume of water in the tank decreased at the average rate of 5 gallons per hour. Now consider the following more general situation.

Suppose that $y = f(x)$. Also let us suppose that $y = 17$ when $x = 3$ and that $y = 53$ when $x = 7$. Here, as x increases from 3 to 7, y changes in value from 17 to 53. Thus y has increased by 36 units over this 4-unit interval of $x = 3$ to $x = 7$. Again, we say that, over the interval $x = 3$ to $x = 7$, y increased at the average rate of $36/4 = 9$ units per unit change in x.

A formal definition of an average rate can now be given.

Definition 6.1. *Let y be a function of x. The average rate of change of y per unit change of x over an interval, say $x = x_1$ to $x = x_2$, is defined as the difference in the values of y at the beginning and end of the interval divided by the length of the interval. We can write the definition in symbolic language thus: Let $y = f(x)$, $x = x_1$ to $x = x_2$ the desired interval, and $\overline{R}$ the average rate; then*

$$\overline{R} = \frac{f(x_2) - f(x_1)}{x_2 - x_1}.$$

Example. Referring to Fig. 5.3, find the average rate at which the liquid is cooling over the interval $t = 3$ to $t = 7$.

Solution: $\overline{R} = \dfrac{T_2 - T_1}{t_2 - t_1}$, where T_1 is the value of T when $t = t_1$ and T_2 is the value of T when $t = t_2$.

In this problem $t_1 = 3$ and $t_2 = 7$. Reading from the graph, we find that $T_1 = 67$ and $T_2 = 51$. Therefore

$$\overline{R} = \frac{51 - 67}{7 - 3} = \frac{-16}{4} = -4 \frac{\text{deg}}{\text{min}}.$$

The symbol deg/min should be read "degrees per minute." This is a very common and convenient form of notation and will be used hereafter for expressing the units involved in a rate problem. For example, if y represents a distance in feet and x represents a time in seconds, the average rate will be given the special name of "average speed" and the units expressed as "ft/sec" and read "feet per second." Similarly, if y represents a speed whose units are feet per second and x represents time measured in seconds, the average rate will be referred to as "average acceleration" and the units expressed as "ft/sec^2" and read "feet per second, per second."

2 INSTANTANEOUS RATES FOUND GRAPHICALLY

In Chapter V we discussed the graphs of functions that increased or decreased at a constant rate. Such functions, however, are rather exceptional, as most quantities change at a varying rate. This being the case, we find it convenient to define and use two kinds of rates. The first of these was defined in Section 1 and was called an average rate over an interval. To obtain this rate we divide the change in the function taking place over the interval by the length of the interval, which gives us, as the name implies, an average rate for the whole interval. For instance, a man drives 80 miles in 2 hours. His average speed is 40 miles per hour, but part of the time he may actually have been driving much more slowly than this and part of the time much faster. The second kind of rate we wish to define is an *instantaneous rate*, the rate at some instant. The man, as he drives his car along the highway, looks at his speedometer and sees the indicator pointing to 40 on the dial. He says, "I am driving 40 miles per hour at this instant." He presses the accelerator, and the indicator on the speedometer moves around to 45, then to 50, and then to 60. At each of the instants mentioned the driver observes that he is driving 45, then 50, and then 60 miles per hour. Are these average speeds? Hardly, for an average speed always implies that an interval of time is involved. When you say, "I am driving 40 miles per hour at this instant," you do not mean that you have driven 40 miles in the last hour or that your average speed over the last 10 minutes was 40 miles per hour, or even that this was your average speed over the last two minutes, or the last minute, or the last 30 seconds. You mean by this your speed at an instant, your instantaneous speed. For the time being we shall content ourselves with this intuitive notion of instantaneous speed and postpone a more formal definition to the next chapter. We can, however, find an instantaneous speed, at least an approximate one, from a distance-time graph. A distance (s ft) traveled by an object in t seconds is given by the graph in Fig. 6.1. If the object had continued to travel, after the first 3 seconds, at

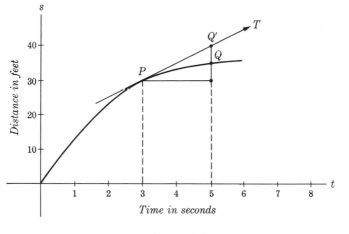

FIGURE 6.1

the same speed at which it had been traveling at $t = 3$, the graph from the point P on, to the right, would have been the straight line PT rather than the actual graph. If an object travels at a constant speed, that is, one whose distance-time graph is a straight line, this speed can be found by calculating the slope of its straight-line graph. This we have already learned to do. In Fig. 6.1 the coordinates of the point P, as read from the graph, are (3, 30) and of Q' are (5, 40). Hence the slope of PT, that is, the speed at the instant $t = 3$, is

$$V = \frac{40 - 30}{5 - 3} = \frac{10}{2} = 5 \text{ ft/sec.}$$

The line PT is called a *tangent line* to the curve at the point P. It is a line that has the same direction as the curve at the point P. A more satisfactory definition of a tangent line will be given later. To draw a tangent line accurately one must place one's ruler in the same direction as the curve at the point. This position can best be found in the following manner. Place the ruler so that one of its edges passes through the fixed point P and the same edge passes through some neighboring variable point Q on the curve (see Fig. 6.1). Now rotate the ruler about the point P in a direction such that Q seems to move toward P on the curve. Continue to turn the ruler slowly, always keeping the edge passing through the fixed point P. When the moving point Q seems to coincide with the fixed point P, stop moving the ruler. Its edge now has the direction of the tangent. With a little practice and care one should be able to draw a reasonably accurate tangent line by this method.

The method just outlined for finding an instantaneous speed from a distance-time graph obviously can be used for finding the instantaneous rate of change of any function per unit change in its independent variable. It is simply a matter of drawing the graph of the function and then drawing a tangent line to this graph at the point in question. The slope of the tangent line gives the slope of the curve at the point of tangency. The slope of the curve is the instantaneous rate of change of the function that the curve represents.

EXERCISES

1. Find the average rate of change of the following functions over the interval indicated.
    a. $f(x) = x^2 + 3x$, from $x = 1$ to $x = 3$.
    b. $f(x) = 4x + 7$, from $x = 3$ to $x = 7$.
    c. $f(x) = 5x^2$, from $x = 1$ to $x = 1.2$.
    d. $f(x) = 3 - 2x$, from $x = 2$ to $x = 5$.
2. Table 1 expresses y as a function of x. Plot the graph. Find the average rate of change of y per unit increase in x over the interval $x = 2$ to $x = 6$, also over the interval $x = 4$ to $x = 8$. What is the instantaneous rate of change of y per unit increase in x at $x = 2$? At $x = 4$?
3. Table 2 expresses y as a function of x. Plot the graph. Find (a) the average rate of change of y per unit change in x from $x = 2$ to $x = 5$, and (b) the instantaneous rate of change of y per unit change in x at $x = 4$.
4. An object travels along a straight line. Its distance (y feet) from a fixed point

after t seconds is given in Table 3 for various values of t. Plot the graph. Find the average speed of the object during the interval $t = 6$ to $t = 12$. Find the instantaneous speed at the instant $t = 6$.

5. As water leaked out of a pail, the volume, V cubic inches, remaining after various intervals of time, t seconds, is given in Table 4. Plot the graph. Find how fast the volume was decreasing at $t = 30$. Find the average rate at which V was decreasing during the first 30 seconds.

TABLE 1		TABLE 2		TABLE 3		TABLE 4	
x	y	x	y	$.t$	y	t	V
0	2	0	0	0	0	0	2000
2	8	1	2	2	72	10	1620
4	14	4	4	4	128	15	1445
6	20	9	6	6	168	20	1280
8	26	16	8	8	192	25	1125
10	32	25	10	10	200	30	980
		36	12	12	192	35	845

6. Table 5 gives the net profit, P dollars, of a certain company as a function of the number of items, N, which the company manufactures. Assuming N a continuous variable, draw a graph of this data and find the instantaneous rate of change of P when N is 450. Find P when N is 330. Find N when P is 1100. Find the average rate of change of P when N increases from 450 to 500.

7. The temperature, T degrees, of a certain vessel of water which is being heated is given in Table 6 as a function of time, t minutes. Draw a graph of this data and find the rate at which the temperature is changing when t is 8 and when t is 10. Find the average rate of change of the temperature between $t = 8$ and $t = 10$.

8. If \$100.00 is invested at 5 percent compounded semiannually, the value of the investment, A dollars, after t years is given by Table 7. Draw a graph of this data and find the instantaneous rate at which the value of the investment is increasing at $t = 5$. What is the rate of increase at $t = 8$? What is the average rate of change between $t = 6$ and $t = 10$ years?

9. The gasoline consumption, G miles per gallon, for a certain car traveling at an average speed of v miles per hour is given by Table 8. What is the instantaneous rate of change of G per unit change in v at $v = 30$ miles per hour? At 40 miles per hour? At 50 miles per hour? What is the average rate of change from $v = 30$ to $v = 50$?

TABLE 5		TABLE 6		TABLE 7		TABLE 8	
N	P	t	T	t	A	v	G
0	0	0	80	0	100.00	10	19.2
100	450	3	110	2	110.38	20	20.3
200	950	6	140	4	121.84	30	20.7
300	1400	9	170	6	134.49	40	19.9
400	1800	12	200	8	148.45	50	18.1
500	2000	15	212	10	163.86	60	15.6
600	2100	18	212	12	180.87	70	12.2

10. The radioactive strength, M millicuries, of a certain isotope t days after being received is given in Table 9. What is the rate of change of M at the time of receipt? At $t = 2$? At $t = 10$? What is the average rate of change from $t = 6$ to $t = 8$? What is the average rate of change from $t - 98$ to $t = 100$? How do these average rates of change compare?

11. The weight, W pounds, of an average Jersey calf m months after birth is given in Table 10. Draw a graph of the weight of this calf. How fast is its weight increasing at 3 months? At 1 year? At 3 years? What is the average rate of change during the first 3 months? What is the average rate of change during the first 3 months of the third year (from 2 years to 2 years and 3 months)?

12. For $y = 60/x$, make a table showing the values of y that correspond to $x = 2$, 4, 6, 8, 10, 12, and 15. Plot the graph. How fast was y decreasing at $x = 4$?

13. The population of the United States at ten-year intervals is given in Table 11. What is the rate of increase of the population in 1900? In 1950? What is the average rate of increase from 1900 to 1950?

TABLE 9		TABLE 10		TABLE 11	
t	M	m	W	Year	Population
				1880	(Millions)
0	4.00	0	53		
5	3.62	3	121	1890	50.16
10	3.27	6	243	1900	62.95
20	2.68	9	360	1910	75.99
50	1.47	12	450	1920	91.97
75	0.89	18	601	1930	105.71
100	0.54	24	733	1940	122.78
		36	855	1950	131.67
					150.70

3 MORE ABOUT AVERAGE RATES

In Section 1 the average rate of change, $\overline{R}$, of a function $f(x)$ over the interval $x = x_1$ to $x = x_2$ was defined as

$$\overline{R} = \frac{f(x_2) - f(x_1)}{x_2 - x_1}.$$

When $f(x)$ is expressed as a formula it is, in general, a very easy task to find $f(x_1)$ and $f(x_2)$ and, hence, $\overline{R}$.

Example. If $f(x) = x^2 + 4$, what is the average rate of change of $f(x)$ over the interval of $x = 2$ to $x = 6$?

Solution: Here we have $x_1 = 2$ and $x_2 = 6$. Hence

$$f(x_2) = f(6) = 6^2 + 4 = 40$$
$$f(x_1) = f(2) = 2^2 + 4 = 8$$

$$\overline{R} = \frac{f(x_2) - f(x_1)}{x_2 - x_1} = \frac{40 - 8}{6 - 2} = \frac{32}{4} = 8.$$

Example. A ball rolled up an inclined plane, its distance S feet from the starting point after t seconds being given by the formula $S = 60t - 3t^2$. Find the average speed of the ball from $t = 3$ to $t = 8$.

Solution: Here $t_1 = 3$ and $t_2 = 8$. Let S_1 be the distance when $t = t_1$ and S_2 be the distance when $t = t_2$. Then we have

$$S_2 = 60(8) - 3(8)^2 = 480 - 192 = 288$$
$$S_1 = 60(3) - 3(3)^2 = 180 - 27 = 153.$$

By the definition of average speed we have

$$\overline{V} = \frac{S_2 - S_1}{t_2 - t_1} = \frac{288 - 153}{8 - 3} = \frac{135}{5} = 27 \text{ ft/sec.}$$

Example. The volume, V cubic inches, of a certain weight of a gas varies as follows with the pressure, P pounds per square inch (pounds per inch, per inch): $V = 40/P$. Find the average rate at which V is changing with P as P increases from $P = 3$ to $P = 7$.

Solution: If $P_1 = 3$ and $P_2 = 7$, then $V_2 = \dfrac{40}{7}$, $V_1 = \dfrac{40}{3}$, and

$$\overline{R} = \frac{V_2 - V_1}{P_2 - P_1} = \frac{40/7 - 40/3}{7 - 3} = \frac{40(1/7 - 1/3)}{4}$$

$$= 10 \left(\frac{1}{7} - \frac{1}{3} \right) = 10 \left(\frac{-4}{21} \right) = -\frac{40 \text{ in.}^3}{21 \text{ lb/in.}^2}.$$

Example. The equation of a curve is $y = x^2 - 5x + 7$. Find the average slope over the interval $x = 2$ to $x = 5$.

Solution: Here $x_1 = 2$, and $x_2 = 5$:

$$y_1 = f(x_1) = f(2) = 4 - 10 + 7 = 1$$
$$y_2 = f(x_2) = f(5) = 25 - 25 + 7 = 7.$$

Hence the average slope $\overline{m}$ is $\overline{m} - \dfrac{y_2 - y_1}{x_2 - x_1} = \dfrac{7 - 1}{5 - 2} = \dfrac{6}{3} = 2.$

EXERCISES

1. The distance S feet fallen by an object in t seconds is given by the relation $S = 16t^2$. Find the average speed (a) during the first 2 seconds, (b) during the first 3 seconds, and (c) during the third second, that is, from $t = 2$ to $t = 3$.
2. A train travels 100 miles in 3 hours and 20 minutes. What is its average speed?
3. A student drove from Knoxville via Nashville to his home near Memphis, a distance of 420 miles, and upon his arrival calculated that he had averaged 40 miles per hour for the trip. Does this imply that he drove through Nashville at 40 miles per hour? How long did it take for the trip?
4. On a 120-mile trip a man averaged 30 miles per hour, but on the return home over the same route he averaged 40 miles per hour. What was his average speed for the round trip? (The answer is not 35 miles per hour.)

5. A straight stretch of a certain highway is 2 miles in length. If one drives the first mile at an average speed of 30 miles per hour, at what average speed must he drive the second mile in order to average for the trip **(a)** 40, **(b)** 50, and **(c)** 60 miles per hour?

6. Find the average rate of change of each of the following functions over the interval indicated.

   a. $f(x) = 5x - x^2$, from $x = 2$ to $x = 4$.
   b. $f(x) = 2x^2 - x + 3$, from $x = 5$ to $x = 8$.
   c. $f(t) = t^3$, from $t = 2$ to $t = 5$.
   d. $f(p) = 20/p$, from $p = 6$ to $p = 10$.
   e. $f(x) = x + 4/x$, from $x = 3$ to $x = 5$.

4   AVERAGE RATES OVER A FLEXIBLE INTERVAL

It is conceivable that one would need to calculate the average rate of change of the same function over several intervals of different lengths but one of whose ends is the same in each case. If so, it would be convenient to have a formula expressing this average rate as a function of the length of the interval.

Example. Suppose we wish to find the average rate of change of the function $f(x) = x^2 + 5x - 7$ over the intervals

$$x = 2 \text{ to } x = 3,$$
$$x = 2 \text{ to } x = 4,$$
$$x = 2 \text{ to } x = 4.5,$$
$$x = 2 \text{ to } x = 3.2,$$
$$x = 2 \text{ to } x = 2.001.$$

Now, rather than calculate each of these separately, as we did in the last section, let us derive a formula in the following manner:

Take $x_1 = 2$ and $x_2 = 2 + h$. The average rate $\overline{R}$ of $f(x)$ over this flexible interval of length h is

$$\overline{R} = \frac{f(2 + h) - f(2)}{h}.$$

But
$$f(2 + h) = (2 + h)^2 + 5(2 + h) - 7,$$
$$= 4 + 4h + h^2 + 10 + 5h - 7,$$
and
$$f(2) = 4 \qquad\qquad + 10 \qquad - 7,$$
So
$$f(2 + h) - f(2) = h^2 + 9h,$$

hence
$$\overline{R} = \frac{h^2 + 9h}{h} = h + 9.$$

This formula gives us the average rate of change of the particular given function over any interval of length h, provided one end of the interval is at $x = 2$. In part (a), the desired interval is from $x_1 = 2$ to $x_2 = 3$ and $x_2 - x_1 = 3 - 2 = 1 = h$. Thus, the average rate in this case is

$$\overline{R} = 9 + h = 9 + 1 = 10.$$

Similarly, for parts (b), (c), (d), and (e) we get

(b) $h = 2$ and $R = 9 + 2 = 11$,
(c) $h = 2.5$ and $R = 9 + 2.5 = 11.5$,
(d) $h = 1.2$ and $R = 9 + 1.2 = 10.2$,
(e) $h = 0.001$ and $R = 9 + 0.001 = 9.001$.

In each of the cases just studied, the left ends of the interval were always the same. The formula works equally well when the right ends are always the same. However, in such case we need to take h as a negative number. For instance, suppose we want $\overline{R}$ over the interval $x = 1$ to $x = 2$; we take $h = -1$ and get

$$\overline{R} = 9 + h = 9 - 1 = 8,$$

which may be easily checked and found to be correct.

Let us look again at part (e) of the example above. Here the length of the interval in question was given to three decimal places, namely $h = 0.001$. To have calculated the average rate over this interval without using the formula we derived would have involved much more labor. To see that such is the case, let us find this average rate directly from the definition, taking $x_1 = 2$, $x_2 - 2.001$, and x_2 $x_1 - 0.001$.

$$f(x_1) = f(2) = 4 + 10 - 7 = 7,$$
$$f(x_2) = f(2.001) = (2.001)^2 + 5(2.001) - 7,$$
$$= 4.004001 + 10.005 - 7,$$
$$= 7.009001,$$

$$\overline{R} = \frac{f(x_2) - f(x_1)}{x_2 - x_1} = \frac{7.009001 - 7}{0.001} = \frac{0.009001}{0.001} = 9.001.$$

EXERCISES

1. Find the average rate of change of the function defined by the equation $f(x) = 5 - 3x - 2x^2$ over the interval $x = 1$ to $x = 1 + h$.
2. Find the average rate of change of the function $f: (x, y)$, defined by the equation $y = x^3 - 3x + 4$, over the interval $x = 2$ to $x = 2 + h$. Use your result to find the average rate of the given function over the interval (a) $x = 2$ to $x = 7$, (b) $x = -2$ to $x = 2$, and (c) $x = 2$ to $x = 2.01$.
3. Given the function defined by the equation $f(x) = 4/x$, find the average rate over the interval $x = 5$ to $x = 5 + h$.
4. Given the function defined by the equation $f(x) = (x + 1)/(x + 2)$, find its average rate of change over the interval $x = x_1$ to $x = x_1 + h$.
5. A ball rolled up an incline, its distance from the starting point after t seconds being $s = 40t - 3t^2$. What was the average speed from $t = 2$ to $t = 4$? During the first 5 seconds?
6. The distance, s miles, of a car from a town t hours after starting was given by the equation $s = 60t + 6t^2 - 2t^3$. Find the average speed of the car during the second hour after starting. If the car started at 12 o'clock, what was its average speed from 1 to 3 o'clock?

7. A bomb was fired straight up, its height, y feet above the ground, being $y = 400t - 16t^2$ t seconds later. Find its average speed from $t = 10$ to $t = 12$, from $t = 10$ to $t = 15$, from $t = 20$ to $t = 22$, and from $t = 10$ to $10 + h$.

8. The speed, v feet per second, of a car t seconds after starting and until full speed was reached, varied thus: $v = 8t - 0.2t^2$. Find the average acceleration from $t = 10$ to $t = 15$ and from $t = 10$ to $t = 10 + h$.

9. Find the average slope of the curve $y = 2x^2$ from the point (1, 2) to the point (3, 18). Draw the curve. Find the average slope from $x = 2$ to $x = 2 + h$. (*Hint:* $\bar{m} = (y_2 - y_1)/(x_2 - x_1)$.)

10. The temperature $T°$ fell, as in the table given below, after various intervals of t minutes. Plot the graph. What was the temperature at $t = 5.2$? At $t = 6.8$? Find the average rate of cooling during this interval. What was the average rate of cooling during the first 2 minutes? During the first 3 minutes?

t min	0	2	4	6	8	10	12	14
$T°$	140	98.7	73.2	57.4	48.5	42.1	37.8	35

11. The time, t hours, required for a certain air trip varies with the mean speed maintained, V miles per hour, according to the equation. $t = 2000/V$. Find the average rate of change of t per unit change in V from $V = 160$ to $V = 180$ and from $V = 160$ to $V = 160 + h$.

12. The temperature $T°$ in a wire varied with the distance, x inches, from one end, thus: $T = 10x - x^2$. Find the average rate at which T changed per unit increase in x from $x = 4$ to $x = 6$ and from $x = 4$ to $x = 4 + h$.

13. The repulsion, F dynes, between a certain pair of electric charges varies with the distance apart, x centimeters, thus: $F = 50/x^2$. Find the average rate of change of F with x from $x = 3$ to $x = 5$ and from $x = 3$ to $x = 3 + h$.

14. A circular metal plate is heated and expands. Find the average rate at which the area A is increasing per unit change in the radius when the radius changes from 4 to 6 centimeters and from 4 to $4 + h$.

5 THE LIMIT CONCEPT

In Section 2 two kinds of rates were mentioned, namely the average rate over an interval and the instantaneous rate, or rate at an instant. We gave a formal definition of an average rate, but we gave only an intuitive notion of an instantaneous rate although we learned how to find it graphically. For us to find an instantaneous rate algebraically it is essential that we have a specific formal definition of it. As an attempt at formulating a satisfactory definition of instantaneous rate, let us first examine our intuitive notion of instantaneous speed. Precisely what is meant by saying that at a certain instant the speed of an object was, say, 10 feet per second? It certainly does not mean that the object traveled 10 feet in the second terminating at that instant. Moreover, it does not mean that the average speed was 10 feet per second, for average speed has to do with an interval of time and an instant has no duration. An *interval of time* is the elapsed time between two different instants; that is, an interval is a length of time, while an instant is not. The radio announcer says, "When you hear the gong it will be exactly ten o'clock." How long was it ten o'clock? It was not ten o'clock for any length of time; it was ten o'clock at the instant. An instant has somewhat the relation to an interval of time that a point has to a line segment: the line segment has length but the point does not. A point may lie on a given line segment; also, an instant may occur within, or during, an interval of time. Now since, as we have seen, an instant has no length, an object cannot travel any distance in an instant. Hence, we could not arrive at the instantaneous speed by dividing the distance traveled in an instant by the length of the instant. In fact, this would be equivalent to attempting to divide zero by zero. Also, we know that, if an object is moving with a varying speed, its speed at a particular instant is not in general equal to its average speed over any interval containing the instant. However, it does seem logical that the average speed calculated over a short interval, including the instant in question, would be a good approximation of the speed at that instant, and that the shorter the interval used the better the approximation. Thus, by taking the intervals shorter and shorter, we should be able to determine average speeds that are nearer and nearer the speed we have in mind when we say "the speed at the instant." To understand this more clearly, let us consider a particular example.

Example.   A ball rolled up an inclined plane, and its distance, y feet, from its starting position after t seconds was given by the relation $y = 90t - 3t^2$. Now, suppose we are interested in knowing the speed at the instant $t = 5$, that is, the speed at the end of 5 seconds. Let us first find the average speed over a flexible interval, $t_1 = 5$ to $t_2 = 5 + h$. Notice that this interval always has the instant $t = 5$ as one end regardless of the value of h. Proceeding as we did in Section 4, we get

$$y_1 = 90(5) - 3(5)^2 = 450 - 75 = 375,$$
$$y_2 = 90(5 + h) - 3(25 + 10h + h^2),$$
$$= 450 + 90h - 75 - 30h - 3h^2,$$
$$= 375 + 60h - 3h^2,$$
$$y_2 - y_1 = 60h - 3h^2,$$

$$\overline{V} = \frac{y_2 - y_1}{t_2 - t_1} = \frac{60h - 3h^2}{h} = (60 - 3h) \text{ ft/sec}, \qquad h \neq 0$$

where $\overline{V}$ is the average speed over an interval beginning at the instant $t = 5$, ending at the instant $t = 5 + h$, and having the length h. This interval is flexible in the sense that we can make its length equal any number we choose by setting h equal to this number. Thus, if we want the average speed over the interval $t = 5$ to $t = 6$, we set $h = 1$ and have

$$\overline{V} = 60 - 3h = 60 - 3 = 57 \text{ ft/sec.}$$

To shorten the interval we take a smaller value for h. To see how this works let's write out a table showing $\overline{V}$ for various values of h.

h	1	0.1	0.01	0.001	0.000001	0.000000000001
$\bar{V}$	57	59.7	59.97	59.997	59.999997	59.999999999997

This table shows that for values of h nearer and nearer zero the corresponding values of $\bar{V}$ get closer and closer to 60. In fact, by taking the values of h near enough to zero we can obtain values of $\bar{V}$ as close to 60 as we choose. This fact is often stated in the following way. The difference between $\bar{V}$ and 60 can be made numerically as small as we please by choosing a value for h that is near enough to zero. This follows at once from our formula for $\bar{V}$. Since $\bar{V} = 60 - 3h$, the difference $60 - \bar{V}$ is $3h$. Thus, the smaller the value of h the smaller the difference $60 - \bar{V}$ becomes.

It should be pointed out that the formula for $\bar{V}$ is valid for both positive and negative values of h but not for $h = 0$. That $h \neq 0$ can be seen in two ways. First, h represents the length of an interval, and an interval cannot have zero length. Second, from a purely algebraic point of view, the original form of the formula is $\bar{V} = (60h - 3h^2)/h$, from which it is seen that zero is not a permissible value of h since division by zero is not a permissible operation. Also, it should be carefully noted that to reduce the formula for $\bar{V}$ to $\bar{V} = 60 - 3h$ it was necessary to divide by h, and this, of course, is valid if and only if h is not zero. By interpreting h as a directed distance rather than as the length of an interval its range may be increased to include negative values. Negative values of h mean that the intervals in question end at the instant $t = 5$, while positive values of h mean that these intervals begin at the instant $t = 5$.

We are now ready to answer the question, What is the speed V of the ball at the instant $t = 5$? Since $\bar{V}$ is an approximation of V and since it is agreed that the shorter the interval over which $\bar{V}$ is calculated the better the approximation for V, then V must be 60 feet per second. For we have just seen that the shorter the length of the interval, that is, the nearer to zero h becomes, the nearer to 60 is $\bar{V}$. In fact, we shall take this as the definition of the speed of the ball at the instant $t = 5$. The process that we have just used in arriving at a value for V when $t = 5$ is called a *limiting process*, and 60 is said to be the limit of $\bar{V}$ as h approaches zero. In this connection we introduce the symbol $\lim\limits_{h \to 0} \bar{V} = 60$, which is read "the limit of $\bar{V}$, as h approaches zero, is 60." This limit process, or limit concept, is such a basic tool in mathematics that it is quite worth while to consider it in more detail and also in a more general sense. Looking again at the example just considered, we are reminded that $\bar{V}$ was a function of the variable h, namely $\bar{V} = (60h - 3h^2)/h$. This suggests that the limit process as used above might be applied to functions in general; when so applied it deals with the value approached by the function as its independent variable approaches some fixed value. To be more specific, let f be a function of the independent variable x defined for all values of x on the open interval (a, b) except, perhaps, for the fixed number c, which belongs to this open interval. Whether f has a value for $x = c$ is immaterial. If there is a number L such that $f(x)$ may be made as close to L as we please by our choosing x close enough to c but different from c, we say that the limit of $f(x)$ as x approaches c is L or, stated in symbols,

$$\lim_{x \to c} f(x) = L.$$

It is important to emphasize the following points in regard to the definition just given.

1.   It makes no difference whether f has a value when $x = c$. That is, the definition is not concerned with the value of $f(x)$ at $x = c$, but is very much concerned with values of $f(x)$ for all other values of x which are sufficiently near c. For example, suppose that

$$f(x) = \frac{x^2 - 1}{x - 1};$$

here $f(x)$ is defined by the given relation for all values of x except $x = 1$. Does $f(x)$ approach a limit as x approaches 1? That it does is easily seen by the following:

$$f(x) = \frac{x^2 - 1}{x - 1} = x + 1, \qquad x \neq 1,$$

which in words is that $(x^2 - 1)/(x - 1)$ and $x + 1$ have the same value for every value of x except $x = 1$. When $x = 1$, then $(x^2 - 1)/(x - 1)$ has no value at all, but $x + 1$ has the value 2. Now, since the existence of the limit of $f(x)$ as x approaches 1 does not depend upon the value of $f(x)$ at $x = 1$, it follows that $(x^2 - 1)/(x - 1)$ will have a limit as x approaches 1 if $x + 1$ has such a limit and, furthermore, that the limits will be the same. Since the limit of $x + 1$ as x approaches 1 is 2, obviously, we have

$$\lim_{x \to 1} \frac{x^2 - 1}{x - 1} = 2.$$

2.   It is not enough that $f(x)$ becomes closer and closer to L as x gets nearer and nearer to c. It must be possible to find an open interval containing c and such that for all values of x in this interval, different from c, the difference $f(x) - L$ will be as near zero as we please. A more precise way to say this is: Given any positive number d, no matter how small, it must be possible to find another positive number k such that the difference $f(x) - L$ will be numerically less than d when x is between $c + k$ and $c - k$ but is different from c.

Let us now rewrite our limit definition definition in precise notation.

Definition 6.2.   *The function f is said to have the* limit L *as x approaches the number c if for every positive number d there exists a positive number k such that $|f(x) - L| < d$ when $0 < |x - c| < k$.*

Example. Suppose that $f(x) = 10 + 2x$. Let us show that $\lim_{x \to 0} f(x) = 10$.

To do this we need to show that for any given positive number d we can find a positive number k such that

$$|(10 + 2x) - 10| < d \qquad \text{when } 0 < |x - 0| < k.$$

Since $|(10 + 2x) - 10| = |2x| = 2|x|$ and $|x - 0| = |x|$, our problem is to find a number k such that

$$2|x| < d \qquad \text{when } |x| < k.$$

It follows at once that

$$2|x| < d \qquad \text{if } |x| < d/2.$$

Hence, no matter what value d may have, if we let $k = d/2$ we have

$$2|x| < d \qquad \text{when } |x| < k,$$

$$\text{or} \qquad |f(x) - 10| < d \qquad \text{when } 0 < |x - 0| < k.$$

This by definition proves that $\lim_{x \to 0} f(x) = 10$.

6 SOME THEOREMS CONCERNING LIMITS

It is rather laborious to resort to the use of the definition of a limit each time it is necessary to evaluate the limit of some function. To expedite the evaluation process we find it convenient to make use of the following theorems, which can be proved from the definition.

Theorem 6.1. $\lim_{x \to c} k = k$, *where k is any constant.*

Theorem 6.2. $\lim_{x \to c} x = c$.

In the following theorems we shall assume that $\lim_{x \to c} f(x) = L$, that $\lim_{x \to c} g(x) = M$, and that n is a positive integer.

Theorem 6.3. $\lim_{x \to c} kf(x) = k \lim_{x \to c} f(x) = kL$.

Theorem 6.4. $\lim_{x \to c} [f(x) + g(x)] = L + M$. *In words: the limit of a sum equals the sum of the limits.*

Theorem 6.5. $\lim_{x \to c} [f(x) \cdot g(x)] = LM$. *In words: the limit of a product is the product of the limits.*

Theorem 6.6. $\text{Lim}_{x \to c} \dfrac{f(x)}{g(x)} = \dfrac{L}{M}$, *if* $M \neq 0$. *In words: the limit of a fraction is the limit of the numerator divided by the limit of the denominator, provided the limit of the denominator is not zero.*

Theorem 6.7. $\text{Lim}_{x \to c} [f(x)]^n = (\lim_{x \to c} f(x))^n = L^n$.

Theorem 6.8. $\text{Lim}_{x \to c} \sqrt[n]{f(x)} = \sqrt[n]{\lim_{x \to c} f(x)} = \sqrt[n]{L}$, *if* $L > 0$ *when* n *is even.*

Theorem 6.9.   *If* $F(x) = f(x)$ *for every* x, *except possibly* $x = c$, *in some interval containing* c, *then* $\lim_{x \to c} F(x) = \lim_{x \to c} f(x) = L$.

To indicate how the definition is used in proving these theorems, we shall prove Theorem 6.4. We shall need the following rather obvious property of the absolute-value symbol. If two numbers a and b have the same sign, then $|a + b| = |a| + |b|$ but, if they have opposite signs, then $|a + b| < |a| + |b|$. Both of these cases are expressed by the inequality

$$|a + b| \leq |a| + |b|.$$

Proof of Theorem 6.4:   It is assumed that

$$\lim_{x \to c} f(x) = L \qquad \text{and} \qquad \lim_{x \to c} g(x) = M.$$

If d_1 and d_2 are any two positive numbers, there must exist corresponding positive numbers k_1 and k_2 such that

$$|f(x) - L| < d_1 \qquad \text{when } 0 < |x - c| < k_1,$$
$$|g(x) - M| < d_2 \qquad \text{when } 0 < |x - c| < k_2.$$

We wish to show that, if d is any positive number, there exists a positive number k such that

$$|[f(x) + g(x)] - (L + M)| < d \qquad \text{when } 0 < |x - c| < k.$$

Let $d_1 = d_2 = d/2$. Now, if k is the smaller of k_1 and k_2, then

$$|f(x) - M| < \frac{d}{2} \qquad \text{and} \qquad |g(x) - L| < \frac{d}{2} \qquad \text{when } 0 < |x - c| < k.$$

By using the property of the absolute-value symbol, mentioned above, we have

$$
\begin{aligned}
|[f(x) + g(x)] - (L + M)| &= |(f(x) - L) + g(x) - M)| \\
&\leq |f(x) - L| + |g(x) - M| \\
&= \frac{d}{2} + \frac{d}{2} = d, \qquad \text{when } 0 < |x - c| < k.
\end{aligned}
$$

Hence, by definition, $\lim_{x \to c} [f(x) + g(x)] = L + M$.

We shall assume the validity of the other theorems given.

7   CONTINUOUS FUNCTIONS

In this section we wish to define a concept, called the *continuity* of a function, which is very basic in mathematics and one which we will find most useful in our further discussion of limits.

Definition 6.3. *A function f which is defined for all values of x in some interval containing the number c is said to be continuous at c provided*

(1) *f has a definite value $f(c)$ at c, and*

(2) $\lim\limits_{x \to c} f(x) = f(c)$.

If f is continuous at each point of a closed interval $[a, b]$, or at each point of the open interval (a, b), then it is said to be continuous on the closed interval, or continuous in the open interval.

Example.   The function f is defined by the equations

$$f(x) = \frac{x^2 - 4}{x - 2}, \qquad \text{for } x \neq 2$$

$$= 4, \qquad \text{for } x = 2.$$

Is f continuous at $x = 2$?

Solution: f is certainly defined in any open interval containing 2, and

(1) $f(2) = 4$, by definition of f, also

(2) $\lim\limits_{x \to 2} \dfrac{x^2 - 4}{x - 2} = \lim\limits_{x \to 2} (x + 2) = 4 = f(2)$.

Therefore since $\lim\limits_{x \to 2} f(x) = f(2)$, f is continuous at $x = 2$ by definition.

The very definition of a continuous function exhibits a property of such functions that makes them important, namely, that the $\lim\limits_{x \to c} f(x)$ is the value of the function at c, which is $f(c)$. Thus, if we know that a particular function is continuous and need its limit as $x \to c$, we simply find $f(c)$. In the next section we shall discover a very important class of continuous functions.

8   POLYNOMIAL FUNCTIONS

Denote by $P(x)$ a general polynomial thus,

(1) $\qquad P(x) = A_0 x^n + A_1 x^{n-1} + \cdots + A_{n-1} x + A_n,$

where n is a positive integer or zero and $A_1, A_2, \cdots, A_n, A_n$ are arbitrary real numbers. For each positive integer n and for each set of real numbers, $\{A_0, A_1, \cdots, A_n\}$, Equation (1) defines a function, called a *polynomial* function. Thus by letting n vary through the set of positive integers by considering all the possible choices for the coefficients $A_0, A_1, \cdots, A_n$, we see that Equation (1) actually defines a whole class of polynomial functions and each such function is defined for all real numbers, that is, for all x such that $-\infty < x < \infty$. Further if $f(x) = x$ and n is a positive integer, then

$$\lim_{x \to c} f(x) = \lim_{x \to c} x = c \qquad \text{(Theorem 6.2)},$$

therefore

$$\lim_{x \to c} [f(x)]^n = \lim_{x \to c} x^n = c^n \qquad \text{(Theorem 6.7)},$$

hence

$$\lim_{x \to c} kx^n = k \lim_{x \to c} x^n = kx^n \qquad \text{(Theorem 6.3)}.$$

So, if P is a polynomial defined by

$$P(x) = A_0x^n + A_1x^{n-1} + \cdots + A_{n-1}x + A_n$$

then

$$\lim_{x \to c} P(x) = \lim_{x \to c} (A_0x^n + A_1x^{n-1} + \cdots + A_{n-1}x + A_n)$$

$$= \lim_{x \to c} A_0x^n + \lim_{x \to c} A_1x^{n-1} + \cdots + \lim_{x \to c} A_{n-1}x + \lim_{x \to c} A_n$$

$$= A_0c^n + A_1c^{n-1} + \cdots + A_{n-1}c + A_n$$

$$= P(c).$$

This proves the following theorem.

Theorem 6.10. *If P is a polynomial function in one variable and c is any real number, then P is continuous at c. That is, P is continuous in the interval $(-\infty, \infty)$.*

Corollary. *If P and Q are polynomial functions in one variable, then the function f defined by the equation*

$$f(x) = \frac{P(x)}{Q(x)}$$

is continuous at c, provided $Q(c) \neq 0$. $f(c) = \dfrac{P(c)}{Q(c)}$ is defined if $Q(c) \neq 0$. Also

$$\lim_{x \to c} f(x) = \lim_{x \to c} \frac{P(x)}{Q(x)}$$

$$= \frac{P(c)}{Q(c)}, \qquad Q(c) \neq 0, \qquad \text{(Theorem 6.6)}.$$

Example. $\lim\limits_{x \to -2} (3x^2 - 5x + 1) = 3(-2)^2 - 5(-2) + 1$

$$= 12 + 10 + 1 = 23.$$

Example. $\lim\limits_{x \to 1} \dfrac{5x^2 + 8x - 3}{x^3 + x} = \dfrac{5 + 8 - 3}{1 + 1} = \dfrac{10}{2} = 5.$

Example. Evaluate the limit: $\lim\limits_{x \to 2} (x^2 + 1)^2.$

Solution: By Theorem 6.7, $\lim\limits_{x \to 2} (x^2 + 1)^2 = [\lim\limits_{x \to 2} (x^2 + 1)]^2 = (5)^2 = 25.$

Example. Evaluate the limit: $\lim\limits_{x \to -1} \sqrt{3x + 19}.$

Solution: By Theorem 6.8, $\lim\limits_{x \to -1} \sqrt{3x + 19} = \sqrt{\lim\limits_{x \to -1} (3x + 19)} = \sqrt{16} = 4.$

Example. Evaluate the limit: $\lim\limits_{x \to 2} \dfrac{5x - 2}{x + 2}.$

Solution: By Theorem 6.6, $\lim\limits_{x \to 2} \dfrac{5x - 2}{x + 2} = \dfrac{\lim\limits_{x \to 2} (5x - 2)}{\lim\limits_{x \to 2} (x + 2)} = \dfrac{10 - 2}{2 + 2} = \dfrac{8}{4} = 2.$

Example. Evaluate the limit: $\lim\limits_{x \to 0} (x^2 + 5)\sqrt{2x + 9}.$

Solution: By Theorem 6.5,

$$\lim\limits_{x \to 0} (x^2 + 5)\sqrt{2x + 9} = \lim\limits_{x \to 0} (x^2 + 5) \lim\limits_{x \to 0} \sqrt{2x + 9}$$

$$= \lim\limits_{x \to 0} (x^2 + 5)\sqrt{\lim\limits_{x \to 0} (2x + 9)}$$

$$= 5\sqrt{9} = 15.$$

Example. Evaluate the limit: $\lim\limits_{x \to 2} \dfrac{x^2 + 5x - 14}{x^2 - x - 2}.$

Solution: We have $\dfrac{x^2 + 5x - 14}{x^2 - x - 2} = \dfrac{(x - 2)(x + 7)}{(x - 2)(x + 1)};$ now let

$$f(x) = \dfrac{x + 7}{x + 1} \quad \text{and} \quad F(x) = \dfrac{x^2 + 5x - 14}{x^2 + x - 2}.$$

Then $F(x) = f(x)$, except when $x = 2$. By Theorem 6.9,

$$\lim\limits_{x \to 2} F(x) = \lim\limits_{x \to 2} f(x) = \lim\limits_{x \to 2} \dfrac{x + 7}{x + 1} = \dfrac{\lim\limits_{x \to 2} (x + 7)}{\lim\limits_{x \to 2} (x + 1)} = \dfrac{9}{3} = 3.$$

9   THE CONCEPT OF INFINITY

We shall not have occasion to use the concept of infinity in the present work, but for the sake of completeness we shall include it here.

It sometimes happens that, as x approaches a, $f(x)$ does not tend to any definite limit but increases beyond all bounds. That is to say, for every positive number M a positive number d can be found such that $f(x) > M$ when $0 < |x - a| < d$. We express this state of affairs by saying that $f(x)$ becomes infinite as x approaches a; in symbols,

$$\lim_{x \to a} f(x) = \infty.$$

It is most important to understand that the symbol ∞ does not represent a number and cannot be used as such in making calculations. In fact, the "equation" above is a shorthand way of saying the following two things.

1. $f(x)$ does not approach a definite limit as $x \to a$.
2.   By taking values of x near enough to a, we can make $f(x)$ as large as we please.

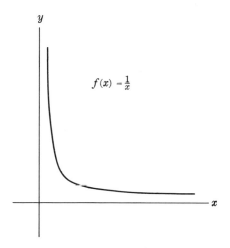

$$f(x) = \frac{1}{x}$$

FIGURE 6.2

Consider as an example the graph of $f(x) = 1/x$, where $x > 0$, in Fig. 6.2:

$$f(1) \;\;\; = 1,$$
$$f(.1) \;\;\; = 10,$$
$$f(.01) = 100,$$
$$\cdot \;\; \cdot \;\; \cdot \;\; \cdot \;\; \cdot \;\; \cdot \;\; \cdot \;\; \cdot \;\; \cdot \;\; \cdot \;\; \cdot \;\; \cdot,$$
$$f(0.000001) = 1{,}000{,}000,$$

for which, obviously, we could write

$$\lim_{x \to 0} \frac{1}{x} = \infty.$$

On the other hand, it might happen that, as x gets larger and larger, $f(x)$ will tend to a definite limit, say L. In symbols we would write this

$$\lim_{x \to \infty} f(x) = L.$$

Again, consider the function $f(x) = 1/x$:

$$\begin{aligned} f(1) &= 1, \\ f(10) &= 0.1, \\ f(100) &= 0.01, \end{aligned}$$
$$. \ . \ . \ . \ . \ . \ . \ . \ . \ . \ .,$$
$$f(1,000,000) = 0.000001,$$

where, clearly, as x increases, $1/x$ is approaching zero; so we write

$$\lim_{x \to \infty} \frac{1}{x} = 0.$$

It follows from the last two examples that, in general,

$$\lim_{x \to 0} \frac{k}{x^n} = \infty \qquad \text{and} \qquad \lim_{x \to \infty} \frac{k}{x^n} = 0,$$

where k is any constant except zero and where n is positive.

Example.   Evaluate the limit $\displaystyle \lim_{x \to \infty} \frac{2x^2 - 3x + 7}{3x^2 + 5x}$.

Solution: To evaluate limits of this type, divide the numerator and denominator by the highest power of x present, whether in the numerator or in the denominator. In this case we divide by x^2 and write

$$\lim_{x \to \infty} \frac{2x^2 - 3x + 7}{3x^2 + 5x} = \lim_{x \to \infty} \frac{2 - (3/x) + (7/x^2)}{3 + (5/x)} = \frac{2}{3}.$$

The last equality is the result of the fact that

$$\lim_{x \to \infty} \frac{k}{x^n} = 0, \qquad k \neq 0, n > 0.$$

EXERCISES

By using the theorems on limits, the properties of polynomials, and limits involving the concept of infinity, evaluate the following.

1. $\displaystyle \lim_{x \to 2} (3x^2 - 7x).$

2. $\displaystyle \lim_{x \to 1} \sqrt{x^2 - 5x + 13}.$

3. $\displaystyle \lim_{x \to 2} \frac{2x + 5}{x - 1}.$

4. $\displaystyle \lim_{x \to 0} \frac{2x^3 + 7x - 4}{x^2 + 8x - 2}.$

5. $\lim\limits_{x\to 5} (x^3 - 100)(3x - 12)$.

6. $\lim\limits_{x\to\infty} \dfrac{2x + 3}{x - 1}$.

7. $\lim\limits_{x\to 2} \dfrac{x^2 - 4}{x - 2}$.

8. $\lim\limits_{x\to 1} \dfrac{x^2 - 1}{x^2 + x - 2}$.

9. $\lim\limits_{x\to 3} (x^3 - 5x^2 + 7x + 10)$.

10. $\lim\limits_{x\to\frac{1}{2}} \dfrac{4}{x^2}$.

11. $\lim\limits_{h\to 0} \dfrac{3h + h^2}{h}$.

12. $\lim\limits_{h\to 0} \dfrac{5xh - 2h - h^2}{h}$.

13. $\lim\limits_{x\to 3} \dfrac{x^2 - 2x - 3}{x^2 - 9}$.

14. $\lim\limits_{x\to 2} \dfrac{x^3 - 8}{x - 2}$.

15. $\lim\limits_{x\to\infty} \dfrac{x^3 + 4x - 1}{x^3 + 5}$.

16. $\lim\limits_{x\to 2} \dfrac{x^2 - 5x + 6}{x^2 - 2x - 2}$.

17. $\lim\limits_{x\to -1} \dfrac{x^3 + 1}{x^2 - 1}$.

18. $\lim\limits_{h\to 0} \dfrac{\sqrt{2 + h} - \sqrt{2}}{h}$.

19. $\lim\limits_{h\to 0} \dfrac{(x + h)^3 - x^3}{h}$.

20. $\lim\limits_{x\to 3} \dfrac{\sqrt{7 - x} - 2}{3 - x}$.

10 INSTANTANEOUS SPEED

The limit idea is essential in defining many important mathematical concepts, one of which, instantaneous speed, we have already mentioned. Because of the importance of this concept let us repeat the definition here in more general form. Let S be the distance, after t units of time, of a moving object from some fixed point. Assume $S = f(t)$. The instantaneous speed V at the instant $t = t_1$ is defined as

$$V = \lim\limits_{h\to 0}\frac{f(t_1 + h) - f(t_1)}{h}.$$

Note: The expression $[f(t_1 + h) - f(t_1)]/h$, it should be emphasized, is precisely the average speed of the object during the interval of time $t = t_1$ to $t = t_1 + h$. Hence V is the limiting value of this average speed as the length of the interval of time over which it was calculated approaches zero. This definition can be stated in other words: The speed of a moving object at an instant is the limit approached by the average speed of the object, calculated over an interval of time containing the instant, as the length of this interval of time is made to approach zero.

Example. A ball was thrown vertically upward. Its distance S feet above the ground after t seconds was $S = 40t - 16t^2$. Find the speed at the instant $t = 1$.

$$t_1 = 1$$
$$f(t) = 40t - 16t^2,$$
$$f(1) = 40 - 16 = 24,$$
$$f(1 + h) = 40(1 + h) - 16(1 + h)^2$$
$$= 40 + 40h - 16 - 32h - 16h^2$$
$$= 24 + 8h - 16h^2,$$
$$f(1 + h) - f(1) = 8h - 16h^2,$$

$$V = \lim_{h \to 0} \frac{8h - 16h^2}{h} = \lim_{h \to 0} (8 - 16h) = 8 \text{ ft/sec.}$$

Example. A particle moved along a straight line in such a way that its distance (x ft) from a fixed point 0 on the line was $x = 10 + 60t - 3t^2$. Find the speed of the particle at the instant $t = t_1$.

$$f(t) = 10 + 60t - 3t^2,$$
$$f(t_1) = 10 + 60t_1 - 3t_1^2,$$
$$f(t_1 + h) = 10 + 60(t_1 + h) - 3(t_1 + h)^2,$$
$$= 10 + 60t_1 + 60h - 3t_1^2 - 6t_1h - 3h^2,$$
$$f(t_1 + h) - f(t_1) = 60h - 6t_1h - 3h^2,$$

$$V = \lim_{h \to 0} \frac{60h - 6t_1h - 3h^2}{h} = \lim_{h \to 0} (60 - 6t_1 - 3h),$$

$$= 60 - 6t_1.$$

Now, since t_1 is arbitrary, we can drop the subscript from the t and have the formula $V = 60 - 6t$ for the speed at any time t.

11   ACCELERATION

As was seen in the last example of Section 10, the speed V may be a varying quantity. The rate at which speed varies with time is called *acceleration*. To be more specific, let V_1 be the speed of an object at the instant t_1 and V_2 be the speed at the instant t_2. We define the average acceleration $\overline{A}$ of the object during the interval of time from $t = t_1$ to $t = t_2$ as

$$\overline{A} = \frac{V_2 - V_1}{t_2 - t_1}.$$

Now let $t_2 = t_1 + h$; then the acceleration A at the instant $t = t_1$ is, by definition,

$$A = \lim_{h \to 0} \overline{A} = \lim_{h \to 0} \frac{V_2 - V_1}{h}.$$

As was pointed out in Section 1, if the variable speed is measured in feet per second, then its acceleration is measured in feet per second per second, which we write symbolically as "ft/sec²."

Example. The speed, V feet per second, of a car t seconds after starting varies thus: $V = 10t - t^2$. What is the average acceleration during the interval $t = 2$ to $t = 2 + h$? Also find the acceleration at the instant $t = 2$.

$$t_1 = 2,$$
$$t_2 = 2 + h,$$
$$V_1 = 20 - 4 = 16,$$
$$V_2 = 10(2 + h) - (2 + h)^2 = 20 + 10h - 4 - 4h - h^2,$$
$$= 16 + 6h - h^2,$$
$$V_2 - V_1 = 6h - h^2,$$

$$\overline{A} = \frac{V_2 - V_1}{t_2 - t_1} = \frac{6h - h^2}{h} = 6 - h,$$

$$A = \lim_{h \to 0} \overline{A} = \lim_{h \to 0} (6 - h) = 6 \text{ ft/sec}^2.$$

12 TANGENT LINE TO A CURVE AT A POINT

In Section 2 we gave an intuitive definition of a line tangent to a curve. We shall now give a formal definition, based on the limit concept and suggested by the intuitive definition.

Consider a smooth curve C which is the graph of a continuous function $y = f(x)$. Let $P(x_1, y_1)$ be a fixed point on C and let $Q(x_1 + h, y_1 + k)$ be a neighboring variable point on C. A line through any two distinct points of a curve is called a *secant line* of the curve. Hence the line through P and Q is a secant line of the curve C. In general, if the secant PQ is made to revolve about the fixed point P in such a way that Q moves along C and approaches P, the

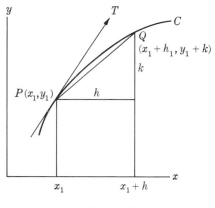

FIGURE 6.3

secant PQ will ultimately assume a limiting position PT (see Fig. 6.3). In such a case PT is called the *tangent* to the curve C at the point P.

Definition 6.4. *A tangent line PT to a curve C, at the fixed point P on C, is the limiting position (if it exists) of a variable secant PQ as Q moves into coincidence with P. P is called the* point of tangency.

It is important to note that this definition does not preclude the possibility of a line tangent to a curve crossing the curve at the point of tangency, or of a curve having two tangent lines at the same point; see Fig. 6.4. How-

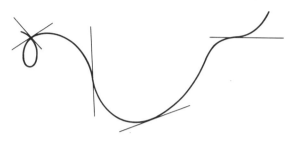

FIGURE 6.4

ever, it does require that a line tangent to a curve will have the same direction as the curve at the point of tangency.

13   SLOPE OF A CURVE AT A POINT

The *average slope* of a curve over an interval is usually defined as the difference in the heights of the curve at the ends of the interval, divided by the length of the interval. From Fig. 6.3 we see that the average slope $\overline{m}$ of the curve C over the interval from $x = x_1$ to $x = x_1 + h$ is

$$\overline{m} = \frac{f(x_1 + h) - f(x_1)}{h}, \qquad h \neq 0.$$

Hence the slope m of the curve C at the point P is defined, provided the limit exists, as follows:

$$m = \lim_{h \to 0} \frac{f(x_1 + h) - f(x_1)}{h}.$$

It should be noted that $\overline{m}$ as just defined is precisely the slope of the secant PQ and, since PQ approaches the position PT as h approaches zero, the slope m' of the tangent line PT is

$$m' = \lim_{h \to 0} \overline{m} = \lim_{h \to 0} \frac{f(x_1 + h) - f(x_1)}{h}.$$

But $m' = m$; hence the slope of the curve C at the point P is the same as the slope of the tangent line to C at the point P. In fact, we could have defined the slope of a curve at a point as the slope of the tangent line to the curve at that point.

14   INSTANTANEOUS RATES IN GENERAL

Instantaneous speed, acceleration, and the slope of a curve at a point are actually particular interpretations of instantaneous rates in general, which we shall now define.

Let y and x be any two varying quantities such that y is a function of x, say $y = f(x)$, defined over a given interval of values of x. The average rate $\overline{R}$ at which y is changing per unit change in x over the interval x_1 to $x_1 + h$ is

$$\overline{R} = \frac{f(x_1 + h) - f(x_1)}{h}.$$

The instantaneous rate R at which y is changing with x per unit change in x at the instant $x = x_1$ is defined as

$$R = \lim_{h \to 0} \overline{R} = \lim_{h \to 0} \frac{f(x_1 + h) - f(x_1)}{h}.$$

Now, if y be interpreted as the distance an object traveled from some fixed point, x units of time after starting, then R is the instantaneous speed of the object when $x = x_1$. Similarly, if $y = f(x)$ is the equation of some curve, then R is the slope of that curve at the point (x_1, y_1). Thus the interpretation that may be given to R depends entirely upon what the quantities x and y represent.

Example.   The volume of a given quantity of a certain gas varied with the pressure in the following way: $V = 400/P$. Find the rate at which the volume was changing per unit change in pressure at the instant $P = 10$.

Here, instead of representing the varying quantities by the letters x and y, we use the letters P and V where V is a function of P.

Solution: Let $P_1 = 10$ and $P_2 = 10 + h$; then

$$V_1 = \frac{400}{P_1} = \frac{400}{10},$$

$$V_2 = \frac{400}{P_2} = \frac{400}{10 + h}.$$

Notice that $400/P$ is playing the role of $f(x)$. Hence,

$$R = \lim_{h \to 0} \frac{400/(10 + h) - 400/10}{h}$$

$$= \lim_{h \to 0} \frac{(4000 - 4000 - 400h)/10(10 + h)}{h}$$

$$= \lim_{h \to 0} \frac{-400}{10(10 + h)} = -\frac{400}{100} = -4.$$

If the volume is measured in cubic inches and the pressure in pounds per square inch, we can say that

$$R = -\frac{4 \text{ in.}^3}{\text{lb/in.}^2}.$$

That is, the volume is decreasing at the rate of 4 cubic inches per unit increase in the pressure. The negative sign tells us that V is decreasing.

EXERCISES

1. A ball rolled up an incline, its distance, s feet from the starting point after t seconds, being $s = 40t - 3t^2$. What was its average speed from $t = 2$ to $t = 2 + h$? What was its instantaneous speed at $t = 2$?

2. The temperature $T°$ in a wire varied with the distance, x inches, from one end according to $T = 10x - x^2$. Find the average rate at which T changed per unit increase in x from $x = 4$ to $x = 4 + h$. Also, find the instantaneous rate at which T was changing at the instant $x = 4$. Could you find a formula that would give the instantaneous rate for any x? Find such a formula. (*Hint:* Find the average rate from x to $x + h$.) Using this formula, find the instantaneous rate of change of T at the instants $x = 6$ and $x = 8$.

3. Using the hint in Exercise 2, find a formula for the slope of each given curve at any point (x, y): **(a)** $y = 3x^2 - 5x + 10$, **(b)** $y = 1/x$, and **(c)** $y = x/(x + 1)$.

4. The speed of a moving object v feet per minute, varied with the time, t minutes, as given in the table below. Plot, and read off the maximum speed. Find the acceleration at $t = 6$ and at $t = 11$.

t min	0	2	4	6	8	10	12	14
v ft/min	0	12	40	72	96	100	72	0

5. The repulsion F, in dynes, between a certain pair of electric charges varies with the distance x centimeters between them; thus: $F = 50/x^2$. Find a formula for the rate of change of F with x. How fast was F changing with x at $x = 2$? What does the minus sign mean?

6. If a ball is thrown upward at an initial speed of 128 feet per second, its height, y feet, above the ground after t seconds is given by the equation $y = 128t - 16t^2$.
   a. Find a formula for its speed at any time.
   b. What was the speed at the end of 2, 4, and 5 seconds?
   c. What is the greatest height attained by the ball?
   d. When did the ball reach the ground and with what speed?
   e. Was the ball rising or falling at the end of 5 seconds?

7. In a right triangle whose hypotenuse is constantly equal to 10 inches, the lengths of the two legs, x and y, are related thus: $y = \sqrt{100 - x^2}$. Find how fast y is changing with x when $x = 6$.

8. **(a)** Find the slope of the curve $y = x^3$ at the point for which $x = 2$. **(b)** Find the rate at which the volume of a cube is changing per unit change in the edge, x inches, when $x = 2$.

9. Find the slope of the tangent line to the curve $y = x^2 - 4x$ at the point $(3, -3)$ and the equation of this line.

10. Find the equation of the line tangent to the curve $y = 2x^2 + 5x + 6$ at the point $(-1, 3)$.

11. A particle moves along the x axis according to the law $x = 2t^3 + 6t^2 - 4t + 1$. Find the acceleration at the instant $t = 2$.

12. Find a formula for the slope of the curve $y = \sqrt{x+1}$ at any point (x, y).

13. The speed, V feet per second, of a car, t seconds after starting, was $V = 0.05t^2 - 0.002t^3$. Find the average acceleration from $t = 20$ to $t = 20 + h$. What was the acceleration at $t = 20$?

14. The force F in pounds, applied to an object, varied with the time t, in minutes, according to $F = 60t - 2t^2$. How fast was F increasing at $t = 10$?

VII

DIFFERENTIATION

1 THE DERIVATIVE OF A FUNCTION

In Chapter VI we learned that finding a slope and finding an instantaneous speed or an instantaneous acceleration or other instantaneous rates are largely one and the same problem. Since this is true, we shall now formulate a procedure for all problems involving the calculations of instantaneous rates.

Definition 7.1. *Let f be the function defined by the equation $y = f(x)$ for all values of x in the open interval (a, b), and let x_1 be any fixed number of this interval. The derivative of y with respect to x at $x = x_1$ is defined, provided the limit exists, as*

$$\lim_{h \to 0} \frac{f(x_1 + h) - f(x_1)}{h}.$$

Various symbols are used to denote this limit, the more common ones being y' (read "y prime"), $f'(x)$ (read "f prime of x"), $D_x y$, and dy/dx (the last two are both read "the derivative of y with respect to x"). The symbols $D_x y$ and dy/dx are interpreted respectively as $D_x y = D_x(y)$ and $dy/dx = d/dx(y)$, where $D_x(\cdots)$ and $d/dx(\cdots)$ each denotes the operation "derivative with respect to x of" the expression following the symbol D_x or d/dx. Note that these symbols do not indicate multiplication. Although we shall for the most part use $D_x y$ and $f'(x)$, the student should learn to recognize each of the symbols mentioned as representing a derivative. Also, since x_1 is an arbitrary number from the interval (a, b), it is common practice to omit the subscript and write the definition of the derivative in either of the forms

$$D_x y = \lim_{h \to 0} \frac{f(x + h) - f(x)}{h} \quad \text{or} \quad f'(x) = \lim_{h \to 0} \frac{f(x + h) - f(x)}{h}.$$

This practice will be adopted here but it must be kept in mind that, for the limit operation, x is a fixed number, h is the variable, and the value of the limit will, in general, be different for different values of x.

It is obvious from our definition that finding the derivative of a function is precisely the same process as finding the instantaneous rate of change of the function. This process is called *differentiation*.

Example.   Find the derivative of $y = f(x) = 3x^2 - 5x + 2$ and evaluate this derivative at $x = 3$.

Solution:
$$\begin{aligned} f(x + h) &= 3(x + h)^2 - 5(x + h) + 2 \\ &= 3x^2 + 6xh + 3h^2 - 5x - 5h + 2. \\ f(x + h) - f(x) &= 6xh - 5h + 3h^2 \end{aligned}$$

$$D_x y = \lim_{h \to 0} \frac{6xh - 5h + 3h^2}{h}$$

$$= \lim_{h \to 0} (6x - 5 + 3h) = 6x - 5.$$

Thus for any x the derivative $D_x y = 6x - 5$. When $x = 3$, $D_x y = 18 - 5 = 13$.

2   Δ NOTATION

Most texts, instead of using the single letter h to denote a change in a variable, use the Greek capital letter *delta*, Δ. The symbol Δx, read "delta x," has precisely the same meaning as h in our notation, and the two may be used interchangeably by means of the simple relation $h = \Delta x$. Again, observe that Δx is a single symbol and does not mean Δ times x. It means an increment of x, that is, a change in x. This notation exhibits the variable whose increment or change is under consideration; thus Δx denotes an increment of x, Δy an increment of y, Δt an increment of t, etc.

In the delta notation we can write

$$\Delta y = f(x + \Delta x) - f(x)$$

and
$$D_x y = \lim_{\Delta x \to 0} \frac{\Delta y}{\Delta x} = \lim_{\Delta x \to 0} \frac{f(x + \Delta x) - f(x)}{\Delta x}.$$

Example.   Use the delta notation to find $D_x y$ if $y = x^2 + 3x - 2$.

Solution: $y + \Delta y = (x + \Delta x)^2 + 3(x + \Delta x) - 2$
$$= x^2 + 2x\,\Delta x + (\Delta x)^2 + 3x + 3\,\Delta x - 2$$

$$y = x^2 \qquad\qquad\qquad\qquad + 3x \qquad\qquad - 2$$

Subtracting: ──────────────────────────────

$$\Delta y = \qquad 2x\,\Delta x + (\Delta x)^2 \qquad\quad + 3\,\Delta x$$

$$\frac{\Delta y}{\Delta x} = 2x + \Delta x + 3$$

$$D_x y = \lim_{\Delta x \to 0} \frac{\Delta y}{\Delta x} = \lim_{\Delta x \to 0} (2x + \Delta x + 3) = 2x + 3.$$

This direct use of the definition in terms of the delta to find a derivative is known as the delta process for finding derivatives.

EXERCISES

In each problem 1 through 14 find $f'(x)$ by using the definition

$$f'(x) = \lim_{h \to 0} \frac{f(x + h) - f(x)}{h}$$

1. $f(x) = 5x - 7.$

2. $f(x) = x^2.$

3. $f(x) = 3x^2 - 8x + 4.$

4. $f(x) = 5 + 6x - 2x^2.$

5. $f(x) = (2x + 3)(5x - 1).$

6. $f(x) = 8 - x - 5x^2.$

7. $f(x) = x^3.$

8. $f(x) = x^4.$

9. $f(x) = 7x^3 - 5x + 10.$

10. $f(x) = \dfrac{x + 3}{x + 2}.$

11. $f(x) = \sqrt{x}.$

12. $f(x) = \sqrt{x + 3}.$

13. $f(x) = \sqrt[3]{x}.$

14. $f(x) = \dfrac{5 - 7x}{3 + 2x}.$

In each problem 15 through 22 find $D_x y$ by using the definition

$$D_x y = \lim_{\Delta x \to 0} \frac{f(x + \Delta x) - f(x)}{\Delta x}.$$

15. $y = f(x) = 8x^2 - 7x + 3.$

16. $y = f(x) = (7x + 2)(3x - 4).$

17. $y = f(x) = (1 - 2x)^2.$

18. $y = f(x) = \dfrac{4}{x}.$

19. $y = f(x) = \dfrac{x - 1}{x + 1}.$

20. $y = f(x) = x + \dfrac{2}{x}.$

21. $y = f(x) = x(x^2 + 3).$

22. $y = \dfrac{10}{x^2}.$

23. If $y = 2x^2 - 5x + 8$, find $\dfrac{dy}{dx}$ at $(1, 5)$.

24. If $S = 20 + 10t - t^2$, find $\dfrac{dS}{dt}$ at the instant $t = 2$.

25. The area A of a circle of radius r is given by the formula $A = \pi r^2$. Find $\dfrac{dA}{dr}$ at $r = 20$.

26. If $W = 10u - u^2$, find $D_u W$ at $u = 3$.

3   RULES FOR DIFFERENTIATION

In each of the last exercises the student was expected to find the derivative by each time applying the definition directly to the specific function involved. The procedure is laborious and rather time-consuming. We shall derive some simple formulas that will reduce the labor involved in finding a derivative and at the same time speed up the operation.

Derivative of a Constant

Let $y = f(x) = C$ for $a < x < b$; then

$$f(x + h) = C,$$
$$f(x + h) - f(x) = 0,$$
$$D_x y = \lim_{h \to 0} \frac{f(x + h) - f(x)}{h} = \lim_{h \to 0} \frac{0}{h} = \lim_{h \to 0} 0 = 0.$$

Hence the derivative of any constant with respect to a variable is zero. In symbols this is written as follows.

Formula 1: $D_x C = 0$, where C is a constant.

Derivative of $y = f(x) = x$ with Respect to x

We have the following equations, which express the fact that the derivative of any variable with respect to itself is equal to 1 (Formula 2, below).

$$f(x + h) = x + h,$$
$$f(x + h) - f(x) = h,$$
$$D_x y = \lim_{h \to 0} \frac{f(x + h) - f(x)}{h} = \lim_{h \to 0} \frac{h}{h} = 1.$$

Formula 2: $D_x x = 1$.

Derivative of x^n Where n Is a Positive Integer

From Formula 2 we have that $D_x x^1 = 1$. In Exercises 2, 7, and 8 of Section 2 we found that

$$D_x(x^2) = 2x,$$
$$D_x(x^3) = 3x^2,$$
$$D_x(x^4) = 4x^3.$$

These equations suggest a third rule, which we shall prove.

Formula 3: $D_x(x^n) = nx^{n-1}$, where n is a positive integer.

Proof: To prove this rule, let us again apply our definition to the function $f(x) = x^n$. If $f(x) = x^n$, then $f(x + h) = (x + h)^n$.
Now applying the binomial theorem, we have

$$f(x + h) = x^n + nx^{n-1}h + \frac{n(n-1)}{2} x^{n-2}h^2 + \cdots + h^n;$$

hence $$f(x + h) - f(x) = nx^{n-1}h + \frac{n(n-1)}{2} x^{n-2}h^2 + \cdots + h^n$$

and $$D_x(x^n) = \lim_{h \to 0} \left(\frac{nx^{n-1}h + \dfrac{n(n-1)}{2} x^{n-2}h^2 + \cdots + h^n}{h} \right),$$

$$= \lim_{h \to 0} \left(nx^{n-1} + \frac{n(n-1)}{2} x^{n-2}h + \cdots + h^{n-1} \right),$$

$$= nx^{n-1}.$$

Example.   Find the derivative of $y = x^{20}$.

Solution: By Formula 3, $D_x y = 20x^{19}$.

Derivative of $kf(x)$ Where k Is a Constant

The derivative of a constant times a function is equal to the constant times the derivative of the function. This is expressed by the following.

Formula 4: $D_x[kf(x)] = kD_x[f(x)]$, where k is a constant and $f(x)$ is a differentiable function of x.

Proof: $$kf(x + h) - kf(x) = k[f(x + h) - f(x)],$$

$$D_x[kf(x)] = \lim_{h \to 0} \frac{k[f(x + h) - f(x)]}{h},$$

$$= k \lim_{h \to 0} \frac{f(x + h) - f(x)}{h},$$

$$= k D_x[f(x)].$$

Example.   Find the derivative of $7x^{10}$.

Solution: By Formula 4, $D_x(7x^{10}) = 7 D_x(x^{10})$;
by Formula 3, $= 7(10x^9)$;
                  $= 70x^9$.

Derivative of $f(x) + g(x)$

Formula 5: $D_x[f(x) + g(x)] = D_x f(x) + D_x g(x).$

Proof: $[f(x + h) + g(x + h)] - [f(x) + g(x)]$
$$= [f(x + h) - f(x)] + [g(x + h) - g(x)].$$

Applying the definition of a derivative and assuming each limit exists, we may write

$$D_x[f(x) + g(x)] = \lim_{h \to 0} \left[\frac{f(x + h) - f(x)}{h} + \frac{g(x + h) - g(x)}{h} \right],$$

$$= \lim_{h \to 0} \frac{f(x + h) - f(x)}{h} + \lim_{h \to 0} \frac{g(x + h) - g(x)}{h},$$

$$= D_x f(x) + D_x g(x).$$

That is, the derivative of the sum of two functions is equal to the sum of the derivatives of each of the functions.

An immediate consequence of Formula 5 is the following theorem.

Theorem 7.1.   *The derivative of the algebraic sum of any finite number of functions is equal to the algebraic sum of the derivatives of the individual functions.*

Example.   Find the derivative of $y = 2x^3 - 7x^2 + 3x - 10$.

Solution: By Formula 5,

$$\begin{aligned} D_x y &= D_x(2x^3 - 7x^2 + 3x - 10), \\ &= D_x(2x^3) + D_x(-7x^2) + D_x(3x) + D_x(-10), \\ &= 6x^2 - 14x + 3 + 0, \\ &= 6x^2 - 14x + 3. \end{aligned}$$

In actual practice all intermediate steps in the solution would be omitted and the result written by inspection wherever possible.

Differentiating Any Polynomial

It should be observed at this point that our special rules now enable us to differentiate at sight any polynomial

$$y = a_0 x^n + a_1 x^{n-1} + \cdots + a_{n-1} x + a_n$$

and, consequently, any expression that can be reduced to a polynomial. Some examples of how this is done follow.

Example.   Find $D_x y$, where $y = x^2(3x - 2)$.

Solution: Multiplying: $y = 3x^3 - 2x^2$.
Differentiating: $D_x y = 9x^2 - 4x$.

Example.   If $y = \dfrac{x^4 - 2x^3 + 7x^2}{3x}$, what is $D_x y$?

Solution: Rewriting, we have $y = \frac{1}{3}x^3 - \frac{2}{3}x^2 + \frac{7}{3}x$; hence $D_x y = x^2 - \frac{4}{3}x + \frac{7}{3}$.

EXERCISES

In each problem 1 through 20 find by inspection the derivative of the given function; the symbols a, b, and c are constants wherever they occur.

1. $y = 7x + 5$.

11. $y = \dfrac{x^3 + x^2}{a + b}$.

2. $y = 3x^4 - 8x^2 - 10$.
3. $y = 5x^{100} - 7^3$.
4. $S = 3t^4 - t^5$.

12. $y = -\frac{5}{7}x^9 + \frac{2}{3}x^4 - \frac{4}{5}$.
13. $y = (2x^3 - 5)^2$.
14. $S = 512 + 20t - 16t^2$.

5. $V = 20t^2 - 5t^4$.

15. $y = \dfrac{x^5 - 4x^3 + x^2}{x^2}$.

6. $y = x^3(5 + 3x^2)$.

16. $y = \dfrac{at - bt^2}{c}$.

7. $S = 4\pi r^2$.
8. $Q = (u^2 - 1)(3u + 2)$.
9. $y = ax^2 + bx + c$.
10. $W = az + b$.

17. $T = u^4 - 2u^3 + 3u + 1$.
18. $y = x + 0.5x^2 + 0.4x^3 + 0.3x^4$.
19. $y = 3x^{17} - 4x^9 + 10^7$.
20. $y = (a^2 - b^2)x^3$.

21.   Use mathematical induction to prove Theorem 7.1. (*Hint:*   Let $F(x) = f_1(x) + f_2(x) + \cdots + f_n(x)$, n a positive integer).

22.   Use the definition of a derivative to prove that if n is a positive integer and $y = \dfrac{k}{x^n}$, then

$$D_x y = -\frac{kn}{x^{n+1}}.$$

23.   Use the result in Problem 22 to find $D_x y$ if

(a) $y = \dfrac{5}{x^2}$.   **(b)** $y = \dfrac{7}{x^4}$.   **(c)** $y = -\dfrac{4}{x^{10}}$.   **(d)** $y = \dfrac{6}{x^{100}}$.

4   DERIVATIVES OF PRODUCTS, QUOTIENTS, AND POWERS

In Section 3 we derived two rules that enabled us to find very quickly the derivative of any polynomial. The first of these two rules was a formula for the derivative of a monomial in x, namely

$$D_x(kx^n) = knx^{n-1}, \qquad n \text{ a positive integer};$$

the second rule stated that the derivative of the sum of a finite number of terms was the sum of their derivatives.

In this section we shall derive rules for finding the derivative with respect to x of the following, where u and v are any differentiable functions of x:

Products, as $y = uv$.
Quotients, as $y = u/v$.
Powers, as $y = u^n$.

Derivative of a Product

To find a rule for the derivative of a product, let $y = uv$, where u and v are differentiable functions of x, let x be given the increment Δx, and let Δy, Δu, and Δv be the corresponding changes in y, u, and v. We can then write

$$y + \Delta y = (u + \Delta u)(v + \Delta v) = uv + u\,\Delta v + v\,\Delta u + \Delta u\,\Delta v.$$

If we subtract from this the equation $y = uv$, we obtain

$$\Delta y = u\,\Delta v + v\,\Delta u + \Delta u\,\Delta v.$$

Now we divide by Δx, getting

$$\frac{\Delta y}{\Delta x} = u\,\frac{\Delta v}{\Delta x} + v\,\frac{\Delta u}{\Delta x} + \Delta u\,\frac{\Delta v}{\Delta x}.$$

Since u and v are assumed differentiable functions of x, it follows that

$$\lim_{\Delta x \to 0} \frac{\Delta u}{\Delta x} = D_x u,$$

$$\lim_{\Delta x \to 0} \frac{\Delta v}{\Delta x} = D_x v,$$

and hence $\lim\limits_{\Delta x \to 0} \Delta u = \lim\limits_{\Delta x \to 0} \Delta v = 0.$

Thus, as Δx approaches zero we have

$$\lim \frac{\Delta y}{\Delta x} = \lim \left(u\,\frac{\Delta v}{\Delta x} + v\,\frac{\Delta u}{\Delta x} + \Delta u\,\frac{\Delta v}{\Delta x} \right),$$

$$= \lim u\,\frac{\Delta v}{\Delta x} + \lim v\,\frac{\Delta u}{\Delta x} + \lim \Delta u\,\frac{\Delta v}{\Delta x},$$

$$= \lim u \lim \frac{\Delta v}{\Delta x} + \lim v \lim \frac{\Delta u}{\Delta x} + \lim \Delta u \lim \frac{\Delta v}{\Delta x},$$

$$= u\,D_x v + v\,D_x u + 0 \cdot D_x v.$$

or, finally, the rule: $D_x y = u\,D_x v + v\,D_x u.$

The rule for differentiating a product may be stated in words thus: *The derivative of the product of two functions is equal to the first function times the derivative of the second function, plus the second function times the derivative of the first function.*

It is important to notice here that the derivative of a product is not the product of the derivatives.

Derivative of a Quotient

To find the derivative of a quotient we let

$$y = \frac{u(x)}{v(x)},$$

where u and v are differentiable functions of x, and consider a value of x, say $x = c$, such that $v(c) \neq 0$. Again let Δy, Δu, and Δv be the increments of y, u, and v corresponding to the increment Δx of x. Let us restrict the values of the increment Δx so that $v + \Delta v \neq 0$. Then for $x = c$ and the restricted Δx we have

$$y + \Delta y = \frac{u + \Delta u}{v + \Delta v}.$$

We now subtract from this $y = u/v$ and obtain

$$\Delta y = \frac{u + \Delta u}{v + \Delta v} - \frac{u}{v} = \frac{(uv + v\,\Delta u) - (uv + u\,\Delta v)}{v(v + \Delta v)} = \frac{v\,\Delta u - u\,\Delta v}{v(v + \Delta v)}.$$

We next divide both sides of the last equation by Δx, keeping in mind that a fraction is divided by a number when we divide its numerator by the number, and we get

$$\frac{\Delta y}{\Delta x} = \frac{v\,\Delta u/\Delta x - u\,\Delta v/\Delta x}{v(v + \Delta v)}.$$

We have assumed that u and v are differentiable functions of x; hence

$$\lim_{\Delta x \to 0} \frac{\Delta u}{\Delta x} = D_x u,$$

$$\lim_{\Delta x \to 0} \frac{\Delta v}{\Delta x} = D_x v,$$

$$\lim_{\Delta x \to 0} \Delta v = 0.$$

Therefore we have that, as Δx approaches zero,

$$\lim \frac{\Delta y}{\Delta x} = \lim \frac{v\dfrac{\Delta u}{\Delta x} - u\dfrac{\Delta v}{\Delta x}}{v(v + \Delta v)} = \frac{\lim \left(v\dfrac{\Delta u}{\Delta x} - u\dfrac{\Delta v}{\Delta x} \right)}{\lim v(v + \Delta v)},$$

or the rule: $$D_x y = \frac{v\,D_x u - u\,D_x v}{v^2}.$$

In words this rule becomes: *The derivative of a quotient is equal to the denominator times the derivative of the numerator, minus the numerator times the derivative of the denominator, all divided by the square of the denominator.*

Example.   Find $D_x y$, given $y = \dfrac{3x + 7}{5 - 2x}$.

Solution: Applying the rule for differentiating a quotient, we have

$$D_x y = \frac{(5 - 2x) \, Dx(3x + 7) - (3x + 7) \, D_x(5 - 2x)}{(5 - 2x)^2},$$

$$= \frac{(5 - 2x)(3) - (3x + 7)(-2)}{(5 - 2x)^2},$$

$$= \frac{15 - 6x + 6x + 14}{(5 - 2x)^2} = \frac{29}{(5 - 2x)^2}.$$

Example. Find $D_x y$, given $y = (3x + 7)(5 - 2x)$.

Solution: We could, of course, easily multiply the product first and then differentiate, but it is as easy to use the rule for differentiating a product. Thus,

$$D_x y = (3x + 7) \, D_x(5 - 2x) + (5 - 2x) \, D_x(3x + 7),$$
$$= (3x + 7)(-2) + (5 - 2x)(3),$$
$$= -6x - 14 + 15 - 6x = 1 - 12x.$$

Derivative of a Power Function

Next consider the power function

$$y = ku^n,$$

where k is a fixed constant, n a positive integer, and u a differentiable function of x. Let Δy and Δu be increments of y and u corresponding to an increment Δx of x. Then,

$$y + \Delta y = k(u + \Delta u)^n$$

$$= k \left[u^n + nu^{n-1} \, \Delta u + \frac{n(n-1)}{2} \, u^{n-2} \, (\Delta u)^2 + \cdots + (\Delta u)^n \right].$$

Subtracting from this the equation $y = ku^n$, we obtain

$$\Delta y = knu^{n-1} \, \Delta u + k \left[\frac{n(n-1)}{2} \, u^{n-2} \mid \cdots + (\Delta u)^{n-2} \right] (\Delta u)^2.$$

Now dividing by Δx, we have

$$\frac{\Delta y}{\Delta x} = knu^{n-1} \frac{\Delta u}{\Delta x} + k \left[\frac{n(n-1)}{2} \, u^{n-2} + \cdots + (\Delta u)^{n-2} \right] \frac{(\Delta u)^2}{\Delta x}.$$

Since u is a differentiable function of x,

$$\lim_{\Delta x \to 0} \frac{\Delta u}{\Delta x} = D_x u.$$

Hence

$$\lim_{\Delta x \to 0} \frac{(\Delta u)^2}{\Delta x} = \lim_{\Delta x \to 0} \frac{\Delta u}{\Delta x} \Delta u = \lim_{\Delta x \to 0} \frac{\Delta u}{\Delta x} \lim_{\Delta x \to 0} \Delta u = D_x u \cdot 0 = 0.$$

Thus, as Δx approaches zero, we have

$$\lim \frac{\Delta y}{\Delta x} = \lim knu^{n-1}\frac{\Delta u}{\Delta x} + \lim k \left[\frac{n(n-1)}{2}u^{n-2} + \cdots + (\Delta u)^{n-2}\right]\frac{(\Delta u)^2}{\Delta x}$$

or the rule: $D_x y = knu^{n-1} D_x u.$

Example. Find $D_x y$, given $y = 8(3 - 4x^3)^{10}.$

Solution: If we take $k = 8$, $n = 10$, and $u = 3 - 4x^3$, we can write $y = 8u^{10}$. Applying the rule just established, we obtain

$$D_x y = 80u^9 D_x u.$$
Since $u = 3 - 4x^3,$
$$D_x u = -12x^2.$$
Therefore $D_x y = 80(3 - 4x^3)^9(-12x^2) = -960x^2(3 - 4x^3)^9.$

Note: It is not necessary actually to replace the quantity within the parentheses by u, as we have done; one can work directly with the quantity, and this is what is usually done.

Corollary. *If $f'(x)$ exists, then*

$$D_x\sqrt{f(x)} = \frac{f'(x)}{2\sqrt{f(x)}}.$$

Proof:

$$D_x\sqrt{f(x)} = D_x[f(x)]^{1/2} = \frac{1}{2}[f(x)]^{-1/2}f'(x) = \frac{f'(x)}{2\sqrt{f(x)}}.$$

Example.

$$D_x\sqrt{7 + x^2} = \frac{2x}{2\sqrt{7 + x^2}} = \frac{x}{\sqrt{7 + x^2}}.$$

Example. Find $D_x y$, given $y = 7(x^2 - 1)^{40}.$

Solution: Applying our rule, we have

$$D_x y = 280(x^2 - 1)^{39} D_x(x^2 - 1) = 280(x^2 - 1)^{39}(2x) = 560x(x^2 - 1)^{39}.$$

Let us now show that the rule is valid when n is a negative integer. Again let

$$y = ku^n, \qquad \text{where } u \neq 0$$

and is a differentiable function of x, n is a negative integer, and k is a fixed constant. Since n is a negative integer, we can write $n = -m$, where m is a positive integer. Hence

$$y = ku^{-m} = \frac{k}{u^m}.$$

We can now apply the rule for differentiating a quotient and write

$$D_x y = \frac{u^m D_x(k) - k D_x u^m}{(u^m)^2}$$

but, since k is a constant,

$$D_x(k) = 0,$$

and, from our rule,

$$D_z u^m = m u^{m-1} D_z u;$$

hence

$$D_z y = \frac{u^m \cdot 0 - k m u^{m-1} D_z u}{(u^m)^2} = -\frac{k m u^{m-1} D_z u}{u^{2m}} = -k m u^{-m-1} D_z u.$$

Replacing $-m$ by n, we obtain

$$D_z y = k n u^{n-1} D_z u$$

and we see that the rule is valid when n is a positive or negative integer. In the special case $u = x$, we have $u^n = x^n$ and $D_z u = 1$; thus,

$$\text{if} \qquad y = kx^n,$$
$$\text{then} \qquad D_z y = k n x^{n-1}.$$

This last result will be recognized as Formula 3 of Section 3, which was shown there to be valid for n a positive integer. Here, however, obtaining it as a special case of a rule valid for n a negative integer shows that it must also be valid for n a negative integer.

Example. Given $y = 3x^{-7}$, find $D_z y$.

Solution: Applying our last rule, we have $D_z y = 21x^{-8}$.

Example. Given $y = \dfrac{10}{(x^2 + 1)^5}$, find $D_z y$.

Solution: $y = \dfrac{10}{(x^2 + 1)^5} = 10(x^2 + 1)^{-5}$. Hence,

$$D_z y = -50(x^2 + 1)^{-6} D_x(x^2 + 1) = -50(x^2 + 1)^{-6}(2x),$$

$$= -100x(x^2 + 1)^{-6} = -\frac{100x}{(x^2 + 1)^6}.$$

Example. Given $y = \dfrac{x^5 + 4x^3 - 2x^2 - 7}{x^2}$, find $D_z y$.

Solution: Dividing each term of the numerator by the denominator, we can write

$$y = x^3 + 4x - 2 - 7x^{-2};$$

thus $\qquad D_z y = 3x^2 + 4 + 14x^{-3} = \dfrac{3x^5 + 4x^3 + 14}{x^3}.$

EXERCISES

Find $D_x y$ in each of the following exercises.

1. $y = 3x^{-2}$.

2. $y = -7x^{-5}$.

3. $y = \dfrac{10}{x^3}$.

4. $y = (x^2 + 5)(1 - x^3)$.

5. $y = \dfrac{x + 1}{x - 1}$.

6. $y = \dfrac{2x + 3}{5x - 7}$.

7. $y = (2x + 1)^3(x^2 - 1)^4$.

8. $y = (x^2 + 4)^6$.

9. $y = (2x - x^2)^4$.

10. $y = 10(x^3 + 5)^{10}$.

11. $y = \dfrac{x^2}{3x + 2}$.

12. $y = x^3 + \dfrac{4}{x}$.

13. $y = \dfrac{10}{1 + x^2}$.

14. $y = \dfrac{10}{(1 + x^2)^2}$.

15. $y = \dfrac{10}{(1 + x)^2}$.

16. $y = \dfrac{x^3 + 2x^2 - x + 5}{x}$.

17. $y = \left(\dfrac{x + 2}{x - 3}\right)^2$.

18. $y = x^2(1 + x)^{20}$.

19. Find the slope of the curve $xy = 12$ at the point (4, 3).
20. The volume of a gas varied with the pressure according to the relation $V = 400/P$. Find how fast V was changing with P at $P = 10$.

5 IMPLICIT DIFFERENTIATION

Most of the functions we have encountered thus far have been of the form $y = f(x)$. We say that in this form y is expressed explicitly as a function of x, that is, that our equation is solved for y in terms of x. In contrast to this we often need to work with equations such as the following.

$$x^2 + y^2 = 25.$$
$$x^2 - 2xy + y^2 = 1.$$
$$3x^2 - 5xy + 9y^2 = 40.$$
$$x^3 + x^2y^2 + 3xy^4 - 8y^5 + 6 = 0.$$

Each of these equations defines y as a function of x in the sense that if x be given a value the resulting equation determines one or more corresponding values of y. In such a case we say that the equation expresses y implicitly as a function of x or that y is an implicit function of x.

It often happens that an equation which determines y as an implicit function of x can be solved for y in terms of x. For example, the first three equations above are of this type. The last equation cannot be solved for y. However, it is possible to find $D_z y$ when it exists without solving for y.

Suppose we have the equation

$$y^2 = x^3$$

and we wish to find $D_z y$. Since y^2 is constantly equal to x^3, each of these quantities must change at the same rate with respect to x; that is,

$$D_z(y^2) = D_z(x^3).$$

Now, if we apply the rule for finding the derivative of a power function (Section 2), we have

$$D_z(y^2) = 2y\, D_z y$$
and
$$D_z(x^3) = 3x^2$$
hence
$$2y\, D_z y = 3x^2.$$

Dividing by $2y$, we obtain

$$D_z y = \frac{3x^2}{2y}, \qquad y \neq 0.$$

This method of differentiation is called *implicit differentiation*.

Example.   Find $D_z y$ at the point $(1, 2)$, given $x^2 - 3xy + 2y^2 = 3$.

Solution: $D_z(x^2 - 3xy + 2y^2) = D_z(3)$. Now, by applying the rules for differentiating a sum, a power u^n, and a product uv, we can find $D_z y$ thus:

$$D_z(x^2) + D_z(-3xy) + D_z(2y^2) = D_z(3),$$
$$2x - 3x\, D_z y + y\, D_z(-3x) + 4y\, D_z y = 0,$$
or
$$2x - 3x\, D_z y - 3y + 4y\, D_z y = 0.$$

Combining like terms, we get

$$2x - 3y - (3x - 4y)\, D_z y = 0.$$

Solving for $D_z y$, we have

$$D_z y = \frac{2x - 3y}{3x - 4y}.$$

At the point $(1, 2)$,

$$D_z y = \frac{2 - 6}{3 - 8} = \frac{-4}{-5} = \frac{4}{5}.$$

We have shown that the equation $D_x(x^n) = nx^{n-1}$ is valid when n is either a positive or a negative integer. We shall now use the method of implicit differentiation to show that this rule is valid for all rational values of n. To do this, let $n = p/q$, where $q > 0$, and consider

$$y = x^{p/q},$$

where p and q are integers. This, of course, means that

$$y^q = x^p.$$

Differentiating implicitly with respect to x, we obtain

$$qy^{q-1} D_x y = px^{p-1}.$$

If $y \neq 0$, then

$$D_x y = \frac{px^{p-1}}{qy^{q-1}}.$$

But

$$y^{q-1} = (x^{p/q})^{q-1} = x^{p-(p/q)}.$$

Hence

$$D_x y = \frac{p}{q} \cdot \frac{x^{p-1}}{x^{p-(p/q)}} = \frac{p}{q} x^{(p/q)-1},$$

which is equivalent to $D_x(x^n) = nx^{n-1}$ with n replaced by p/q. By a similar argument it is easy to generalize this result and thus show that

$$D_x(u^n) = nu^{n-1} D_x u$$

if u is a differentiable function of x and n is a rational number.

Example.   Given $y = x^{5/3}$, find $D_x y$.

Solution: $D_x y = \frac{5}{3}x^{5/3-1} = \frac{5}{3}x^{2/3}$.

Example.   Given $y = 7\sqrt{x^3}$, find $D_x y$.

Solution: In exponential form, $y = 7x^{3/2}$; hence $D_x y = \frac{21}{2}x^{1/2} = \frac{21}{2}\sqrt{x}$.

Example.   Given $y = 10/\sqrt{x}$, find $D_x y$.

Solution: $y = 10/\sqrt{x} = 10/x^{1/2} = 10x^{-1/2}$. Differentiating, we get

$$D_x y = -5x^{-3/2} = -\frac{5}{x^{3/2}} = -\frac{5}{\sqrt{x^3}}.$$

Example.   Given $y = \sqrt[3]{7 + 2x^4}$, find $D_x y$.

Solution: $y = \sqrt[3]{7 + 2x^4} = (7 + 2x^4)^{1/3}$.
Using the rule for differentiating u^n, we obtain

$$D_x y = \frac{1}{3}(7 + 2x^4)^{-2/3} D_x(7 + 2x^4),$$
$$= \frac{1}{3}(7 + 2x^4)^{-2/3}(8x^3),$$

$$= \frac{8x^3}{3(7 + 2x^4)^{2/3}} = \frac{8x^3}{3\sqrt[3]{(7 + 2x^4)^2}}.$$

EXERCISES

Find $D_x y$ in each of the following problems.

1. $y = 3x^{-5}$.

2. $y = \dfrac{10}{x^5}$.

3. $y = (x^2 + 5)(1 - x^3)$.

4. $y = \dfrac{x + 1}{x - 1}$.

5. $y = \dfrac{2x + 3}{5x - 7}$.

6. $y = \dfrac{x^2}{4 + x^2}$.

7. $y = (x^3 + 1)^{10}$.

8. $y = (4 - x^2)^8$.

9. $y = x^2 + \dfrac{7}{x} + \sqrt{x}$.

10. $y = \sqrt{4 - x^2}$.

11. $y = x^2\sqrt{x^2 + 1}$.

12. $y = 6\sqrt{x^3}$.

13. $y = (x^3 + 7)^{3/2}$.

14. $x^2 + xy = 4$.

15. $2x^2 + 3y^2 = 5$.

16. $y = \dfrac{10}{\sqrt{x^3}}$.

17. $y = \sqrt{x} + \dfrac{1}{\sqrt{x}}$.

18. $y = \dfrac{10}{(1 + x^2)^2}$.

19. $y = \left(\dfrac{x + 2}{x - 3}\right)^2$.

20. $y = \dfrac{x^3 - x + 5}{x}$.

21. $x^2 - 3xy - 2y^2 = 10$.

22. $x^2 - y^2 = 7$.

23. $xy + 3x - 2y = 4$.

24. $y = x^3\left(\sqrt{x} + \dfrac{1}{\sqrt{x}}\right)$.

25. $y = (x^2 + 2x)^{20}$.

26. $y = \dfrac{10}{1 + x^2}$.

27. $y = \dfrac{4}{(1 + x)^3}$.

28. $y = \sqrt[3]{3x - 7}$.

29. $y = \dfrac{5}{\sqrt{2x + 3}}$.

30. $x^2 + y^2 - 4x + 6y - 8 = 0$.

31. $y = \sqrt{x^2 - 2x + 5}$.

32. $y = \sqrt{1 - x^4}$.

33. $x^{2/3} + y^{2/3} = 4$.

6 SOME IMPORTANT THEOREMS

In this section we shall have a look at some theorems which are basic to the discussions to follow in the remainder of this chapter. The first two of these theorems we shall state without proof, however, both seem true intuitively.

Theorem 7.2. *If f is a function continuous on the closed interval* $[a, b]$, *then f has a maximum value, M, and a minimum value, m, on* $[a, b]$.

Theorem 7.3.   Intermediate Value Theorem. *If f is a continuous function on the closed interval* $[a, b]$, *with maximum value M and minimum value m, and* *if k is a number between m and M, then there is at least one number c on $[a, b]$ such that $f(c) = k$.*

Theorem 7.4.   *Suppose f is a function continuous on the closed interval $[a, b]$ with maximum value M and minimum value m on $[a, b]$. If $f(x_1) = M$ (or $f(x_1) = m$), where $a < x_1 < b$, and f is differentiable at x_1, then $f'(x_1) = 0$.*

We shall prove the theorem for the case $f(x_1) = M$. The proof for the case $f(x_1) = m$ is obtained with precisely the same type of argument.

Proof: Since $f(x_1) = M$, the maximum value of f on $[a, b]$, then $f(x_1 + h) - f(x_1) \le 0$ for all values of $h \ne 0$, and such that $a < x_1 + h < b$. Hence

$$\frac{f(x_1 + h) - f(x_1)}{h} \le 0 \quad \text{if} \quad h > 0 \quad \text{and} \quad \frac{f(x_1 + h) - f(x_1)}{h} \ge 0 \quad \text{if} \quad h < 0.$$

It follows that

$$\lim_{h \to 0} \frac{f(x_1 + h) - f(x_1)}{h} \le 0 \quad \text{if} \quad h > 0 \quad \text{and}$$

$$\lim_{h \to 0} \frac{f(x_1 + h) - f(x_1)}{h} \ge 0 \quad \text{if} \quad h < 0.$$

Now if f is differentiable at x_1, these two limits must have the same value, namely $f'(x_1)$. Therefore $f'(x_1) \le 0$ and $f'(x_1) \ge 0$, that is $f'(x_1) = 0$, which proves our theorem.

Theorem 7.5.   Rolle's Theorem.   *Let f be a function continuous on $[a, b]$ and differentiable in (a, b), and suppose $f(a) = f(b)$. Then there is at least one number $c \in (a, b)$ such that $f'(c) = 0$.*

Proof: Let M and m be the maximum and minimum values, respectively, of f on $[a, b]$. We need to consider two cases.

Case 1.   If $M = m$, then $f(x) = M = m$ for all $x \in [a, b]$ and $f'(x) = 0$ at each point of $[a, b]$ and the theorem is certainly true in this case.

Case 2.   Suppose $M \ne m$, that is $M > m$. Since $f(a) = f(b)$, f cannot have both its maximum value and its minimum value at an end point. Suppose $f(a) = f(b) \ne M$. Hence there is at least one point $x_1 \in (a, b)$ such that $f(x_1) = M$. By Theorem 7.3, $f'(x_1) = 0$ and our theorem is proved.

Theorem 7.6.   The Mean Value Theorem.   *Let f be a function continuous on $[a, b]$ and differentiable in (a, b). Then there is at least one number $c \in (a, b)$ such that*

$$\frac{f(b) - f(a)}{b - a} = f'(c).$$

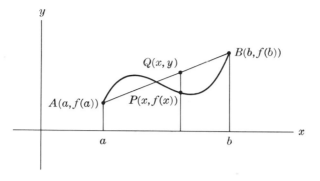

FIGURE 7.1

Proof: The endpoints of the graph of f are $A(a, f(a))$ and $B(b, f(b))$. See Fig. 7.1. The slope of the segment AB is

$$m = \frac{f(b) - f(a)}{b - a}.$$

Let $Q(x, y)$ and $P(x, f(x))$ be points on line AB and the graph of f, respectively, for each $x \in (a, b)$. Then

$$y = \frac{f(b) - f(a)}{b - a}(x - a) + f(a) \qquad \text{(Equation of line } AB\text{)}.$$

Now let $F(x) = y - f(x)$

$$= \frac{f(b) - f(a)}{b - a}(x - a) + f(a) - f(x).$$

Obviously F is continuous on $[a, b]$ and differentiable in (a, b). Also it is easily seen that $F(a) = 0 = F(b)$. Thus F satisfies the hypothesis of Rolle's Theorem and hence for some $c \in (a, b)$, $F'(c) = 0$. But

if $\qquad F'(x) = \dfrac{f(b) - f(a)}{b - a} - f'(x), \qquad$ and $\qquad F'(c) = 0$

$$\frac{f(b) - f(a)}{b - a} = f'(c).$$

This proves our theorem.

An obvious geometrical interpretation of the Mean Value Theorem is that there is at least one point of the graph of f, between $A(a, f(a))$ and $B(b, f(b))$ at which the slope of the tangent to the graph is parallel to the chord AB.

Theorem 7.7. *If the functions f and g are differentiable on $[a, b]$ and $f'(x) = g'(x)$ for all $x \in [a, b]$, then $g(x) = f(x) + c$, c a constant.*

Proof: Let $F(x) = g(x) - f(x)$, then F is continuous and differentiable on $[a, b]$ and the Mean Value Theorem applies. Hence for each x on $[a, b]$ there is a $c \in (a, b)$ such that

$$\frac{F(x) - F(a)}{b - a} = F'(c).$$

But, since $f'(x) = g'(x)$ all $x \in [a, b]$, $F'(c) = 0$, and so

$$F(x) = F(a)$$

for all $x \in [a, b]$, that is

$$g(x) - f(x) = F(a)$$

or $g(x) = f(x) + c$, where $c = F(a)$.

7   INTERPRETATIONS OF A DERIVATIVE

In Section 1 it was pointed out that *derivative* was a general name given to all instantaneous rates. Hence, if one wishes the instantaneous rate of change of a function, he finds its derivative. The interpretation given to such a derivative depends upon the kind of quantity represented by the function. We have previously introduced the word *speed* to denote the instantaneous rate of change of distance with respect to time. Thus, if the formula $S = f(t)$ gives the distance S, in feet, traveled by an object in t seconds, then $D_t S$ is the speed of the object and we write $V = D_t S$. Similarly, the instantaneous rate of change of speed is called *acceleration* and is written $A = D_t V$.

Example. A particle moves along a straight line in such a way that its distance, S feet, from the starting point after t seconds is given by the formula $S = t^4 - 12t^3 + 40t^2$. Find (a) the speed at any time, (b) the acceleration at any time, and (c) the speed and acceleration at $t = 2$.

Solution: $S = t^4 - 12t^3 + 40t^2$.

(a) Speed: $V = D_t S = 4t^3 - 36t^2 + 80t$.
(b) Acceleration: $A = D_t V = 12t^2 - 72t + 80$.
(c) When $t = 2$: $V = 4(2)^3 - 36(2)^2 + 80(2) = 32 - 144 + 160$,
                  $= 48$ ft/sec.
                  $A = 12(2)^2 - 72(2) + 80 = 48 - 144 + 80$,
                  $= -16$ ft/sec².

The negative sign here means that the speed V was decreasing at $t = 2$.

We defined the slope of a curve at a point on the curve as the instantaneous rate at which the height of the curve was changing at the point. For example, if $y = f(x)$ is the equation of the curve, the slope m at the point (x_1, y_1) on the curve can then be expressed in the following manner:

$$m = D_x y]_{x = x_1} \quad \text{or} \quad m = f'(x_1).$$

The symbol $D_x y]_{x = x_1}$ is read "the derivative of y with respect to x at $x = x_1$."

The instantaneous rate of change of slope is called the *flexion* of the curve. Thus, flexion $= D_x m$.

Example.   Find the slope of the curve $y = x^3 - 2x^2 + 3x - 5$ at the point for which $x = 1$.

Solution:

$$y = x^3 - 2x^2 + 3x - 5,$$
$$m = D_x y = 3x^2 - 4x + 3,$$
$$m = 3 - 4 + 3 = 2, \quad \text{when } x = 1.$$

Example.   As water leaks out of a tank, the quantity, Q gallons, remaining in the tank after t minutes is given by the formula $Q = 500 - 40t + 0.6t^2$.

How fast was Q changing at the end of 10 minutes?

Solution:

$$Q = 500 - 40t + 0.6t^2,$$
$$D_t Q = -40 + 1.2t \quad \text{(rate of change for any } t),$$
$$D_t Q = -40 + 12 = -28 \text{ gal/min}, \quad \text{when } t = 10.$$

In economics it is frequently necessary to make use of the rate of change of one variable with respect to another. For instance, the *marginal cost* M_c is defined as the rate of change of the total cost of production with respect to the number of units produced. Thus, if n is the number of units produced and C is the total cost of producing these n units, the marginal cost indicates the increase in total cost of production per additional unit produced. If we treat n as a continuous variable we see that the marginal cost is just the derivative of the cost C with respect to n or, in symbols,

$$M_c = D_n C.$$

If M_c is less than the selling price it pays to increase production, whereas if M_c is greater than the selling price there is a loss on each item produced.

Similarly, *marginal revenue* M_r is defined as the rate of increase of total revenue R with respect to the increase in output x. Hence,

$$M_r = D_x R,$$

where, again, we have a particular interpretation of a derivative.

Example.   Find the marginal cost of producing n units when the cost is given by the relation $C = 15 + 8n - 4n^2 + n^3$.

Solution: By definition, $M_c = D_n C$,
$$= 8 - 8n + 3n^2.$$

Figure 7.2 shows the graphs of the cost and the marginal cost plotted on the same coordinate axes. We see from these graphs that, while the cost continues to rise, the marginal cost decreases at first and then starts to rise

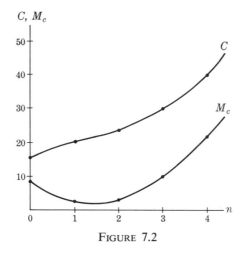

FIGURE 7.2

again between $n = 1$ and $n = 2$. Thus, after a certain point the marginal cost increases as more units are produced.

EXERCISES

1. An object is thrown from the top of a building in such a way that its height, y feet, above the ground t seconds after it is released is given by the formula $y = 100 + 80t - 16t^2$. Find:
    a. A formula for the speed at any time t.
    b. A formula for the acceleration at any time t.
    c. The initial speed (speed at $t = 0$).
    d. The height, speed, and acceleration at the end of 2 seconds, and at the end of 6 seconds.
2. The distance, x miles, of a car from a certain point t hours after passing the point is given by the relation $x = 60t - 5t^2$. Derive formulas for its speed and acceleration at any time t hours later. Suppose that for a second car the distance, x miles, from the same point at the same time t is $x = 12 + 60t - 5t^2$. Derive formulas for the speed and acceleration of the second car. Compare the results for the two cars. What is the significance of the constant term 12 in the distance formula for the second car?
3. In Exercise 2, when did the first car stop and reverse its direction? How far was it from the given point when it stopped?
4. A car travels a distance of S miles from its starting point in t hours, and $S = t^3 - 0.25t^4$. Find the speed and acceleration of the car at the instants $t = 0$, $t = 1$, $t = 2$, and $t = 3$. On the same axes draw graphs representing S, V, and A, each as a function of t. Could you have anticipated the graph of V from the graph of S?
5. A ball was rolled up an inclined plane and its distance, S feet, from the starting point after t seconds was $S = 20t - 2t^2$. What was its speed when $t = 3$? When $t = 6$? How far above the starting point did it go?
6. The cost of producing N radios in a certain factory is given by the relation $C = 2000 + 25N + 2N^2$, where C is in dollars. What is the marginal cost when the factory is producing 100 radios?

7. The revenue is defined as the product of the price of a commodity and the number of items of that commodity sold. If the price, P dollars, of a certain commodity is $P = 45 - 0.01x$, where x is the output per week, what are the weekly revenue R and the marginal revenue M_r when $x = 500$?

In each of the following exercises find the slope of the given curve at the point indicated.

8. $y = \frac{1}{4}x^2$ at $(2, 1)$.
9. $y = x^3$ at $(0, 0)$.
10. $y = x^2 - 3x + 2$ at $(2, 0)$.
11. $y = 3x - 5$ at $(4, 7)$.
12. $y = x^3 - x^2 + 6x - 8$ at $(-1, -16)$.

13. $y = x^2 - 6x$ at $(3, -9)$.
14. $y = 1/x$ at $(1, 1)$.
15. $y = 2x^3 - x^4$ at $(2, 0)$.
16. $x^2 + y^2 = 25$ at $(3, -4)$.
17. $x^2 - y^2 = 7$ at $(4, 3)$.

18. $x^2 + y^2 - 2x + 4y - 4 = 0$ at $(1, 1)$.
19. $y^2 = 4x$ at $(4, 4)$.
20. $x^2 - 2xy + 3y^2 = 11$ at $(-2, 1)$.
21. $3x^2 + 4y^2 = 7$ at $(1, -1)$.
22. Write the equation of the tangent line to the given curve at the given point in each of the Problems 20 and 21.
23. The formula for the volume of a sphere is $V = \frac{4}{3}\pi r^3$. Find the rate of change of the volume with respect to its radius.
24. At what points on the curve $y = x^3 - 3x^2 - 12x + 10$ is the slope -3?
25. At what point on the curve $y = 4x - x^2$ is the tangent line parallel to the line $2x + y = 7$?

8 SUCCESSIVE DIFFERENTIATION

The derivative $D_x y$ of a function $y = f(x)$ is, in general, another function of x, say $f'(x)$. This function $f'(x)$ may have a derivative $f''(x)$, which in turn may have a derivative $f'''(x)$, and so on. In this connection we define the following symbols:

$$f''(x) = D_x f'(x) = D_x(D_x y) = D_x^2 y = \frac{d^2 y}{dx^2},$$

where the symbols $D_x^2 y$ and $d^2 y/dx^2$ are each read "the second derivative of y with respect to x." (The superscripts "2" appearing in the symbols $D_x^2 y$ and $d^2 y/dx^2$ are not exponents and do not indicate a power of D_x or d or x. Note also the relative position of these superscripts to D_x and y and to d and y.) The *second derivative* is the derivative of the first derivative, $D_x y$. In the same manner,

$$f'''(x) = D_x f''(x) = D_x(D_x^2 y) = D_x^3 y = \frac{d^3 y}{dx^3},$$

where $D_x^3 y$ and $d^3 y/dx^3$ are read "the third derivative of y with respect to x," the third derivative being the derivative of the second derivative. It is possible that one differentiate a function successively any number of times, say n times, so we make the general definition

$$D_x^n y = D_x(D_x^{n-1} y) = \frac{d^n y}{dx^n},$$

where n is a positive integer.

We have already met situations in which it was necessary to find the second derivative of a given function. For example, to find the acceleration of any object when its distance from some fixed point is given as a function of the elapsed time, we first differentiated the distance function to find the speed V and then differentiated the speed to obtain the acceleration. Thus, if the distance S be given by the relation $S = f(t)$, the speed V is

$$V = D_t S$$

and the acceleration A is

$$A = D_t V = D_t(D_t S) = D_t^2 S.$$

Similarly, if $y = f(x)$ is the equation of a given curve, the slope m is

$$m = D_x y,$$

and the flexion m' is

$$m' = D_x m = D_x(D_x y) = D_x^2 y.$$

To find the rate at which the acceleration is changing we take the derivative of the acceleration, which gives

$$D_t A = D_t(D_t^2 S) = D_t^3 S,$$

a third derivative. So derivatives of higher order than the first are not at all unusual in mathematics.

Example. A particle traveled in such a way that its distance S feet from a given point after t seconds was $S = 20t^3 - t^4$. Find how fast the acceleration was changing at $t = 2$.

Solution:

$$S = 20t^3 - t^4,$$
$$V = D_t S = 60t^2 - 4t^3,$$
$$A = D_t V = D_t^2 S = 120t - 12t^2,$$
$$R = D_t A = D_t^3 S = 120 - 24t.$$

Therefore, when $t = 2$, $R = 120 - 48 = 72$ ft/sec³.

9   INCREASING AND DECREASING FUNCTIONS

A function $f(x)$ is said to be an *increasing function* on the interval (a, b) if $f(x_1) < f(x_2)$ for any two numbers x_1 and x_2 in the interval such that $x_1 < x_2$. Similarly, $f(x)$ is said to be a *decreasing function* on the interval (a, b) if $f(x_1) > f(x_2)$ for any two numbers x_1 and x_2 in the interval such that $x_1 < x_2$.

It follows from these definitions that the graph of a function $y = f(x)$ rises as x increases over any interval where $f(x)$ is an increasing function, and that it falls as x increases over any interval where $f(x)$ is a decreasing function. In Fig. 7.3 the curve rises as x increases from $x = b$ to $x = c$, falls from $x = c$

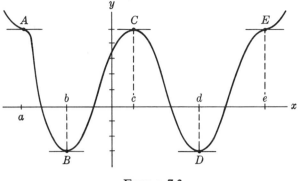

FIGURE 7.3

to $x = d$, and then rises again for values of x greater than $x = d$. A study of this graph suggests that the value of the derivative of a function for a particular value of x should determine whether the function is increasing or decreasing as x increases through that value. Some of these facts are expressed by the following theorems.

Theorem 7.8.   *If $f'(x) > 0$ for all x in some open interval (a, b), then $f(x)$ is an increasing function on the interval (a, b).*

Theorem 7.9.   *If $f'(x) < 0$ for all x in the open interval (a, b), then $f(x)$ is a decreasing function on the interval (a, b).*

We will prove Theorem 7.8. The proof of Theorem 7.9 is obtained in a similar manner.

   Proof: Let x_1 and x_2 be any two numbers such that $a < x_1 < x_2 < b$. Applying the Mean Value Theorem to the interval $[x_1, x_2]$, there is a number $c \in (x_1, x_2)$ such that

$$f(x_2) - f(x_1) = (x_2 - x_1)f'(c).$$

We have given that $f'(x) > 0$ for all $x \in (a, b)$, so $f'(c) > 0$. Also, since $x_1 < x_2$, $x_2 - x_1 > 0$, hence

$$f(x_2) - f(x_1) > 0 \quad \text{or} \quad f(x_1) < f(x_2).$$

Thus by definition, f is an increasing function in (a, b).

   It follows from Theorem 7.8 that, if $f'(x_1) > 0$ and $f'(x)$ is continuous, there must exist some open interval including x_1 on which $f(x)$ is increasing. Hereafter we shall imply this by the briefer statement "if $f'(x_1) > 0$, $f(x)$ is increasing at $x = x_1$." Similarly, the statement "$f(x)$ is decreasing at $x = x_1$" shall mean that there exists an open interval including x_1 on which $f(x)$ is a decreasing function.

   If $f'(x_1) = 0$ the function is said to be stationary at $x = x_1$. At such a point (see points A, B, C, D, and E, Fig. 7.3) the curve has zero slope and hence the line tangent to the curve at that point is parallel to the x axis. We shall refer to such a tangent line as a horizontal tangent.

Furthermore, if $f'(x_1) = 0$ the function could be increasing at $x = x_1$ (see point E, Fig. 7.3). It could also be decreasing at $x = x_1$ (see point A, Fig. 7.3). On the other hand, the function may be neither increasing nor decreasing at $x = x_1$ (see points B, C, and D, Fig. 7.3).

Example.   Determine whether the function $y = f(x) = x^3 - 4x^2 + 3x - 5$ is increasing or decreasing at $x = 1$.

Solution:

$$D_x y = f'(x) = 3x^2 - 8x + 3,$$
$$f'(1) = 3 - 8 + 3 = -2.$$

Hence $f(x)$ is decreasing at $x = 1$.

Example.   A stone is thrown vertically upward and its height, y feet, above the ground t seconds later is given by the formula $y = 80t - 16t^2$. Was the stone rising or falling when $t = 2$, when $t = 3$, and when $t = 2.5$?

Solution:

$$y = f(t) = 80t - 16t^2,$$
$$D_t y = f'(t) = 80 - 32t,$$
$$f'(2) = 80 - 64 = 16 \text{ ft/sec.}$$

Since $f'(2) > 0$, the function $f(t)$ was increasing at $t = 2$; that is, the stone was rising at $t = 2$.

For $t = 3$ we have $f'(3) = 80 - 96 = -16$ ft/sec. Since $f'(3) < 0$, the stone was falling at $t = 3$.

For $t = 2.5$ we have $f'(2.5) = 80 - 80 = 0$. Thus at $t = 2.5$ the speed $D_t y = 0$, so the stone was neither rising nor falling. Here it reached its highest point and was instantaneously at rest.

Example.   For the curve $y = x^2 - 4x - 2$, find the range of values of x where the derivative is positive, and the range where the derivative is negative. With the aid of this information graph the function.

Solution: $D_x y = 2x - 4 = 2(x - 2)$.

Therefore $D_x y > 0$ where $x > 2$,
and $D_x y < 0$ where $x < 2$;
also, $D_x y = 0$ where $x = 2$.

This analysis shows, the curve has a horizontal tangent at the point $(2, -6)$, that for all points to the left of $(2, -6)$, y decreases as x increases, and that for all points to the right of $(2, -6)$, y increases as x increases; see Fig. 7.4.

Concavity

It follows from Theorem 7.8 that if $f''(x) > 0$ for all values of x in an open interval, then $f'(x)$ increases with x on that interval. Likewise it follows from Theorem 7.9 that if $f''(x) < 0$ for all values of x on an open interval,

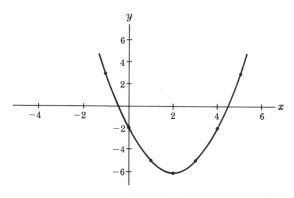

FIGURE 7.4

$f'(x)$ is a decreasing function on that interval. Also if $f'(x)$ exists for each x in an interval, the graph of the function f is a continuous curve with a tangent line at each point. If we think of a point P as moving along the curve, the tangent line at P will also move along the curve having at each point the direction of the curve at that point. We say the curve has a continuously turning tangent. If $f'(x)$ increases with x, the tangent line turns in a counterclockwise manner and hence always lies below the curve, whereas if $f'(x)$ decreases with increasing x, the tangent line turns in a clockwise manner and lies above the curve. A curve is said to be *concave upward* at a point if the curve lies above its tangent line at the point and is said to be *concave downward* if the curve lies below its tangent line at the point. For example, the curve in Fig. 7.5 is concave downward at A and at all the points between A and C. It is concave upward at all the points between C and E. However, at C the curve is changing

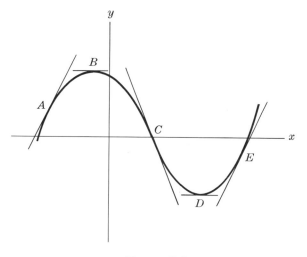

FIGURE 7.5

from concave downward to concave upward and the tangent line to the curve at C crosses the curve there.

The curve is said to have a *point of inflection* at C. In general, a point at which a curve changes from concave downward to being concave upward, or vice-versa, is called a point of inflection. More precisely, a curve $y = f(x)$, with a continuously turning tangent, has a point of inflection at $(x_0, f(x_0))$ if for some interval containing x_0 the curve has one direction of concavity at all the points $(x, f(x))$ in the interval such that $x < x_0$ and has the opposite direction of concavity at all points $(x, f(x))$ in the interval such that $x > x_0$.

The results of the above discussion may be summarized in the following two theorems.

Theorem 7.10.   *The graph of the function $y = f(x)$ is concave downward at $x = x_1$ if $f''(x_1) < 0$ and is concave upward at $x = x_1$ if $f''(x_1) > 0$.*

This theorem follows from the fact that if $f''(x) < 0$ for all values of x in some interval, $f'(x)$ is a decreasing function in the interval and if $f''(x) > 0$ for all values of x in an interval, $f'(x)$ increases with increasing x in the interval.

Theorem 7.11.   *If (x_1, y_1) is a point of inflection of the curve $y = f(x)$ and if $f''(x_1)$ exists, then $f''(x_1) = 0$.*

Proof: If (x_1, y_1) is a point of inflection then there exists an open interval containing x_1 and such that $f'(x_1)$ is either a maximum, or minimum, value of the function $f'(x)$ in that interval, and hence it follows from Theorem 7.3 that $f''(x_1) = 0$, if it exists.

Theorems 7.10 and 7.11 suggest the following test for a point of inflection. The point (x_1, y_1) is a point of inflection of the curve $y = f(x)$ if

1. $f''(x_1) = 0$, and
2. $f''(x)$ changes sign as x increases through x_1.

Further, if $f''(x_1) = 0$, but $f''(x)$ does not change sign as x increases through x_1, then (x_1, y_1) is not a point of inflection.

Example.   Test the curve $y = f(x) = x^3 - 3x^2 - 9x + 7$ for points of inflection.

Solution: We apply the test suggested above as follows.
$$y = f(x) = x^3 - 3x^2 - 9x + 7,$$
$$f'(x) = 3x^2 - 6x - 9,$$
$$f''(x) = 6x - 6 = 6(x - 1).$$
So $f''(x) = 0$ when $x = 1$.

If $x < 1, f''(x) < 0$ and if $x > 1, f''(x) > 0$, hence $f''(x)$ changes sign as x increases through $x = 1$. Therefore $(1, -4)$ is a point of inflection.

EXERCISES

1. Find $D_x^4 y$ if
   a. $y = x^6 - 3x^2$.
   c. $y = x^5 - x^4 + 2x^3 - 5x^2 + 8x - 20$.
   b. $y = 4x^3 - x^5$.
   d. $y = x^4$.

2. The distance traveled by a particle in t seconds was $S = 10t^3 - t^4$. Was the speed increasing or decreasing at $t = 3$? Was the acceleration increasing or decreasing at $t = 3$?

3. Find the slope and the flexion of the curve $y = x^3 - 4x + 10$ at the point $(1, 7)$. Was the slope increasing or decreasing at this point?

4. In t seconds after the brakes were applied a train traveled a distance, S feet, given by the formula $S = 35t - 2t^2$. How fast was the speed decreasing at $t = 5$?

5. A particle moves along the x axis according to the law $x = 7 - 15t + 9t^2 - t^3$. Find the speed at the instant the acceleration is zero. Also find the acceleration at each instant the speed is zero.

6. A ball was thrown vertically upward from a rooftop 112 feet high. Its height, y feet, above the ground after t seconds, was $y = 112 + 96t - 16t^2$. Find the interval of time during which y was increasing. When was the ball highest, that is, when was the speed zero? How high above the ground did the ball rise? When did the ball reach the ground and with what speed?

7. A particle moves along the x-axis in such a way that its distance, x feet, from the origin t seconds after starting is given by the formula $x = t^3 - 6t^2 + 9t + 4$. Find the position, speed, and direction of the particle at the start. Also find when and where the particle stopped and reversed its direction.

8. Same as Problem 7, for $x = 2t^3 - 21t^2 + 60t - 10$.

9. Find $D_x^2 y$ if

   a. $y = \dfrac{10}{x}$.
   b. $y = \dfrac{x + 1}{x - 1}$.
   c. $y = x^2 + \dfrac{1}{x}$.

For each of the following functions find the intervals in which f is increasing, f is decreasing, the graph is concave upward, concave downward, and the values of x where $f'(x) = 0$. Sketch the graph of each function.

10. $f(x) = x^2 - 10x$.
11. $f(x) = 3 + 4x - x^2$.
12. $f(x) = x^3$.

15. $f(x) = x^3 - 3x^2 + 3x + 5$.
16. $f(x) = x^3 - 12x - 10$.
17. $f(x) = 3x^4 - 4x^3 - 5$.

13. $f(x) = x^4$.

18. $f(x) = x + \dfrac{4}{x}$.

14. $f(x) = 2x^3 - 3x^2 - 12x + 5$.

19. $f(x) = \sqrt{4 - x^2}$.

20. For the graph of each function listed in Problems 12 through 17 find the point of inflection if such exists.

10 MAXIMA AND MINIMA VALUES

Let f be a function continuous in a closed interval $[a, b]$. The function f is said to have a *relative maximum* value at $x = x_1$ if any one of the following three sets of conditions hold.

1. x_1 is not an endpoint of the interval (a, b) and for some $h > 0$, $f(x_1) \geq f(x)$ when $x_1 - h < x < x_1 + h$.

2. x_1 is the left-hand endpoint of the interval $[a, b]$, that is $x_1 = a$, and for some $h > 0$, $f(x_1) \geq f(x)$ when $x_1 < x < x_1 + h$.

3. x_1 is the right-hand endpoint of $[a, b]$, that is $x_1 = b$, and for some $h > 0$, $f(x_1) \geq f(x)$ when $x_1 - h < x < x_1$.

Similarly, the function f is said to have a *relative minimum* value at $x = x_2$ if one of the following three sets of conditions hold.

1. x_2 is not an endpoint of the interval (a, b) and for some $h > 0$, $f(x_2) \leq f(x)$ when $x_2 - h < x < x_2 + h$.

2. x_2 is the left-hand endpoint of the interval $[a, b]$, that is $x_2 = a$, and for some $h > 0$, $f(x_2) \leq f(x)$ when $x_2 < x < x_2 + h$.

3. x_2 is the right-hand endpoint of $[a, b]$, that is $x_2 = b$, and for some $h > 0$, $f(x_2) \leq f(x)$ when $x_2 - h < x < x_2$.

It is important to understand that the word *relative* as used in the above definitions means that $f(x_1)$ is a maximum, or minimum, when compared with $f(x)$ at values of x nearby x_1. In such a case $f(x_1)$ may or may not be the largest, or smallest, value of f on $[a, b]$. If it happens that $f(x_1) \geq f(x)$ for all values of x on $[a, b]$, that is $f(x_1) = M$ (see Theorem 7.2), then $f(x_1)$ is called the *absolute maximum* value of f on $[a, b]$. If $f(x_2) \leq f(x)$ for $x \in [a, b]$, that is if $f(x_2) = m$, then $f(x_2)$ is called the *absolute* minimum value of f on $[a, b]$. It should be noted that every absolute maximum is automatically a relative maximum and every absolute minimum is at the same time a relative minimum.

The geometrical meanings of the above definitions may be made more clear by considering the graph shown in Fig. 7.6. This graph is a function-

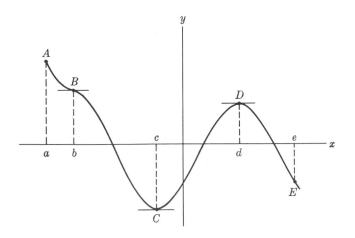

FIGURE 7.6

graph. So, let it be the graph of a function f continuous on a closed interval $[a, e]$. Here $f(a)$ and $f(d)$ are relative maximum values and $f(c)$ and $f(e)$ are relative minimum values. Note that $f(a)$ is also an absolute maximum value and $f(c)$ is an absolute minimum value of f on $[a, e]$. Points such as A and D are called *relative maximum points* and points like C and E are called *relative minimum points*.

It is obvious from the above figure that, for a function f defined on a closed interval, the values of f at the endpoints can be among the relative maxima and relative minima values of the function, and they generally are. Thus if we are investigating a function, defined on a closed interval, to find all of its relative maxima and relative minima values, we *must always check the values at the endpoints*. Checking the endpoints is routine and easily done. However, relative maxima and minima values may occur at any x within the interval and these are not so easily found.

To aid us in finding maxima and minima values which occur at interior points of the interval we prove the following theorem.

Theorem 7.12. *Suppose f is a function continuous on a closed interval $[a, b]$ and suppose $a < x_1 < b$. If $f(x_1)$ is a relative maximum (minimum) value of f and $f'(x_1)$ exists, then $f'(x_1) = 0$.*

Proof: This theorem follows as a direct consequence of Theorem 7.4 and the definitions of maximum and minimum values at interior points of an interval. For if $f(x_1)$ is a relative maximum value of f and $a < x_1 < b$, there exists an interval $(x_1 - h, x_1 + h)$, contained in (a, b), such that $f(x_1)$ is the maximum value of f in $(x_1 - h, x_1 + h)$. Hence, by Theorem 7.4, if $f'(x_1)$ exists, then $f'(x_1) = 0$. A similar statement holds if $f(x_1)$ is a relative minimum.

Unfortunately, the converse of Theorem 7.12 is not true. Referring again to Fig. 7.6, we see that the curve has a horizontal tangent at the point B. Hence $f'(b) = 0$, but $f(b)$ is neither a relative maximum nor a relative minimum value. Thus $f'(x_1) = 0$ does not imply that $f(x_1)$ is a relative maximum

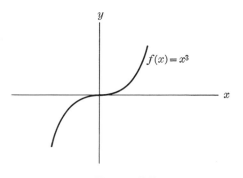

FIGURE 7.7

or a relative minimum, it may be neither. For example, let f be defined by the equation $f(x) = x^3$. Then $f'(x) = 3x^2$ and $f'(0) = 0$. However, $f(0)$ is neither a relative maximum nor a relative minimum because $f'(x) > 0$ if $x \neq 0$, hence f is an increasing function on both sides of $x = 0$. See Fig. 7.7.

The above discussion and example show that $f'(x_1) = 0$ is no guarantee $f(x_1)$ is a relative maximum or minimum even though x_1 is not an endpoint of the domain of definition of f. We must also point out that $f'(x_1)$ does not even need to exist for $f(x_1)$ to be a relative maximum or minimum. To see this consider the function $f(x) = |x|$ defined on the closed interval $[-2, 2]$. The graph of f is shown in Fig. 7.8 and obviously consists of two straight

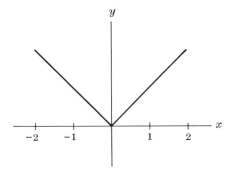

FIGURE 7.8

line segments. The portion of the graph that lies in the first quadrant is a segment of the line $y = x$ and the portion of the graph that lies in the second quadrant is a segment of the line $y = -x$. Thus for our function, $f(x) = |x|$, we see that $f'(x) = 1$ when $x > 0$ and $f'(x) = -1$ when $x < 0$. Although f is continuous at $x = 0$, it is obvious that $f'(0)$ does not exist. It is equally obvious that $f(0)$ is a relative minimum value of f.

To summarize: for a function f defined on a closed interval $[a, b]$, in order to find all the relative maxima and minima values of f on $[a, b]$, we must examine

(1)   all points in (a, b) at which $f'(x) = 0$,
(2)   all points in (a, b) at which $f'(x)$ fails to exist, and
(3)   the two endpoints $x = a$ and $x = b$.

A number x_1 in (a, b) at which $f'(x_1) = 0$ or at which $f'(x_1)$ fails to exist will be called a *critical value* of x, and the corresponding point $(x_1, f(x_1))$ is called a *critical point*. Hence *all* interior relative maxima and relative minima points are critical points but the converse is not true, some critical points are neither. It is, therefore, desirable to have a simple test we can apply to each critical value x_1 and thereby determine whether $f(x_1)$ is a relative maximum, a relative minimum or neither. Each of the following tests serve that purpose if it is applicable to the case under consideration.

The First Derivative Test.   Suppose f is a function defined on $[a, b]$ and differentiable in (a, b) except perhaps at one or more critical values. Let x_1 be a critical value of x. Then

(a) $f(x_1)$ is a relative maximum if $f'(x)$ changes sign from positive to negative as x increases through x_1.

(b) $f(x_1)$ is a relative minimum if $f'(x)$ changes sign from negative to positive as x increases through x_1.

(c) $f(x_1)$ is neither a relative maximum nor a relative minimum if $f'(x)$ does not change sign as x increases through x_1.

Obviously, this test reduces to the problem of solving the inequalities $f'(x) < 0$ and $f'(x) > 0$. Methods of solving such inequalities were studied in Chapter IV and the student might do well at this point to review that section. We shall illustrate with the following example, a typical procedure for applying the First Derivative Test.

Example.   For the function $f(x) = x^4 - 8x^2 + 10$, $[-3, 3]$, find all the critical values of x and determine for each whether the corresponding value of the function is a relative maximum, a relative minimum, or neither.

Solution:

$$f(x) = x^4 - 8x^2 + 10,$$
$$f'(x) = 4x^3 - 16x = 4x(x - 2)(x + 2).$$

The critical values in this case are the solutions of $f'(x) = 0$, namely $x = -2$, $x = 0$, and $x = 2$.

To apply the First Derivative test we need to find where $f'(x) < 0$ and where $f'(x) > 0$. To do this we proceed as in Section 27 of Chapter IV. Recall that the solid portion of the line shows where the indicated factor is positive and the dotted portion shows where the factor is negative. See Fig. 7.9.

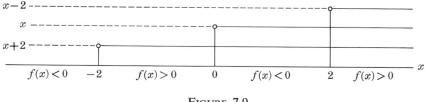

FIGURE 7.9

Inspection of this figure shows that $f'(x) < 0$ for $x < -2$, $f'(x) > 0$ in the interval $(-2, 0)$, $f'(x) < 0$ in $(0, 2)$, and $f'(x) > 0$ for $x > 2$. Thus $f(-2) = -6$ and $f(2) = -6$ are relative minima values and $f(0) = 10$ is a relative maxima value. This information is very helpful in sketching the graph of f. We locate the minima points $(-2, -6)$ and $(2, -6)$ and the maximum point

(0, 10). These are the turning points of the graph. Also the graph has a horizontal tangent at each of these points. The graph of f is shown in Fig. 7.10.

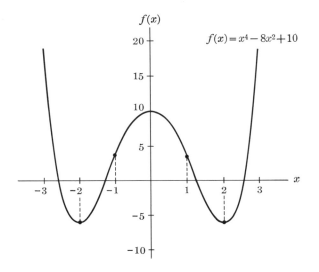

FIGURE 7.10

Second Derivative Test.   Suppose f is a function defined on $[a, b]$ and differentiable in (a, b). Let x_1 be a value of x such that $f'(x_1) = 0$. Then

(a) $f(x_1)$ is a relative maximum if $f''(x_1) < 0$
(b) $f(x_1)$ is a relative minimum if $f''(x_1) > 0$
(c) test fails if $f''(x_1) = 0$.

This is by far the simplest test to use if it is applicable, especially in cases where the second derivative is easy to calculate. The last example above is a case in point. We repeat the solution of that example here, but using the Second Derivative Test.

Solution.

$$f(x) = x^4 - 8x^2 + 10$$
$$f'(x) = 4x^3 - 16x = 4x(x + 2)(x - 2)$$
$$f''(x) = 12x^2 - 16.$$

The critical values of x are -2, 0, and 2. $f''(-2) = 32 > 0$, $f''(0) = -16 < 0$, and $f''(2) = 32 > 0$, showing that $f(-2)$ and $f(2)$ are relative minima values and that $f(0)$ is a relative maximum value. This agrees with the results found by the First Derivative Test.

To determine the absolute maximum value and the absolute minimum value of a function f, defined in a closed interval $[a, b]$, we find $f(a), f(b)$, and the value of f at each critical value of x. The largest of these is the absolute maximum and the smallest is the absolute minimum value of f. In the above example, the function f is defined in the closed interval $[-3, 3]$ and we have found the critical values of x to be -2, 0, and 2. To find the maximum value of f in the given interval we compare the values $f(-3) = 19, f(-2) = -6$, $f(0) = 10, f(2) = 6$, and $f(3) = 19$. The absolute maximum value of f is 19 and the absolute minimum value of f is -6.

EXERCISES

For each of the following functions, Problems 1 through 16, find all the critical values of x and determine for each whether the corresponding value of f is a relative maximum, a relative minimum, or neither. Use this information to sketch the graph of the function.

1. $f(x) = 6x - x^2$.

2. $f(x) = 5 + 12x - 3x^2$.

3. $f(x) = x^3 - 3x + 1$.

4. $f(x) = 2x^3 + 6x^2 - 18x + 5$.

5. $f(x) = x^3 - 6x^2 - 20$.

6. $f(x) = x^4 - 4x^3 + 12$.

7. $f(x) = x^3 - 3x^2 + 3x + 1$.

8. $f(x) = 3x^4 - 4x^3 - 12x^2 + 12$.

9. $f(x) = |x - 1|$.

10. $f(x) = 3x^{2/3}$.

11. $f(x) = 10x^3 - 6x^5 - 2$.

12. $f(x) = x^3 - 6x^2 + 9x + 4$.

13. $f(x) = x + \dfrac{4}{x}, \quad x > 0$.

14. $f(x) = x + \dfrac{4}{x - 2}, \quad x \neq 2$.

15. $f(x) = 4\sqrt{x} - x$.

16. $f(x) = |x^2 - 4|$.

17. Find the absolute maximum value and the absolute minimum value of the function $f(x) = x^3 - 3x^2 - 9x + 10$ on the closed interval $[-2, 4]$.

18. What is the absolute minimum value of f if $f(x) = 2x + \dfrac{32}{x}, \quad x > 0$.

11   APPLIED PROBLEMS IN MAXIMA AND MINIMA

The theory of relative maximum and minimum values discussed in the preceding section is of great use in the solution of problems that require the determination of maximum or minimum values of a quantity when the quantity is expressible as a function of a single independent variable defined over some interval. Let us consider two examples.

Example.   A farmer has 100 yards of fencing with which he wishes to enclose a rectangular area. What dimensions should he use if he wishes the enclosed area to be a maximum? See Fig. 7.11 on page 278.

Solution: Let x = length, y = width, A = area enclosed. Then, first, $A = xy$ and, second, $2x + 2y = 100$. A is the quantity whose maximum value is required.

Hence it is necessary to express A as a function of one independent variable. To do this, solve the first equation for y and substitute into the second equation.

Solving for y, we get $y = 50 - x$.

Substituting we get $A = f(x) = x(50 - x)$, where $0 \le x \le 50$.

Since $A = 0$ at both endpoints of the interval, the maximum value must occur at some value of x within the interval. Also, D_xA exists through the interval; hence $D_xA = 0$ where A is a maximum. Differentiating, we find

$$D_xA = f'(x) = 50 - 2x.$$

Now, $D_xA = 0$ when $50 - 2x = 0$, and solving this equation for x we have

$$2x = 50,$$
$$x = 25.$$

Also, $f'(24) = +2$ and $f'(26) = -2$. Therefore A is a relative maximum when $x = 25$. Since this is the only relative maximum on the interval, A has its maximum value at $x = 25$. Also, when $x = 25$, then $y = 25$. These are the required dimensions.

Example. A rectangular box is to be made from a piece of cardboard 8 inches long and 5 inches wide by cutting out same-sized squares from each corner and turning up the cardboard to form the sides and ends of the box. Find the volume of the largest such box that can be made from the given piece of cardboard. See Fig. 7.12.

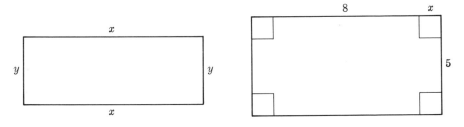

FIGURE 7.11   FIGURE 7.12

Solution: Let $x =$ length of edge of square cut out. After folding up the resulting edges, we find that the length of the box is $8 - 2x$, the width is $5 - 2x$, and the depth is x. Hence the volume V is given by the relation

$$\begin{aligned} V &= f(x) \\ &= x(8 - 2x)(5 - 2x), \qquad 0 \le x \le \tfrac{5}{2}. \end{aligned}$$

Obviously, the maximum value of V occurs for a value of x within the interval of definition and for which $D_xV = 0$. Differentiating,

$$f'(x) = D_xV = 12x^2 - 52x + 40.$$
$$\text{Here} \quad f'(x) = D_xV = 0, \quad \text{when } 12x^2 - 52x + 40 = 0.$$

Dividing by 4 and factoring, we get

$$(3x - 10)(x - 1) = 0.$$

Therefore $x = \tfrac{10}{3}$ or $x = 1$.

But $x = \tfrac{10}{3}$ is outside the interval of definition, so $x = 1$ should give V its maximum value. To check this, find

$$f'(\tfrac{1}{2}) = 12(\tfrac{1}{4}) - 52(\tfrac{1}{2}) + 40 = 17.$$
$$f'(2) = 12(4) - 52(2) + 40 = -16.$$

This shows that V has its maximum value when $x = 1$; hence the solution to our problem is $V_{\max} = 4 - 26 + 40 = 18$.

It is important to observe the difference in the information sought in these two examples. In the first we were asked to find the dimensions of the rectangle for which the area was a maximum; the maximum area was not requested. In the second, however, the maximum volume was the quantity desired.

EXERCISES

1. Find the dimensions of the rectangle with maximum area, the sum of three of whose sides is 40.
2. A long rectangular piece of tin 20 inches wide is to be made into a gutter by bending up the two long sides vertically. How many inches should be turned up at each side to give the gutter the greatest cross-sectional area?
3. The cost of producing u units of a certain item per day is $C = 400 + 12u - (4 - u)^3$. When is the marginal cost a minimum?
4. A rectangular box with open top is to be made from a square piece of cardboard 24 inches on a side by cutting same-sized squares from each corner and turning up the resulting edges vertically. What is the volume of the largest box that can be so made?
5. A carpenter has 300 square feet of lumber from which he wishes to make a rectangular box with a square base and no top. Find the dimensions of the largest box that he can make, assuming no loss of material from cutting or overlapping.
6. A particle moves along the x axis in such a way that its distance, x feet, from the origin after t seconds is $x = 10t^3 - t^4$. Find the speed at which the acceleration is a maximum.
7. Find the dimensions of the largest rectangular flower bed that can be made in a right-triangular lot whose hypotenuse is 50 feet and whose legs are 30 feet and 40 feet, respectively, if two sides of the bed lie along the two legs of the triangular lot.
8. The manager of a theater found that with an admission charge of 50 cents per person the average daily attendance was 1200, while with every increase of 5 cents the attendance dropped 60. What should be the admission price for the daily receipts to be a maximum?
9. Farmer Jones estimates that if he digs his potatoes now he will have 150 bushels worth $2.00 per bushel but, if he waits, the crop will grow 25 bushels per week while the price will drop 20 cents per bushel per week. When should he dig them to get the largest cash return?
10. Postal regulations specify that for a package to be sent by parcel post the sum of its length and girth must not exceed 100 inches. Find the volume of the largest rectangular package with square ends that would come within the above regulations.

11. A farmer wishes to lay out a rectangular lot whose area is 400 square yards. What dimensions should he use if the length of fence needed is to be a minimum?

12. A rectangular box with a square base and no top is to be built out of plywood to contain a volume of 32 cubic feet. Neglecting thickness and waste from cutting, what dimensions should be used to require the least amount of material?

13. An open rectangular box with a square base is to contain 18 cubic feet. The material for the base is to cost 8 cents per square foot and for the sides 6 cents per square foot. Find the minimum total cost for building such a box.

14. At what point of the curve $y = 24x^2 - x^4$ is the slope increasing most rapidly?

15. A cylindrical can with a top and a bottom is to be made from tin and is to contain 250π cubic inches. What dimensions should be used if the amount of material needed for the can is to be a minimum?

16. A printed page is to allow 108 square inches for printed matter and have a margin of 1.5 inches at each side and 2 inches at the top and bottom. What dimensions of paper will the page require if its area is to be a minimum?

17. At a price of x each, the manufacturer of a certain type of transistor radio can sell weekly a number $n = 180 - 5x$, the cost of which to him was $C = 600 + 4n$ (dollars). What price x will maximize his profit?

18. A man is stranded on a level desert 5 miles from A, the nearest point on a straight highway. A town B on this highway is 12 miles from A. If the man can walk 3 miles per hour through the sand and 5 miles per hour along the highway, what is the shortest possible time for him to get to B, assuming he walks all the way.

12 THE CHAIN RULE FOR DIFFERENTIATION

Let us suppose that $y = f(u)$ is a differentiable function of u and $u = g(x)$ is a differentiable function of x. We wish to show that $y = f[g(x)]$ is a differentiable function of x and that

$$D_x y = D_u y \, D_x u.$$

This equation is called the *chain rule of differentiation*.

To establish this result, give x the increment $\Delta x \neq 0$ and denote by Δy and Δu the corresponding changes in y and u, respectively. Since y is a differentiable function of u and u is a differentiable function of x, we have

$$\lim_{\Delta u \to 0} \frac{\Delta y}{\Delta u} = D_u y,$$

$$\lim_{\Delta x \to 0} \frac{\Delta u}{\Delta x} = D_x u.$$

We now define the number d as follows:

$$d = \frac{\Delta y}{\Delta u} - D_u y, \qquad \Delta u \neq 0,$$

$$= 0, \qquad\qquad\quad \Delta u = 0.$$

Hence

$$\Delta y = D_u y\, \Delta u + d\, \Delta u,$$

where d approaches zero as Δu approaches zero. Now divide this by Δx,

$$\frac{\Delta y}{\Delta x} = D_u y\, \frac{\Delta u}{\Delta x} + d\, \frac{\Delta u}{\Delta x},$$

and take the limit as Δx approaches zero. Since u is a differentiable function of x, it follows that Δu approaches zero as Δx does, and hence that

$$\lim_{\Delta x \to 0} d = 0.$$

Therefore

$$\lim_{\Delta x \to 0} \frac{\Delta y}{\Delta x} = \lim_{\Delta x \to 0} D_u y\, \frac{\Delta u}{\Delta x} + \lim_{\Delta x \to 0} d\, \frac{\Delta u}{\Delta x}$$

and we have $D_x y = D_u y\, D_x u$, the desired result. Observe that the rule we established for differentiating a power u^n is a special case of the chain rule with $f(u) = u^n$.

Example. Given $y = u^3$ and $u = x^2 + x$, find $D_x y$ at $x = 1$.

Solution: Using the chain rule, $D_x y = D_u y\, D_x u$, we find $D_x y = 3u^2(2x + 1)$. But $u = 2$ when $x = 1$; therefore $D_x y = (12)(3) = 36$.

13 RELATED RATES

If two or more related variables are each a function of time t and if we know rates at which all of these variables, except one, are changing, then the rate at which the one variable is changing with respect to time can often be found by applying the chain rule.

Example. The area, A square inches, of a square is related to the length of one of its sides, x inches, according to the relation $A = x^2$. If the length of each side is increased at the constant rate of 2 inches per minute, how fast is the area increasing at the instant $x = 10$?

Solution: Given $A = x^2$ and $D_t x = 2$, we are to find $D_t A$ when $x = 10$. Using the chain rule, $D_t A = D_x A\, D_t x$, we have

$$D_t A = D_x(x^2)\, D_t x = 2x\, D_t x = 20(2) = 40 \text{ in.}^2/\text{min.}$$

Example. A north-south highway and an east-west highway intersect at A. Two trucks leave A at the same time, one traveling north at 30 miles per hour and the other traveling east at 40 miles per hour. How fast was the distance between them increasing at the end of 2 hours?

Solution: Let B and C be the respective positions of the two trucks at the end of t hours. Denote the distance AC by x, the distance AB by y, and the distance BC by z (see Fig. 7.13). Then

$$z^2 = x^2 + y^2, \qquad y = 30t, \qquad x = 40t.$$

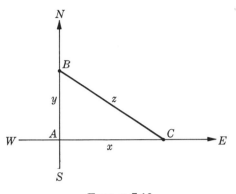

FIGURE 7.13

Differentiating implicitly with respect to t, we get

$$2z\frac{dz}{dt} = 2x\frac{dx}{dt} + 2y\frac{dy}{dt}, \qquad \frac{dy}{dt} = 30, \qquad \frac{dx}{dt} = 40.$$

When $t = 2$, then $x = 80$, $y = 60$, and $z = 100$; therefore

$$200\frac{dz}{dt} = 160(40) + 120(30)$$

$$\frac{dz}{dt} = \frac{6400 + 3600}{200} = 50 \text{ mph.}$$

Example. A north-south highway and an east-west highway intersect at A; a truck leaves A, traveling east at 40 miles per hour, 2 hours before a second truck traveling at 30 miles per hour and coming from the south arrives at A. How fast is the distance between the two trucks changing 1 hour after the east-bound truck leaves A?

Solution: Let B and C be the respective positions of the two trucks t hours after the east-bound truck leaves A. Denote the distance AB by x, the distance AC by y, and the distance BC by z (see Fig. 7.14). Then

$$z^2 = x^2 + y^2, \qquad x = 40t, \qquad y = 60 - 30t.$$

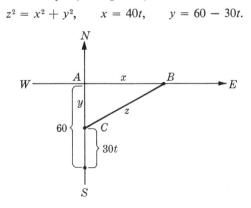

FIGURE 7.14

Differentiating with respect to t, we have

$$2z\frac{dz}{dt} = 2x\frac{dx}{dt} + 2y\frac{dy}{dt}, \quad \frac{dx}{dt} = 40, \quad \frac{dy}{dt} = -30, \quad \text{or} \quad z\frac{dz}{dt} = x\frac{dx}{dt} + y\frac{dy}{dt}.$$

When $t = 1$, then $x = 40$, $y = 30$, and $z = 50$; therefore

$$50\frac{dz}{dt} = 40(40) + 30(-30), \quad \text{and} \quad \frac{dz}{dt} = \frac{1600 - 900}{50} = \frac{700}{50} = 14 \text{ mph.}$$

EXERCISES

1. A ladder 30 feet long has one end resting on the level ground and the top end resting against a vertical wall. If the lower end is pulled away from the wall at the rate of 0.2 feet per minute in a direction perpendicular to the wall, how fast is the top descending when 18 feet high?

2. A baseball diamond is a square 90 feet on each side. If the batter bats a ball down the third-base line at the rate of 120 feet per second, how fast was its distance from first base changing at the end of 1 second? When it passed third base?

3. A cube was expanding at the rate of 300 cubic inches per minute at the instant the edge was 20 inches. How fast was the edge then changing?

4. The radius of a circle is being increased at the constant rate of 0.4 feet per second. How fast is the area increasing at the instant the radius is 2 feet?

5. Two cars leave the same intersection at 10 o'clock. One is traveling north at 40 miles per hour and the other is traveling east at 30 miles per hour. How fast is the distance between them changing 1 hour later, assuming they traveled at a constant speed?

6. A north-south and an east-west highway intersect at point A. At 9 o'clock one car is 90 miles west of A and traveling toward A at the constant speed of 50 miles per hour. At this same time a second car is leaving A and traveling north at a constant speed of 30 miles per hour. How fast is the distance between them changing at 10 o'clock? Is this distance increasing or decreasing at that time?

7. A rectangular tank has a square base 10 by 10 feet, and water is running into the tank at the uniform rate of 40 cubic feet per minute. Show that the surface is rising at a constant rate and find that rate.

8. A man 6 feet tall is walking directly away from a street light at the constant rate of 3 feet per second. If the street light is 15 feet above the street, how fast is the tip of his shadow moving?

9. Gas is being forced into a spherical balloon in such a way that the radius is increasing at the constant rate of 0.2 feet per minute. How fast is the volume of the balloon increasing at the instant the radius is 10 feet?

10. A man is standing on a river bridge 30 feet above the water in the river below just as a boat passes beneath him. If the boat travels in a straight line and at a rate of 8 ft/sec, how fast is the distance between the boat and the man on the bridge changing 5 sec later?

11. Sand falling at the rate 100 in.³/min forms a conical pile whose radius always equals twice the height. Find the rate at which the height is changing at the instant the height is 10 in. [*Hint:* $V = \frac{1}{3}\pi r^2 h$.]

VIII

INTEGRATION

1 INTRODUCTION

In Chapter V it was stated that one of the objectives in this course was to investigate two major problems concerning the mode of variation of two related quantities. The first problem, that of finding the instantaneous rate at which one variable is changing with respect to another, when a relation between the two variables is known, was studied in some detail in Chapters V, VI, and VII. We learned that finding instantaneous rates was actually one and the same problem and that every such rate was called a derivative. The process of finding a derivative we called differentiation. Thus the first problem could be stated briefly as, "given a function, find its derivative." We derived formulas for differentiating various types of algebraic functions and discovered many applications of derivatives. In this chapter we wish to examine the second major problem which as we shall see turns out to be, in a certain sense, an inverse of the problem of differentiation. This second problem is that of finding the functional relation between two variables when the derivative of one of the variables with respect to the other is known. For example, suppose we have a formula which expresses the speed of a certain object as a function of t, the number of seconds the object has been traveling since it started, and suppose we need to find the distance traveled by the object in a given interval of time. Since speed is the rate of change of distance with respect to time, our problem may be considered as one of finding a function of t whose derivative is the given formula.

2 DIFFERENTIATION REVERSED

Let us suppose that it is desired to express y as a function of x when the only information we have concerning y and x is that $D_x y = 6x^2$. Our problem then, is to find a function of x whose derivative is $6x^2$. Recalling the rule for differentiating kx^n and reversing the operation, it is easy to see that $y = 2x^3$ defines a function whose derivative is $6x^2$. Could there be other functions having this same derivative? The answer to this question is given in Theorem 7.7 of Chapter VII, which says that if two functions, $f(x)$ and $g(x)$, are so related that $f'(x) = g'(x)$ for all x in the domain of definition of both, then $g(x) = f(x) + c$. Therefore $y = 2x^3 + c$, where c is an arbitrary constant, represents every possible function whose derivative is $6x^2$. This shows that the derivative alone is not sufficient to completely determine a function. If, however, in addition to knowing the derivative, we also know the value of the function for at least one value of the independent variable, then the function is completely determined. For example, suppose we have given

$$D_x y = 6x^2 \quad\text{and}\quad y = 3 \quad\text{when } x = 1.$$

We first write

$$y = 2x^3 + c.$$

Now substituting $y = 3$ and $x = 1$, we get

$$3 = 2(1^3) + c,$$

or

$$c = 1,$$

and hence $y = 2x^3 + 1$ is the desired function.

The process of finding a function whose derivative is given is called *integration*. The required function is called an *integral* of the given derivative. In symbols, if $D_x y = f(x)$ and $F'(x) = f(x)$, then $y = F(x) + c$. We say that $F(x)$ is an *integral* of $f(x)$ with respect to x. The constant c is called a *constant of integration*. When integrating, the constant c is an important part of the integral function $F(x)$ and to omit it is to assume $c = 0$.

3 SOME INTEGRATION FORMULAS

Based on the definition of integration given in the last section, the process of integration is in a sense a trial and error type operation. That is, we are given a function $f(x)$ and are required to find a function $F(x)$ such that $F'(x) = f(x)$. So, we guess a function $F(x)$ which seems a likely prospect to have $f(x)$ as its derivative and then we check by differentiation to see if we have been successful. Recalling the rules for differentiation from Chapter VII and reversing them we obtain the following formulas which should reduce the number of trials to a minimum.

FORMULAS

I.   If $D_x y = 0$, then $y = c$ (constant) for $D_x c = 0$.

II. If $D_x y = 1$, then $y = x + c$ for $D_x(x + c) = 1$.

III. If $D_x y = k$, then $y = kx + c$ for $D_x(kx + c) = k$.

IV. If $D_x y = kx^n$, then $y = \dfrac{kx^{n+1}}{n+1} + c$, for $D_x \left(\dfrac{kx^{n+1}}{n+1} + c \right) = kx^n, n \neq -1$.

V.   If $D_x y = kf(x)$ and $F'(x) = f(x)$, then $y = kF(x) + c$ for $D_x[kF(x) + c] = kF'(x) = kf(x)$.

VI. If $D_x y = f(x) + g(x)$ and $F'(x) = f(x)$ and $G'(x) = g(x)$, then $y = F(x) + G(x) + c$ for $D_x[F(x) + G(x) + c] = F'(x) + G'(x) = f(x) + g(x)$.

In words, Formula V states "the integral of the product of a constant and a function is the product of that same constant and the integral of the function." Similarly Formula VI states "the integral of the sum of two functions is the sum of the integrals of the functions." In fact this rule can be generalized to state "the integral of the algebraic sum of any finite number of functions is the algebraic sum of the integrals of those functions."

It should be emphasized that the acid test of whether or not a function $F(x)$ is an integral of a function $f(x)$ is the following:

$F(x)$ is an integral of $f(x)$ if and only if $F'(x) = f(x)$. The student is encouraged to guess an integral when not sure but he should always check his guess by differentiation. The following examples may help the student to see how the above formulas are used.

Example. Find y if $D_x y = 7x^4$.

Solution: By Formula IV, $y = \dfrac{7x^{4+1}}{4+1} + c = \dfrac{7}{5}x^5 + c$.

Check: $D_x(\tfrac{7}{5}x^5 + c) = \dfrac{35x^4}{5} = 7x^4$.

Example. Find y if $D_x y = \dfrac{3}{\sqrt{x}}$.

Solution: Rewriting gives $D_x y = 3x^{-1/2}$. By Formula IV,

$$y = \frac{3x^{-1/2+1}}{-\tfrac{1}{2}+1} + c = \frac{3x^{1/2}}{\tfrac{1}{2}} + c = 6x^{1/2} + c = 6\sqrt{x} + c.$$

Check: $D_x(6\sqrt{x} + c) = D_x(6x^{1/2} + c) = \tfrac{1}{2} \cdot 6x^{-1/2} = 3x^{-1/2} = \dfrac{3}{\sqrt{x}}.$

Example. Find y if $D_x y = 8x^3 - 3x^2 + 6x + 5$.

Solution: By Formulas IV and VI

$$y = \frac{8x^4}{4} - \frac{3x^3}{3} + \frac{6x^2}{2} + 5x + c$$

$$= 2x^4 - x^3 + 3x^2 + 5x + c.$$

Check: $D_x(2x^4 - x^3 + 3x^2 + 5x + c) = 8x^3 - 3x^2 + 6x + 5).$

The student should find that with a little practice he will be able to write the integrals of polynomial functions by inspection in simplified form in one step. See the next example.

Example. Find y if $D_x y = 3x^2 - 4x + 5$ and $y = 3$ when $x = 1$.

Solution: $y = x^3 - 2x^2 + 5x + c$, substituting $y = 3$ and $x = 1$ gives

$$3 = 1 - 2 + 5 + c$$

or

$$c = -1,$$

hence

$$y = x^3 - 2x^2 + 5x - 1.$$

EXERCISES

In Problems 1 through 12, find y and check your answer in each case if

1. $D_x y = 3x^7$.

2. $D_x y = x^{3/2}$.

3. $D_x y = x^3 + 7x^2 - 5x - 4$.
4. $D_x y = \sqrt[3]{x}$.

5. $D_x y - 2x^{-3}$.

6. $D_x y = 3x^2 - \dfrac{4}{x^2}$.

7. $D_x y = x(x^2 - 1)$.
8. $D_x y = (2x + 5)(3x - 2)$.

[*Hint:* In Problems 7 and 8 multiply before integrating.]

9. $D_x y = 40x^{19}$.
10. $D_x y = 8\sqrt[5]{x^4}$.

11. $D_x y = (x^2 + 1)^3$.
12. $D_x y = 4 + x(x - 1)$.

13. Find y if $D_x y = 5x^4 - 3x^2 + 2$, and $y = 5$ when $x = -1$.
14. Find y if $D_x y = x^4 + 5x^2 - 3x + 1$, and $y = 5$ when $x = 2$.
15. Find S if $D_t S = 80 - 32t$.
16. Find U if $D_v U = 4v^3 - 4v^2 + 4v - 4$.
17. Find V if $D_t V = -32$ and $V = 50$ when $t = 0$.
18. Find Z if $D_y Z = y^5 + y^3 + y$.
19. Find V if $D_r V = 4\pi r^2$ and $V = 0$ when $r = 0$.
20. Find S if $D_t S = 96 - 32t$ and $S = 256$ when $t = 0$.

4 SPEED AND DISTANCE

We now return to our original problem, remarked on in the beginning of this chapter: we are given a formula for the speed of a moving object and are asked to find a formula that will give the distance traveled for a given time t. Let us consider, for example, that our speed from noon to two o'clock is given by the expression

$$V = 120t - 60t^2,$$

where V is in miles per hour and t is the number of hours after twelve o'clock. Thus, at noon $t = 0$ and $V = 0$; at 12:30, $t = \frac{1}{2}$ and $V = 45$, etc. We now wish to know where we can expect to be at two o'clock. Obviously, our location at two o'clock will depend not only on our speed, which determines how far we travel between noon and that time, but also upon where we were at noon. If we were 75 miles from Knoxville at noon and were headed away from Knoxville, we can now determine our location relative to Knoxville at two o'clock, for when $t = 0$ the distance, S miles, from Knoxville will be 75. Referring to Chapter VI, we remember that $V = D_t S$:

	$V = D_t S;$
thus	$V = 120t - 60t^2$
is equivalent to	$D_t S = 120t - 60t^2$
with the added condition that	$S = 75 \quad$ when $t = 0;$
by integration,	$S = 60t^2 - 20t^3 + C;$

substituting $S = 75$ and $t = 0$ we get

	$75 = 0 - 0 + C,$
or	$C = 75,$
and therefore	$S = 60t^2 - 20t^3 + 75.$

With this distance formula we may determine our distance from Knoxville not only at two o'clock but at any time during the two-hour period after noon. In particular, at two o'clock,

$$t = 2$$
$$S = 60(2)^2 - 20(2)^3 + 75 = 240 - 160 + 75 = 155,$$

whence we know that we were 155 miles from Knoxville at two o'clock. Similarly, at 12:30

$$t = 1/2$$
$$S = 60(\tfrac{1}{2})^2 - 20(\tfrac{1}{2})^3 + 75 = 15 - 2.5 + 75 = 87.5,$$

which shows that at that time our distance from Knoxville was 87.5 miles.

In this example the condition that $S = 75$ when $t = 0$ is called *the initial condition*. Thus, our example suggests that, in general, if a formula for the speed V is given and the initial condition is known, a formula for the traveled distance S can be found by integration.

Similarly, if a formula for the acceleration of a body is given and the initial conditions are known, formulas for the speed and distance can be found by integration. It should be noted that in such case the initial conditions are the initial speed and the initial position of the moving object, that is, the value of V and the value of S when $t = 0$.

Example.   At the instant the brakes were applied, a train was moving at the rate of 44 feet per second, and thereafter, until it stopped, the speed decreased at the constant rate of 4 feet per second, per second. Find (a) formulas for the distance traveled and the speed t seconds after the brakes were applied, (b) the number of seconds required for the train to stop, and (c) how far the train traveled after the brakes were applied.

Solution:
(a)   The speed was decreasing at the constant rate of 4 feet per second per second. This is equivalent to the statement

(Eq. 1) $D_t V = -4.$

The initial conditions are $V = 44$ feet per second and $S = 0$ when $t = 0$. Integrating the expression in Equation 1 we get

$$V = -4t + C_1.$$

But $V = 44$ when $t = 0$; therefore

$$44 = 0 + C_1$$
or $C_1 = 44$
(Eq. 2)   and $V = 44 - 4t.$

This is our formula for the speed at any time t seconds after the brakes were applied. Since $V = D_t S$, it follows from Equation 2 that

$$D_t S = 44 - 4t;$$
by integration, $S = 44t - 2t^2 + C_2.$

Notice here that subscripts are used to indicate the fact that the two constants of integration, C_1 and C_2, are in general different. Now, since $S = 0$ when $t = 0$, we have the following formula, one which gives the distance S, in feet, traveled by the train after the brakes were applied:

(Eq. 3) $S = 44t - 2t^2.$

(b)   The train stopped when $V = 0$. So in Equation 2 we set V equal to 0 and solve for t, which will be the time the train required before coming to a stop after the brakes were applied.

$$44 - 4t = 0$$
$$4t = 44$$
$$t = 11 \text{ sec.}$$

(c)   To find how far the train traveled after the brakes were applied we substitute $t = 11$ in Equation 3 and set

$$S = 44(11) - 2(11)^2 = 484 - 242 = 242 \text{ ft;}$$

hence the train moved 242 feet after the brakes were applied before it stopped.

5 FREELY FALLING BODIES

Another application of integration, which is really just a special case of the one discussed in the last section, is that of finding the height after t seconds of a body that has been released from rest at a certain height or has been projected vertically from some fixed point. We shall assume that the only force acting on the body after its release or projection is the pull of gravity. A body in flight after such conditions is called a *freely falling body*. The acceleration of a freely falling body is known to be approximately constant, and we shall take it to be numerically equal to 32 feet per second per second.

To express this fact mathematically, let y feet represent the height of the body above the ground at any time t. Now, recalling that the acceleration is the second derivative of the height, we can write

(Eq. 1) $D_t^2 y = -32.$

The negative sign is caused by the fact that y is positive upward and the acceleration due to gravity is toward the center of the earth. Equation 1 can be used to solve most problems in freely falling bodies if we understand the process of integration.

Example. An object is thrown vertically downward from an airplane at an altitude of 7200 feet with an initial speed of 40 feet per second. What will be the speed of the object after 8 seconds, and how far will it have fallen during these 8 seconds?

Solution: Starting with Equation 1 and recall that

(Eq. 2) $D_t^2 y = D_t V.$

Hence we can write $D_t V = -32.$

Integrating we have $V = -32t + C_1.$

But $V = -40$ when $t = 0$, the minus sign being necessary since the height, y feet, of the object is decreasing and V, the rate of change of y, is negative. So,

$$-40 = 0 + C_1$$

(Eq. 3) $V = -32t - 40.$

This is the formula for the speed of the object t seconds after being thrown from the airplane. After 8 seconds, when $t = 8$,

$$V = -32(8) - 40 = -296 \text{ ft/sec.}$$

Now, since $V = D_t y$, Equation 3 becomes

$$D_t y = -32t - 40.$$

Integrating again, we obtain the result

$$y = -16t^2 - 40t + C_2.$$

Here y is to represent the height of the falling object t seconds after being thrown; hence $y = 7200$ when $t = 0$. Thus,

$$C_2 = 7200$$

(Eq. 4)
$$y = -16t^2 - 40t + 7200.$$

Formula 4 gives the height, y feet, of the object above the ground t seconds after being thrown; hence, at the end of 8 seconds, $t = 8$ and

$$y = -16(8)^2 - 40(8) + 7200 = -1024 - 320 + 7200 = 5856 \text{ ft.}$$

If we wish to know when the object hits the ground, we simply find the value of t in Equation 4 for which $y = 0$, that is, the value of t for which

$$0 - -16t^2 - 40t + 7200.$$

This reduces to the quadratic equation $2t^2 + 5t - 900 = 0$, which can be solved by factoring thus: $(t - 20)(2t + 45) = 0$. Hence $t = 20$ or $t = -22.5$. Since t must be positive to satisfy the physical conditions involved, $t = 20$ is the required solution.

Example. A ball is thrown vertically upward from a tower 100 feet high at an initial speed of 64 feet per second. Find when the ball was highest and how high it was.

Solution: Again we start with the basic Equation 1, namely $D_t^2 y = -32$.

We write its equivalent, $\quad D_t V = -32.$
Integrating, we obtain $\quad V = -32t + C_1.$

From the statement of the problem we find the initial conditions to be $V = 64$ and $y = 100$ when $t = 0$. Substituting $V = 64$ and $t = 0$ in the last equation we determine C_1 as follows:

$$64 = 0 + C_1$$
$$C_1 = 64.$$

(Eq. 5)   We now have $\qquad V = 64 - 32t.$
Again recalling that $\qquad V = D_t y$
we obtain the relation $\qquad D_t y = 64 - 32t.$
Integrating once more, $\qquad y = 64t - 16t^2 + C_2.$

But $y = 100$ when $t = 0$; therefore $C_2 = 100$, and our formula for the height, y feet, of the ball above the ground t seconds after being thrown vertically upward is

(Eq. 6) $y = 100 + 64t - 16t^2.$

When the ball reached its highest point, V was zero; hence from Equation 5 we have

$$0 = 64 - 32t$$
$$32t = 64, \quad \text{and} \quad t = 2.$$

The ball reached its highest point above the ground at the end of 2 seconds. To find this maximum height we substitute $t = 2$ in Equation 6:

$$y = 100 + 64(2) - 16(2)^2 = 100 + 128 - 64 = 164.$$

The maximum height of the ball above the ground was 164 feet.

EXERCISES

1. A certain object moves with a speed $V = 30t^2 - 4t^3$. Find the distance traveled from $t = 0$ to $t = 4$ if $S = 0$ when $t = 0$. Also, find this distance if $S = 25$ when $t = 0$, and if $S = -35$ when $t = 0$. Does the value of S when $t = 0$ affect the distance covered between $t = 0$ and $t = 4$?

2. An object initially at the point $(18, 0)$ on the x axis is projected toward the left along the x axis with an initial speed of 20 feet per second. If the acceleration is thereafter constantly equal to 4 feet per second per second, what is a formula for the distance (x feet) of the object from the origin after t seconds? When does the object pass through the origin? When and where does it stop and reverse its direction?

3. An object moves along a straight line in such a way that its acceleration is given by the formula $A = 6t + 4$. If $V = 4$ and $S = 5$ when $t = 1$, what are the speed and position of the object when $t = 5$?

4. A ball is thrown vertically upward from the edge of a roof 128 feet high with an initial speed of 32 feet per second. With what speed does the ball hit the ground? At what time, after $t = 0$, is the object again 128 feet above the ground?

5. If an object travels with a speed $V = 100 - 20t$, and if $S = 40$ when $t = 1$, what are S and A when $t = 9$?

6. An antiaircraft shell is fired vertically upward at an initial speed of 4096 feet per second. Neglecting air resistance, how long will it take to reach the highest point of its path? How high will this be?

7. If the speed of an object is given by the function $V = 12t - 3t^2$, and if $S = 5$ when $t = 0$, where is the object when the speed is a maximum?

8. What is the distance traveled by an object in the first 10 seconds if the acceleration is given by the relation $A = 12t - 4$ feet per second per second and if the initial speed is 2 feet per second.

9. An object falls from rest from a height of 256 feet. With what speed does it hit the ground?

10. A train was traveling at the rate of 60 miles per hour at the instant the brakes were applied. The speed thereafter decreased at the rate of 1200 miles per hour, per hour. Find when the train stopped and how far it moved in stopping.

11. Babe Ruth is supposed to have caught a baseball dropped from the top of the Washington Monument, 576 feet high. Assuming no air resistance and that the ball was caught at ground level, find the speed of the ball when caught.

12. What should be the initial upward speed of a body if it goes to a maximum height of 4900 feet?

6   THE EQUATION OF A CURVE

We have made frequent use, heretofore, of the fact that the slope of the line tangent to a curve at a point (or the slope of the curve at the point) is the value of the derivative $D_x y$ at the point. Thus, if m is the slope of the curve $y = f(x)$ at a general point (x, y) on the curve, then

$$D_x y = m.$$

If m is a function of x we can frequently find y by integration and so find the equation of the curve, if we have sufficient information to determine the constant of integration. For the special case $m = $ constant, the curve represented is always a straight line, as was pointed out in Chapter VI. Hence, if a formula for the slope m of a curve is known, the equation of the curve can often be found by integration.

Example. Find the equation of the curve whose slope is given by the relation $m = 2x - 3$ and whose y intercept is -2.

Solution: Here $D_x y = 2x - 3$ and, by integration, we get $y = x^2 - 3x + C$.

This last equation does not represent one curve, but a family of curves: one curve for each different value of C. Figure 8.1 shows the graph of this equation for

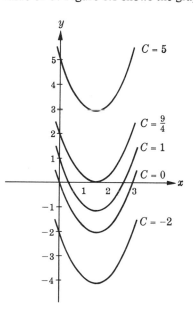

FIGURE 8.1

several values of C. Note that the curves all have the same shape. Also, for the same value of x each curve has the same slope. So far, we have not made use of the second condition stated in our problem, namely that the y intercept is -2. This condition, when applied, has the effect of singling out one particular curve of the family in question. To completely determine a curve we need to be given a formula for its slope at any point and the coordinates of one point on the curve. In this case, knowing that the y intercept is -2 is equivalent to knowing that the curve passes through the point $(0, -2)$. Thus our second condition is $y = -2$ when $x = 0$. From this we find that $C = -2$; hence

$$y = x^2 - 3x - 2$$

is the required equation. Notice that its graph is the bottom curve in the figure.

From the discussion in this example we can conclude that, if a formula for the slope of a curve is given, integration will provide the equation of a whole family of curves having the same slope formula. An equation for a single curve is obtained only when sufficient information is available to determine the constant of integration.

EXERCISES

Find the equations of the curves with the following slope formulas. Where the coordinates of a point are given, find the equation of the particular curve which passes through the given point.

1. $m = 2x$.
2. $m = \frac{2}{3}$.
3. $m = 9x^2 - 12x$.
4. $m = 2x + 3$.
5. $m = -5$.
6. $m = -\frac{2}{5}$.

7. $m = 3x^2$; $(2, 1)$.
8. $m = 5x$; $(-1, 3)$.
9. $m = 4$; $(0, 2)$.
10. $m = -1$; $(3, 0)$.
11. $m = x^2 + x - 1$; $(-2, -3)$.
12. $m = 5x^4 + x^3 - x - 4$; $(2, -1)$.

13. The slope of a certain suspension cable at a distance x feet from the center is $0.004x$. Find the height, y feet, at any point if $y = 25$ when $x = 0$.
14. At every point of a curve, $D_x^2 y = 6x$; at the point $(0, 5)$ the slope is 4. Find the equation of the curve.
15. At every point of a curve, $D_x^2 y = -12$; it passes through $(1, 2)$ and has the slope -6 at that point. Find the equation of the curve.

7 INTEGRAL NOTATION

We are already familiar with the use of symbols in mathematics to indicate operations that are to be performed. For example, the symbol $+$ indicates the operation of addition, the radical $\sqrt{}$ indicates the operation of extracting a square root, and in the last chapter we used a capital D with a subscript, say D_x, to indicate the operation of taking a derivative. We now find it convenient to introduce a symbol to indicate the operation of integration.

The integral of any function $f(x)$ with respect to x will be denoted by

$$\int f(x)\, dx.$$

To be more specific, we define this new symbol in the following way:

$$\int f(x)\, dx = F(x) + C,$$

where $F(x)$ is a function of x such that $F'(x) = f(x)$. The symbol $\int$ is called an *integral sign*, and the equation is read, "the integral, with respect to x, of $f(x)$ is $F(x)$ plus C." We are thus interpreting the symbol $\int(\cdots)\, dx$ as the inverse of the symbol $D_x(\cdots)$. The function $f(x)$ is commonly called the *integrand.* We have used x as the independent variable in stating our definition, but any other variable would have been equally good; for instance,

$$\int f(t)\, dt = F(t) + C \qquad \text{if } F'(t) = f(t),$$

$$\int g(y)\, dy = G(y) + C \qquad \text{if } G'(y) = g(y).$$

Using this new notation we may write

$$\int 3x^2\, dx = x^3 + c$$

$$\int 5t^4 dt = t^5 + c$$

$$\int (6y^2 - 4y + 7)\, dy = 2y^3 - 2y^2 + 7y + c.$$

The integration formulas of Section 3 when written in integral notation become

I. $\displaystyle\int 0\, dx = c$

II. $\displaystyle\int dx = x + c$

III. $\displaystyle\int k\, dx = kx + c$

IV. $\displaystyle\int kx^n\, dx = \frac{kx^{n+1}}{n+1} + c, \qquad n \neq -1$

V. $\displaystyle\int kf(x)\, dx = k\int f(x)\, dx, \qquad k \neq 0$

VI. If $F'(x) = f(x)$ and $G'(x) = g(x)$, then $\displaystyle\int [f(x) + g(x)]\, dx = F(x) + G(x) + c.$

Let us add to our list a new formula which is a generalization of Formula IV. If $u(x)$ is a differentiable function of x, then

$$D_x \left(\frac{u^{n+1}(x)}{n+1} \right) = u^n(x) \cdot u'(x).$$

Therefore by the definition of an integral

VII. $\displaystyle\int u^n(x)u'(x)\, dx = \frac{u^{n+1}(x)}{n+1} + c, \qquad n \neq -1.$

For the special case $n = -\frac{1}{2}$ we have the following useful formula.

VIII. $\displaystyle\int \frac{u'(x)\, dx}{\sqrt{u(x)}} = 2\sqrt{u(x)} + c.$

For the sake of brevity we shall write "integrate: $\int f(x)\, dx$" to mean, "find the function $F(x) + c$ represented by the symbol $\int f(x)\, dx$."

Example.   Integrate: $\int (x^4 + 1)^{19}4x^3 \, dx$.

Solution: If we let $u(x) = x^4 + 1$, then $u'(x) = 4x^3$, and hence

$$\int (x^4 + 1)^{19}4x^3 \, dx = \int u^{19}(x)u'(x) \, dx$$

$$= \frac{u^{20}(x)}{20} + c \qquad \text{(Formula VII)}$$

$$= \frac{(x^4 + 1)^{20}}{20} + c.$$

Check: $D_x[\frac{1}{20}(x^4 + 1)^{20}] = (x^4 + 1)^{19} \cdot 4x^3.$

Example.   Integrate: $\int x\sqrt{x^2 + 4} \, dx$.

Solution: $\int x\sqrt{x^2 + 4} \, dx = \int (x^2 + 4)^{1/2}x \, dx$. Let $u(x) = x^2 + 4$, then $u'(x) = 2x$. In our integral we only have x rather than $2x$. However, since only the *constant factor* 2 is missing, we can supply this factor and compensate for it by a factor of $\frac{1}{2}$ in front of the integral (by Formula V). We may therefore write

$$\int (x^2 + 4)^{1/2}x \, dx = \frac{1}{2} \int (x^2 + 4)^{1/2}2x \, dx$$

$$= \frac{1}{2} \int u^{1/2}(x)u'(x) \, dx$$

$$= \frac{1}{2} \frac{u^{3/2}(x)}{\frac{3}{2}} + c \qquad \text{(Formula VII)}$$

$$= \tfrac{1}{3}u^{3/2}(x) + c = \tfrac{1}{3}(x^2 + 4)^{3/2} + c.$$

Check: $D_x[\frac{1}{3}(x^2 + 4)^{3/2}] = \frac{1}{3} \cdot \frac{3}{2}(x^2 + 4)^{1/2}.$

Example.   Integrate: $\displaystyle\int \frac{x^2 \, dx}{\sqrt{x^3 - 7}}.$

Solution:

$$\int \frac{x^2 \, dx}{\sqrt{x^3 - 7}} = \frac{1}{3} \int \frac{3x^2 \, dx}{\sqrt{x^3 - 7}} \quad [u = x^3 - 7, \, u' = 3x^2]$$

$$= \frac{1}{3} \int \frac{u'(x) \, dx}{\sqrt{u(x)}}$$

$$= \tfrac{1}{3} \cdot 2\sqrt{u(x)} + c \qquad \text{(Formula VIII)}$$

$$= \tfrac{2}{3}\sqrt{x^3 - 7} + c.$$

Check:

$$D_x[\tfrac{2}{3}\sqrt{x^3 - 7}] = D_x[\tfrac{2}{3}(x^3 - 7)^{1/2}] = [\tfrac{2}{3} \cdot \tfrac{1}{2}(x^3 - 7)^{-1/2} \cdot 2x]$$

$$= \frac{x}{\sqrt{x^3 - 7}}.$$

8   THE DIFFERENTIAL OF A FUNCTION

Let $y = f(x)$ be the value of a function of x defined on the interval $a \leq x \leq b$ and having a derivative at each point of this interval. We wish now to define a quantity which we shall represent by dy and call the differential of $f(x)$ or, more simply, the differential of y. Before giving our definition let us first introduce the new symbol dx for an arbitrary increment of the independent variable x. Note that since dx is arbitrary, that is, can be assigned any value whatever, it is in reality an independent variable. In fact, dx is the same type of variable as was h or Δx in Chapters VI and VII, except that $x + h$ and $x + \Delta x$ must belong to the domain of f, while dx is unrestricted. This symbol dx is called the *differential of x* and its range is $-\infty < dx < \infty$.

The *differential dy* of the function $y = f(x)$ is defined by the relation

$$dy = D_x y \, dx.$$

An equivalent notation is $df(x) = D_x y \, dx$.

Again, it should be emphasized that dx, as also dy, represents one number only, and is not d times x and should never be thought of as such.

It follows from our definition that, if $dx \neq 0$, then

$$\frac{dy}{dx} = D_x y.$$

This is the source of the notation dy/dx for the derivative of y with respect to x, mentioned in the first section of Chapter VII. The notation has the advantage that with it the derivative can always be regarded as a quotient of differentials.

Example. If $y = 3x^2$, then $D_x y = 6x$ and $dy = 6x \, dx$. We now list a few numerical values of dy for various values of x and dx.

When	$x = 1$	and	$dx = 0.2,$	then	$dy = 1.2$
	$x = 3$		$dx = 5,$		$dy = 90$
	$x = 2$		$dx = -1,$		$dy = -12$
	$x = 2$		$dx = 0.01,$		$dy = 0.12$
	$x = -1$		$dx = 100,$		$dy = -600.$

Thus dy is, in fact, a function of two independent variables, x and dx.

Example. If $y = 2x^2 - 7x + 8$, what is dy?

Solution: By definition, $dy = D_x y \, dx = (4x - 7) \, dx$.

A geometrical interpretation of the differential may be given as follows. Consider the graph of the curve $y = f(x)$; see Fig. 8.2. Let $P_1(x_1, y_1)$ be a point on the curve. For $x = x_1$ the ratio of dy to dx is the slope of the curve $y = f(x)$ at the point P_1. Hence the point R with coordinates $(x_1 + dx, y_1 + dy)$ lies on the tangent to the curve at the point P_1, no matter what value may be

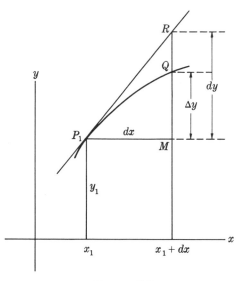

FIGURE 8.2

assigned dx. So, in Fig. 8.2 the differentials dx and dy are represented by the directed segments

$$dx = P_1M, \qquad dy = MR.$$

In the figure, Q is the point where the segment MR intersects the curve $y = f(x)$. Denote MQ by Δy. It follows that

$$\Delta y = f(x_1 + dx) - f(x_1).$$

As dx approaches zero, so does Δy. Similarly, as dx approaches zero, so does dy. This suggests one application of the differential dy, namely as an approximation for Δy when dx is sufficiently small but not zero.

The application we are particularly interested in at the moment, however, is that of representing any derivative as the ratio of two differentials. This trick is a boon to integration. For example, if we have been given

$$D_x y = f(x),$$

we can replace this with the equivalent relation

$$\frac{dy}{dx} = f(x).$$

Since the left member of this equation is a fraction, dy divided by dx, we can multiply both members of the equation by dx and get

$$dy = f(x)\, dx.$$

Now integrating both sides,

$$\int dy = \int f(x)\,dx$$

or
$$y + C_1 = F(x) + C_2$$

and finally
$$y = F(x) + C,$$

where $F'(x) = f(x)$ and $C_2 - C_1 = C$.

The advantage of using differentials is much more obvious in cases like the following. Suppose we have been given

$$D_x y = f(x)/g(y).$$

To integrate such a problem seems almost hopeless. But now let us rewrite this equation in the form

$$\frac{dy}{dx} = \frac{f(x)}{g(y)}.$$

Clearing fractions, we have

$$g(y)\,dy = f(x)\,dx.$$

Integration can now be indicated thus:

$$\int g(y)\,dy = \int f(x)\,dx.$$

Example. Find the equation of the curve passing through the point $(2, 1)$, whose slope is given by the relation

$$m = \frac{2x + 1}{2y - 1}.$$

Solution:

$$m = \frac{dy}{dx}.$$

Therefore
$$\frac{dy}{dx} = \frac{2x + 1}{2y - 1}.$$

Clearing fractions, $(2y - 1)\,dy = (2x + 1)\,dx.$

Integrating, $\int (2y - 1)\,dy = \int (2x + 1)\,dx$

or $y^2 - y = x^2 + x + C.$

Since $y = 1$ when $x = 2$ we find, by substitution, that $C = -6$. The required equation can now be written: $x^2 - y^2 + x + y = 6$.

An equation involving one or more derivatives is called a *differential equation*. $D_x y = 6x$, $D_t V = 4 - 2t$, $D_t^2 y = -32$, and $dy/dx = (2x + 1)/(2y - 1)$ are examples of differential equations. These are, of course, of the simplest possible type, but they are sufficient for our present purposes. The equation free of derivatives, obtained by integrating a differential equation, is called a *solution of the differential equation*. Thus $x^2 - y^2 + x + y = 6$ is a solution of the differential equation $dy/dx = (2x + 1)/(2y - 1)$.

Example. If $y = x^3$, approximately how much does y increase when x increases from $x = 10$ to $x = 10.02$? Exactly how much?

Solution: Since the increase in x is small, dy is probably a good approximation of the change in y. Let us calculate dy by letting $dx = \Delta x = 0.02$:

$$dy = 3x^2\, dx = 3(10)^2(0.02) = 6.$$

This says that y increases about 6 units when x increases from $x = 10$ to $x = 10.02$. The exact increase in y is, of course,

$$\Delta y = (10.02)^3 - 10^3.$$

This difference can be found by direct calculation, but the following procedure may be easier in many cases.

$$y = x^3,$$
$$y + \Delta y = (x + dx)^3,$$
$$= x^3 + 3x^2(dx) + 3x(dx)^2 + (dx)^3,$$
whence $\qquad \Delta y = 3x^2(dx) + 3x(dx)^2 + (dx)^3.$

Now let $x = 10$ and $dx = 0.02$:

$\Delta y = 3(10^2)(0.02) + 3(10)(0.02)^2 + (0.02)^3 = 6 + 0.012 + 0.000008 = 6.012008,$
from which it is seen that the error made by taking dy as an approximation of Δy is $\Delta y - dy = 0.012008.$

EXERCISES

Perform each indicated integration.

1. $\displaystyle\int x^5\, dx.$

2. $\displaystyle\int 3dx.$

3. $\displaystyle\int 4t^3\, dt.$

4. $\displaystyle\int (5 - 2t)\, dt.$

5. $\displaystyle\int dy.$

6. $\displaystyle\int (x^2 - ax)\, dx.$

7. $\displaystyle\int (5x^4 + 8x^3 - 3x^2 + 6x - 7)\, dx.$

8. $\displaystyle\int (\tfrac{2}{3}x^2 - \tfrac{5}{7}x + 4^2)\, dx.$

9. $\displaystyle\int (7 + 4y - 9y^2)\, dy.$

10. $\displaystyle\int x(5x^2 - 2)\, dx.$

11. $\displaystyle\int \frac{10}{x^2}\, dx.$

12. $\displaystyle\int (40 - 32t + 4t^3)\, dt.$

13. $\displaystyle\int (x + 1)^3\, dx.$

14. $\displaystyle\int \sqrt{2y + 3}\, dy.$

15. $\displaystyle\int x^2(10 + x^3)\, dx.$

16. $\displaystyle\int \frac{(2x + 3)\, dx}{\sqrt{x^2 + 3x - 5}}.$

17. $\displaystyle\int \frac{x\, dx}{\sqrt{4 - x^2}}.$

18. $\displaystyle\int \frac{x\, dx}{(4 + x^2)^2}.$

19. $\displaystyle\int (t^{19} - 7t^8 + 4)\, dt.$

22. $\displaystyle\int 7x(3 + 4x^2)^{10}\, dx.$

20. $\displaystyle\int (x + 1)(2x + 4)\, dx.$

23. $\displaystyle\int \frac{dy}{\sqrt{2y + 1}}.$

21. $\displaystyle\int (ax^2 + bx + c)\, dx.$

24. $\displaystyle\int \frac{(x - 3)\, dx}{\sqrt{x^2 - 6x + 10}}.$

25. Find the equation of the curve which passes through (2, 1) and whose slope at any point (x, y) on the curve is $m = \dfrac{x + 5}{y}.$

26. Find the equation of the curve which passes through (0, 5) and whose slope at any point on the curve is $m = \dfrac{2}{y}.$

27. Find a solution of the differential equation $\dfrac{dy}{dx} = \dfrac{4 + x}{2 - y}$ if $y = 3$ when $x = 0$.

28. About how much would y change if x increased from $x = 1$ to $x = 1.01$ and $y = x^3 + 3x^2 + 10x - 7$?

29. Find a solution of the differential equation $\dfrac{dy}{dx} = x^2 y^2$ if $y = 1$ when $x = 1$.

30. The speed of an object t seconds after starting was $V = \dfrac{20}{\sqrt{4t + 1}}.$ If $S = 10$ when $t = 0$, find S when $t = 6$.

9   AREAS FOUND BY INTEGRATION

One important practical use of the process of integration is that of finding the area bounded by two or more curves. We wish to show here that an area frequently can be found by integration, provided the equation of the curve is given.

Area Under a Curve

Let us consider the area below the curve whose equation is $y = f(x)$ and which is above the x axis and bounded on the left by the line $x = a$ and on the right by the line $x = b$ (Fig. 8.3).

For simplicity of argument we shall assume that $y = f(x)$ is a rising curve in the interval $a \le x \le b$. Select x_1 such that $a < x_1 < b$ and let A represent the area lying between the lines $x = a$ and $x = x_1$. As x_1 increases, the area A also increases. It is thus helpful to think of A as a growing area whose value depends upon the value of x_1; then A is a function of x_1. Denote by ΔA the increase in A when x is increased from $x = x_1$ to $x = x_1 + \Delta x$. In Fig. 8.3, ΔA represents the area above the x axis, under the curve, and bounded on the sides by the lines $x = x_1$ and $x = x_1 + \Delta x$. Now let us compare this area with the areas of the two rectangles $MNRP$ and $MNQS$.

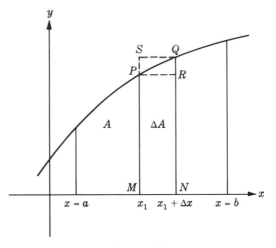

FIGURE 8.3

It is apparent from the figure that ΔA is larger than the area of rectangle $MNRP$ and smaller than the area of $MNQS$. In symbols,

(Eq. 1) $$\Delta x f(x_1) < \Delta A < \Delta x f(x_1 + \Delta x).$$

Since Δx is a positive number, we can divide by Δx and the resulting inequality will still hold; thus,

(Eq. 2) $$f(x_1) < \frac{\Delta A}{\Delta x} < f(x_1 + \Delta x).$$

We are assuming that $y = f(x)$ is a continuous function; hence

$$\lim_{\Delta x \to 0} f(x_1 + \Delta x) = f(x_1).$$

It follows from the last inequality that

$$f(x_1) \leq \lim_{\Delta x \to 0} \frac{\Delta A}{\Delta x}$$

and $$\lim_{\Delta x \to 0} \frac{\Delta A}{\Delta x} \leq \lim_{\Delta x \to 0} f(x_1 + \Delta x) = f(x_1).$$

Therefore, the equality sign must hold, and

$$\lim_{\Delta x \to 0} \frac{\Delta A}{\Delta x} = f(x_1).$$

But ΔA is the change in A produced by the increase Δx in x; so $\Delta A / \Delta x$ is the average rate of change of A over the interval Δx, and by the definition of a derivative,

$$\lim_{\Delta x \to 0} \frac{\Delta A}{\Delta x} = D_x A.$$

This gives the important result

$$D_x A = f(x_1).$$

Since x_1 was any value of x on the interval (a, b) we can now drop the subscript and write

(Eq. 3) $$D_x A = f(x).$$

In words, this result says that the rate at which the area A is changing at any distance x from the y axis is always equal to the height of the curve at that distance.

If we make the assumption that our curve is a falling curve over the interval (a, b) instead of a rising curve, the same argument will hold throughout if we simply reverse the direction of the inequalities in Equations 1 and 2. With a slight modification in argument, Equation 3 can be shown to hold for any continuous curve.

To complete our discussion of finding areas by integration, let us return to Equation 3 and write it in the equivalent form

$$\frac{dA}{dx} = f(x)$$

or $$dA = f(x)\,dx.$$

Integrating, $$\int dA = \int f(x)\,dx.$$

Let $F(x)$ be a function such that $F'(x) = f(x)$; then

$$A = \int f(x)\,dx = F(x) + C.$$

A represents the area under the curve and between the lines $x = a$ and $x = x_1$. Hence, if x_1 decreases, so does A, and when $x_1 = a$, then $A = 0$. So in general we can say that $A = 0$ when $x = a$, and determine C as follows:

$$0 = F(a) + C \quad \text{or} \quad C = -F(a).$$

Our expression for the area between the fixed ordinate at $x = a$ and a variable ordinate at x now becomes

(Eq. 4) $$A = F(x) - F(a),$$

which verifies our earlier contention that A was a function of x. To find the area bounded by $x = a$ and $x = b$ we need only substitute $x = b$ in Equation 4 and we obtain

(Eq. 5) $$A = F(b) - F(a).$$

It is convenient to represent this area by the symbol

(Eq. 6) $$A = \int_a^b f(x)\,dx.$$

The a at the bottom of the integral sign is the initial value of x, or the value of x at which the area in question begins, and is called the *lower limit of integration.* The *b* at the top of the integral sign is the terminal value of *x*, or the value of *x* at which the area stops, and is called the *upper limit.*

From our definition and by combining Equations 5 and 6, we have

(Eq. 7) $$\int_a^b f(x)\, dx = F(b) - F(a),$$

where $F(x)$ is a function whose derivative is $f(x)$. We shall refer to the integral symbol, such as that in Equation 7, involving upper and lower limits, as a *definite integral,* to distinguish it from the integral symbol originally defined and commonly called an *indefinite integral.* Equation 7, in practice, is always written in slightly more detail, as

(Eq. 8) $$\int_a^b f(x)\, dx = F(x)\Big]_a^b = F(b) - F(a).$$

The added detail, $F(x)\Big]_a^b$, is important in that it exhibits the actual function $F(x)$ being employed.

It is convenient to use the definite integral in many problems other than those involving area.

Example.   Find the value of the definite integral $\int_1^3 (4x - 1)\, dx$.

Solution: The rules of integration previously stated still apply in finding $F(x)$:

$$\int_1^3 (4x - 1)\, dx = 2x^2 - x\Big]_1^3 = [2(3)^2 - 3] - [2(1)^2 - 1],$$

$$= (18 - 3) - (2 - 1) = 14.$$

Example.   Find the area under the curve $y = x^3 - x^2 + 3$, above the *x* axis, and between the lines $x = -1$ and $x = 2$ (the shaded area in Fig. 8.4).

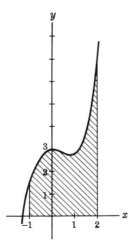

FIGURE 8.4

Solution: Here $A = \int_{-1}^{2} (x^3 - x^2 + 3)\, dx,$

$$= \frac{x^4}{4} - \frac{x^3}{3} + 3x \Big]_{-1}^{2},$$

$$= \left(4 - \frac{8}{3} + 6\right) - \left(\frac{1}{4} + \frac{1}{3} - 3\right),$$

$$= \frac{39}{4}.$$

In our discussion we have restricted ourselves to areas that lie wholly above the x axis. By similar arguments, we would find that the area below the x axis, above the curve $y = f(x)$ and between the lines $x = a$ and $x = b$, is given by the relation

$$A = - \int_{a}^{b} f(x)\, dx.$$

The minus sign is needed in this case because each ordinate $f(x)$ is negative, and without this change of sign the area would turn out to be negative.

If the curve $y = f(x)$ crosses the x axis between $x = a$ and $x = b$, so that a part of the area in question is above and a part below the x axis, each of these parts should be calculated separately and then the results added, to give the total area required. Otherwise, the area below the x axis tends to cancel out the area above the axis, and one gets the algebraic sum of the areas rather than the actual sum.

Example.   Sketch the graph of the curve $y = x(x - 2)(x - 4)$ and find the area bounded by this curve and the x axis.

Solution: An inspection of the equation shows that the curve crosses the x axis at the points $(0, 0)$, $(2, 0)$, and $(4, 0)$, and only at these points. The graph is shown in Fig. 8.5. Since the portion of the area between $x = 2$ and $x = 4$ is below the

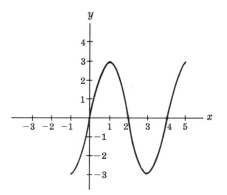

FIGURE 8.5

x axis, we express the total area as the algebraic sum of the two definite integrals:

$$A = \int_0^2 (x^3 - 6x^2 + 8x)\, dx - \int_2^4 (x^3 - 6x^2 + 8x)\, dx,$$

$$= \frac{x^4}{4} - 2x^3 + 4x^2 \bigg]_0^2 - \left[\frac{x^4}{4} - 2x^3 + 4x^2\right]_2^4,$$

$$= \frac{16}{4} - 16 + 16 - [(64 - 128 + 64) - (4 - 16 + 16)],$$

$$= 4 - (-4) = 8.$$

Area Between Two Curves

Suppose that the graphs of the equations $y = f(x)$ and $y = g(x)$ are the curves shown in Fig. 8.6. Let A be the area bounded above by the curve whose

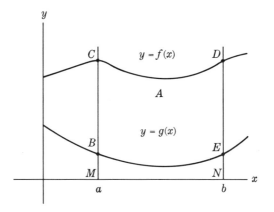

FIGURE 8.6

equation is $y = f(x)$ and below by the curve whose equation is $y = g(x)$, and bounded on the left by the line $x = a$ and on the right by the line $x = b$. It follows from our discussion regarding areas under a curve that

$$A = \int_a^b f(x)\, dx - \int_a^b g(x)\, dx$$

(Eq. 9)   or that $A = \int_a^b [f(x) - g(x)]\, dx.$

Example.   Find the area bounded above by the curve $y = x^2 + 2$ and below by the curve $y = x^2 + 1$, and lying between the lines $x = 1$ and $x = 3$ (Fig. 8.7).

Solution: Here $f(x) = x^2 + 2$, $g(x) = x^2 + 1$, $a = 1$, and $b = 3$. Substituting into Equation 9 we get

$$A = \int_1^3 [(x^2 + 2) - (x^2 + 1)]\, dx,$$

$$= \int_1^3 1\, dx = x \bigg]_1^3 = 3 - 1 = 2.$$

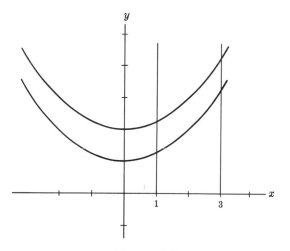

FIGURE 8.7

It can be shown that Equation 9 is valid in the following more general case. Let the equations

$$y = f(x) \quad \text{and} \quad y = g(x)$$

define two functions of x that are continuous on the closed interval $[a, b]$. Suppose also that

$$g(x) \le f(x) \quad \text{on } [a, b].$$

Then the area bounded above by the curve $y = f(x)$, below by the curve $y = g(x)$, and on the sides by the vertical lines $x = a$ and $x = b$ is given by Equation 9. It should be observed that one or both of the given curves may lie wholly or partially below the x axis in the interval $[a, b]$.

Example. Find the area bounded by the curve $y = x^2 - 2x$ and the line $y = 3$ (see Fig. 8.8).

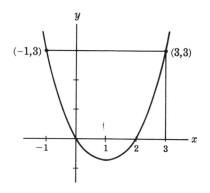

FIGURE 8.8

Solution: Referring to Equation 9, we find $f(x) = 3$, $g(x) = x^2 - 2x$, $a = -1$, and $b = 3$. Therefore,

$$A = \int_{-1}^{3} [3 - (x^2 - 2x)] \, dx,$$

$$= \int_{-1}^{3} (3 + 2x - x^2) \, dx,$$

$$= 3x + x^2 - \frac{x^3}{3} \Big]_{-1}^{3} = (9 + 9 - 9) - \left(-3 + 1 + \frac{1}{3}\right),$$

$$= 9 + 2 - \frac{1}{3} = \frac{32}{3}.$$

EXERCISES

Find the value of each definite integral in Problems 1 through 9.

1. $\int_{1}^{6} 2x \, dx.$ **2.** $\int_{-2}^{5} 4 dx.$ **3.** $\int_{-1}^{4} (3x^2 + 5).$

4. $\int_{0}^{6} (t^3 + t + 3) \, dt.$ **7.** $\int_{0}^{4} \frac{dx}{\sqrt{2x + 1}}.$

5. $\int_{2}^{4} (x^2 - 3x + 1) \, dx.$ **8.** $\int_{1}^{16} \sqrt{x} \, dx.$

6. $\int_{-1}^{0} (5x^4 + 3x^2 - 4x) \, dx.$ **9.** $\int_{-4}^{-2} x \, dx.$

10. Find the area above the x-axis, below the curve $y = 6x^2$ and between the lines $x = 1$ and $x = 5$.

11. Find the area above the x-axis, below the curve $y = \frac{40}{x^2}$ and between the lines $x = 2$ and $x = 10$.

12. Find the area above the x-axis and below the curve $y = 9 - x^2$.

13. Find the area above the x-axis, below the line $y = 2x + 3$, and between the lines $x = 1$ and $x = 6$. Check by geometry.

14. Find the area above the x-axis, below the curve $y = x^3 - 3x + 2$ and between $x = -2$ and $x = 1$. Draw the graph of the curve.

15. Find the area bounded by the curve $y = x^2$ and the line $y = 4$.

16. Find the area bounded by the curve $y = 25 - x^2$ and the line $y = 9$.

17. Find the area bounded by the curve $y = x^2 - 4x$ and the line $y = x$.

18. Find the area bounded by the two curves $y = x^2$ and $x = y^2$.

19. Find the area bounded by the parabola $y = x^2$ and the line $y = x + 2$.

20. Find the area above the x-axis, below the curve $y = x\sqrt{3x^2 + 4}$, and between the lines $x = 0$ and $x = 2$.

10 VOLUMES OF SOLIDS

In this section we wish to indicate how the volumes of certain solids may be found by the method of integration. Let Fig. 8.9 represent a solid, and let V

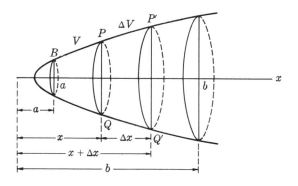

FIGURE 8.9

be the volume of that portion of the solid lying between a fixed plane AB, which is a units from some fixed point O, and a variable plane PQ, which is parallel to the fixed plane AB and a distance x units from O. Let A_x denote the area of the cross section of the solid, made by the plane PQ. We shall assume that A_x is a continuous increasing function of x for $a \leq x \leq b$.

If ΔV is the volume of that portion of the solid between the plane PQ and another plane $P'Q'$ which is parallel to PQ and a distance $x + \Delta x$ from O, then

$$A_x \Delta x \leq \Delta V \leq A_{x+\Delta x} \cdot \Delta x \qquad \text{or} \qquad A_x \leq \frac{\Delta V}{\Delta x} \leq A_{x+\Delta x}.$$

Now, since A_x is continuous,

$$\lim_{\Delta x \to 0} A_{x+\Delta x} = A_x$$

hence

(Eq. 1)
$$\frac{dV}{dx} = \lim_{\Delta x \to 0} \frac{\Delta V}{\Delta x} = A_x.$$

Thus the instantaneous rate at which the volume is changing per unit increase in x, at a point within the solid and at a distance x units from 0, is equal in value to the area of a cross section made by a plane x units from O. It can be shown that the assumption that A_x is an increasing function is unnecessary; A_x only needs to be continuous. From Equation 1 we get

(Eq. 2)
$$V = \int_a^b A_x \, dx$$

as the volume of the solid between the parallel planes at $x = a$ and $x = b$.

This discussion suggests that we can use integration to find the volume of a solid if we can do two things: first, express the area A_x of a typical cross section as a function of its distance, x units, from some convenient fixed point and, second, integrate the function so obtained.

Example.   In a certain cone each section perpendicular to the axis of the cone is a circle whose radius r varies with its distance, x inches, from the vertex according to the equation $r = 0.3x$. Find the volume of the portion of the cone extending from $x = 2$ to $x = 10$.

Solution: Since each section is a circle, we have

$$A_x = \pi r^2 = \pi(0.3x)^2 = 0.09\pi x^2.$$

Substituting into Equation 2, we obtain

$$V = \pi \int_2^{10} 0.09x^2 \, dx = \pi(.03x^3)\Big]_2^{10} = \pi[(30) - (0.24)] = 29.76\pi \text{ in.}^3$$

Example.   Find the volume of a solid hemisphere of radius 10 inches.

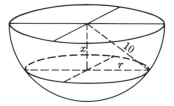

FIGURE 8.10

Solution: Each section parallel to the flat side is a circle. Let r be the radius of a circular section x units from the flat side (see Fig. 8.10). From the figure,

$$A_x = \pi r^2$$
$$\text{and} \qquad x^2 + r^2 = 10^2,$$
$$\text{whence} \qquad r^2 = 100 - x^2$$
$$\text{and} \qquad A_x = \pi(100 - x^2).$$

Using Equation 2, we have

$$V = \pi \int_0^{10} (100 - x^2) \, dx.$$

Integrating, we get

$$V = \pi\left[100x - \frac{x^3}{3}\right]_0^{10} = \pi\left[\left(1000 - \frac{1000}{3}\right) - (0 - 0)\right] = \frac{2000\pi}{3} \text{ in.}^3$$

Check: We can check our result by using a formula from geometry for the volume of a sphere, namely,

$$V = \tfrac{4}{3}\pi r^3,$$

where r is the radius of the sphere. Since ours is half a sphere we would use the formula

$$V = \tfrac{2}{3}\pi r^3;$$

thus $V = \tfrac{2}{3}(\pi)(10)^3 = 2000\pi/3$ in.^{3}, which verifies our answer.

EXERCISES

1. A certain horn has an axis of symmetry. Each section perpendicular to this axis is a circle whose radius r varies thus with the distance x units from one end: $r = 0.04x^2$. Find the volume of the space within the horn from $x = 1$ to $x = 8$.

2. Every horizontal section of a solid is a square whose side S feet varies thus with the distance x feet from the top: $S = 0.2x^2$. Find the volume if the total height is 20 feet.

3. A right circular cone has an altitude of 10 inches and a radius of base 5 inches. Find by integration the volume of the cone. (*Hint:* Show that a circular cross section x inches from the vertex has radius $r = 0.5x$.)

4. Find by integration the volume cut from a sphere of radius 5 inches by a plane 3 inches from the center.

5. Use integration to derive a formula for the volume of a sphere of radius a.

6. Find the volume of the solid generated by revolving about the x axis the area bounded by the curve $y = 2x^2$, the line $x = 1$, and the line $x = 5$.

7. A hemispherical cistern of radius 5 feet has the flat side up and has sand in the bottom to a depth of 1 foot in the middle. The cistern is filled with water to a level 1 foot below the top. Find the volume of water in the cistern above the sand.

8. The base of a solid is a circle of radius 10 inches. Every section perpendicular to one diameter is an isosceles triangle whose altitude equals half its base. Find the volume.

IX

SIMULTANEOUS LINEAR EQUATIONS AND INEQUALITIES LINEAR PROGRAMMING

1 SYSTEMS OF TWO LINEAR EQUATIONS IN TWO VARIABLES

We define the solution set of the linear equation $ax + by + c = 0$ as the set consisting of all the ordered pairs (x, y) such that $ax + by + c = 0$ or, stated symbolically, as the set $S = \{(x, y) \mid ax + by + c = 0\}$. For example, the solution set S of the linear equation $2x - 3y = 12$ is the set $S = \{(x, y) \mid 2x - 3y = 12\}$. In this section we are interested in the solution set, not of one equation, but of a pair of linear equations in x and y. For example, consider the pair of equations

$$\begin{cases} 2x - 3y = 12 \\ x - y = 5. \end{cases}$$

A pair such as this is commonly referred to as a system of two simultaneous linear equations in two variables, or in two unknowns. Let S_1 be the solution set of $2x - 3y = 12$ and S_2 be the solution set of $x - y = 5$. The solution set of the system is the set of ordered pairs that are elements of both S_1 and S_2. Symbolically, the solution set of the system is the set $S = S_1 \cap S_2$. It is easily verified that $(3, -2)$ is a solution of the system and, as we shall show in the next section, it is the only solution. Hence, $S = \{(3, -2)\}$. We shall now describe some simple methods of finding solution sets of systems of linear equations and systems of linear inequalities.

2 GRAPHICAL METHOD FOR EQUATIONS AND INEQUALITIES IN TWO VARIABLES

It was shown in Chapter V, Section 12, that every linear equation in x and y has for its graph a straight line. An obvious method of solving a system of two linear equations in x and y is to draw the two lines that are the graphs of the two equations involved, and to read from the graph the coordinates of the points the two lines have in common. Figure 9.1 shows the graphical solution

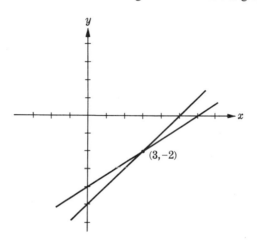

$(3,-2)$

FIGURE 9.1

of the system mentioned above. Since the two lines are distinct and not parallel, they intersect in one and only one point, and this shows that the solution set of the system consists of a single ordered pair, namely $(3, -2)$.

Now consider the system

$$\begin{cases} a_1x + b_1y + c_1 = 0 \\ a_2x + b_2y + c_2 = 0, \end{cases}$$

where a_1, b_1, c_1, a_2, b_2, and c_2 are arbitrary real numbers, it being understood that a_1 and b_1 are not both zero and the same for a_2 and b_2. Since the coefficients a_1, b_1, etc., are arbitrary, they may be assigned any real values whatever with the exceptions just mentioned. This system represents *all* systems of two linear equations in two unknowns. Let S_1 be the solution set of $a_1x + b_1y + c_1 = 0$ and let S_2 be the solution set of $a_2x + b_2y + c_2 = 0$, that is,

$S_1 = \{(x, y) \mid a_1x + b_1y + c_1 = 0\}$ and $S_2 = \{(x, y) \mid a_2x + b_2y + c_2 = 0\}$.

The solution set S of the system is defined as $S = S_1 \cap S_2$.

The graphical method of solving systems of two linear equations has the disadvantage that it is not always possible to read accurately from the graph the coordinates of the point of intersection of the two lines involved. It does, however, suggest the following important facts regarding the solution set of the system just discussed.

1. The solution set S of the system will consist of one and only one element if $a_1/b_1 \neq a_2/b_2$.

2. The solution set S will be the empty set if $a_1/a_2 = b_1/b_2 \neq c_1/c_2$.

3. The solution set S will contain infinitely many elements if $a_1/b_1 = a_2/b_2 = c_1/c_2$.

The truth of these statements follows immediately from a consideration of the graphs of the two equations that define the system. The slope of the line whose equation is $a_1x + b_1y + c_1 = 0$ is $-a_1/b_1$ and the slope of the line $a_2x + b_2y + c_2 = 0$ is $-a_2/b_2$. Hence, if $a_1/a_2 \neq b_1/b_2$, the lines are not parallel and therefore intersect in one and only one point. On the other hand, if $a_1/b_1 = a_2/b_2 \neq c_1/c_2$, the two lines are parallel and distinct and hence have no point in common. Finally, if $a_1/a_2 = b_1/b_2 = c_1/c_2$, the two equations are equivalent and so every solution of either of the equations is also a solution of the other; the solution set therefore contains infinitely many elements.

3   THE METHOD OF ELIMINATION BY ADDITION AND SUBTRACTION FOR EQUATIONS

As was pointed out in the last section, the graphical method for solving systems of linear equations is limited by the accuracy with which one is able to read from the graph the coordinates of the point of intersection of two lines. The graphical method is also limited for all practical purposes to systems involving two equations and two unknowns. We wish to review a method which will obviate both of these objections and also with which you are undoubtedly already familiar. This method is called the method of *elimination* by addition and subtraction, and consists of transforming a given system into an equivalent system whose solution set can be found by inspection. Two systems of equations are said to be equivalent if they have the same solution set.

We first apply the method to a system of two linear equations in two variables. Consider the system

(Syst. 1) $\begin{cases} a_1x + b_1y + c_1 = 0, \\ a_2x + b_2y + c_2 = 0, \end{cases}$ a_1 and b_1 not both zero
a_2 and b_2 not both zero.

It is obvious that if either or both of these equations are replaced by a non-zero multiple of themselves the new system thus obtained is equivalent to the original, for the solution set of each equation remains unchanged. That is, the system

(Syst. 2) $\quad \begin{cases} k_1(a_1x + b_1y + c_1) = 0, & k_1 \neq 0 \\ k_2(a_2x + b_2y + c_2) = 0, & k_2 \neq 0 \end{cases}$

is equivalent to System 1. Further, we can prove that the following system is also equivalent to System 1.

Theorem 9.1. *The system*

(Syst. 3) $\quad \begin{cases} a_1x + b_1y + c_1 = 0 \\ k_1(a_1x + b_1y + c_1) + k_2(a_2x + b_2y + c_2) = 0, & k_2 \neq 0 \end{cases}$

is equivalent to System 1.

Proof: If (x_1, y_1) is a solution of System 1, then

$$\begin{cases} a_1x_1 + b_1y_1 + c_1 = 0 \\ a_2x_1 + b_2y_1 + c_2 = 0, \end{cases}$$

obtains; hence, (x_1, y_1) is a solution of System 3. To verify this, note that if x_1 and y_1 are substituted for x and y respectively in the second equation of System 3 we get

$$k_1(a_1x_1 + b_1y_1 + c_1) + k_2(a_2x_1 + b_2y_1 + c_2) = k_1(0) + k_2(0) = 0,$$

which shows that (x_1, y_1) is a solution of this equation. Thus (x_1, y_1) is a solution of the system. Thus every solution of System 1 is also a solution of System 3. Next, suppose that (x_2, y_2) is a solution of System 3, then

$$a_1x_2 + b_1x_2 + c_1 = 0,$$
$$k_1(a_1x_2 + b_1y_2 + c_1) + k_2(a_2x_2 + b_2y_2 + c_2) = 0;$$

therefore $\quad\quad\quad k_2(a_2x_2 + b_2y_2 + c_2) = 0$

and, since $k_2 \neq 0$, $\quad\quad\quad a_2x_2 + b_2y_2 + c_2 = 0,$

which shows that (x_2, y_2) is also a solution of System 1.

Let us now use Theorem 9.1 to solve System 1:

$$\begin{cases} a_1x + b_1y + c_1 = 0, & a_1 \text{ and } b_1 \text{ not both zero} \\ a_2x + b_2y + c_2 = 0, & a_2 \text{ and } b_2 \text{ not both zero.} \end{cases}$$

Solution: Assume that $a_1 \neq 0$ and let $k_1 = -a_2$ and $k_2 = a_1$; then System 3 becomes

$$\begin{cases} a_1x + b_1y + c_1 = 0 \\ -a_2(a_1x + b_1y + c_1) + a_1(a_2x + b_2y + c_2) = 0 \end{cases}$$

or, when simplified,

(Syst. 4) $\quad \begin{cases} a_1x + b_1y + c_1 = 0 \\ (a_1b_2 - a_2b_1)y + (a_1c_2 - a_2c_1) = 0, \end{cases}$

which is equivalent to System 1 (Theorem 9.1). If $a_1b_2 - a_2b_1 \neq 0$, we can solve the second equation of System 4 for y and get

$$y = -\frac{a_1c_2 - a_2c_1}{a_1b_2 - a_2b_1}$$

which, when substituted for y in the first equation of System 4, gives

$$x = -\frac{b_2c_1 - b_1c_2}{a_1b_2 - a_2b_1};$$

the solution set of System 1 in this case is the set

$$\left\{\left(-\frac{b_2c_1 - b_1c_2}{a_1b_2 - a_2b_1}, \quad -\frac{a_1c_2 - a_2c_1}{a_1b_2 - a_2b_1}\right)\right\}.$$

If $a_1b_2 - a_2b_1 = 0$ and $a_1c_2 - a_2c_1 \neq 0$, the second equation of System 4 has no solution, System 4 has no solution, and hence System 1 has no solution. This is, of course, the case in which the graphs of the two equations defining the system are parallel lines and consequently have no points in common.

Finally, if $a_1b_2 - a_2b_1 = 0$ and if $a_1c_2 - a_2c_1 = 0$, the second equation of System 4 has infinitely many solutions, System 4 therefore has infinitely many solutions, and System 1, being equivalent to System 4, likewise has a solution set containing infinitely many elements. In this case each of the two equations of System 1 has the same line as its graph.

At the outset of our solution we assumed that $a_1 \neq 0$. We could just as well have assumed that $b_1 \neq 0$; then, had we chosen $k_1 = b_2$ and $k_2 = -b_1$, we would have obtained the equivalent system

(Syst. 5) $\qquad \begin{cases} a_1x + b_1y + c_1 = 0 \\ (a_1b_2 - a_2b_1)x + (b_2c_1 - b_2c_2) = 0 \end{cases}$

and could then have used System 5 to arrive at the same conclusions as before regarding the solution set of System 1.

Example.   Solve the system $\begin{cases} 2x - 3y - 12 = 0 \\ x - y - 5 = 0. \end{cases}$

Solution: Let $k_1 = -1$ and $k_2 = 2$. A system equivalent to the given system is

$$\begin{cases} 2x - 3y - 12 = 0 \\ -(2x - 3y - 12) + 2(x - y - 5) = 0 \end{cases}$$

or

$$\begin{cases} 2x - 3y - 12 = 0 \\ y + 2 = 0. \end{cases}$$

The solution set of the last system is obviously the number pair $(3, -2)$; hence the solution set of the given system is the set $\{(3, -2)\}$.

It should be observed that the important step in solving a system of two linear equations in two variables is in choosing k_1 and k_2 such that

$$k_1(a_1x + b_1y + c_1) + k_2(a_2x + b_2y + c_2) = 0$$

reduces to a form that is either free of x or free of y.

Example. Solve the system $\begin{cases} 3x + 2y + 8 = 0 \\ 5x - y + 9 = 0. \end{cases}$

Solution: Multiply the second equation by 2, add the result to the first equation, and then replace the second equation by this sum to obtain the equivalent system

$$\begin{cases} 3x + 2y + 8 = 0 \\ 13x + 26 = 0. \end{cases}$$

Solve the second equation for x and get $x = -2$. Substitute this value of x in the first equation and solve for y, obtaining $y = -1$. The solution of the given system is the set $\{(-2, -1)\}$.

The elimination method discussed above obviously can be used to solve systems of linear equations involving more than two variables. We illustrate this fact by solving the following system:

$$\begin{cases} 3x + 4y - 2z = 17 \\ x - y + z = -4 \\ 2x - 3y + z = -7. \end{cases}$$

Solution: We obtain an equivalent system by replacing the second equation by the sum of the first equation and 2 times the second equation and then replacing the third equation by the third equation minus the second equation:

$$\begin{cases} 3x + 4y - 2z = 17 \\ 5x + 2y = 9 \\ x - 2y = -3; \end{cases}$$

in this new system replace the third equation by the sum of the second equation and third equation to get the equivalent system

$$\begin{cases} 3x + 4y - 2z = 17 \\ 5x + 2y = 9 \\ 6x = 6, \end{cases}$$

from which by inspection we see that $x = 1$, $y = 2$, and $z = -3$. The solution set of the given system is therefore the set $\{(1, 2, -3)\}$. Note that a solution of a single linear equation in three variables is an ordered triple rather than an ordered pair.

EXERCISES

In problems 1 through 6 solve graphically each given system of linear equations.

1. $2x + 3y = 12$
$4x - 5y = 2.$

2. $2x + 3y = 5$
$3x - 2y = -12.$

3. $4x - y = 7$
$8x - 2y = 3.$

4. $4x + 5y = 23$
$2x - 3y = -5.$

5. $x - 3y = 3$
$4x - 12y = 12.$

6. $7x - 4y = 25$
$x + y = 2.$

In problems 7 through 22 solve each given system of linear equations by the elimination process.

7. $x + 4y = 1$
$2x - y = -7.$

9. $4x + 3y = 10$
$3x + 2y = 5.$

11. $8x - 4y + 17 = 0$
$16x + 12y + 9 = 0.$

8. $5x + 6y = 17$
$6x + 5y = 16.$

10. $5x - 7y = 13$
$3x - 8y = 23.$

12. $15x - 8y = 12$
$11x + 5y = -9.$

13. $-113x + 203y = 400$
$97x + 141y = 200.$

18. $2x - 3y + 4z = 8$
$3x + 4y - 5z = -4$
$4x - 5y + 6z = 12.$

14. $175x - 85y = 69$
$300x + 70y = 32.$

19. $4x - y + 5z = 21$
$3x + 7y - 2z = -17$
$2x + 6y + 9z = 17.$

15. $\dfrac{3}{x} - \dfrac{1}{y} = 5$

$\dfrac{3}{x} + \dfrac{2}{y} = 2.$

20. $3x - y + z = 7$
$5x + 3y - 2z = 11$
$7x - 5z = -6.$

16. $\dfrac{2}{x} - \dfrac{1}{y} - 2 = 0$

$\dfrac{4}{x} + \dfrac{5}{y} - \dfrac{5}{3} = 0.$

21. $2x - 4y + 5z = -7$
$3x + 5y - 2z = 21$
$8x - 3y + 7z = 11.$

17. $3x - y + 2z = 9$
$2x + y - z = 7$
$x + 2y - 3z = 4.$

22. $3x + 5y + 2z = 4$
$-2x + 4y + 7z = 37$
$5x + 8y + 4z = 8.$

23. Two numbers differ by 7; the smaller number exceeds one-half the larger number by 1. Find the two numbers.

24. A person invests part of $6000 at 4 percent and the rest at 6 percent. Find each part, given that the annual income from the first investment equals the income from the second investment.

25. An airplane travels 1450 miles in the time required for a car to travel 300 miles. If the rates of each are constant and the plane travels 230 miles per hour faster than the car, what is the rate of each?

26. Ten horses and seven cows can be bought for $1985 and seven horses and ten cows can be bought for $1925. If each of the horses has the same value and each of the cows costs the same, what is the price of each?

27. A man has several coins consisting of quarters, dimes, and nickels, the total worth $3.30. He observes that if each nickel were exchanged for a quarter, each quarter for a dime, and each dime for a half-dollar, he would have $7.30, but that, if he had three times as many nickels, twice as many dimes, and the same number of quarters that he has, he would have $5.30. How many coins of each kind does he have?

28. A candy store wishes to mix 175 pounds of candy, to be sold at 85¢ per pound, by mixing candy worth 79¢ per pound and candy worth $1.00 per pound. How many pounds of each kind should he use?

4 THE METHOD OF DETERMINANTS

In this article we introduce the concept of a determinant, which is useful in the study of the solutions of systems of linear equations. Let us consider again a typical system of two linear equations in two variables. For convenience let us write the system in the form

(Eq. 1)
$$\begin{cases} a_1x + b_1y = r_1 \\ a_2x + b_2y = r_2 \end{cases}$$

where the coefficients a_1, b_1, r_1, etc., are real numbers. This system can be solved by the elimination method discussed in Section 4 and, if $a_1b_2 - a_2b_1 \neq 0$, the solution is

(Eq. 2)
$$x = \frac{r_1b_2 - r_2b_1}{a_1b_2 - a_2b_1}, \qquad y = \frac{a_1r_2 - a_2r_1}{a_1b_2 - a_2b_1}.$$

The student should verify, by direct substitution from Equations 2 back into Equations 1, that the ordered pair (x, y) given in Equations 2 is a solution of Equations 1.

The method of determinants consists of using Equations 2 as formulas, after first expressing them in terms of symbols called *determinants*. The symbol

$$\begin{vmatrix} a & c \\ b & d \end{vmatrix}$$

where a, b, c, and d are any four real numbers, is called a *determinant of the second order* and is defined by the equation

$$\begin{vmatrix} a & c \\ b & d \end{vmatrix} = ad - bc.$$

Some examples are

$$\begin{vmatrix} 7 & 3 \\ 5 & 4 \end{vmatrix} = 28 - 15 = 13, \qquad \begin{vmatrix} 2 & 6 \\ 3 & 4 \end{vmatrix} = 8 - 18 = -10,$$

$$\begin{vmatrix} 5 & -1 \\ 2 & 3 \end{vmatrix} = 15 - (-2) = 17, \qquad \begin{vmatrix} -6 & -4 \\ 3 & 1 \end{vmatrix} = (-6) - (-12) = 6.$$

Using this notation, Equations 2 can now be written

Eq. 3
$$x = \frac{\begin{vmatrix} r_1 & b_1 \\ r_2 & b_2 \end{vmatrix}}{\begin{vmatrix} a_1 & b_1 \\ a_2 & b_2 \end{vmatrix}}, \qquad y = \frac{\begin{vmatrix} a_1 & r_1 \\ a_2 & r_2 \end{vmatrix}}{\begin{vmatrix} a_1 & b_1 \\ a_2 & b_2 \end{vmatrix}}.$$

It should be noted that the denominators of the fractions in the right members of Equations 3 are identical, and also that the numbers a_1, b_1, a_2, b_2, which form the determinant appearing in the denominators of the right members of Equations 3, are the coefficients of x and y in the two equations of the given system and occur in exactly the same order as they occur in the system. Further, the determinant in the numerator of the fraction in the right member of the first of Equations 3 is the same as the determinant in the denominator of that same fraction, except that the coefficients of x, namely a_1 and a_2, have been respectively replaced by the constant terms r_1 and r_2, whose algebraic signs are those that these numbers have in Equations 1. Similarly, the determinant in the numerator of the fraction in the right member of the second equation of Equations 3 is obtained from the determinant in the denominator by replacing b_1 and b_2, the coefficients of y, by r_1 and r_2 respectively.

Example.   Use determinants to solve the system $\begin{cases} 3x + 7y = 10 \\ 2x + 5y = 6. \end{cases}$

Solution:

$$x = \frac{\begin{vmatrix} 10 & 7 \\ 6 & 5 \end{vmatrix}}{\begin{vmatrix} 3 & 7 \\ 2 & 5 \end{vmatrix}} = \frac{50 - 42}{15 - 14} = \frac{8}{1} = 8,$$

$$y = \frac{\begin{vmatrix} 3 & 10 \\ 2 & 6 \end{vmatrix}}{\begin{vmatrix} 3 & 7 \\ 2 & 5 \end{vmatrix}} = \frac{18 - 20}{15 - 14} = \frac{-2}{1} = -2.$$

Check: $3(8) + 7(-2) = 24 - 14 = 10,$
$2(8) + 5(-2) = 16 - 10 = 6.$

Hence the solution set consists of the single element $(8, -2)$.

Let us now extend the method of determinants to systems of three linear equations in three variables. We shall start by applying the method of elimination to a typical system of three equations which, for convenience, we write in the form

$$a_1x + b_1y + c_1z = r_1$$
$$a_2x + b_2y + c_2z = r_2$$
(Eq. 4) $\qquad\qquad a_3x + b_3y + c_3z = r_3,$

where $a_1, b_1, c_1, r_1, a_2, b_2, c_2, r_2, a_3, b_3, c_3, r_3$ are arbitrary but fixed real numbers. If we replace the second equation by c_2 times the first equation, minus c_1 times the second equation, and replace the third equation by c_3 times the first equation, minus c_1 times the third equation, we obtain the equivalent system

$$a_1x + b_1y + c_1z = r_1$$
$$(a_1c_2 - a_2c_1)x + (b_1c_2 - b_2c_1)y = r_1c_2 - c_1r_2$$
(Eq. 5) $\qquad (a_1c_3 - a_3c_1)x + (b_1c_3 - b_3c_1)y = r_1c_3 - c_1r_3.$

Now, if we replace the third equation here by $b_1c_3 - b_3c_1$ times the second equation, minus $(b_1c_2 - b_2c_1)$ times the third equation, we obtain the system

$$a_1x + b_1y + c_1z = r_1$$
$$(a_1c_2 - a_2c_1)x + (b_1c_2 - b_2c_1)y = r_1c_2 - c_1r_2$$
$$[(a_1c_2 - a_2c_1)(b_1c_3 - b_3c_1) - (a_1c_3 - a_3c_1)(b_1c_2 - b_2c_1)]x$$

(Eq. 6)
$$= (r_1c_2 - c_1r_2)(b_1c_3 - b_3c_1) - (r_1c_3 - c_1r_3)(b_1c_2 - b_2c_1).$$

It follows from the manner in which Equations 6 were obtained that they are equivalent to Equations 5 and, hence, to Equations 4. By expanding the products in the third equation of Equations 6, combining terms where possible, and factoring out c_1 in each member, one can write it in the form

$$c_1[a_1b_2c_3 + a_2b_3c_1 + a_3b_1c_2 - a_1b_3c_2 - a_2b_1c_3 - a_3b_2c_1]x$$

(Eq. 7)
$$= c_1[r_1b_2c_3 + r_2b_3c_1 + r_3b_1c_2 - r_1b_3c_2 - r_2b_1c_3 - r_3b_2c_1]$$

or, if $c_1 \neq 0$, in the form

$$[a_1b_2c_3 + a_2b_3c_1 + a_3b_1c_2 - a_1b_3c_2 - a_2b_1c_3 - a_3b_2c_1]x$$

(Eq. 8)
$$= r_1b_2c_3 + r_2b_3c_1 + r_3b_1c_2 - r_1b_3c_2 - r_2b_1c_3 - r_3b_2c_1.$$

If $c_1 = 0$, then $c_2 \neq 0$ or $c_3 \neq 0$, and we can arrive at the same result by a different order of steps.

Let us examine the coefficient of x in Equation 8 a bit more closely. For convenience we denote this coefficient by D; then

(Eq. 9) $D = a_1b_2c_3 + a_2b_3c_1 + a_3b_1c_2 - a_1b_3c_2 - a_2b_1c_3 - a_3b_2c_1,$

where the right member consists of six terms, each of which is a product of the three letters a, b, and c and where the subscripts of these letters, are the numbers 1, 2, and 3, arranged differently in each of the six terms. We observe also that a plus sign is attached to exactly three of the six products and a minus sign to the other three (a rule for determining which sign to attach to which product will be given later). Although these facts are helpful in theoretical considerations, they are of little use for finding the value of D in cases in which the literal coefficients of x, y, and z have been replaced by numerical coefficients. We now look for simpler ways of expressing D and of arriving at its value. We introduce a new symbol called a *determinant of the third order*. The symbol

$$\begin{vmatrix} a_1 & b_1 & c_1 \\ a_2 & b_2 & c_2 \\ a_3 & b_3 & c_3 \end{vmatrix},$$

where a_1, a_2, a_3, b_1, b_2, b_3, c_1, c_2, c_3 are any nine real numbers, is defined by the equation

$$\begin{vmatrix} a_1 & b_1 & c_1 \\ a_2 & b_2 & c_2 \\ a_3 & b_3 & c_3 \end{vmatrix} = a_1b_2c_3 + a_2b_3c_1 + a_3b_1c_2 - a_1b_3c_2 - a_2b_1c_3 - a_3b_2c_1$$

(Eq. 10)
$$= a_1(b_2c_3 - b_3c_2) - a_2(b_1c_3 - b_3c_1) + a_3(b_1c_2 - b_2c_1).$$

By making use of second-order determinants, Equation 10 can be written

$$\begin{vmatrix} a_1 & b_1 & c_1 \\ a_2 & b_2 & c_2 \\ a_3 & b_3 & c_3 \end{vmatrix} = a_1 \begin{vmatrix} b_2 & c_2 \\ b_3 & c_3 \end{vmatrix} - a_2 \begin{vmatrix} b_1 & c_1 \\ b_3 & c_3 \end{vmatrix} + a_3 \begin{vmatrix} b_1 & c_1 \\ a_2 & b_2 \end{vmatrix}.$$

(Eq. 11)

The numbers $a_1, b_1, \cdots, c_3$ which form the determinant are called *ele-ments* or *entries*. The rows are numbered from top to bottom and the columns are numbered from left to right. This helps to describe the position of any element of the determinant. For example, the element c_2 lies in the second row and third column, the element a_3 lies in the third row and first column, and so on. It is also helpful, purely as a memory device, to assign plus and minus signs alternately, beginning in the upper left-hand corner, to each of the nine positions of the determinant, as indicated in the schematic diagram of Fig. 9.2.

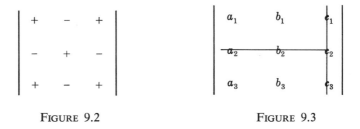

FIGURE 9.2   FIGURE 9.3

It must be clearly understood that the signs shown in this figure have abso-lutely nothing to do with the algebraic signs of the elements standing in those positions. To understand the usefulness of such a device we need to define what is called the *minor* of an element of a determinant.

Each element of a determinant can be located by giving the number of the row and the number of the column in which it lies. Now if we cross out the row and column in which a particular element is located, just four ele-ments remain. The second-order determinant formed by these four elements in their natural positions is called the minor of that element. For example, the element c_2 lies in the second row and third column; to find its minor, cross out the second row and third column, as in Fig. 9.3. The minor of c_2, denoted by the capital letter C_2, is

$$C_2 = \begin{vmatrix} a_1 & b_1 \\ a_3 & b_3 \end{vmatrix},$$

and the minors A_1 and B_3 of a_1 and b_3, respectively, and of the other elements, are found in the same way:

$$A_1 = \begin{vmatrix} b_2 & c_2 \\ b_3 & c_3 \end{vmatrix} \quad \text{and} \quad B_3 = \begin{vmatrix} a_1 & c_1 \\ a_2 & a_2 \end{vmatrix}.$$

Equation 11 may now be written in the form

(Eq. 12)
$$\begin{vmatrix} a_1 & b_1 & c_1 \\ a_2 & b_2 & c_2 \\ a_3 & b_3 & c_3 \end{vmatrix} = a_1A_1 - a_2A_2 + a_3A_3.$$

Observe that the right member of this equation consists of three terms, each of which is the product of an element and its minor, and that the three elements a_1, a_2, and a_3 exhibited in the products are all from the same column. Note further that the products a_1A_1 and a_3A_3 carry plus signs and the elements a_1 and a_3 each stand in a positive position, while the product a_2A_2 carries a negative sign and the element a_2 stands in a negative position. Equation 12 is called the *evaluation of the determinant by minors of the first column*. Could we have expanded by minors of some other column or by some row? The answer is, Yes, if we use the proper sign with each product involved.

To simplify our discussion, let us define the *cofactor* of an element of a determinant.

Cofactor: The cofactor of an element of a determinant is either the minor of that element or the negative of the minor of that element, depending upon whether the element is in a positive position in the determinant or in a negative position. If the element is in a positive position, its cofactor is the same as its minor, and if in a negative position, its cofactor is the negative of its minor.

Let us use primed capitals to denote cofactors. For example, the cofactor of a_1 is A_1', of a_2 it is A_2', of a_3 it is A_3', and so on. Thus, expressing the cofactors in terms of corresponding minors, we can write $A_1' = A_1$, $A_2' = -A_2$, $\cdots$, $C_2' = -C_2$, and $C_3' = C_3$. In terms of the cofactor notation, the rule for expanding a determinant by minors may be summarized in the following theorem.

Theorem 9.2.   *If each element of a row (or column) of a determinant is multiplied by its own cofactor, the sum of the resulting products is equal to the value of the determinant.*

Proof: That this theorem is true is easily verified by actual calculation with each of the six possibilities. We have already seen (in Equation 11) that the theorem is true for elements of the first column. We shall verify the theorem for elements of the second row. We wish to verify that

$$\begin{vmatrix} a_1 & b_1 & c_1 \\ a_2 & b_2 & c_2 \\ a_3 & b_3 & c_3 \end{vmatrix} = a_2A_2' + b_2B_2' + c_2C_2'.$$

By definition,

$$A_2' = -\begin{vmatrix} b_1 & c_1 \\ b_3 & c_3 \end{vmatrix} = -(b_1c_3 - b_3c_1),$$

$$B_2' = \begin{vmatrix} a_1 & c_1 \\ a_3 & c_3 \end{vmatrix} = a_1c_3 - a_3c_1, \qquad C_2' = -\begin{vmatrix} a_1 & b_1 \\ a_3 & b_3 \end{vmatrix} = -(a_1b_3 - a_3b_1).$$

Substituting these values for A_2', B_2', and C_2' we have

$$a_2A_2' + b_2B_2' + c_2C_2' = -a_2(b_1c_3 - b_3c_1) + b_2(a_1c_3 - a_3c_1) - c_2(a_1b_3 - a_3b_1)$$
$$= -a_2b_1c_3 + a_2b_3c_1 + a_1b_2c_3 - a_3b_2c_1 - a_1b_3c_2 + a_3b_1c_2.$$

Comparing this with the definition given by Equation 10 we see that this is the value of the determinant. The verification for the other two rows and two columns is left for the student.

Another important theorem in this connection is the following.

Theorem 9.3.   *If each element of a row (or column) of a determinant is multiplied by the cofactor of the corresponding element of another row (or column) of that determinant, the sum of the resulting products is zero.*

The proof here, as in Theorem 9.2, consists of verifying the theorem for each of the six possible cases. We shall leave such verification to be made by the student.

Example.   Find the value of the determinant

$$\begin{vmatrix} 3 & 5 & -2 \\ -1 & -2 & 12 \\ -4 & 1 & 7 \end{vmatrix}.$$

Solution: We shall expand by minors of the elements of the first column:

$$\begin{vmatrix} 3 & 5 & -2 \\ -1 & -2 & 12 \\ -4 & 1 & 7 \end{vmatrix} = 3\begin{vmatrix} -2 & 12 \\ 1 & 7 \end{vmatrix} - (-1)\begin{vmatrix} 5 & -2 \\ 1 & 7 \end{vmatrix} + (-4)\begin{vmatrix} 5 & -2 \\ -2 & 12 \end{vmatrix},$$

$$= 3(-14 - 12) + (35 + 2) - 4(60 - 4),$$
$$= -78 + 37 - 224 = -265.$$

Example.   Form the sum of the products of the elements of the first column and the cofactors of the corresponding elements of the second column for the determinant in the example above.

Solution: Forming the required sum, we get

$$-3\begin{vmatrix} -1 & 12 \\ -4 & 7 \end{vmatrix} - 1\begin{vmatrix} 3 & -2 \\ -4 & 7 \end{vmatrix} + 4\begin{vmatrix} 3 & -2 \\ -1 & 12 \end{vmatrix}$$

$$= -3(-7 + 48) - 1(21 - 8) + 4(36 - 2)$$
$$= -123 - 13 + 136 = 0.$$

This result is in agreement with the conclusion of Theorem 4.11.

We are now ready to return to our original problem, namely that of solving a system of three linear equations in three variables by the method of determinants. Comparing Equations 9 and 10 we see that

(Eq. 13)
$$D = \begin{vmatrix} a_1 & b_1 & c_1 \\ a_2 & b_2 & c_2 \\ a_3 & b_3 & c_3 \end{vmatrix}.$$

Now denote the right member of Equation 8 by N_x; then

$$N_x = r_1b_2c_3 + r_2b_3c_1 + r_3b_1c_2 - r_1b_3c_2 - r_2b_1c_3 - r_3b_2c_1.$$

Comparing this with the right member of Equation 9 we see that we can get N_x from Equation 9 by replacing a_1, a_2, a_3 with r_1, r_2, r_3, respectively. Hence,

(Eq. 14)
$$N_x = \begin{vmatrix} r_1 & b_1 & c_1 \\ r_2 & b_2 & c_2 \\ r_3 & b_3 & c_3 \end{vmatrix}.$$

Equation 8 now becomes

$$Dx = N_x$$

and, if $D \neq 0$, we have

(Eq. 15)
$$x = \frac{N_x}{D}.$$

We could complete our solution of Equations 4 by substituting from Equation 15 into Equations 6, but a more direct method is to use a rule called *Cramer's Rule*.

Cramer's Rule: If the determinant D, of the coefficients of x, y, z in a system of three linear equations in x, y, z, is not zero, then the equations have a solution set consisting of a single element. In the solution, the value of each variable may be expressed as a fraction which is the ratio of two determinants. The denominator of the fraction is D and the numerator is a determinant obtained from D by replacing the column of coefficients of the variable in question by the constant terms r_1, r_2, and r_3.

Proof: Suppose (x, y, z) is an ordered triple of real numbers that satisfy the system Equations 4. Now, if we multiply each by non-zero constants and add, we obtain a new equation. By repeating this process twice more, but using different sets of constants each time, we get two more new equations each of which has (x, y, z) as a solution. Thus the system formed by these three new equations also has the triple (x, y, z) as a solution. It can be shown that the converse is also true, and hence this new system is equivalent to Equations 4.

The determinant D of the coefficients of x, y, and z in Equations 4 is given by Equation 13. We calculate the cofactors A_1', A_2', and A_3' of the elements of the first column of D. Next we multiply the first equation by A_1' the second by A_2', the third by A_3', and add. The new equation is

(Eq. 16)
$$(a_1A_1' + a_2A_2' + a_3A_3')x + (b_1A_1' + b_2A_2' + b_3A_3')y$$
$$+ (c_1A_1' + c_2A_2' + c_3A_3')z = r_1A_1' + r_2A_2' + r_3A_3'.$$

It follows from Theorem 8.6 that the coefficient of x is D, and from

Theorem 8.7 that the coefficients of y and z are both zero. The right member, by Theorem 8.6, is N_x. Equation 16 therefore reduces to

(Eq. 17)
$$x \begin{vmatrix} a_1 & b_1 & c_1 \\ a_2 & b_2 & c_2 \\ a_3 & b_3 & c_3 \end{vmatrix} = \begin{vmatrix} r_1 & b_1 & c_1 \\ r_2 & b_2 & c_2 \\ r_3 & b_3 & c_3 \end{vmatrix},$$

or, if $D \neq 0$, to $x = N_x/D$, which agrees with the value found in Equation 15 and also with the statement in Cramer's Rule. Similarly, to obtain an equation involving only the value of y, we calculate B_1', B_2', and B_3', the cofactors of the elements in the second column of D. Then, multiplying the first equation of Equations 4 by B_1', the second by B_2', and the third by B_3', we have, after adding,

(Eq. 18)
$$(a_1 B_1' + a_2 B_2' + a_3 B_3')x + (b_1 B_1' + b_2 B_2' + b_3 B_3')y \\ + (c_1 B_1' + c_2 B_2' + c_3 B_3')z = r_1 B_1' + r_2 B_2' + r_3 B_3'.$$

This time the coefficients of x and z are zero, the coefficient of y is D and the right member is D, whose b's are replaced by r's. Let us denote right member by N_y; then Equation 18 becomes

$$Dy = N_y$$

(Eq. 19)
$$y = \frac{N_y}{D}.$$

Using the same type of argument and the cofactors of the elements in the third column of D, we obtain a third new equation,

(Eq. 20)
$$z = \frac{N_z}{D},$$

where $N_z = r_1 C_1' + r_2 C_2' + r_3 C_3'$. Now, if we replace the first equation of Equations 4 by Equation 17, the second by Equation 19, and the third by Equation 20, we have a system equivalent to Equations 4. Since the solution set of this new system, if $D \neq 0$, is obviously the single triple of numbers N_x/D, N_y/D, N_z/D, it follows that Equations 4 have the same solution set, and our proof of Cramer's Rule is complete.

It should be emphasized that, if $D = 0$, Cramer's Rule does not apply. In such case the solution set would either contain infinitely many elements or be the empty set, the best procedure would be the method of elimination.

Example. Use Cramer's Rule to solve the system

$$\begin{aligned} 2x - 3y + 4z &= -1 \\ 3x + y &= 5 \\ x + y - z &= 3. \end{aligned}$$

Solution: We first calculate D, N_x, N_y, and N_z:

$$D = \begin{vmatrix} 2 & -3 & 4 \\ 3 & 1 & 0 \\ 1 & 1 & -1 \end{vmatrix} = 2 \begin{vmatrix} 1 & 0 \\ 1 & -1 \end{vmatrix} - 3 \begin{vmatrix} -3 & 4 \\ 1 & -1 \end{vmatrix} + \begin{vmatrix} -3 & 4 \\ 1 & 0 \end{vmatrix},$$

$$= 2(-1 - 0) - 3(3 - 4) + (0 - 4),$$
$$= -2 + 3 - 4 = -3;$$

$$N_x = \begin{vmatrix} -1 & -3 & 4 \\ 5 & 1 & 0 \\ 3 & 1 & -1 \end{vmatrix} = -1 \begin{vmatrix} 1 & 0 \\ 1 & -1 \end{vmatrix} - 5 \begin{vmatrix} -3 & 4 \\ 1 & -1 \end{vmatrix} + 3 \begin{vmatrix} -3 & 4 \\ 1 & 0 \end{vmatrix},$$

$$= -(-1 - 0) - 5(3 - 4) + 3(0 - 4),$$
$$= 1 + 5 - 12 = -6;$$

$$N_y = \begin{vmatrix} 2 & -1 & 4 \\ 3 & 5 & 0 \\ 1 & 3 & -1 \end{vmatrix} = 2 \begin{vmatrix} 5 & 0 \\ 3 & -1 \end{vmatrix} - 3 \begin{vmatrix} -1 & 4 \\ 3 & -1 \end{vmatrix} + \begin{vmatrix} -1 & 4 \\ 5 & 0 \end{vmatrix},$$

$$= 2(-5 - 0) - 3(1 - 12) + (0 - 20),$$
$$= -10 + 33 - 20 = 3;$$

$$N_z = \begin{vmatrix} 2 & -3 & -1 \\ 3 & 1 & 5 \\ 1 & 1 & 3 \end{vmatrix} = 2 \begin{vmatrix} 1 & 5 \\ 1 & 3 \end{vmatrix} - 3 \begin{vmatrix} -3 & -1 \\ 1 & 3 \end{vmatrix} + \begin{vmatrix} -3 & -1 \\ 1 & 5 \end{vmatrix},$$

$$= 2(3 - 5) - 3(-9 + 1) + (-15 + 1),$$
$$= -4 + 24 - 14 = 6.$$

Hence $x = \dfrac{N_x}{D} = \dfrac{-6}{-3} = 2$, $y = \dfrac{N_y}{D} = \dfrac{3}{-3} = -1$, $z = \dfrac{N_z}{D} = \dfrac{6}{-3} = -2$.

Check: $2(2) - 3(-1) + 4(-2) = 4 + 3 - 8 = -1$,
$3(2) + 1(-1) + 0(-2) = 6 - 5 = 5$,
$1(2) + 1(-1) - 1(-2) = 2 - 1 + 2 = 3$.

Although Cramer's Rule was stated for a system of three linear equations in three unknowns, it can be generalized to apply to a system of n linear equations in n unknowns, provided the determinant of the coefficients of the system is not zero. In fact, Theorems 9.2 and 9.3 are both valid for a determinant of any order. However, Cramer's Rule has little practical value if n is large, and even for small values of n the elimination method is often much faster. The real value of Cramer's Rule, therefore, lies in its theoretical importance.

EXERCISES

Evaluate each of the following determinants.

1. $\begin{vmatrix} 3 & 1 \\ 4 & 2 \end{vmatrix}$.

2. $\begin{vmatrix} 0 & 3 \\ -1 & 2 \end{vmatrix}$.

3. $\begin{vmatrix} ab & ac \\ bd & cd \end{vmatrix}$.

4. $\begin{vmatrix} x & x+1 \\ x-1 & x \end{vmatrix}$.

5. $\begin{vmatrix} 1 & 3 & 0 \\ 2 & 1 & 4 \\ -1 & 2 & -3 \end{vmatrix}$.

6. $\begin{vmatrix} 2 & 1 & 5 \\ 0 & 3 & 1 \\ 1 & 1 & 2 \end{vmatrix}$.

7. $\begin{vmatrix} 1 & 1 & -1 \\ 2 & 0 & 3 \\ 1 & 2 & 2 \end{vmatrix}$.

8. $\begin{vmatrix} 1 & 2 & 3 \\ 4 & 5 & 6 \\ 7 & 8 & 9 \end{vmatrix}$.

9. $\begin{vmatrix} 3 & -2 & 1 \\ 7 & 1 & -1 \\ 6 & -1 & 2 \end{vmatrix}$.

10. $\begin{vmatrix} 1 & -2 & 3 \\ 2 & -3 & 1 \\ 4 & -8 & 12 \end{vmatrix}$.

11. $\begin{vmatrix} 2 & -3 & 4 \\ 3 & 4 & -5 \\ 4 & -5 & 6 \end{vmatrix}$.

12. $\begin{vmatrix} 1 & 1 & 1 & 1 \\ 1 & 2 & 3 & 4 \\ 1 & 3 & 6 & 10 \\ 1 & 4 & 10 & 20 \end{vmatrix}$.

Solve systems 13–18.

13. $3x - 8y = 6$
$6x + 2y = 3.$

14. $x + y = 2$
$3x - 2y = -4.$

15. $x + 3y - z = 7$
$5x - 7y + z = 3$
$2x - y - 2z = 0.$

16. $x + y - z = 0$
$3x + 6y - 4z = 0$
$x + y + z = 1.$

17. $x - 2y + z = 12$
$x + 2y + 3z = 48$
$6x + 4y + 3z = 84.$

18. $2x - y + 3z = 4$
$x + 3y + 3z = -2$
$3x + 2y - 6z = 6.$

19. Prove: $\begin{vmatrix} a_1 & b_1 & c_1 \\ a_2 & b_2 & c_2 \\ a_3 & b_3 & c_3 \end{vmatrix} = \begin{vmatrix} a_1 & a_2 & a_3 \\ b_1 & b_2 & b_3 \\ c_1 & c_2 & c_3 \end{vmatrix}$.

20. Prove: $\begin{vmatrix} a_1 & ka_1 & c_1 \\ a_2 & ka_2 & c_2 \\ a_3 & ka_3 & c_3 \end{vmatrix} = 0.$

21. Prove: $\begin{vmatrix} a_1 + kb_1 & b_1 & c_1 \\ a_2 + kb_2 & b_2 & c_2 \\ a_3 + kb_3 & b_3 & c_3 \end{vmatrix} = \begin{vmatrix} a_1 & b_1 & c_1 \\ a_2 & b_2 & c_2 \\ a_3 & b_3 & c_3 \end{vmatrix}$.

22. Show that the following is the equation of the line determined by the points $(2, 3)$ and $(-1, 5)$:

$$\begin{vmatrix} x & y & 1 \\ 2 & 3 & 1 \\ -1 & 5 & 1 \end{vmatrix} = 0.$$

23. Show that the following is the equation of the line through $(2, 3)$ and $(5, -4)$:

$$\begin{vmatrix} x & 2 & 5 \\ y & 3 & -4 \\ 1 & 1 & 1 \end{vmatrix} = 0.$$

24. Show that $\begin{vmatrix} a & d & g \\ b & e & h \\ c & f & j \end{vmatrix} = - \begin{vmatrix} a & d & g \\ c & f & j \\ b & e & h \end{vmatrix}$.

5 SYSTEMS OF LINEAR INEQUALITIES

To solve a system of two or more linear inequalities the best method available is the graphical method. A typical system of two linear inequalities in x and y is the following.

$$\begin{cases} a_1x + b_1y + c_1 > 0, & a_1 \text{ and } b_1 \text{ not both zero} \\ a_2x + b_2y + c_2 > 0, & a_2 \text{ and } b_2 \text{ not both zero,} \end{cases}$$

where the coefficients a_1, b_1, etc., are real numbers. The solution set S of this system is the set $S = S_1 \cap S_2$, where

$$S_1 = \{x \mid a_1x + b_1y + c_1 > 0\} \qquad \text{and} \qquad S_2 = \{x \mid a_2x + b_2x + c_2 > 0\}.$$

The graph of the solution set S_1 is a half-plane, as is the graph of the solution set S_2 (see Section 14 of Chapter V). The solution set S is therefore the intersection of these two half-planes. The graph of the solution set of an inequality $ax + by + c > 0$ is an open half-plane, since it does not contain the points on the line $ax + by + c = 0$. The graph of the solution set of $ax + by + c \geq 0$ does contain the points on the line $ax + by + c = 0$ and hence is a closed half-plane. Thus in our typical system mentioned above, the graphs of S_1 and S_2 are open half-planes.

Example. Find the solution set of the system $\begin{cases} x - y - 2 < 0 \\ 3x + y - 2 > 0. \end{cases}$

Solution: We first draw the lines $L_1: x - y - 2 = 0$ and $L_2: 3x + y - 2 = 0$; they intersect at $(1, -1)$.

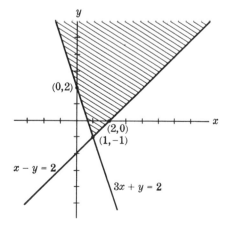

FIGURE 9.4

The solution set S_1 of $x - y - 2 < 0$ is the left half-plane determined by L_1, while the solution set S_2 of $3x + y - 2 > 0$ is the right half-plane determined by L_2. The solution set S of the given system is $S = S_1 \cap S_2$ and is represented graphically by the shaded portion in Fig. 9.4.

The procedure used in this example works equally well for determining the solution set of a system involving three or more linear inequalities in two variables.

Example.   Determine the solution set of the system

$$\begin{cases} x - \ y - 2 \le 0 \\ 3x + \ y - 2 \ge 0 \\ x + 3y - 6 \le 0. \end{cases}$$

Solution: Draw each of the lines $x - y - 2 = 0$, $3x + y - 2 = 0$, and $x + 3y - 6 = 0$. These lines intersect in pairs in the three points $(0, 2)$, $(1, -1)$, and $(3, 1)$, and thus determine a triangle. The graph of the desired solution set is the set of all points inside the triangle and on the sides. See Fig. 9.5.

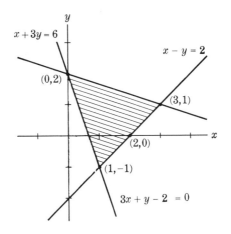

FIGURE 9.5

Example.   Determine the solution set of the system

$$\begin{cases} 2x + y - 5 \ge 0 \\ x - y - 1 \le 0 \\ x - 1 \ge 0 \\ x + y - 5 \le 0. \end{cases}$$

Solution: It is easily verified that the solution set of this system has for its graph all points inside and on the sides of the quadrilateral, shaded region, shown in Fig. 9.6.

The graphs of the solution sets of the systems of linear inequalities discussed above possess a rather obvious useful common property, namely

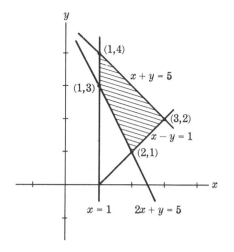

FIGURE 9.6

that, if any two points of the graph are joined by a line segment having the two points as endpoints, every point on the segment is also a point of the graph. A set of points having this property is called a *convex* set.

Definition 9.1.   *A set of points is said to be* convex *if for each pair of points P_1 and P_2 which are members of the set, every point of the line segment having P_1 and P_2 as endpoints also is a member of the set.*

For future reference, we state and prove the following theorem.

Theorem 9.4.   *The intersection of two convex sets is convex.*

Proof: Let S_1 and S_2 be two convex sets. If P_1 and P_2 are any two points in the set $S = S_1 \cap S_2$, then these two points are both in S_1. By definition of a convex set, all the points on the line segment having these points as endpoints are also in S_1. Similarly, since P_1 and P_2 are in S_2, all the points on this same line segment are also in S_2. Hence, all the points of the segment P_1P_2 belong to the set $S = S_1 \cap S_2$.

Definition 9.2.   *The intersection of two or more closed half-planes is called a* polygonal convex set.

The graphs of the solution sets shown in Figs. 9.5 and 9.6 are typical examples of polygonal convex sets. Some applications of solution sets of systems of linear inequalities will be discussed in the next section.

EXERCISES

Draw the graph of the solution set of each of the following systems of linear inequalities.

1. $x + y - 3 > 0$
$\qquad y - 1 > 0.$

4. $\qquad x \geq 0$
$\qquad\qquad y \geq 0$
$\qquad x + y \leq 5.$

7. $\qquad x - 2y + 10 \geq 0$
$\qquad 4x + 3y - 26 \geq 0$
$\qquad 3x - 4y - \ 7 \leq 0$
$\qquad x + \ y - 14 \leq 0.$

2. $x - 2 \geq 0$
$\qquad y + 5 \leq 0.$

5. $\qquad x \geq 1$
$\qquad\qquad y \leq 4$
$\qquad x - y \leq 0.$

8. $\qquad x - \ y + \ 3 \geq 0$
$\qquad 2x + 3y + \ 6 \geq 0$
$\qquad 2x - 5y - 10 \leq 0$
$\qquad 3x + 5y - 15 \leq 0.$

3. $\quad x - 2y > 0$
$\qquad 3x - \ y < 0.$

6. $x - y - 3 \leq 0$
$\qquad x + 1 \geq 0$
$\qquad\qquad y \leq 3.$

9. $\qquad x - 2y - 2 \geq 0$
$\qquad 3x + \ y - 2 \leq 0$
$\qquad\qquad y + 4 \geq 0.$

6 LINEAR PROGRAMMING

Suppose we are given a convex polygonal set S in the xy-plane and a linear polynomial $f(x, y) = ax + by + c$, where a, b, and c are real numbers and a and b are not both zero. Suppose further that we are required to find the point or points of S at which $f(x, y)$ has its maximum (or minimum) value. Such a problem is called a *linear programming* problem in two variables. It is the purpose of this section to investigate a procedure for solving such problems.

Since a polygonal convex set is the intersection of two or more closed half-planes, such a set consists of the interior of a region together with the line segments which form its boundary. This region may, of course, be finite or infinite. If the region is finite, the boundary is a polygon in which case we shall refer to the polygon and its interior as a *convex polygon*.

A property of polygons, well known to all who have studied high school geometry, is that a polygon with n sides has n vertices. That is, a polygon with three sides is a triangle and has three vertices, a polygon with four sides has four vertices, and with five sides has five vertices, and so on. The solution set of the system of inequalities in the last example of the last section is a convex polygon of four sides and four vertices (see Fig. 9.6). The coordinates of the vertices are the ordered pairs (1, 3), (2, 1), (3, 2), and (1, 4) as shown in this figure.

We return now to the linear programming problem stated at the beginning of this section. To aid us in the solution of this problem we need the following theorems.

Theorem 9.5.   *Let $P_1(x_1, y_1)$ and $P_2(x_2, y_2)$ be the endpoints of a line segment and let $P(x', y')$ be any point of the segment P_1P_2. If*

$$\frac{P_1P}{P_1P_2} = r, \qquad 0 \leq r \leq 1,$$

then

$$x' = x_1 + r(x_2 - x_1) \qquad and \qquad y' = y_1 + r(y_2 - y_1).$$

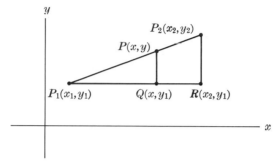

FIGURE 9.7

Proof: From similar triangles (Fig. 9.7),

$$\frac{P_1P}{P_1P_2} = \frac{x_1 - x'}{x_2 - x_1} = r \qquad and \qquad \frac{P_1P}{P_1P_2} = \frac{y' - y_1}{y_2 - y_1} = r$$

when simplified these equations become

$$x' = x_1 + r(x_2 - x_1) \qquad and \qquad y' = y_1 + r(y_2 - y_1),$$

which proves our theorem.

Note that if

$$r = 0, \qquad P = P_1$$
$$r = \tfrac{1}{2}, \qquad P \text{ is midpoint of } P_1P_2$$
$$r = 1, \qquad P = P_2.$$

Theorem 9.6.   *Let $P_1(x_1, y_1)$ and $P_2(x_2, y_2)$ be the endpoints and let $P(x', y')$ be any point of a line segment P_1P_2. Denote by $f(x, y)$ the value of the linear polynomial $ax + by + c$ at (x, y), that is, $f(x, y) = ax + by + c$. If $f(x_1, y_1) = m$ and $M = f(x_2, y_2)$, where $m \leq M$, then*

$$m \leq f(x', y') \leq M.$$

Proof: From Theorem 9.5 we have

$$x' = x_1 + r(x_2 - x_1) \qquad and \qquad y' = y_1 + r(y_2 - y_1), \qquad 0 \leq r \leq 1.$$

Thus

$$f(x', y') = ax' + by' + c$$
$$= a[x_1 + r(x_2 - x_1)] + b[y_1 + r(y_2 - y_1)] + c$$
$$= (1 - r)[ax_1 + by_1] + r(ax_2 + by_2) + c$$
$$= (1 - r)(ax_1 + by_1 + c) + r(ax_2 + by_2 + c)$$
$$= (1 - r)m + rM$$
$$= m + r(M - m).$$

Since $0 \le r \le 1$, it is easy to verify that

$$m \le m + r(M - m) \le M$$

and our theorem is proved.

We are now ready to prove a theorem which is of vital importance in the solution of two dimensional linear programming problems.

Example. Find the maximum and minimum values of the polynomial $f(x, y) = 3x + 2y - 5$ on the convex polygon which is the solution set of the system

$$2x + y - 5 \ge 0$$
$$x - y - 7 \le 0$$
$$x - 1 \ge 0$$
$$x + y - 5 \le 0.$$

The solution set of this system is the convex polygon shown in Fig. 9.6. The vertices are the points $(1, 3)$, $(2, 1)$, $(3, 2)$, and $(1, 4)$.

$$f(1, 3) = 3 + 6 - 5 = 4$$
$$f(2, 1) = 6 + 2 - 5 = 3$$
$$f(3, 2) = 9 + 4 - 5 = 8$$
$$f(1, 4) = 3 + 8 - 5 = 6.$$

Theorem 9.7. *A linear polynomial, $f(x, y) = ax + by + c$, defined on a convex polygon has its maximum (and minimum) value at a vertex of the convex polygon.*

Proof: As was stated above, a convex polygon is a convex set of finite area consisting of a polygon together with its interior. The proof is the same regardless of the number of sides the polygon may have so long as this number is finite. So, for simplicity, we shall in our proof refer to the convex polygon $ABCDE$ shown in Fig. 9.8. Also we shall use the symbol $f(P)$ to denote the value of f at the point P. For example, $f(A)$ represents the value of f at the vertex A, $f(B)$ represents the value of f at vertex B, $f(C)$ represents the value of f at vertex C, and so on.

Suppose we have calculated the value of f at each of the five vertices. Let M and m denote the largest and the smallest of these five values respectively. Next, suppose $f(E) = M$ and $f(D) = m$. Now, let P be any point on the convex polygon. Join vertex E, a vertex at which f has its largest value, to the point P by a line segment and continue the segment until it intersects

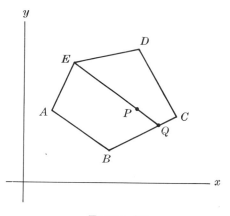

FIGURE 9.8

the polygon again, say at Q. It follows from Theorem 9.6 that $f(Q)$ lies between $f(B)$ and $f(C)$. By hypothesis $f(B)$ and $f(C)$ both lie between M and m. Hence $m \leq f(Q) \leq M$. Similarly, by Theorem 9.7, $f(Q) \leq f(P) \leq f(E)$. But $f(E) = M$ and $m \leq f(Q)$, therefore

$$m \leq f(P) \leq M.$$

Since P was any point on the convex polygon our theorem is proved.

Example.   Find the maximum and minimum value of the polynomial

$$f(x, y) = 5x - 2y + 7$$

over the convex polygon determined by the following system of inequalities

$$\begin{aligned}
x + 3y - 8 &\geq 0 \\
2x + y - 6 &\geq 0 \\
x - y + 3 &\geq 0 \\
4x - y - 19 &\leq 0 \\
x + 3y - 21 &\leq 0.
\end{aligned}$$

Solution: The solution set of the given system is the convex polygon shown in Fig. 9.9. It follows from Theorem 9.7 that the maximum (and minimum) values of f on a convex polygon occurs at a vertex. Hence to find the maximum and minimum values of $f(x, y) = 5x - 2y + 7$ over the convex polygon of Fig. 9.9 we calculate the value of f at each vertex and compare as follows:

$$\begin{aligned}
f(1, 4) &= 5 - 8 + 7 = 4 \\
f(2, 2) &= 10 - 4 + 7 = 13 \\
f(5, 1) &= 25 - 2 + 7 = 30 \\
f(6, 5) &= 30 - 10 + 7 = 27 \\
f(3, 6) &= 15 - 12 + 7 = 10,
\end{aligned}$$

which shows the maximum value of f to be 30 and the minimum value to be 4.

In the above discussions we have considered the maxima and minima values of a linear polynomial, $f(x, y) = ax + by + c$, only over convex poly-

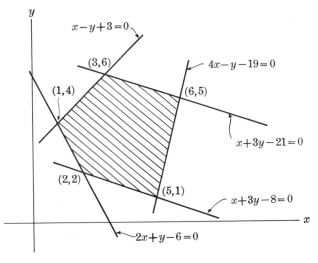

FIGURE 9.9

gons. If the polygonal convex set S over which f is defined has an infinite area, then one and only one of the following possibilities can exist.

(1) f has neither a maximum value nor a minimum value over S.
(2) f has a maximum value but no minimum value over S.
(3) f has a minimum value but no maximum value over S.

If f does have a maximum (or minimum) value over S, then it must occur at a vertex or corner point.

Example. The polynomial $f(x, y) = 3x + y$ has neither a maximum value nor a minimum value over the convex set determined by the system of inequalities

$$x - y \geq 0$$
$$x + y \leq 0.$$

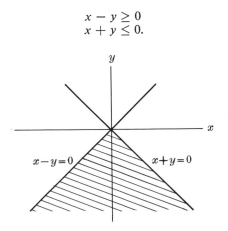

FIGURE 9.10

Proof: The solution set of the given system is the convex set S shown in Fig. 9.10. To see that f has no maximum value over this convex set, note that for any number $M > 0$, the point $(M, -M)$ belongs to S and $f(M, -M) = 3M - M = 2M > M$. Thus there is no largest value of f on S. Similarly, for any $M > 0$, the point $(-M, -M)$ belongs to S and $f(-M, -M) = -3M + M = -2M < -M$, which shows that f has no minimum value on S.

Example. Find the minimum value of the linear polynomial $f(x, y) = 4x + 3y + 5$ over the convex set determined by the system of inequalities

$$2x - y + 2 \geq 0,$$
$$2x + 3y - 6 \geq 0,$$
$$x - 3y - 3 \leq 0.$$

Solution: We first solve the given system of inequalities and find the solution set to be the polygonal convex set shown as the shaded area of Fig. 9.11. Denote

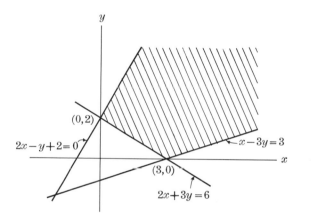

FIGURE 9.11

this set by S. Inspection of the graph shows that S has an infinite area and two corner points, namely $(0, 2)$ and $(3, 0)$. We next calculate the value of f at each corner point.

$$f(0, 2) = 0 + 6 + 5 = 11$$
$$f(3, 0) = 12 + 0 + 5 = 17.$$

Thus the minimum value of f at a corner point is 11. How can we be sure that this is the minimum value of f on S, since Theorem 9.8 does not apply? Suppose (x', y') is any point of S, not a corner point, then it follows from the second inequality of our system that $2x' + 3y' \geq 6$. Also $x' > 0$ and $y' > 0$. Therefore

$$f(x', y') = 4x' + 3y' + 5 > 2x' + 3y' + 5 \geq 6 + 5 = 11,$$

which proves that the minimum value of f on S is 11. Obviously f has no maximum value on S.

In the examples of linear programming problems discussed above we have used a graphical method of solution which necessitated that we restrict ourselves to problems involving only two independent variables. Methods are available for handling problems involving more than two variables but any worthwhile treatment of such methods would carry us too far afield so no attempt will be made here.

In summary, we have outlined a procedure for finding the maximum (and minimum) value of a linear polynomial $f(x, y) = ax + by + c$ on a polygonal convex set determined by a system of linear inequalities in x and y. The inequalities of such a system are called *constraints* and each point of the convex set is called a feasible point. A point of the set at which f has a maximum (or minimum) value is called an *optimal point*. We have found that such a maximum (or minimum) value always occurs at a corner point of the polygon boundary of the set. The above procedure makes possible the solution of an important class of practical problems. We close this section with an example, a hypothetical case illustrating such a problem.

Example.   A nutritionist in a school cafeteria wishes to insure that the diet in the cafeteria will contain at least 12 units of Vitamin R, 5 units of Vitamin S, and 8 units of Vitamin T, for a given meal. She tests foods A and B and finds that each pound of food A contains 2 units of Vitamin R, 1 unit of Vitamin S, and 4 units of Vitamin T. On the other hand, each pound of food B contains 3 units, 1 unit, and 1 unit of Vitamins R, S, and T, respectively. Therefore she can fulfill the minimum requirements with 6 pounds of food A or with 8 pounds of food B or with various combinations of some of each of the two foods. However, the nutritionist wishes to minimize the cost, and discovers that food A costs 60 cents per pound while food B costs 40 cents per pound. The question then arises which of the possible combinations of food A and food B will fulfill the minimum requirement and yet at minimum cost.

Solution: Suppose we purchase x pounds of A and y pounds of food B. Since we cannot purchase a negative amount of either food then $x \geq 0$ and $y \geq 0$. For a minimum of 12 units of Vitamin R, 5 units of Vitamin S, and 8 units of Vitamin

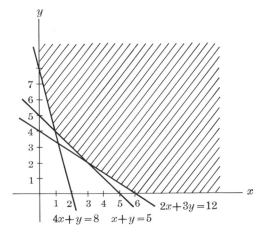

FIGURE 9.12

T, the following inequalities must be satisfied: $2x + 3y \geq 12$, $x + y \geq 5$, and $4x + y \geq 8$. The cost C of x pounds of food A and y pounds of food B is given by the relation $C = 0.60x + 0.40y$.

Our problem reduces to that of minimizing C over the polygonal convex set determined by the following system of restraints.

$$x \geq 0$$
$$y \geq 0$$
$$2x + 3y \geq 12$$
$$x + y \geq 5$$
$$4x + y \geq 8.$$

The graph of the solution set of the given system is the polygonal set shown as the shaded area in Fig. 9.12. The coordinates of the corner points are $(0, 8)$, $(1, 4)$, $(3, 2)$, and $(6, 0)$. We calculate the value of C at each corner point.

$$C(0, 8) = 0.60(0) + 0.40(8) = 3.20,$$
$$C(1, 4) = 0.60(1) + 0.40(4) = 2.20,$$
$$C(3, 2) = 0.60(3) + 0.40(2) = 2.60,$$
$$C(6, 0) = 0.60(6) + 0.40(0) = 3.60.$$

We see that $2.20 is the minimal cost. The corresponding purchases would be 1 pound of food A and 4 pounds of food B.

EXERCISES

1. Find the maximum value of the polynomial $f(x, y) = 5x - 2y + 12$ over the convex polygon determined by the following system of inequalities.

$$3x + 2y - 11 \geq 0,$$
$$5x - 4y + 11 \geq 0,$$
$$4x - y - 11 \leq 0.$$

2. Find the maximum value and the minimum value of $f(x, y) = 7x - 3y + 6$ over the convex closed polygon determined by the following system of inequalities:

$$2x - y + 2 \geq 0$$
$$x + y \geq 5$$
$$5x + 2y \leq 22.$$

3. Find the maximum and minimum values of $f(x, y) = -8x + 10y + 15$ on the convex polygon given by the inequalities

$$y + 3 \geq 0$$
$$x - y + 5 \geq 0$$
$$x + y + 5 \geq 0$$
$$x - 2 \leq 0.$$

4. Find the minimum value of $f(x, y) = 4x + 3y$ subject to the following restraints:

$$x + y \geq 7$$
$$x + 2y \geq 9$$
$$3x + y \geq 8.$$

5. A convex polygon has the points (2, 5), (3, 1), (3, 10), and (14, 8) as corner points. Find a set of inequalities which defines the convex polygon having these corner points.

6. Draw a quadrilateral and a pentagon neither of which is a convex polygon. Is every triangle a convex polygon?

7. Consider the convex polygon defined by the inequalities

$$x \geq 0$$
$$y \geq 0$$
$$x + y \leq 7.$$

Find the maximum value of the polynomial $f(x, y) = 3x + 3y + 8$ over this polygon. Does f take on this maximum value at a point of the convex polygon that is not a corner point? If so, explain how this may happen.

8. Given the polynomial $f(x, y) = 20 - 2x - 3y$.
   a. Find a polygonal convex set such that over this set f has a maximum value but no minimum.
   b. Find a polygonal convex set such that over this set f has a minimum value but no maximum value.

9. Find the maximum and minimum values, when they exist, of the polynomial $f(x, y) = 7x - 10y - 15$ over each of the convex polygons given in problems 7, 8, and 9 of the set of exercises following section 5.

X

TRIGONOMETRIC FUNCTIONS

1 ANGLES

For the purposes of our discussion here we shall say that an angle AOB has been generated when a half-line, having one end at O, is rotated about O from an initial position OA to a terminal position OB. The amount of this rotation is called the *magnitude of the angle*. Obviously, such a rotation could take place in either of two directions. It is conventional to consider an angle positive when the rotation is counterclockwise and negative when it is clockwise. In drawing an angle the direction of rotation should be indicated with a curved arrow to prevent any confusion. See Fig. 10.1.

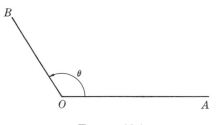

FIGURE 10.1

The point O is the *vertex of the angle*, OA is the *initial side*, and OB is the *terminal side*. When three letters are used to denote an angle, as angle "AOB," the middle letter always designates the vertex, the first two letters the initial side, and the last two letters the terminal side. Angle *AOB* is often called angle *O*. Small Greek letters, such as θ, also are frequently used to denote angles.

Since the magnitude of an angle is the amount of rotation necessary to move the initial side into the position of the terminal side, an obvious unit of measure for angles is a complete rotation, or one revolution. See Fig. 10.2.

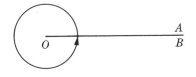

FIGURE 10.2

For convenience, $\frac{1}{360}$ of a revolution is frequently used as a unit; it is called a *degree*. In symbols,

$$1° = 1/360 \text{ rev.} \quad \text{or} \quad 360° = 1 \text{ rev.}$$

To obtain still smaller units, we define one *minute* as $\frac{1}{60}$ of a degree and one *second* as $\frac{1}{60}$ of a minute. In symbols these become

$$60' = 1°, \quad 60'' = 1'.$$

If an angle has a magnitude of 90° (that is, $\frac{1}{4}$ rev.), it is called a *right angle*, and its sides are said to be *perpendicular* to each other. Angles less than 90°

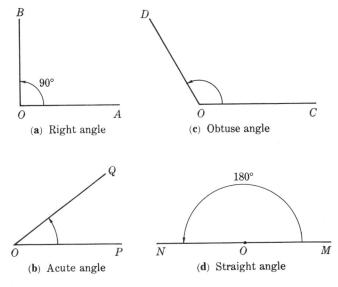

(a) Right angle

(c) Obtuse angle

(b) Acute angle

(d) Straight angle

FIGURE 10.3

are called *acute angles*. Angles greater than 90° and less than 180° are called *obtuse angles*. If the magnitude of an angle is 180°, the angle is called a *straight angle*. See Fig. 10.3.

For certain purposes it is more convenient to use $\dfrac{1}{2\pi}$ times a revolution as a unit (π is the ratio of the circumference of a circle to its diameter). This unit is called a *radian*. Since one revolution contains 2π radians, a half-revolution (a straight angle) contains π radians. In symbols,

$$\pi \text{ radians} = 180°, \qquad 1 \text{ radian} = (180/\pi)°, \qquad 1° = (\pi/180) \text{ radians},$$

and when the symbol for degrees, minutes, or seconds is omitted, we shall understand that the unit of angular measurement is the radian.

From geometry we know that in any circle the length of an arc subtending a central angle is proportional to the central angle. See Fig. 10.4. If

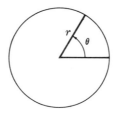

FIGURE 10.4

the central angle is doubled, the arc is doubled, etc. The circumference of the entire circle can be considered as the arc of a sector with a central angle of one revolution, or 2π radians. Since this circumference is 2π times the radius, and since one radian is $\dfrac{1}{2\pi}$ times one revolution, the length of arc subtending an angle of 1 radian is exactly equal to the length of the radius. Similarly, the length of arc subtending an angle of θ radians is θ times the radius. If the arc has a length of s units and the radius has a length of r units, the same units being used for both measurements, then

$$s = \theta r$$

if θ is measured in radians. Thus, for example, the arc of one quadrant of a circle has a length given by the expression

$$s = \frac{\pi}{2} r = \frac{\pi r}{2}$$

since a right angle is $\pi/2$ radians.

If a particle is in motion on the circumference of a circle, the angle measured from some fixed position is then changing, and the length of arc from the corresponding fixed position is also changing. The corresponding rates of change may be obtained immediately by differentiation. The radius is constant; consequently,

$$D_t s = r D_t \theta$$

and the rate of change of arc length with respect to the variable t is the radius times the rate of change of the central angle (measured in radians) with respect to the same variable t. If t denotes units of time, $D_t s$ and $D_t \theta$ are velocities. In this case $D_t s$ is rate of change of the number of linear units of arc with respect to the number of units of time. Similarly, $D_t \theta$ is the rate of change of the number of radians in the central angle with respect to the number of units of time. Therefore, $D_t s$ is a velocity of the type we have previously discussed, and $D_t \theta$ is an *angular velocity*. (Note that the results obtained here are valid only when the central angle is measured in radians.)

In similar fashion, we can differentiate the equation relating the velocities, and we obtain

$$D_t^2 s = r D_t^2 \theta,$$

which states that the linear acceleration on the circumference of a circle is the radius multiplied by the *angular acceleration* of the central angle if the central angle is measured in radians. The interpretation of the angular acceleration as the rate of change of angular velocity with respect to time should be apparent.

2   TRIANGLES

If three points, not in a straight line, are joined in succession by line segments, the figure formed is called a *triangle*. The three line segments are called the *sides*. Each vertex and the two sides meeting at that vertex form an angle. Every triangle has three sides and three angles, which are often referred to as the parts of the triangle.

A very important theorem from plane geometry states that the sum of the three angles of any triangle is 180° (or π radians). We shall assume that this statement is true (and in so doing we are using Euclidean geometry).

A triangle one of whose angles is a right angle is called a *right triangle*, a triangle having two equal sides is an *isosceles triangle*, and a triangle having three equal sides is an *equilateral triangle*. A triangle that does not contain a right angle is an *oblique triangle*.

EXERCISES

1. Draw angles of 120°, 37°, $\pi/4$, $\pi/12$, $7\pi/6$, 475°.
2. Convert to radians the angles 270°, $-15°$, 67°30′, 42°, 220°.
3. How many degrees are in 1 radian? How many radians in 1 degree?
4. Convert to degrees the angles $\pi/3$, $7\pi/12$, $-4\pi/15$, -2, 0.1.

5. Find the third angle of a triangle if two of the angles are as given.
   a. 47° and 92°.   **b.** 12°10′12″ and 47°58′56″.   **c.** $\pi/8$ and $\pi/3$.
6. A wheel 28 inches in diameter revolves at a rate of 60 revolutions per minute. How fast is a point on the circumference moving? (Use $\pi = 22/7$.)

3   THE TRIGONOMETRIC FUNCTIONS

An angle will be said to be in standard position if its vertex is at the origin of a rectangular coordinate system and its initial side coincides with the positive x axis. It is said to be in a certain *quadrant* if it is in standard position and its terminal side lies in that quadrant. For example, if drawn in standard position, 110° is in the second quadrant, 315° is in the fourth quadrant, and $-100°$ is in the third quadrant.

An angle that is in standard position and whose terminal side coincides with one of the coordinate axes is called a *quadrantal angle*. Examples of quadrantal angles are 90°, 180°, 270°, $-90°$, $-450°$, etc.

Two or more angles are said to be *coterminal* if they are in standard position and have the same terminal side. For example, 0° and 360° in standard position are coterminal angles; so are 120°, 480°, and also $7\pi/6$, $-5\pi/6$, and $19\pi/6$. See Fig. 10.5.

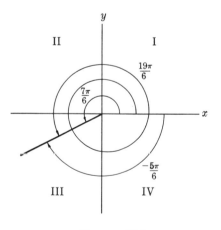

FIGURE 10.5

Consider an angle θ in standard position relative to a given coordinate system, Fig. 10.6. Now select an arbitrary but fixed point P, not the origin, on the terminal side of θ and let the coordinates of P be represented by (x, y). Let the distance of the point P from the origin be represented by the letter r. We shall assume that r is always positive. It follows from the right triangle relation that $x^2 + y^2 = r^2$. We have thus associated with the angle θ in standard position three coordinates x, y, and r. These three coordinates determine

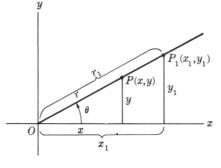

FIGURE 10.6

six possible ratios, namely y/r, x/r, y/x, r/x, r/y, and x/y. It is easy to show that the values of these six ratios are independent of the choice of the fixed point P. To show this, select a second point, say $P_1(x_1, y_1)$ in Fig. 10.6, on the terminal side of θ and distinct from P. Denote by r_1 the distance of P_1 from the origin. The right triangles OMP and OM_1P_1 have an acute angle in common and hence are similar. It follows that the ratios of their corresponding sides are equal. That is,

$$\frac{y}{r} = \frac{y_1}{r_1}, \qquad \frac{x}{r} = \frac{x_1}{r_1}, \qquad \frac{y}{x} = \frac{y_1}{x_1}, \qquad \frac{x}{y} = \frac{x_1}{y_1}, \qquad \frac{r}{x} = \frac{r_1}{x_1}, \qquad \text{and} \qquad \frac{r}{y} = \frac{r_1}{y_1}.$$

Thus, when θ is given, each of these ratios that exists can be determined. Furthermore, if θ is changed, the value of each of these ratios will in general be changed. That is, each of the six ratios determined by the coordinates x, y, and r of a point P on the terminal side of θ is a function of θ. To emphasize this fact and also as a matter of convenience in computation, each of these ratios is given a special name which associates it with the specific angle involved. The names and definitions of the six functions of θ are

$$\sin \theta = \frac{y}{r}, \qquad \csc \theta = \frac{r}{y},$$

$$\cos \theta = \frac{x}{r}, \qquad \sec \theta = \frac{r}{x},$$

$$\tan \theta = \frac{y}{x}, \qquad \cot \theta = \frac{x}{y},$$

where sin, cos, tan, cot, sec, and csc are abbreviations for sine, cosine, tangent, cotangent, secant, and cosecant respectively. These six functions are called the *six trigonometric functions of angle θ*.

Trigonometry is the detailed study of the six trigonometric functions and their applications.

Example. Given $P(-12, 5)$, a point on the terminal side of the angle θ (see Fig. 10.7), find the six trigonometric functions of θ.

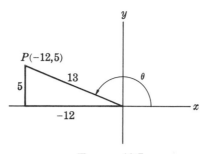

FIGURE 10.7

Solution: $r^2 = (-12)^2 + (5)^2 = 144 + 25 = 169; r = 13.$

$$\sin \theta = \tfrac{5}{13}, \qquad \csc \theta = \tfrac{13}{5},$$
$$\cos \theta = -\tfrac{12}{13}, \qquad \sec \theta = -\tfrac{13}{12},$$
$$\tan \theta = -\tfrac{5}{12}, \qquad \cot \theta = -\tfrac{12}{5}.$$

EXERCISES

Find the six trigonometric functions of the angles in Exercises 1 to 8.

1. The angle in standard position and $P(4, 3)$ on the terminal side.
2. The angle in standard position and $P(5, -12)$ on the terminal side.
3. The angle in standard position and $P(-1, 3)$ on the terminal side.
4. The angle in standard position and $P(-8, -15)$ on the terminal side.
5. The angle in standard position and $P(2, -5)$ on the terminal side.
6. The angle in standard position and $P(-\sqrt{5}, -2)$ on the terminal side.
7. The angle in standard position and $P(a, b)$ on the terminal side.
8. The angle in standard position and $P(r, \sqrt{s^2 - r^2})$ on the terminal side.
9. By placing the angle in standard position, find the six trigonometric functions of each of the following.
   a. 30°.   c. 45°.   e. 150°.   g. 300°.
   b. 60°.   d. 120°.   f. −120°.   h. −210°.
10. Find those trigonometric functions of the given quadrantal angles which exist: (a) 90°, (b) 180°, and (c) 270°.
11. Find the six trigonometric functions of the angle (or angles) placed in standard position, whose point on the terminal side 17 units from the origin has an abscissa of −8.
12. Find the six trigonometric functions of the angle (or angles) placed in standard position, whose point on the terminal side 25 units from the origin has an ordinate of 24.
13. If $\tan \theta = -\tfrac{3}{4}$ and θ lies in quadrant IV, what are the other five trigonometric functions of θ?
14. If $\sec \theta = -5$ and θ lies in quadrant II, what are the other five trigonometric functions of θ?
15. What relationship exists between the corresponding functions of two angles in standard position when $P_1(a, b)$ is on the terminal side of one and $P_2(-a, b)$ is on the terminal side of the other? What is the relationship between the two angles? Make a similar comparison with angles determined by $P_3(a, -b)$ and $P_4(-a, -b)$.

4   RELATED ANGLES

The *related angle* of a given angle θ is the positive acute angle determined by the terminal side of θ and the x axis when θ is in standard position; for example, $30°$ is the related angle of $150°$, $\pi/3$ is the related angle of $4\pi/3$, and $\pi/5$ is the related angle of $-4\pi/5$. We can now state an important theorem which we shall refer to as *the related-angle theorem*.

Theorem 10.1.   (Related-Angle Theorem).   *The absolute value of any trigonometric function of an angle θ is equal to the same function of its related angle.*

Proof: Let θ be any angle and let θ_1 be its related angle. Draw θ and θ_1 in standard position (Fig. 10.8). Select on the terminal side of θ a point P

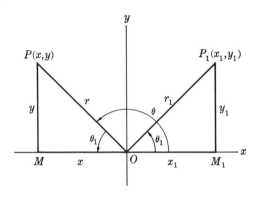

FIGURE 10.8

with coordinates (x, y) and a corresponding value of r. Now locate the point $P_1(x_1, y_1)$ on the terminal side of θ_1 such that $r_1 = OP_1 = OP = r$; the two right triangles OMP and OM_1P_1 are congruent. Therefore, since x_1 and y_1 are nonnegative,

$$|x| = x_1, \qquad |y| = y_1, \qquad |r| = r_1.$$

From the definitions in Section 3 and the relations given above, we have

$$|\sin \theta| = \frac{|y|}{|r|} = \frac{y_1}{r} = \sin \theta_1,$$

$$|\cos \theta| = \frac{|x|}{|r|} = \frac{x_1}{r} = \cos \theta_1,$$

$$|\tan \theta| = \frac{|y|}{|x|} = \frac{y_1}{x_1} = \tan \theta_1,$$

the other three functions being represented in a similar manner. This completes our proof.

The theorem permits the following symbolic statement:

Any function of $\theta = \pm$ the same function of θ_1,

where θ is any angle and θ_1 is the related angle of θ. The proper sign in the right member here is determined by the quadrant in which the given angle θ lies and by the function involved. To determine the proper sign, one needs to recall the definition of the function in question and the algebraic signs that x and y have in each quadrant and to remember that r is always positive. For cxamplc, x and y arc both positive for every point in quadrant I, x is negative and y is positive in quadrant II, x and y are both negative in quadrant III, and x is positive and y negative in quadrant IV. Suppose we wish to know the algebraic sign for each of the functions sin 140°, cos 140°, and tan 140°. In standard position, 140° is an angle in quadrant II and, for any point (x, y) in quadrant II, x is negative, y is positive, and r is positive. So we have

$$\sin 140° = \frac{y}{r} = \frac{+}{+} = +, \quad \cos 140° = \frac{-}{+} = -, \quad \tan 140° = \frac{y}{x} = \frac{+}{-} = -.$$

The importance of our theorem lies in the fact that it enables us to express any function of an angle that is not an acute angle in terms of the same function of an acute angle. In particular, it enables us to determine the following relations between the functions of an angle θ and its negative:

$$\sin(-\theta) = -\sin\theta, \quad \csc(-\theta) = -\csc\theta,$$
$$\cos(-\theta) = +\cos\theta, \quad \sec(-\theta) = +\sec\theta,$$
$$\tan(-\theta) = -\tan\theta, \quad \cot(-\theta) = -\cot\theta.$$

Example. Express the sine, cosine, and tangent of 200° in terms of the related angle.

Solution: 200°, in standard position, is an angle in quadrant III with a related angle of 20°. Consequently, $\sin 200° = -\sin 20°$, $\cos 200° = -\cos 20°$, $\tan 200° = \tan 20°$.

Example. Express the sine, cosine, and tangent of $(-2\pi/3)$ in terms of $(2\pi/3)$.

Solution: $\sin(-2\pi/3) = -\sin 2\pi/3$, $\cos(-2\pi/3) = \cos 2\pi/3$, $\tan(-2\pi/3) = -\tan 2\pi/3$.

Example. Given θ an angle in the third quadrant such that $\sec\theta = -2$, find the other functions of θ.

Solution: Since $\sec\theta = -2 = 2/-1$, we may let $r = 2$ and $x = -1$ (note that r is always positive, and therefore the negative sign must be associated with x). By the relation $x^2 + y^2 = r^2$, we have $y^2 = 3$. In the third quadrant, y is negative and hence $y = -\sqrt{3}$ (see Fig. 10.9). The other functions can now be written at once:

$$\sin\theta = -\sqrt{3}/2, \quad \cos\theta = -1/2, \quad \tan\theta = +\sqrt{3},$$

$$\cot\theta = +\left(\frac{1}{\sqrt{3}}\right), \quad \csc\theta = -2/\sqrt{3}.$$

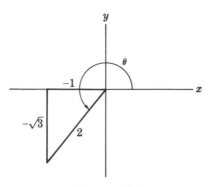

FIGURE 10.9

It should be pointed out that any choice of r and x such that $r/x = -2$ would serve equally well and would yield the same results.

EXERCISES

1. What is the related angle of each of the following: $-470°$, $189°17'$, $144°32'17''$, $-23°18'$, $35°$, $4\pi/3$, -6.2, $8\pi/15$?

2. List the functions that are negative in the second quadrant; in the third quadrant; in the fourth quadrant. In how many lists does each function occur?

Find the other five functions of θ in each of the following cases:

3. $\sin \theta = \frac{24}{25}$, and θ in quadrant I.
4. $\cos \theta = \frac{4}{5}$, and θ in quadrant IV.
5. $\tan \theta = -3$, and θ in quadrant II.
6. $\cot \theta = \frac{1}{2}$, and θ in quadrant III.
7. $\sec \theta = -\sqrt{5}$, and θ in quadrant II.
8. $\csc \theta = -\frac{13}{12}$, and θ in quadrant IV.
9. Express the sine, cosine, and tangent of each of the following angles in terms of its related angle.
   a. $150°$. **c.** $315°$. **e.** $-250°$. **g.** $(-140°)$. **i.** $1475°$.

   b. $240°$. **d.** $420°$. **f.** $(-70°)$. **h.** $780°$. **j.** $\dfrac{11\pi}{6}$.

5 BASIC IDENTITIES AMONG THE TRIGONOMETRIC FUNCTIONS

The trigonometric functions are interrelated such that the value of any one of the functions for a given angle determines the absolute values of the other five (see the last example in the previous section). It is the purpose of this section to examine some of these relationships.

As you have probably noticed, the names of the six trigonometric functions come in pairs: sine and cosine, tangent and cotangent, and secant and cosecant. This is no accident. For example, "cosine" is short for "complement's sine," "cotangent" is an abbreviation of "complement's tangent," etc. To understand this we need to recall that two acute angles are said to be complementary if their sum is 90°. We shall extend this statement and say that any two angles are *complementary* if their algebraic sum is a right angle. Thus, angles of 120° and −30° are complementary since $120° + (−30°) =$ 90°. Similarly, $5\pi/6$ and $−\pi/3$ are complementary since the angle $5\pi/6 + (−\pi/3) = \pi/2$ radians is a right angle.

Theorem 10.2.   *If α and β are complementary angles, then*

$$\sin \alpha = \cos \beta, \qquad \cos \alpha = \sin \beta,$$
$$\tan \alpha = \cot \beta, \qquad \cot \alpha = \tan \beta,$$
$$\sec \alpha = \csc \beta, \qquad \csc \alpha = \sec \beta.$$

Proof: Let $P_\alpha(x_\alpha, y_\alpha)$ and $P_\beta(x_\beta, y_\beta)$ be points on the terminal sides of α and β respectively, such that $OP_\alpha = OP_\beta = r$ (see Fig. 10.10). Since α and β

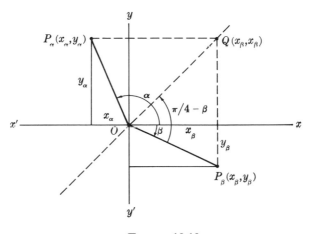

FIGURE 10.10

are complementary, $\alpha + \beta = \pi/2$, or $\alpha − \pi/4 = \pi/4 − \beta$. Let Q be the point with coordinates (x_β, x_β). Then angle $XOQ = \pi/4$, or angle $X'OQ = \pi/4$. Consequently, triangle $P_\alpha OQ$ is congruent to triangle $P_\beta OQ$, since two sides $(OP_\alpha$ and $OQ)$ and the included angle (either $\alpha − \pi/4$ or its supplement) of triangle $P_\alpha OQ$ equal, respectively, two sides $(OP_\beta$ and $OQ)$ and the included angle (either $\pi/4 − \beta$ or its supplement) of triangle $P_\beta OQ$. Since angle $OQP_\beta = \pi/4$, angle $OQP_\alpha = \pi/4$ and QP is parallel to the x axis. Hence $y_\alpha = x_\beta$. Similarly, $y_\beta = x_\alpha$. Since $r = r$, the theorem follows at once, with an examination of the definitions. For instance,

$$\sin \alpha = y_\alpha/r = x_\beta/r = \cos \beta.$$

The results of Theorem 10.2 are of particular importance in the construction of tables of values of trigonometric functions, as we shall see later. Another set of identical relationships of great importance in our further development of trigonometry involve only a single angle. These identities are listed here:

(1) $\sin \theta = 1/\csc \theta$, $\csc \theta = 1/\sin \theta$, $(\theta \neq n\pi)$
(2) $\cos \theta = 1/\sec \theta$, $\sec \theta = 1/\cos \theta$, $(\theta \neq \pi/2 + n\pi)$
(3) $\tan \theta = 1/\cot \theta$, $\cot \theta = 1/\tan \theta$, $(\theta \neq n\pi/2)$
(4) $\tan \theta = \sin \theta/\cos \theta$, $(\theta \neq \pi/2 + n\pi)$
(5) $\cot \theta = \cos \theta/\sin \theta$, $(\theta \neq n\pi)$
(6) $\sin^2 \theta + \cos^2 \theta = 1$,
(7) $1 + \tan^2 \theta = \sec^2 \theta$, $(\theta \neq \pi/2 + n\pi)$
(8) $\cot^2 \theta + 1 = \csc^2 \theta$. $(\theta \neq n\pi)$

Note that the square of $\sin \theta$ is normally written $\sin^2 \theta$, and the same form is used for the other functions. The exclusions noted at the right of seven of the eight relationships merely exclude angles for which one or more of the functions involved is undefined. The symbol n denotes an integer. Any integer $(0, \pm 1, \pm 2,$ etc.$)$ provides a value of θ that must be excluded in each case.

The proofs of these relationships are given for (1), (4), and (7). The other proofs can be worked out as these are.

Proof of (1):   Refer to Fig. 10.5: $\sin \theta = y/r$ and $\csc \theta = r/y$, and therefore, if $\theta \neq n\pi$, we have

$$1/\csc \theta = \frac{1}{r/y} = y/r = \sin \theta \quad \text{and} \quad 1/\sin \theta = \frac{1}{y/r} = r/y = \csc \theta.$$

If $\theta = 0, \pm \pi,$ or $\pm 2\pi$, etc., then $\csc \theta$ is not defined. This can be summarized by the statement that if $\theta = n\pi$, where n is understood to be an integer, then $\csc \theta$ is not defined.

Proof of (4):   In Fig. 10.5, $\sin \theta = y/r$, $\cos \theta = x/r$, and $\tan \theta = y/x$. Therefore, $\sin \theta/\cos \theta = (y/r)/(x/r) = y/r \cdot r/x = y/x = \tan \theta$. If $\theta = \pm \pi/2$, $\pm 3\pi/2$, etc., then $\cos \theta = 0$ and neither side of the resulting equation is defined.

Proof of (7):   In Fig. 10.5, $\tan \theta = y/x$ and $\sec \theta = r/x$. Since triangle OMP is a right triangle, $x^2 + y^2 = r^2$. In all cases in which $x^2 \neq 0$ (for example, $\theta \neq \pm \pi/2, \pm 3\pi/2$, etc.), we can divide by x^2 and obtain $1 + (y/x)^2 = (r/x)^2$. Therefore, $1 + \tan^2 \theta = \sec^2 \theta$.

Note that the exceptions cited above, those in which $x = 0$, can be summarized in the statement $\theta = \pi/2 + n\pi$, where $n = 0, \pm 1, \pm 2$, etc.

EXERCISES

1. Prove identity (2).
2. Prove identity (3).

3. Prove identity (5).
4. Prove identity (6).

5. Prove identity (8).
6. Use these relations to find $\cos \theta$, given $\sin \theta = 0.6$. Do you get a single answer? Explain.
7. Use these relations to find $\sin \theta$, given $\cot \theta = 2$. Do you get a single answer? Explain.
8. Use these relations to find $\tan \theta$, given $\cot \theta = 3$. Do you get a single answer? Explain.

In each of the following problems, using one or more of the 8 basic identities listed in this section, reduce the given expression to simplest form.

9. $\sin \theta \csc \theta$.

10. $\cos \theta \tan \theta$.

11. $\dfrac{\cot \theta}{\csc \theta}$.

12. $\dfrac{\cos^2 \theta}{1 - \sin \theta}$.

13. $\dfrac{\csc \theta - \sin \theta}{\cot \theta}$.

14. $\dfrac{\sec \theta - \cos \theta}{\tan \theta}$.

15. $\dfrac{\sec^2 \theta - \tan^2 \theta}{\csc \theta}$.

16. $(\tan \theta + \cot \theta)\sin \theta \cos^2 \theta$.

17. $\dfrac{\cos \theta}{1 + \sin \theta} + \dfrac{1 + \sin \theta}{\cos \theta}$.

18. $\dfrac{\tan \theta + \sin \theta}{\cot \theta + \csc \theta}$.

19. $\dfrac{\tan \theta + \cot \theta}{\sec \theta}$.

20. $\dfrac{\sin \theta}{\cos \theta \tan^2 \theta}$.

21. $\sin^4 \theta + 2 \sin^2 \theta \cos^2 \theta + \cos^4 \theta$.

22. $\dfrac{\tan^2 \theta}{\sec \theta + 1} + \dfrac{\cot^2 \theta}{\csc \theta - 1}$.

6 THE TRIGONOMETRIC FUNCTIONS OF 0, $\pi/6$, $\pi/4$, $\pi/3$, AND $\pi/2$

If we know the values of the trigonometric functions for acute angles, the relationships thus far derived permit us to obtain the functions of all angles. For this reason we shall concentrate, in this section and in the next, on the problem of determining the functions of the acute angles. Examples will be given to indicate how these results may be extended to determine the functions of angles that are not acute. In this section we shall determine values of the functions of certain angles which yield readily to geometric analysis.

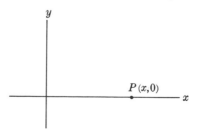

FIGURE 10.11

If $\theta = 0$ (see Fig. 10.11), the terminal side of θ is the x axis. A point P on the terminal side must have coordinates $(x, 0)$ and $r = x$. Hence,

$$\sin 0 = y/r = 0/r = 0, \qquad \cot 0 = x/y = r/0 \quad \text{(does not exist)},$$
$$\cos 0 = x/r = r/r = 1, \qquad \sec 0 = r/x = r/r = 1,$$
$$\tan 0 = y/x = 0/r = 0, \qquad \csc 0 = r/y = r/0 \quad \text{(does not exist)}.$$

Since 0 and $\pi/2$ are complementary, the results of the last section yield

$$\sin \pi/2 = 1, \qquad \cot \pi/2 = 0,$$
$$\cos \pi/2 = 0, \qquad \sec \pi/2 \quad \text{(does not exist)}$$
$$\tan \pi/2 \quad \text{(does not exist)} \qquad \csc \pi/2 = 1.$$

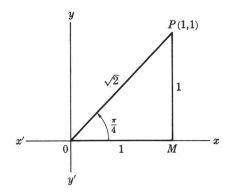

FIGURE 10.12

Let $\theta = \pi/4$; see Fig. 10.12. The point P in this case may be any point on the terminal side of θ. For convenience, let us select the point $(1, 1)$. In this case $x = y = 1$ and $r = \sqrt{2}$. Therefore,

$$\sin \pi/4 = 1/\sqrt{2} = \sqrt{2}/2, \qquad \cot \pi/4 = 1,$$
$$\cos \pi/4 = 1/\sqrt{2} = \sqrt{2}/2, \qquad \sec \pi/4 = \sqrt{2}/1 = \sqrt{2},$$
$$\tan \pi/4 = 1, \qquad \csc \pi/4 = \sqrt{2}/1 = \sqrt{2}.$$

To obtain the functions of $\theta = \pi/6$ (Fig. 10.13), let $P(x, y)$ be a point on the terminal side of $\pi/6$. Since the sum of the angles in a triangle is π and angle $PMO = \pi/2$, the angle θ and the angle OPM are complementary; thus, angle OPM is $\pi/3$. Now consider the triangle OPP_1 where P_1 has the coordinates $(x, -y)$. Angle OP_1M is $\pi/3$ and angle P_1OP is $2\pi/6 = \pi/3$; therefore, triangle OPP_1 is equiangular and, hence, equilateral. This result states that the side PP_1 has the same length as the side OP (that is, $2y = r$); thus $y = r/2$.

Since $x^2 + y^2 = r^2$,

$$x^2 + r^2/4 = r^2 \qquad \text{and} \qquad x^2 = 3r^2/4,$$

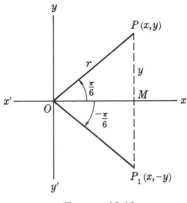

FIGURE 10.13

Since x is positive, $x = r\sqrt{3}/2$; therefore,

$$\sin \pi/6 = y/r = \frac{r/2}{r} = \frac{1}{2},$$

$$\cos \pi/6 = x/r = \frac{r\sqrt{3}/2}{r} = \sqrt{3}/2,$$

$$\tan \pi/6 = y/x = \frac{r/2}{r\sqrt{3}/2} = 1/\sqrt{3} = \sqrt{3}/3,$$

$$\cot \pi/6 = x/y = \frac{r\sqrt{3}/2}{r/2} = \sqrt{3},$$

$$\sec \pi/6 = r/x = \frac{r}{r\sqrt{3}/2} = 2/\sqrt{3} = 2\sqrt{3}/3,$$

$$\csc \pi/6 = r/y = \frac{r}{r/2} = 2.$$

Since the angles $\pi/6$ and $\pi/3$ are complementary,

$$\begin{aligned} \sin \pi/3 &= \sqrt{3}/2, & \cot \pi/2 &= \sqrt{3}/3, \\ \cos \pi/3 &= 1/2, & \sec \pi/3 &= 2, \\ \tan \pi/3 &= \sqrt{3}, & \csc \pi/3 &= 2\sqrt{3}/3. \end{aligned}$$

7 TABLES OF TRIGONOMETRIC FUNCTIONS

Trigonometric functions are used in so many different types of problems that tables of their values have been compiled and are easily available to anyone needing them.

The most common type of trigonometric table gives, correct to five significant digits, the values of the sine, cosine, tangent, and cotangent of each angle from 0° to 90° at intervals of 1'. Table I in the back of this book is such a table, and a small portion of it is reproduced here.

35°

1'	sin	tan	cot	cos	1'
0	.57358	.70021	1.4281	.81915	60
1	.57381	.70064	1.4273	.81899	59
2	.57405	.70107	1.4264	.81882	58
3	.57429	.70151	1.4255	.81865	57
—					—
—					—
17	.57762	.70760	1.4132	.81631	43
18	.57786	.70804	1.4124	.81614	42
19	.57810	.70848	1.4115	.81597	41
—					—
—					—
59	.58755	.72610	1.3772	.80919	1
60	.58779	.72654	1.3764	.80902	0
1'	cos	cot	tan	sin	1'

54°

Notice how the table utilizes the fundamental principle regarding cofunctions of complementary angles stated in Section 4. The degrees, from 0° to 44°, are at the tops of the pages and the minutes, from 0' to 60' (reading down), are listed in the first column on each page; the degrees, from 45° to 89°, are at the bottoms of the pages and the minutes, from 0' to 60' (reading up), are listed in the last column of each page. Thus the degrees at the top of a page and any minutes in the first column, are the complement of the degrees at the bottom and the minutes immediately across in the last column. For example, 35°17' is the complement of 54°43'. Note how the remaining four columns are labeled and that the label at the top of a column is the cofunction of the label at the bottom.

To see how the table is used, let us find sin 35°18'. Since 35° occurs at the top of the table, we move down the first column to 18' and across to the entry in the column labeled "sin" at the top. Thus, sin 35°18' = 0.57786. To find tan 54°41', we move up the last column to 41' and read the entry in the column labeled "tan" at the bottom. Thus, tan 54°41' = 1.4115. We can also use such a table to find an acute angle if any one of the four functions sine, cosine, tangent, and cotangent of the given angle is known.

Example.   Given sin A = 0.57405, find A.

Solution: We search for this number in either of the sine columns of our table in which it might occur. If it occurs in the column labeled "sin" at the top, we read the angle in degrees from the top of the table and the correct minutes from the minutes column on the left. If it occurs in the column labeled "sin" at the bottom, we read the degrees at the bottom and the minutes from the minutes column on the right. Since 0.57405 is found in the sine column at the top, we read $A = 35°2'$.

By using straight-line interpolation (see Section 9 of Chapter V) it is possible to find from a table of trigonometric functions the functions of angles that lie between consecutive entries in the table.

Example.   Find tan 35°18.4′.

Solution: We arrange our work in tabular form thus:

$$
1' \left\{ 0.4' \begin{cases} \text{angle} \\ 35°18' \\ 35°18.4' \\ 35°19' \end{cases} \quad \begin{array}{c} \text{tan} \\ \left. \begin{array}{c} 0.70804 \\ ? \\ 0.70848 \end{array} \right\} d \end{array} \right\} 0.00044
$$

$$
\frac{d}{.00044} = \frac{.4}{1}.
$$

$d = 0.000176 = 0.00018$ (rounded off to five places),
tan 35°18.4′ $= 0.70804 + 0.00018 = 0.70822$.

Example.   Given sin $A = 0.81621$, find A correct to $\frac{1}{10}$ minute.

Solution: Arranging our work in tabular form, we have

$$
1' \left\{ d \begin{cases} \text{angle} \\ 54°42' \\ ? \\ 54°43' \end{cases} \quad \begin{array}{c} \text{sin} \\ \left. \begin{array}{c} 0.81614 \\ 0.81621 \end{array} \right\} 0.00007 \\ 0.81631 \end{array} \right\} 0.00017
$$

$$
\frac{d}{1} = \frac{0.00007}{0.00017} = \frac{7}{17} = 0.41.
$$

$d = 0.4$ (rounding off to tenths),
$A = 54°42' + 0.4' = 54°42.4'$.

EXERCISES

Using Table I, find the value of the following functions.

1. sin 14°23′.	**6.** cot 25°54′.	**11.** cos 4°3′.
2. tan 36°17′.	**7.** cos 71°37′.	**12.** cos 36°.
3. cos 29°43′.	**8.** cot 58°20′.	**13.** sin 32°24.6′.
4. tan 54°7′.	**9.** sin 44°45′.	**14.** tan 18°40.7′.
5. sin 67°30′.	**10.** tan 85°58′.	**15.** cos 27°16.3′.

From Table I find A for each of the following given functions, interpolating where necessary.

16. sin $A = .53411$.	**18.** cos $A = 0.90948$.	**20.** sin $A = 0.85264$.
17. tan $A = 0.32042$.	**19.** cot $A = 1.7045$.	**21.** tan $A = 1.5070$.

22.	$\cos A = 0.52175.$	**25.**	$\tan A = 4.4676.$	**28.**	$\sin A = 0.64536.$
23.	$\cot A = 0.77848.$	**26.**	$\cos A = 0.21104.$	**29.**	$\tan A = 0.73160.$
24.	$\sin A = 0.97176.$	**27.**	$\sin A = 0.70711.$	**30.**	$\cos A = 0.83651.$

8 SOLUTION OF RIGHT TRIANGLES

In plane geometry it is shown that a right triangle is completely determined either if two sides or if one side and an acute angle are known. In this section we shall indicate ways of using the given parts of a right triangle to find all the parts not given. This procedure is called *solving the triangle*.

For convenience we shall adopt the following notation. We shall denote the vertices of our triangle by the capital letters A, B, and C, the right angle being at the vertex C. We shall also denote the angle at a vertex by the letter at that vertex. That is, the angle at vertex A will be called angle A, the angle at vertex B will be called angle B, and the right angle will be called angle C. The small letters a, b, and c will be used to denote the lengths of the sides that are opposite A, B, and C respectively. Thus a is the length of the side joining B and C, b is the length of the side joining A and C, and c is the length of the side joining A and B (see Fig. 10.14). Hence c is the length of the hy-

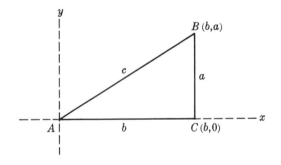

FIGURE 10.14

potenuse, a is the length of the side opposite angle A, and b is the length of the side adjacent to angle A.

Let us now construct a rectangular coordinate system in the plane of triangle ABC such that the origin is at A and C is a point on the positive x axis with coordinates $(b, 0)$. Vertex B will be a point in the first quadrant with coordinates (b, a). From the definitions of the six trigonometric functions of an angle, it is apparent that these functions of angle A can be written as follows.

$$\sin A = \frac{a}{c} = \frac{\text{length of opposite side}}{\text{length of hypotenuse}}, \quad \csc A = \frac{c}{a} = \frac{\text{length of hypotenuse}}{\text{length of opposite side}},$$

$$\cos A = \frac{b}{c} = \frac{\text{length of adjacent side}}{\text{length of hypotenuse}}, \quad \sec A = \frac{c}{b} = \frac{\text{length of hypotenuse}}{\text{length of adjacent side}},$$

$$\tan A = \frac{a}{b} = \frac{\text{length of opposite side}}{\text{length of adjacent side}}, \quad \cot A = \frac{b}{a} = \frac{\text{length of adjacent side}}{\text{length of opposite side}}.$$

Example. Solve the right triangle ABC in which $c = 100$ and $A = 35°18'$.

Solution: $B = 90° - 35°18' = 54°12'$.

By definition, $a/c = \sin A$, or $a = c \sin A$; hence $a = 100 \sin 35°18'$.

From Table I, $\sin 35°18' = 0.57786$; therefore $a = 100 \sin 35°18' = 100(0.57786) = 57.786$, or, rounding off to four places, $a = 57.79$.

Similarly, $b/c = \cos A$, or $b = c \cos A$. From this, after substituting $c = 100$ and $A = 35°18'$, we have $b = 100 \cos 35°18' = 100(0.81614) - 81.61$.

Example. Solve the right triangle ABC in which $c = 100$ and $a = 66$.

Solution: By definition, $\sin A = a/c$; substituting for a and c, we get

$$\sin A = \frac{66}{100} = 0.66.$$

From Table I, $A = 41°18'$; therefore $B = 90° - 41°18' = 48°42'$.

Again, by definition, we have $\sin B = b/c$ or $b = c \sin B$; substituting the known values of B and c we get

$$b = 100 \sin 48°42' = 100(0.75126) = 75.13, \text{ to four places.}$$

EXERCISES

Solve the following right triangle.

1. $A = 26°10'$, $a = 120$.
2. $B = 54°18'$, $a = 75$.
3. $c = 200$, $a = 148.6$.
4. $a = 96.44$, $b = 64.32$.
5. $A = 41°20'$, $c = 140$.
6. $B = 57°32'$, $c = 0.482$.
7. $a = 0.0648$, $c = 0.9724$.
8. $b = 240$, $c = 350$.

9. $A = 72°30'$, $b = 150$.
10. $a = 0.6478$, $c = 2$.
11. $B = 44°35'$, $c = 1000$.
12. $A = 54°12'$, $b = 40$.
13. $a = 486$, $b = 600$.
14. $a = 32$, $c = 64$.
15. $b = 707.11$, $c = 1000$.
16. $B = 58°14'$, $a = 250$.

17. Using the fact that the area of a right triangle is one-half the product of the two perpendicular legs, find the area of each of the right triangles given above.
18. Read from the triangle shown below the six trigonometric functions of angle B of that triangle.

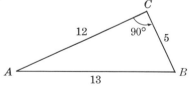

19. Read from the triangle shown below the six trigonometric functions of 30° and 60°.

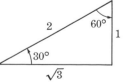

9   ANGLES OF ELEVATION AND ANGLES OF DEPRESSION

An *angle of elevation* is the angle, measured from the horizontal, through which an observer would have to elevate his normal line of sight, *EH*, in order to see an object *O* situated above *EH*. In Fig. 10.15, angle *E* is the angle of elevation.

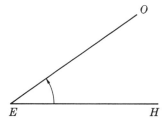

FIGURE 10.15

An *angle of depression* is the angle, measured from the horizontal, through which an observer would have to depress his normal line of sight, *DH*, in order to see an object *O* situated below *DH*. In Fig. 10.16, angle *D* is the angle of depression.

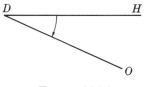

FIGURE 10.16

Example.   Find the length of the shadow cast by a tree 50 feet tall at the instant that the angle of elevation of the sun is 45°.

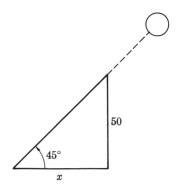

FIGURE 10.17

Solution: Let x be the length of the shadow; from Fig. 10.17 we can write

$$\frac{x}{50} = \cot 45°.$$

Hence $x = 50 \cot 45° = 50(1) = 50$ feet.

Example. As seen from the top of a tower, the angle of depression of an object on the level ground 100 feet from the base of the tower is 28°46′. Find the height of the tower.

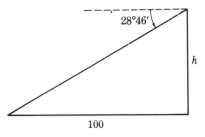

28°46′

h

100

FIGURE 10.18

Solution: Let h be the height of the tower; from Fig. 10.18 we have

$$\frac{h}{100} = \tan 28°46′.$$

From Table I, $\tan 28°46′ = 0.54900$; hence $h = 54.9$ feet.

EXERCISES

1. A ladder 30 feet long has one end on the ground and the other end against a wall. If the ladder makes an angle of 68° with the level ground, how far up the wall does it reach?
2. A tree 48 feet tall is casting a shadow 32 feet long. What is the angle of elevation of the sun at that moment?
3. From the top of a vertical cliff 80 feet high on one bank of a river, the angle of depression of a point on the opposite bank directly across the river is 20°. How wide is the river at this point?
4. At the instant that the angle of elevation of the sun is 48°, a boy standing erect casts a shadow 4.9 feet in length. How tall is the boy?
5. Find the height of a kite when 180 feet of string are out and the angle of elevation of the kite is 37°20′.
6. The angle of depression of a boat, as seen from a vertical cliff 225 feet high, is 29°20′. Find the distance of the boat from the foot of the cliff.
7. From a point on a bridge 75 feet above the water, the angles of depression of two boats, on the river and in the same straight line with a point on the water directly below the observer, are 16°20′ and 24°40′. Find the distance between the boats.
8. From a window in a building across a level street from a skyscraper, the angle of elevation of the top of the skyscraper is 56°40′ and the angle of depression of the base is 37°26′. The window is 75 feet above the street level. Find the height of the skyscraper and the width of the street.

9. It takes the Earth 6 hours to rotate through 90°. Assuming this rotation uniform, each degree of elevation of the sun will correspond to $\frac{6}{90}$ of an hour, or 4 minutes. A vertical stick 16.4 inches high casts a horizontal shadow 8 inches long. What time is it, if the sun rose at 6:00 A.M. and will be directly overhead at noon?
10. From a point on the ground and 100 feet from the base of a building, the angles of elevation of the bottom and top of a flagpole standing on top of the building are 24°10′ and 33°32′, respectively. Find the length of the flagpole.
11. Two straight highways, A and B, intersect at a point O, and the smallest angle between them is 58°. A service station is located on highway A, 500 yards from the intersection. Where is the point on highway B that is nearest to the service station, and how near is it?
12. The sides of an isosceles triangle are 20, 20, and 16. Find the magnitudes of the angles.

10 PROJECTIONS, VECTORS, AND COMPONENTS OF VECTORS

Before discussing vectors, we need to introduce the notion of projections. This we shall do next.

The *projection of a point P* on a line L is the point Q of the intersection of L and the line drawn through P perpendicular to L; see Fig. 10.19. If P is on L, P and Q will coincide and P projects into itself.

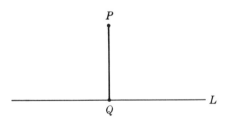

FIGURE 10.19

The *projection of a line segment AB* on a line L is the segment $A'B'$, where A' is the projection of A on L and B' is the projection of B on L; see Fig. 10.20.

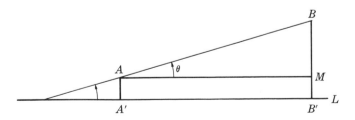

FIGURE 10.20

If the segment AB lies on a line perpendicular to L, A' and B' will coincide and the projection of AB on L is a single point. If the line AB is parallel to L, then $A'B' = AB$. If AB is neither perpendicular nor parallel to L, it will intersect L at some acute angle θ. Through A draw a line parallel to L and let it intersect BB' in a point M. Now

$$A'B' = AM = AB \cos \theta,$$

which proves the following theorem.

Theorem 10.3.   *The length of the projection of a line segment AB on a line L is equal to the length of AB times the cosine of the angle between AB and L.*

Vectors

In the study of physics and mechanics, two common types of quantities are encountered. The first is a quantity that has magnitude but no direction; positive and negative numbers, speed, temperature, volume, mass, etc., are of this kind. Such a quantity is called a *scalar*. The second is a quantity that has both magnitude and direction; velocities, forces, and displacements are of this type. Such a quantity is called a *vector quantity*.

It is convenient to represent a vector quantity by a straight arrow whose length represents the magnitude of the quantity and whose direction indicates the direction of the quantity. Such a directed line segment is called a *vector*. We shall use small letters to designate vectors, as a, b, c, etc. We shall denote the length of a vector a by the notation $|a|$.

Two vectors are said to be equal if they are of the same length, are parallel, and point in the same direction. In Fig. 10.21, $a = b$.

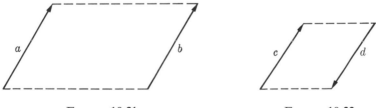

FIGURE 10.21   FIGURE 10.22

If two vectors have the same length, are parallel, but point in opposite directions, they are said to be the negatives of each other. In Fig. 10.22, $c = -d$ and $d = -c$.

Hence a vector can be moved from one position to another without being changed if its direction and magnitude are kept unchanged.

Consider two vectors a and b and a point P. Place the initial end of vector a at the point P. Move vector b until its initial end coincides with the terminal end of vector a. Draw the vector c with initial end at P and terminal end at the terminal end of b, Fig. 10.23 (left). Vector c is called the *resultant*, or *sum*, of the vectors a and b, and is written $c = a + b$.

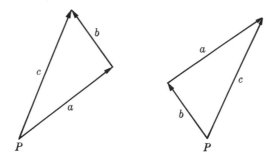

FIGURE 10.23

If we reverse the process by starting with vector b, placing its initial end at P, and moving vector a until its initial end coincides with the terminal end of b, we find the same vector c as a resultant, Fig. 10.23 (right). Thus $c = a + b = b + a$.

If a and b are parallel vectors, the resultant c is parallel to a and to b (Fig. 10.24).

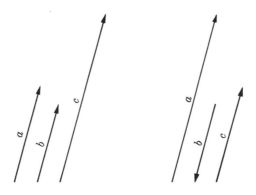

FIGURE 10.24

Now consider the case in which a and b are not parallel, and place the initial end of a at P and the initial end of b at P. Complete the parallelogram having a and b as adjacent sides. The diagonal from P to the opposite vertex determines a vector c, and again $c = a + b$, Fig. 10.25. Thus, the sum of two vectors may be found graphically by drawing a triangle, as in Fig. 10.23, or by drawing a parallelogram, as in Fig. 10.25.

In a similar manner, three or more vectors may be added graphically by finding the resultant of two of the vectors, adding a third vector to this

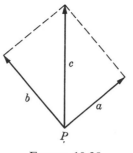

FIGURE 10.25

resultant, then adding a fourth vector to the resultant of the first three, and so on. The order in which vectors are added does not change the sum.

Components of Vectors

The *component* of a vector a along a line L, or in the direction of L, is a vector having the same direction as the line L and whose magnitude is the length of the projection of a upon L. Thus, if θ is the angle between L and the direction of a, and if b is the component of a in the direction of L, as in Fig. 10.26, then $|b| = |a| \cos \theta$.

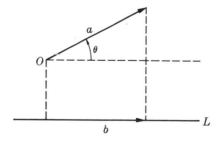

FIGURE 10.26

Two components of a vector that are often useful are the horizontal component and the vertical component. If a is a vector whose direction makes an angle θ with the horizontal and a_h and a_v are its horizontal and vertical components, then by definition $|a_h| = |a| \cos \theta$ and $|a_v| = |a| \sin \theta$. Moreover, $a = a_h + a_v$; see Fig. 10.27.

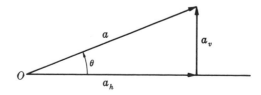

FIGURE 10.27

Example. A force of 50 pounds acts in a direction making an angle of 30° with the horizontal. Find the magnitude of the horizontal and vertical components of the force.

Solution: From Fig. 10.27 we have

$$|a_h| = 50 \cos 30° = 25\sqrt{3} \text{ lb,}$$
$$|a_v| = 50 \sin 30° = 25 \text{ lb.}$$

Example. A force of 40 pounds and a force of 60 pounds act on the same point O in directions that are at right angles with each other. Find the resultant of these two forces and the angle it makes with the direction of the 60-pound force.

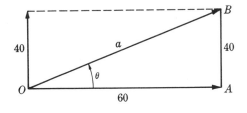

FIGURE 10.28

Solution: Complete the rectangle determined by the vectors representing the given forces; see Fig. 10.28. The diagonal of this rectangle, with O as initial point, is a vector a which represents the resultant of the given forces. Let θ represent the angle the resultant makes with the 60-pound force. Then from the figure we have

$$\tan \theta = \frac{40}{60} = \frac{2}{3} = 0.66667$$

which gives $\theta = 33°41'$ correct to the nearest minute.

Next let $R = |a|$ represent the magnitude of the resultant. Referring again to the figure, we find

$$40/R = \sin \theta$$
$$40 = R \sin \theta$$

$$R = \frac{40}{\sin \theta} = \frac{40}{\sin 33°41'} = \frac{40}{0.5546} = 72.11.$$

EXERCISES

1. Find the horizontal and vertical projections of a line segment 40 inches long and inclined at an angle of 32° with the horizontal.
2. A line segment inclined 60° with the horizontal has a horizontal projection of 20 feet. Find the length of the segment.
3. A line segment 50 feet long has a vertical projection 30 feet long. Find the angle the line makes with the horizontal.
4. If a ship is sailing 30° north of east at the rate of 20 miles per hour, what are the components of its speed eastward and northward?

5. A force of 100 pounds and a force of 50 pounds act at a common point O and at right angles to each other. Find the resultant of these two forces and the angle this resultant makes with the 100-pound force.

6. A 4000-pound car is parked on a hill inclined at an angle of 10° with the horizontal. What force must the brakes overcome, to keep the car from rolling down the hill? With what force is the car pressing against the hill?

7. A cake of ice weighing 100 pounds is held on a smooth plane, inclined 20° with the horizontal, by a single force acting along the plane. Find the magnitude of the force.

8. A lawnmower weighing 30 pounds is pushed on level ground with a force of 40 pounds directed along the handle, which is inclined 32° with the ground. How large is the force that produces the forward motion? With what total force do the wheels press against the ground?

11 OBLIQUE TRIANGLES

An oblique triangle was defined earlier in this chapter as one not containing a right angle. Thus the ratio of two sides of an oblique triangle does not represent a function of one of the angles of the triangle. Hence the method used in solving right triangles does not apply here. In fact, to solve oblique triangles we shall need two additional formulas, namely the law of sines and the law of cosines.

Law of Sines

In any triangle the sides are proportional to the sines of the opposite angles or, in symbols,

$$\frac{a}{\sin A} = \frac{b}{\sin B} = \frac{c}{\sin C}.$$

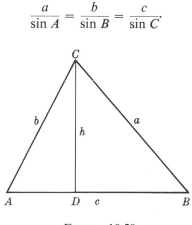

FIGURE 10.29

Proof 1: All angles are acute. Let h be the length of the perpendicular CD from the vertex C to the side AB; see Fig. 10.29. From the right triangles ACD and BCD we find

$$\sin A = \frac{h}{b} \quad \text{and} \quad \sin B = \frac{h}{a},$$

$$h = b \sin A \quad \text{and} \quad h = a \sin B.$$

Equating these two values for h, we have

$$a \sin B = b \sin A.$$

After dividing by $\sin A \sin B$, we get

$$\frac{a}{\sin A} = \frac{b}{\sin B}.$$

In a similar manner we can show that

$$\frac{a}{\sin A} = \frac{c}{\sin C},$$

Consequently, our theorem is proved.

Proof 2: One angle is obtuse. Suppose that angle B is obtuse. Let h be the length of the perpendicular CD drawn from the vertex C to the side

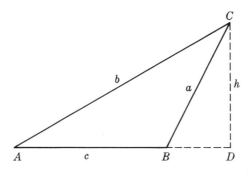

FIGURE 10.30

AB extended; see Fig. 10.30. From the right triangles ADC and BDC we have the two following relations:

$$\sin A = \frac{h}{b}, \quad \text{or} \quad h = b \sin A,$$

$$\text{and} \quad \sin (CBD) = \frac{h}{a}, \quad \text{or} \quad h = a \sin (CBD).$$

But angle CBD is the angle related to the obtuse angle B; thus,

$$\sin (CBD) = \sin B;$$

hence $h = a \sin B.$

Again, if we equate the two values found for h, $a \sin B = b \sin A$, or

$$\frac{a}{\sin A} = \frac{b}{\sin B}.$$

It follows from Proof 1 that

$$\frac{a}{\sin A} = \frac{c}{\sin C}.$$

Consequently, our theorem is proved.

It is shown in plane geometry that if one side and any other two parts of a triangle are given, there is in general one and only one triangle so determined. (There is one exception to this general law which will be explained in a moment.) There are four ways of combining one side of a triangle with two other parts:

Case 1. Given one side and two angles.
Case 2. Given two sides and the angle opposite one of them.
Case 3. Given two sides and the included angle.
Case 4. Given three sides.

The law of sines is equivalent to the three formulas

$$\frac{a}{\sin A} = \frac{b}{\sin B}, \qquad \frac{a}{\sin A} = \frac{c}{\sin C}, \qquad \frac{b}{\sin B} = \frac{c}{\sin C}.$$

It is obvious from an inspection of these three formulas that the law of sines is adequate for solving oblique triangles when the given information is either that in Case 1 or Case 2. The exceptional case mentioned earlier comes under Case 2. When the given angle is acute and the given side opposite this angle is shorter than the other given side, there may be two, one, or no solutions. If the given angle is obtuse and the given side opposite this angle is shorter than the other given side, then there is no solution. These last two statements are easily verified by drawing a figure for each one. We shall not consider problems of the ambiguous type here.

Example. Given $A = 70°$, $B = 30°$, and $b = 40$, find angle C, side a, and side c.

Solution: $A + B + C = 180°$,
$$C = 180° - (A + B) = 180° - 100° = 80°.$$

From the law of sines we have

$$\frac{a}{\sin A} = \frac{b}{\sin B} \qquad \text{and} \qquad \frac{c}{\sin C} = \frac{b}{\sin B},$$

or
$$a = \frac{b \sin A}{\sin B} \qquad \text{and} \qquad c = \frac{b \sin C}{\sin B}.$$

Substituting the values given for A, B, and b and the value found for C, we obtain the following:

$$a = \frac{40 \sin 70°}{\sin 30°} = \frac{40(0.93969)}{0.5}, \qquad \text{and} \qquad c = \frac{40 \sin 80°}{\sin 30°} = \frac{40(0.98481)}{0.5},$$

$$= 80(0.93969), \qquad\qquad\qquad\qquad = 80(0.98481),$$
$$= 75.18, \text{ approximately} \qquad\qquad = 78.78, \text{ approximately.}$$

We shall assume that all data given in triangle problems are exact.

Law of Cosines

The square of any side of a triangle is equal to the sum of the squares of the other two sides minus twice the product of those sides and the cosine of the angle between them, or in symbols,

$$a^2 = b^2 + c^2 - 2bc \cos A,$$
$$b^2 = a^2 + c^2 - 2ac \cos B,$$
$$c^2 = a^2 + b^2 - 2ab \cos C.$$

Proof: Consider the triangle ABC of Fig. 10.31. We shall follow the same convention regarding notation as was used in the discussion of right triangles, with the exception that neither of the angles is necessarily a right angle. In the plane of triangle ABC, construct a rectangular coordinate system with the origin at vertex A and the positive x axis passing through B (Fig. 10.31). Relative to this coordinate system, the coordinates of A, B, and

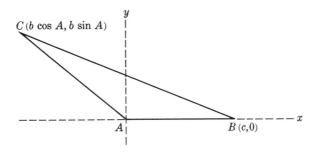

FIGURE 10.31

C respectively are $(0, 0)$, $(c, 0)$, and $(b \cos A, b \sin A)$. Using the distance formula to calculate $d(B, C)$, noting that according to our notation $d(B, C) = a$, and remembering that $\cos^2 A + \sin^2 A = 1$, we obtain

$$a^2 = (b \cos A - c)^2 + (b \sin A - 0)^2$$
$$= b(\cos^2 A + \sin^2 A) - 2bc \cos A + c^2$$
$$= b^2 + c^2 - 2bc \cos A.$$

By rearranging the letters A, B, C, a, b, and c on our triangle, we find that the relations for b^2 and c^2 follow.

Example.   Given $a = 14$, $b = 8$, $C = 40$, find side c.

Solution: To find side c we use:

$$c^2 = a^2 + b^2 - 2ab \cos C,$$
$$= 196 + 64 - 2(14)(8) \cos 40°,$$
$$= 260 - 224 \cos 40°,$$
$$= 260 - 224(0.7660) = 88.42 \text{ (approximately)},$$
$$c = 9.40.$$

Example.   Given $a = 20$, $b = 14$, and $c = 10$, find angle A.

Solution: To find angle A, we use $a^2 = b^2 + c^2 - 2bc \cos A$ and solve for $\cos A$. The result is

$$\cos A = \frac{b^2 + c^2 - a^2}{2bc} = \frac{196 + 100 - 400}{280} = -0.37143.$$

If A_1 is the related angle, then $\cos A_1 = 0.37143$ and $A_1 = 68°12'$; therefore, $A = 180° - 68°12' = 111°48'$.

EXERCISES

Find the unknown parts of the given triangles in Exercises 1 to 10.

1. $A = 72°$, $C = 64°10'$, $c = 20$.
2. $A = 100°$, $B = 34°45'$, $b = 50$.
3. $B = 80°$, $C = 70°$, $a = 100$.
4. $A = 60°$, $a = 10$, $b = 8$.
5. $A = 110°$, $C = 40°$, $b = 20$.

6. $A = 120°$, $a = 30$, $b = 20$.
7. $b = 30$, $c = 40$, $A = 60°$.
8. $a = 6$, $b = 7$, $c = 8$.
9. $a = 20$, $b = 24$, $C = 40°$.
10. $a = 60$, $c = 50$, $B = 110°$.

11. A force of 60 pounds and a force of 100 pounds act at the same point on an object. If the angle between the two forces is 60°, what are the direction and magnitude of the resultant?
12. Two points A and B are separated by a pond. If the distance from A to a third point C is 316 yards, the distance from C to B is 346 yards, and the angle ACB is 41°15′, how far is it from A to B?
13. How long is the chord subtending an angle of 40° at the center of a circle of radius 15 feet?
14. Prove that the area of any triangle is equal to one-half the product of any two sides and the sine of the angle between those sides.
15. Two adjacent sides of a parallelogram are 16 feet and 25 feet, and the angle between them is 50°. Find the length of each diagonal.

12   FUNCTIONS OF $(A + B)$, $(A - B)$, AND $2A$

It is a simple matter to show that in general

$$\sin (A + B) \neq \sin A + \sin B$$

or that

$$\sin 2A \neq 2 \sin A.$$

For example, $\sin 30° = \dfrac{1}{2}$, $\sin 60° = \dfrac{\sqrt{3}}{2}$, and $\sin 90° = 1$. Since $30° + 60° = 90°$ and $\dfrac{1}{2} + \dfrac{\sqrt{3}}{2} \neq 1$, then

$$\sin (30° + 60°) = \sin 90° \neq \sin 30° + \sin 60°.$$

Similarly, since $60° = 2 \cdot 30°$, and $2 \cdot \dfrac{1}{2} = 1 \neq \dfrac{\sqrt{3}}{2}$, then

$$\sin 60° = \sin 2 \cdot 30° \neq 2 \sin 30°.$$

We may therefore ask, is it possible to express $\sin (A + B)$, or in fact any function of $(A + B)$ or $(A - B)$ in terms of functions of A and functions of B? To answer such questions we prove the following identities. We shall start by proving if A and B are any two angles, then

(1) $$\cos (A - B) = \cos A \cos B + \sin A \sin B.$$

Since $\cos (-\theta) = \cos \theta$ and $\sin (-\theta) = -\sin \theta$ for all angles θ, if A and B are interchanged in (9) both sides of the equation remain unchanged. We may therefore assume $A > B$. Also since $\sin (\theta \pm 2\pi) - \sin \theta$ and $\cos (\theta \pm 2\pi) = \cos \theta$ are identities, we may assume without loss of generality that $0 \leq A \leq 2\pi$ and $0 \leq B \leq 2\pi$.

Draw a unit circle on a rectangular coordinate system and place angles A and B in standard position on this same system (see Fig. 10.32). Let

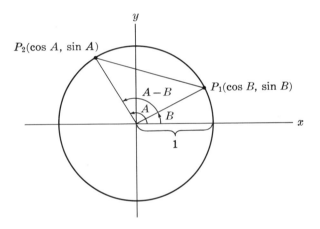

FIGURE 10.32

$P_1(x_1, y_1)$ be the point of intersection of terminal side of B and unit circle, and let $P_2(x_2, y_2)$ be point of intersection of terminal side of A and the circle. By definition,

$$\cos B = \frac{x_1}{1} = x_1 \qquad \cos A = \frac{x_2}{1} = x_2$$

$$\sin B = \frac{y_1}{1} = y_1 \qquad \sin A = \frac{y_2}{1} = y_2$$

and hence $(x_1, y_1) = (\cos B, \sin B)$ and $(x_2, y_2) = (\cos A, \sin A)$ as shown in the figure. Applying the Law of Cosines,

$$\overline{P_1 P_2^2} = 1^2 + 1^2 - 2 \cdot 1 \cdot 1 \cos (A - B)$$
$$= 2 - 2 \cos (A - B).$$

Now using the distance formula to find $\overline{P_1P_2^2}$ we set

$$\overline{P_1P_2^2} = (\cos A - \cos B)^2 + (\sin A - \sin B)^2$$
$$= \cos^2 A - 2\cos A \cos B + \cos^2 B + \sin^2 A - 2\sin A \sin B + \sin^2 B$$
$$= (\cos^2 A + \sin^2 A) + (\cos^2 B + \sin^2 B) - 2\cos A \cos B - 2\sin A \sin B$$
$$= 2 - 2\cos A \cos B - 2\sin A \sin B.$$

Equating the two expressions for $P_1P_2^2$ and simplifying we obtain

$$\cos(A - B) = \cos A \cos B + \sin A \sin B,$$

and our identity is proved.

Since Equation (1) holds for all angles A and B we can replace B by $(-B)$, which gives

$$\cos[A - (-B)] = \cos A \cos(-B) + \sin A \sin(-B).$$

But $\cos(-B) = \cos B$ and $\sin(-B) = -\sin B$, hence

(2) $$\cos(A + B) = \cos A \cos B - \sin A \sin B.$$

Example.   If

$$\sin A = \tfrac{12}{13}, \qquad A \text{ in quadrant II}$$
$$\text{and} \qquad \cos B = \tfrac{4}{5}, \qquad B \text{ in quadrant IV,}$$

find $\cos(A - B)$ and $\cos(A + B)$.

Solution: Before we can calculate $\cos(A - B)$ and $\cos(A + B)$ we need to calculate $\cos A$ and $\sin B$. To do this place A and B in standard position on coordinate system as shown in Fig. 10.33. From the figure we see that $\cos B = -\tfrac{5}{13}$ and $\sin B = -\tfrac{3}{5}$.

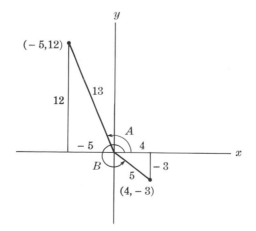

FIGURE 10.33

We now substitute the known values for $\cos A$, $\sin A$, $\cos B$, and $\sin B$ into Equation (1), giving

$$\cos (A - B) = (-\tfrac{5}{13})(\tfrac{4}{5}) + (\tfrac{12}{13})(-\tfrac{3}{5})$$
$$= -\tfrac{20}{65} - \tfrac{36}{65} = -\tfrac{56}{65}.$$

To find $\cos (A + B)$ we use Equation (10) and find that

$$\cos (A + B) = -\tfrac{20}{65} + \tfrac{36}{65} = \tfrac{16}{65}.$$

The angles $\dfrac{\pi}{2} - \theta$ and θ are complementary angles and hence for any angle θ (Theorem 10.2),

$$\cos \left(\frac{\pi}{2} - \theta\right) = \sin \theta$$

$$\sin \left(\frac{\pi}{2} - \theta\right) = \cos \theta.$$

To obtain a formula for $\sin (A + B)$ we proceed as follows:

$$\sin (A + B) = \cos \left[\frac{\pi}{2} - (A + B)\right],$$

$$= \cos \left[\left(\frac{\pi}{2} - A\right) - B\right],$$

$$= \cos \left(\frac{\pi}{2} - A\right) \cos B + \sin \left(\frac{\pi}{2} - A\right) \sin B,$$

and finally

(3) $$\sin (A + B) = \sin A \cos B + \cos A \sin B,$$

since $\cos \left(\dfrac{\pi}{2} - A\right) = \sin A$ and $\sin \left(\dfrac{\pi}{2} - A\right) = \cos A$. If in Equation (3) we replace B by $-B$, we obtain

(4) $$\sin (A - B) = \sin A \cos B - \cos A \sin B.$$

The details are left to the student.

We can now obtain a formula for $\tan (A - B)$ in the following way.

$$\tan (A - B) = \frac{\sin (A - B)}{\cos (A - B)} \qquad \text{(Identity 4, Sec. 10.5)}$$

$$= \frac{\sin A \cos B - \cos A \sin B}{\cos A \cos B + \sin A \sin B} \qquad \text{(Expanding)}$$

$$\tan (A - B) = \frac{\dfrac{\sin A \cos B}{\cos A \cos B} - \dfrac{\cos A \sin B}{\cos A \cos B}}{\dfrac{\cos A \cos B}{\cos A \cos B} + \dfrac{\sin A \sin B}{\cos A \cos B}} \qquad \text{(Divide by $\cos A \cos B$)}$$

then

(5) $$\tan (A - B) = \frac{\tan A - \tan B}{1 + \tan A \tan B}.$$

Replacing B by $-B$ and recalling that $\tan (-B) = -\tan B$, Identity (5) becomes

(6) $$\tan (A + B) = \frac{\tan A + \tan B}{1 - \tan A \tan B}.$$

It should be emphasized that Identities (5) and (6) are valid only for those angles for which the functions involved are defined and for which the denominators are not zero.

Definition.   *The inclination of a line L is the angle ϕ measured counterclockwise from the x-axis to the line. The angle ϕ satisfies the inequality*

$$0° \leq \phi < 180°$$

and $\phi = 0$ if and only if L is parallel to the x-axis.

See Figure 10.34.

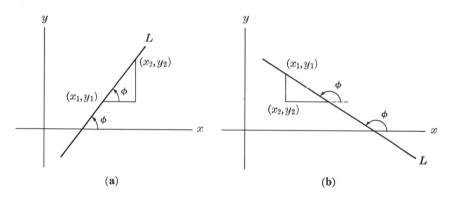

(a)

(b)

FIGURE 10.34

It is obvious from Fig. 10.34 that the slope m of line L is equal to the tangent of the angle of inclination ϕ of L. That is,

$$m = \frac{y_2 - y_1}{x_2 - x_1} = \tan \phi.$$

Let L_1 and L_2 be two lines, with inclination angles ϕ_1 and ϕ_2 respectively, which intersect at P, and let θ be the angle of intersection of L_1 and L_2 measured from L_1 counterclockwise around to L_2. (See Fig. 10.35).

Then $\theta = \phi_2 - \phi_1$ and

$$\tan \theta = \tan (\phi_2 - \phi_1) = \frac{\tan \phi_2 - \tan \phi_1}{1 + \tan \phi_2 \tan \phi_1}.$$

If we denote the slopes of L_1 and L_2 by m_1 and m_2 the last equation can be written in the form

$$\tan \theta = \frac{m_2 - m_1}{1 + m_1 m_2}.$$

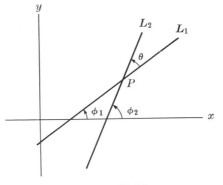

FIGURE 10.35

Example. Find the tangent of the acute angle θ between L_1 and L_2 if $L_1: 2x - y = 3$ and $L_2: 3x + y = 7$.

Solution: Here $m_1 = 2$ and $m_2 = -3$, hence

$$\tan \theta = \frac{m_2 - m_1}{1 + m_1 m_2} = \frac{-3 - 2}{1 - 6}$$

$$= 1$$

so $\tan \theta = 1$ and $\theta = 45°$.

Double Angle Formulas

If in Identity (2) we let $B = A$, it becomes

(7) $\cos 2A = \cos^2 A - \sin^2 A.$

Similarly by setting $B = A$ in Identity (3) we obtain

(8) $\sin 2A = 2 \sin A \cos A.$

Formulas (7) and (8) are called double angle formulas because the angle exhibited on the left is double the angle exhibited on the right.

EXERCISES

1. If $\cos A = -\frac{3}{5}$, A in quadrant II, and $\cos B = \frac{15}{17}$, B in quadrant I, find
   a. $\sin (A + B)$.   d. $\cos (A - B)$.   g. $\cos 2A$.
   b. $\sin (A - B)$.   e. $\tan (A + B)$.   h. $\sin 2B$.
   c. $\cos (A + B)$.   f. $\tan (A - B)$.   i. $\cos 2B$.
2. If $\tan A = \frac{1}{2}$, $\tan B = \frac{1}{3}$, and A and B are both acute angles, find $\tan (A + B)$ and thus show that $A + B = 45°$.
3. Simplify each of the following expressions and then find its value.
   a. $\cos 40° \cos 20° - \sin 40° \sin 20°$.   e. $\cos 75° \cos 15° + \sin 75° \sin 15°$.
   b. $\sin 70° \cos 40° - \cos 70° \sin 40°$.   f. $\sin 40° \cos 50° + \cos 40° \sin 50°$.

   c. $\cos^2 15° - \sin^2 15°$.   g. $\dfrac{\tan 25° + \tan 20°}{1 - \tan 25° \tan 20°}$.

   d. $2 \sin 15° \cos 15°$.   h. $\dfrac{\tan 200° - \tan 65°}{1 + \tan 200° \tan 65°}$.

4. By regarding 3θ as $2\theta + \theta$ and using Formulas (7) and (8) show that $\sin 3\theta = 3 \sin \theta - 4 \sin^3 \theta$.

5. Find the tangent of the acute angle of intersection of each given pair of lines.
  a. $3x + y = 7, x - y = 3$.   **b.** $2x + 3y = 8, 2x + y = 4$.

6. Express each of the following as a function of θ only.
  a. $\cos (90° + \theta)$.   **b.** $\sin (180° - \theta)$.   **c.** $\sin (270° - \theta)$.

7. If $\sin A = -\frac{4}{5}$, $\cos B = -\frac{5}{13}$, and A and B are in the same quadrant, find $\sin (A + B)$ and $\cos (A - B)$.

8. The angle of intersection of two intersecting curves is defined as the angle of intersection of the tangents to the two curves drawn at the point of intersection. Using this definition, find the tangent of the angle of intersection of the parabolas $y = x^2$ and $y^2 = x$.

9. Using the identities $\cos^2 \theta + \sin^2 \theta = 1$ and $\cos^2 \theta - \sin^2 \theta = \cos 2\theta$, show that

$$\sin^2 \theta = \frac{1 - \cos 2\theta}{2}$$

and

$$\cos^2 \theta = \frac{1 + \cos 2\theta}{2}.$$

10. Identify each given statement as true or false and give a reason. Do not use tables.
  a. $\cos^2 18° = \sin^2 18° + \cos 36°$.   **c.** $\cos 80° = 1 - 2 \sin^2 40°$.

  b. $\cos^2 \frac{\theta}{2} + \sin^2 \frac{\theta}{2} = \frac{1}{2}$.   **d.** $\sin^2 70 + \sin^2 20 = 1$.

XI

SIMPLE AND COMPOUND INTEREST

1 INTRODUCTION

Interest is the rental paid for the use of borrowed money. The rent depends upon how much money is borrowed, the length of time the money is used, and the interest rate. The sum of money borrowed is called the *principal*. The *interest rate* is that fraction of the principal which is to be paid for its use for a specified unit period of time.

We shall consider two kinds of interest, simple interest and compound interest. If interest is computed on the original principal only, it is called *simple interest*. If the interest for a given unit period is added to the principal on which it was computed, and the interest for the next period is computed on this new principal, the sum by which the original principal has been increased is called the *compound interest* for the two unit periods.

It is common practice to express interest rates as percentages rather than as common fractions. In this connection it should be pointed out that the applications of percentage to business are countless. In fact, percentage is used in so much of the computation in the business world, particularly in commercial problems, that its importance can hardly be overemphasized. For this reason we next review briefly the notion of percentage.

2 PERCENTAGE

The word *percent* comes from the Latin phrase *per centum*, which means "by the hundred." Thus percentage refers to calculations in which hundredths are used as the basis of comparison. Therefore, a percent always stands for a fraction whose denominator is 100. The symbol for percent is %. Thus, 6% means $\frac{6}{100}$, 17% means $\frac{17}{100}$, 123% means $\frac{123}{100}$, etc. For example, 5% of 60 means $\frac{5}{100}$ of 60, which is 3. In making calculations involving percents it is always necessary to express each percent as an equivalent fraction before carrying out the computation. This may be done either as a decimal fraction or a common fraction. Thus $25\% = \frac{25}{100} = 0.25 = \frac{1}{4}$. Similarly, we can express any number as a percent by multiplying it by 100 and attaching the percent sign; for example, $\frac{3}{4} = \frac{300}{4}\% = 75\%$. The following illustrative examples show how elementary algebra can often be used to solve problems involving percentage. The student is advised to study these examples very carefully before attempting to solve the problems in the exercises.

Example. Find the number which is 7% of 280.

Solution: Let x be the desired number.

$$\text{Then} \qquad x = 7\% \text{ of } 280,$$

$$\text{that is} \qquad x = \frac{7}{100}(280)$$

$$\text{or} \qquad 100x = 7(280) = 1960,$$
$$\text{hence} \qquad x = 19.6.$$

Example. What percent of 500 is 85?

Solution: Let x be the number of the percent.

$$\text{Then} \qquad x\% \text{ of } 500 - 85;$$

$$\text{that is,} \qquad \frac{x}{100}(500) = 85$$

$$\text{or} \qquad 500x = 8500,$$
$$\text{hence} \qquad x = 17 \qquad \text{and 85 is 17\% of 500.}$$

Check: $17\% \text{ of } 500 = \frac{17}{100}(500) = 17(5) = 85.$

Example. If 15% of a number is 36, what is the number?

Solution: Let x be the number.

$$\text{Then} \qquad 15\% \text{ of } x = 36;$$

$$\text{that is,} \qquad \frac{15}{100}x = 36$$

$$\text{or} \qquad 15x = 3600,$$
$$\text{hence} \qquad x = 240.$$

Check: 15% of $240 = \dfrac{15}{100}(240) = 0.15(240) - 36.$

Example.   In a class of 150 students, 117 received passing grades. What percent of the class failed?

Solution: Let x be the number of the percent that failed.

Then $x\%$ of $150 = 33;$

that is, $\dfrac{x}{100}(150) = 33$

or $150x = 3300,$
hence $x = 22$ and so 22% of the class failed.

Check: 22% of $150 = \dfrac{22}{100}(150) = 0.22(150) = 33.$

Example.   A man's salary for 1956 was $6720. This was 12% more than his salary for 1955. What was his salary for 1955?

Solution: Let x be the salary for 1955.

Then $x + 12\%$ of $x = 6720;$

that is, $x + \dfrac{12}{100}x = 6720$

or $100x + 12x = 672000,$
which reduces to $112x = 672000,$
and solving for x we get $x = 6000.$

EXERCISES

1.   Express each of the following as a common fraction.
    a. 4%.   **b.** 12.5%.   **c.** 125%.   **d.** 7%.   **e.** $16\frac{2}{3}\%$.
2.   Express each of the following as a decimal fraction.
    a. 6%.   **b.** 17%.   **c.** 32%.   **d.** 140%.   **e.** 300%.
3.   Express each of the following as a percent.
    a. $\frac{1}{8}$.   **b.** $\frac{1}{3}$.   **c.** $\frac{2}{5}$.   **d.** $\frac{7}{4}$.   **e.** $\frac{17}{25}$.
4.   Express each of the following as a percent.
    a. 0.08.   **b.** 0.26.   **c.** 1.17.   **d.** 0.3247.   **e.** 0.005.
5.   Find: **(a)** 10% of 460, **(b)** 5% of 275, **(c)** 5.2% of 150, **(d)** 22% of 897.
6.   What percent of **(a)** 60 is 3, **(b)** 40 is 32, **(c)** 48 is 60, **(d)** 1000 is 5?
7.   **a.**   300 is 6% of what number?   **c.**   8.4 is $33\frac{1}{3}\%$ of what number?
    b.   60 is 75% of what number?   **d.**   42 is 12% of what number?
8.   In a class of 50 students, 12% failed. How many students passed?
9.   A piece of real estate, for taxation purposes, is evaluated at $7500. If the tax rate is 4.8%, what is the amount of the tax?

10. The R & H Radio Company sells a radio for $40. The purchase price was $32. The gain is what percent of the purchase price? Of the selling price?
11. The real estate tax on a man's home was $280. Find the valuation of the home if the tax rate was 4%.
12. If your average grade on hour tests is 76 and counts for 60% of your final grade, what grade must you make on the final examination to receive a grade of 80 in the course?
13. How much milk containing 5% butterfat should be mixed with 50 pounds of milk containing 3% butterfat to obtain milk that is 4% butterfat?
14. A piano was sold for $850. If this is 15% less than the list price, what is the list price?
15. How many gallons of cream that is 23% butterfat can a farmer separate from 1000 gallons of milk giving 5% butterfat, if the milk left must have 3% butterfat?

3 SIMPLE INTEREST DEFINED

By definition, simple interest is the percent of the given principal that is to be paid for its use for a given unit of time. Let P be the principal in dollars, r the yearly interest rate, t the number of years the principal is used, I the total interest in dollars, and S the amount in dollars of the principal and interest at the end of t years. The following formulas involving simple interest follow immediately from the definition.

$$I = Ptr,$$
$$S = P + I;$$

therefore, $\qquad S = P + Ptr, \qquad$ or $S = P(1 + tr).$

Example. Find the simple interest on $300 for 7 years at 5%. Also find the amount.

Solution: We have $P = 300$, $t = 7$, and $r = 0.05$; substituting in the formula $I = Ptr$ we get

$$I = (300)(7)(0.05) = \$105;$$
from $S = P + I,$ $\qquad S = 300 + 105 = \$405.$

Example. Find the simple interest on $500 for 9 months if the rate is 4%.

Solution: Here $P = \$500$, $t = \frac{9}{12} = \frac{3}{4}$, and $r = 0.04$; so

$$I = 500(\tfrac{3}{4})(0.04) = \$15.$$

Example. What principal will amount to $399 in 2 years at 7% simple interest?

Solution: In this problem, we know that $S = 399$, $t = 2$, and $r = 0.07$. We wish to find P. To do this we use the formula $S = P(1 + rt)$. Solving for P, we get

$$P = \frac{S}{1 + rt}.$$

Substituting the known values for S, r, and t, we find

$$P = \frac{399}{1 + (2)(0.07)} = \frac{399}{1.14} = \$350.$$

Example.   What is the rate of simple interest if \$375 amounts to \$412.50 in $2\frac{1}{2}$ years?

Solution: Here $P = 375$, $S = 412.50$, and $t = \frac{5}{2}$. We wish to find r. First we find I:

$$I = S - P = 412.50 - 375 = 37.50;$$

now $$r = \frac{I}{Pt} = \frac{37.50}{(375)(\frac{5}{2})} = 0.04 = 4\%.$$

EXERCISES

1.   Find the simple interest and amount of a principal of \$800 for $3\frac{1}{2}$ years at 6%.
2.   Find the simple interest and amount of a principal of \$2400 for 8 months at $4\frac{1}{2}\%$.
3.   How long will it take \$1200 to yield \$35 at $3\frac{1}{2}\%$ simple interest?
4.   Mr. Spendthrift pays a bank \$291.20 in settlement of a loan and 6% interest on it for 8 months. How much has he borrowed?
5.   Find the rate of simple interest if a principal of \$400 amounts to \$445 in $2\frac{1}{2}$ years.
6.   A certain used car can be bought for \$800 cash or for \$844 due in 6 months. If the second plan is accepted, what rate of simple interest does the buyer pay?
7.   In how many years will \$480 amount to \$507 at $4\frac{1}{2}\%$ simple interest?
8.   What is the rate of interest if \$324 amounts to \$328.05 in 3 months?
9.   Mr. Smith gives a check for \$576.80 in settlement of a loan of \$560 with simple interest at 4%. How long did he use the money?
10.   What principal will amount to \$397.10 in 9 months at 6% simple interest?

4   PRESENT VALUE AT SIMPLE INTEREST

The *maturity value* of a financial obligation due at some future date is that amount of money which will settle the obligation on the day it is due. Denote by S the maturity value of an obligation due in t years. The present value of this obligation at the simple interest rate r is that principal P which, if invested now at the rate r, will amount to S in t years.

Since a principal P invested at the rate r will amount to $P(1 + tr)$ in t years, we have the following relation between S and P: $S = P(1 + tr)$. Solving for P, we get

$$P = \frac{S}{1 + tr},$$

the difference, $S - P$, between the maturity value and the present value at simple interest, is called the *simple discount on S* and is usually denoted by *D*. Thus,

$$D = S - P.$$

In the business world it is assumed that money always has rental value. You and I are aware that this is certainly true to a limited extent at least. The local banks and Federal Building and Loan Associations are constantly urging us to put our money in a savings account and watch it grow. Since money always has rental value, it is convenient to think of a sum of money as a growing quantity whose value increases from day to day. We frequently say that, if money earns interest at the rate *r*, it is worth *r*. In what follows, an expression such as "money is worth 4%" shall mean that said money can be invested to earn 4%.

Our discussion suggests that in dealing with a sum of money it is very important that the date on which we speak of the value of the sum of money and any interest rates involved be known. In fact, the following *fundamental principle* can be stated: *If the value of a sum of money on any particular day is known and the worth of money is assumed, the value of the sum on any other day can be found.*

Example.   Find the present value of $200 due in 1 year if the money is worth 5%.

Solution: Substituting $S = 200$, $t = 1$, and $r = 0.05$ in $P = S/(1 + tr)$, we have

$$P = \frac{200}{1 + 1(0.05)} = \left(\frac{200}{1.05}\right) = \$190.48.$$

The simple discount is $D = 200 - 190.48 = \$9.52$.

This means that a principal of $190.48, if invested at 5%, will earn $9.52 interest in 1 year.

Example.   A debt of $1000 is due in 6 months. Find the value of this debt today if the money is worth 4%.

Solution: Here $S = 1000$, $t = \frac{1}{2}$, and $r = 0.04$; substituting in $P = S/(1 + tr)$, we get

$$P = \frac{1000}{1 + \frac{1}{2}(0.04)} = \left(\frac{1000}{1.02}\right) = \$980.39.$$

EXERCISES

In the following exercises, assume one day to be $\frac{1}{360}$ of a year and one month to be $\frac{1}{12}$ of a year.

1.   A non-interest-bearing note for $300 is due in 60 days. Find the present value of the note if the money is worth 5%.
2.   What is the present value at 4% of a $1200 debt due in 8 months? What is the simple discount?

3. A non-interest-bearing note for $1000 is due in 6 months. Assuming money is worth 5%, find the value of this note (a) 2 months hence, (b) 4 months hence, (c) 6 months hence, and (d) 10 months hence.

4. Mr. A borrows $500 from Mr. B and gives him a note for $500 with interest at 4% due in 6 months. Four months later B sells the note to C. If B and C agree that money is worth 6% at that time, how much does C pay B for the note? How much does the holder of the note get for it on the day it is due?

5. A note for $600 bearing 5% interest is due in 8 months. What is the present value of this note at 7% simple interest? What is the simple discount?

6. Find the present value at 6% of a debt of $800 due in 10 months with interest at 4%. How much is the simple discount?

7. A note for $400 with interest at $5\frac{1}{2}\%$ and dated July 1, 1956, is due in 90 days. What should one pay for this note on August 30 to realize 4% simple interest on his investment?

5   COMPOUND INTEREST DEFINED

It should be recalled that, in dealing with sums of money involving simple interest, the original principal remains unchanged. That is, the interest for the second, or third, or fourth year is exactly the same as for the first year. In fact, the interest for *n* years is *n* times the interest for 1 year. For example, simple interest at 5% for 1 year on $100 is $5, for 7 years it is $35, for 10 years it is $50, etc.

In transactions in which compound interest is used, the principal does not remain the same. In fact, it is increased at the end of each interest period, the increase being the interest earned during that period. When interest is added to the principal in this manner to obtain a new principal, it is said to be *converted*, or *compounded*. If the interest is added to the principal at the end of each year, it is said to be *converted annually* and the conversion period is one year. If the interest is added at the end of every six months, the principal is said to be *converted semiannually* and the conversion period is six months. The conversion period could be four months, three months, one month, or any convenient interval of time; in actual practice it usually is one year or less. The total amount due at the end of the last conversion period is called the *compound amount*. The difference between the compound amount and the original principal is called the *compound interest*.

This discussion may be clarified by the following example.

Example. Find the compound amount at the end of 3 years of $100 invested at 4% interest compounded semiannually.

Solution:	Original principal	$100.00
	Interest for the first 6 months	2.00
	Principal at end of first 6 months	$102.00
	Interest for second 6 months	2.04
	Principal at end of second 6 months	$104.04
	Interest for third 6 months	2.081

Principal at end of third 6 months	$106.121
Interest for fourth 6 months	2.122
Principal at end of fourth 6 months	$108.243
Interest for fifth 6 months	2.165
Principal at end of fifth 6 months	$110.408
Interest for sixth 6 months	2.208
Principal at end of sixth 6 months	$112.616

Hence the compound amount at the end of 3 years, of $100 invested at 4% compounded semiannually, is $112.62. Note also that the compound interest in this case is $112.62 − $100 = $12.62.

6 SOME TERMINOLOGY

Herafter in any discussion or problem the word *interest* shall be understood to mean compound interest unless otherwise specified. Further, if no conversion period is specifically stated it shall be understood that interest is converted annually. For example, that money is worth 6% will mean 6% converted annually.

If, in a statement regarding a certain sum's being due at a specified time, no mention is made of interest, it will be understood that the sum is due without interest. For example, "$500 due in 2 years" means that $500 paid at the end of 2 years will cancel the debt.

Interest period is the same as the conversion period, that is, the time between two successive conversions of interest.

Frequency of conversion is the number of conversion periods per year. Thus, if interest is converted quarterly, there are 4 conversion periods per year and the frequency of conversion is 4.

It is common practice to express interest on an annual basis, regardless of how many times per year the interest is converted. Interest rate per conversion period is found by dividing this annual rate by the frequency of conversion. Thus, if interest is 8% converted quarterly, the interest rate per conversion period is 8% divided by 4, or 2% per quarter. In general, if r is the annual rate, k the frequency of conversion, and i the interest rate per conversion period, then

$$i = \frac{r}{k}.$$

7 A FORMULA FOR COMPOUND AMOUNT

In the example of Section 5, an arithmetic step-by-step method was used for finding the compound amount. It is obvious that this is tedious and could be quite long. It is our purpose here to derive a general formula for finding compound amounts.

The example just mentioned suggests that the compound amount of a given principal depends upon two things: the total number of conversion periods and the interest rate per conversion period. Let us denote by t the total number of conversion periods and by i the interest rate per conversion period. Then, if the original principal is P, the interest for the first conversion period is Pi. The principal at the end of the first interest period is $P + Pi = P(1 + i)$. Thus, to find the principal at the end of any interest period, we multiply the principal at the beginning of that period by the quantity $(1 + i)$. Hence, since the principal at the end of the first period is $P(1 + i)$, the principal at the end of the second period is $P(1 + i)(1 + i) = P(1 + i)^2$. Similarly, the principal at the end of the third period is $P(1 + i)^3$, or the principal at the end of t periods is $P(1 + i)^t$. So if S denotes the compound amount of an original principal P compounded for t periods at an interest rate i per conversion period, then we have the general formula

$$S = P(1 + i)^t.$$

In using this formula it must be kept in mind that t is the total number of interest periods and would be the number of years the investment ran only if the conversion or interest period were 1 year. Similarly, the interest rate i in the formula is not, in general, the quoted rate, which is an annual rate, but the interest rate per conversion period.

We often refer to the compound amount of a given principal as the accumulation of that principal. Thus, to accumulate a given principal for a specified time is to find its compound amount at the end of that time. The quantity $(1 + i)^t$ is called an *accumulation factor*, because multiplying any principal P by this factor gives the compound amount of P at the end of t periods at the rate i per period. In fact, the quantity $(1 + i)^t$ is itself the compound amount of $1 compounded for t periods at the rate i.

One of the main reasons that the formula $S = P(1 + i)^t$ is preferable to the step-by-step method is that the value of the accumulation factor $(1 + i)^t$ can be found in a table such as Table II for various values of i and all values of t from 1 to 100.

Example. Find the compound amount at the end of 7 years of $500 at 6% compounded quarterly.

Solution: Here $P = 500$, $t = 28$, and $i = 1\frac{1}{2}\%$; substituting in the formula $S = P(1 + i)^t$, we have $S = 500(1.015)^{28}$.

In Table II we find that $(1.015)^{28} = 1.517222$, correct to six decimal places. Therefore $S = 500(1.51722) = \$758.61$.

Example. A man deposits $1000 with Home Federal Savings and Loan Association, which pays 3% compounded semiannually. How much will he have to his credit at the end of 10 years?

Solution: $P = 1000$, $t = 20$, and $i = 1\frac{1}{2}\%$; therefore,
$$S = 1000(1.015)^{20} - 1000(1.346855) = \$1346.86,$$

from Table II, used to evaluate $(1.015)^{20}$. Actually, this table is not sufficiently accurate to give all results correct to the nearest cent. However, in this case it is. A general rule that expresses the decimal-place accuracy needed in evaluating $(1 + i)^t$ to obtain the product $P(1 + i)^t$ correct to the nearest cent is: Compute $(1 + i)^t$ accurately to as many decimal places as there are dollar and cents places in P.

EXERCISES

1. What is the compound amount of $200 at the end of 12 years if interest is at 6% (a) compounded annually, (b) compounded semiannually, and (c) compounded quarterly?
2. If you accumulate $350 for 15 years at 7% compounded semiannually, how much is the compound interest?
3. If you accumulate $500 for 40 years at (a) 2%, (b) 3%, (c) 4%, (d) 5%, and (e) 6%, what is the compound interest in each case?
4. On a boy's first birthday his grandfather deposited for him $1000 with a trust company, which pays 4% interest compounded semiannually. How much was to the boy's credit on his eighteenth birthday?
5. Ten years ago a trust fund amounting to $9500 was invested at 3% compounded semiannually. Find the value of the fund now.
6. A certain firm increases its employees' annual salaries 5% each year for the first 15 years of employment. Find the salary, for 1957, of a man who started working for this firm in 1945 at an annual salary of $4000.
7. Use Table II to evaluate $(1.03)^{20}(1.05)^{12}$ correct to four decimal places.
8. If $(1 + i)^{40} = 7.0400$ and $(1 + i)^{30} = 4.3219$, what is the value of $(1 + i)^{70}$ correct to four decimal places?

8 PRESENT VALUE

The *present value* of a sum S due at some future date is the principal P whose compound amount on that date is S. If the due date is t interest periods from now and money is worth i, then, in effect, S is the compound amount of P at the end of t periods at the rate i. Thus we have the general formula met with in Section 7, $S = P(1 + i)^t$, or

$$P = \frac{S}{(1 + i)^t} = S(1 + i)^{-t}.$$

To discount an obligation by using a compound interest rate is to find its value on some date before the due date. The date that one chooses to call the present, in dealing with problems involving money invested at compound interest, is a matter of convenience and is absolutely arbitrary. Hence, if the date on which an obligation is to be discounted is called the present, then to discount the obligation is to find its present value. For this reason the quantity

$(1 + i)^{-t}$ is often called the *discount factor*. Note that $(1 + i)^{-t}$ is actually the present value of \$1 due in t periods with money worth i per period. Table III gives the value of $(1 + i)^{-t}$ for several values of i and values of t from 1 to 100.

Example. What is the present value of \$1000 due at the end of 3 years if money is worth 4% compounded semiannually?

Solution: $S = 1000$, $t = 6$, and $i = 0.02$; substituting in the formula

$$P = S(1 + i)^{-t}$$

we have

$$P = S(1 + i)^{-t} = 1000(1.02)^{-6}$$

or, from Table III,

$$P = 1000(0.887971) = \$887.97.$$

This means that \$887.97 invested now at 4% compounded semiannually will amount to \$1000 at the end of 3 years.

Example.   A \$500 debt bearing 5% interest is due in 4 years. Find the present value of the debt if money is worth 6% converted semiannually.

Solution: First we need to find the maturity value of the debt; for this, $P = 500$, $t = 4$, and $i = 0.05$. Hence

$$S = 500(1.05)^4 = \$607.75.$$

Now we find the present value of \$607.75 at 6% converted semiannually. Here $S = 607.75$, $t = 8$, and $i = 0.03$.
Therefore, $P = 607.75(1.03)^{-8}$, or $P = 607.75(0.78941) = \$479.76.$

EXERCISES

1. What is the value of a \$100 investment at the end of 10 years if it earns 4% the first 6 years and 5% the last 4 years?
2. Smith deposited \$1000 on January 1, 1946, with a trust company paying 3% interest compounded semiannually. Beginning January 1, 1953, the trust company raised its rates to 4% compounded annually. Find the amount to Smith's credit on January 1, 1957.
3. Find the compound amount of \$400 at the end of 20 years for interest at 4% converted quarterly.
4. Use the binomial theorem to compute the value of $(1.02)^{40}$ correct to six decimal places.
5. Find the present value of \$2000 due in 5 years if money is worth 5%.
6. A debt of \$1000, bearing interest at 4% converted semiannually, is due in 5 years. Find the present value of this debt assuming money worth 4%.
7. A debt of \$800 is due in 3 years. Find the present value at **(a)** 5% compound interest and **(b)** 5% simple interest.
8. John borrows \$700 for his last year at college, agreeing to repay it in 5 years with interest at 4%. Three years later he wishes to settle the debt. If it is agreed that money at this time is worth 5% and he is permitted to repay the loan, how much should he pay?

9. Smith borrows $1000 from Jones and gives him a note for $1000 due in 5 years with interest at 5% compounded annually. Two years later Jones sells the note to Brown. If Jones and Brown agree that money is worth 4% compounded semiannually, what does Brown pay for the note?

10. How much should a father deposit in his daughter's name on her first birthday so that she will have $2000 to her credit on her sixteenth birthday if the deposit earns 3% converted semiannually?

11. A lot can be bought for $1125 cash or $1200 due in 2 years. Which is the better proposition if money is worth 4%?

12. Jones has two debts, $1000 due in 1 year and $2000 due in 2 years. If money is worth 5% and he is permitted to pay the debts now, how much will cancel both debts?

9   EQUATION OF VALUE

As has been pointed out, it is desirable to consider a sum of money as a growing quantity. Its value today is different from what it will be a year from today. Two sums of money are said to be equivalent on a certain date if they have the same value on that date, assuming the same rate of interest as the worth of money in both cases. For example, if money is worth 4%, $100 due today is equivalent to $104 due 1 year from today.

If a sum of money has the value X on a certain date and money is assumed to be worth i per period, its value t periods after that date is $X(1 + i)^t$. Its value t periods before that date is $X(1 + i)^{-t}$. Thus, if we know the value of an obligation on any certain date, we can find its value on any other date, given the worth of money. Furthermore, it can be shown that, if two sums of money are equivalent on any one date, they will be equivalent on any other date if compound interest is the basis of our computation of value.

It is often desirable to exchange one set of obligations due at various times for an equivalent set due at various other times. This is referred to as *commuting* the one set of obligations into the other set. The procedure for commuting a set of obligations into another set is first to select a convenient date, known as the *focal date,* and then to determine the second set in such a way that both sets have the same value on the focal date. The equation that expresses this equivalence is called the *equation of value.* The following examples may help to clarify the idea.

Example.   A debt of $200 due 1 year hence and another debt of $500 due 4 years hence are to be discharged by a payment of $300 now and a second payment 3 years hence. If money is worth 5%, how much is this second payment?

Solution: Let x be the amount of the second payment and the time of it, 3 years hence, be the focal date. We now find the value of each obligation at the focal date and determine x so that the sum of the values at the focal date of the original debts is equal to the sum of the values of the two new obligations at the focal date.

Focal date, 3 years hence

Old debts	Value at focal date	New obligations	Value at focal date
\$200 due in 1 year	$200(1.05)^2 = 220.50$	\$300 due now	$300(1.05)^3 = 347.29$
\$500 due in 4 years	$500(1.05)^{-1} = 476.19$	x due in 3 years	x
	Total 696.69		Total $x + 347.29$

The equation of value is $x + 347.29 = 696.69$; hence $x = \$349.40$.

The answer would have been the same had we chosen any other date as focal date.

Example.   A debt of \$1000 due 2 years hence is to be discharged by two equal payments, one due 1 year hence and the other due 3 years hence. If money is worth 4% converted semiannually, how much should each of these payments be?

Solution: Let x be each payment and the time 3 years hence be the focal date.

Focal date, 3 years hence

Old debts	Value at focal date	New obligations	Value at focal date
\$1000 due in 2 years	$1000(1.02)^2 = 1040.40$	x due in 1 year	$x(1.02)^4 = 1.082432x$
		x due in 3 years	x
			Total $2.082432x$

Therefore $2.082432x = 1040.40$ and $x = 1040.40/2.082432 = \$499.61$.

EXERCISES

1. A debt of \$600 is due in 5 years. Given that money is worth 4%, find the value of this debt **(a)** now, **(b)** 2 years hence, **(c)** 4 years hence, **(d)** 5 years hence, and **(e)** 7 years hence.

2. Solve Example 1, using 1 year hence as the focal date.

3. Solve Example 2, assuming the original debt discharged by 3 equal payments, made in 1 year, 2 years, and 3 years.

4. A debt of \$400 due now is to be paid in two equal installments, the first due in 1 year and the second due in 2 years. If money is worth 5%, how much should each of these payments be?

5. Mr. Cox buys a car on the following terms: \$500 down, \$1000 at the end of each year for 2 years. If money is worth 6% converted semiannually, what single cash payment on day of purchase is equivalent to these terms?

6. A debt of \$200 due in 2 years and another of \$400 due in 4 years are to be discharged by a payment of \$100 in 1 year, \$300 in 3 years, and a final payment in 5 years. Assuming money worth 8% converted quarterly, how much should the final payment be?

7. A note for \$800 with interest at 5% is due in 4 years. Assuming money worth 6%, what single payment 2 years hence would settle this debt?

8. John, aged 14, and Carolyn, aged 12, have just inherited an estate of $8000. The will specifies that the money is to be invested at 5% converted annually and that each shall receive the same amount when 21 years of age. How much will each receive?

9. If money is worth 6%, what single payment 3 years hence will settle debts of $400 and $600 due in 2 and 5 years, respectively?

10. If money is worth 5%, when will $1000 cancel the two debts of Exercise 9?

XII

SEQUENCES, SERIES, AND ANNUITIES

1 SEQUENCES

A *sequence of numbers* is an ordered set of numbers $a_1, a_2, a_3, \cdots, a_n, \cdots$, formed by some fixed rule. Some examples of sequences are:

$1, 2, 4, 8, 16, \cdots, 2^{n-1}, \cdots$.
$2, 5, 8, 11, 14, \cdots, (3n - 1), \cdots$.
$7, 3, -1, -5, -9, \cdots, (11 - 4n), \cdots$.
$1, 4, 9, 16, 25, \cdots, n^2, \cdots$.
$12, 6, 3, \dfrac{3}{2}, \dfrac{3}{4}, \cdots, \dfrac{12}{2^{n-1}}, \cdots$.

Usually a sequence is defined by giving a formula for the nth term in terms of n. Then, by assigning to n the values 1, 2, 3, etc., one can obtain the first, second, third, etc. terms. For example, if $a_n = (n + 1)/n$, the sequence is

$$2, \frac{3}{2}, \frac{4}{3}, \frac{5}{4}, \frac{6}{5}, \cdots.$$

The sum

$$a_1 + a_2 + a_3 + \cdots + a_n +$$

of a sequence $a_1, a_2, a_3, \cdots, a^n, \cdots$ is called a *series*. If the number of terms in the series is finite, the series is called a *finite series*. If the number of terms is unlimited, the series is called an *infinite series*.

In this chapter we shall confine our attention to two special types of sequences known as arithmetic progressions and geometric progressions, and to their corresponding series.

2 ARITHMETIC PROGRESSIONS

A sequence, each term of which after the first is obtained from the preceding term by adding a fixed number that is positive, zero, or negative, is called an *arithmetic progression*. We shall hereafter refer to such a progression as an A.P. The fixed number referred to in the definition, being the difference between any two consecutive terms of the sequence, is called the *common difference* of the A.P. If we denote the first term by a and the common difference by d, an A.P. is defined by the sequence

$$a, (a + d), (a + 2d), (a + 3d), \cdots a + (n - 1)d, \cdots,$$

and if we denote the nth term by L we then have the formula

(Eq. 1) $$L = a + (n - 1)d.$$

The L in an A.P. having n terms is often referred to as the last term. It is frequently necessary to find the sum S_n of the first n terms of an A.P. and, if n is large, term-by-term addition becomes laborious. For this reason a formula for S_n is needed. To find such a formula, we first write the sum in the natural order, then in reverse order, and add the two sums term by term, thus:

$$
\begin{aligned}
S_n &= \quad a \quad + (a + d) + (a + 2d) + (a + 3d) \mid \cdots + (L - d) + \quad L \\
S_n &= \quad L \quad + (L - d) + (L - 2d) + (L - 3d) + \cdots + (a + d) + \quad a \\
\hline
2S_n &= (a + L) + (a + L) + (a + L) \ + (a + L) \ + \cdots + (a + L) + (a + L)
\end{aligned}
$$

We observe that the sum of each corresponding pair of terms of the two sums gives rise to the same quantity, $a + L$. Since there were n terms in the original series, we can now write

$$2S_n = n(a + L),$$

(Eq. 2)   or $$S_n = \frac{n}{2}(a + L).$$

Another very useful formula is obtained when, in Equation 2, we replace L by its value from Equation 1 and get

(Eq. 3) $$S_n = \frac{n}{2}[2a + (n - 1)d].$$

It follows from the discussion above that there are five quantities involved in an A.P.; they are

a, the first term,
d, the common difference,
n, the number of terms,

L, the nth or last term,

S_n, the sum of n terms.

These five quantities are connected by Equations 1, 2, and 3; if any three of them are known, the other two can be determined.

Example.   Find the twentieth term and the sum of the first 20 terms of the A.P.

$$2, 5, 8, 11, \cdots.$$

Solution: Here $a = 2, d = 3$, and $n = 20$. To find L, we substitute these values in Equation 1 and get

$$L = 2 + (20 - 1)3 = 59.$$

Similarly, to find S_{20}, we use Equation 2; then

$$S_{20} = \frac{20}{2}(2 + 59) = 610.$$

Example.   If $a = 7, d = -4$, and $S_n = -143$, what are n and L?

Solution: Since Equation 3 involves only one of the two unknowns, we use it to find n. Substituting into Equation 3 we have

$$-143 = \frac{n}{2}[14 + (n - 1)(-4)] = 7n - 2n^2 + 2n,$$

or $2n^2 - 9n - 143 = 0;$
factoring, we have $(2n + 13)(n - 11) = 0.$

Solving for n, we find $n = -13/2$, or $n = 11$.

Since n must be a positive integer, the desired solution is $n = 11$; using this value for n and the given values of a and d, we obtain from Equation 1

$$L = 7 + (11 - 1)(-4) = -33.$$

Example.   Find the sum of all the integers lying between 100 and 600 that end in 3.

Solution: The numbers whose sum we are to calculate obviously define an A.P. with $a = 103$, $d = 10$, and $L = 593$. The value of n can be found either by inspection or by using Equation 1. Let us use Equation 1;

then $593 = 103 + (n - 1)10,$
which gives $10(n - 1) = 593 - 103 = 490$
or $n - 1 = 49,$
and so $n = 50.$

Now applying Equation 2 we have $S_{50} = \dfrac{50}{2}(103 + 593) = 17{,}400.$

Caution: Before attempting to apply Equations 1, 2, and 3 to a given sequence, make sure your sequence is an A.P.; otherwise, these formulas are not valid.

3 ARITHMETIC MEANS

The terms between the first term and the last term of an A.P. are called the *arithmetic means* between those two numbers. The first and last terms are called the *extremes*. In particular, if x, y, and z are any three consecutive terms of an A.P., then y is called the *arithmetic mean* between x and z. It follows from the definition of an A.P. that

$$y - x = z - y$$
$$\text{or} \qquad 2y = x + z;$$
$$\text{hence} \qquad y = \frac{x + z}{2}.$$

The last equation says that the arithmetic mean between two given numbers is the average value of the given numbers. Our definition can now be stated in a more general form.

Definition (Arithmetic Mean)

The numbers $x_1, x_2, x_3, \cdots, x_k$ are k arithmetic means between the two numbers a and L if and only if the sequence $a, x_1, x_2, x_3, \cdots, x_k, L$ is an A.P.

Thus, to insert k arithmetic means between two given numbers x and y, we simply consider the A.P. having $a = x$, $n = k + 2$, and $L = y$ and use Equation 1 of the last section to calculate the common difference d.

Example.   Find the arithmetic mean between -6 and 28.

Solution: Since the arithmetic mean x between two numbers is the average value of the two numbers, we have

$$x = \frac{-6 + 28}{2} = 11.$$

Example.   Insert six arithmetic means between -4 and 17.

Solution: The two given numbers together with the six arithmetic means determine an A.P. of eight terms having $a = -4$, $n = 8$, and $L = 17$:

$$\text{therefore} \quad 17 = -4 + (8 - 1)d,$$
$$\text{or} \qquad 7d = 21,$$
$$\text{whence} \quad d = 3.$$

The six arithmetic means between -4 and 17 are $-1, 2, 5, 8, 11, 14$.

EXERCISES

Show that each of the following sequences is an A.P. and find d, L, and S_n in each case.

1. $1, 2, 3, 4, \cdots, (n = 50)$.
2. $-17, -12, -7, -2, \cdots, (n = 10)$.
3. $10, 7, 4, 1, \cdots, (n = 20)$.
4. $14, 11\frac{1}{2}, 9, 6\frac{1}{2}, \cdots, (n = 21)$.

5. $4.00, 3.80, 3.60, 3.40, \cdots, (n = 40)$.
6. $12, 13.2, 14.4, 15.6, \cdots, (n = 50)$.
7. $-5, -3\frac{1}{2}, -2, -\frac{1}{2}, \cdots, (n = 10)$.

8. Given $a = 5$, $d = -5/2$, and $L = -105$, find n and S_n.
9. The fifth term of an A.P. is 12 and the tenth term is 14. Find the first term and the common difference.
10. Find the arithmetic mean of -17 and 105.
11. Find the arithmetic mean of $a - 3b$ and $a + 5b$.
12. Insert three arithmetic means between 3 and 19.
13. Insert five arithmetic means between 19 and -11.
14. Find the sum of the first 100 positive even integers.
15. Find the sum of all the integers lying between 100 and 500 that are exactly divisible by 7.
16. A man earns \$300 per month as a starting salary and receives a \$10-per-month pay increase at the end of every six months thereafter. What is his salary for the last month of his ninth year? How much does he earn during his first 9 years?

4 GEOMETRIC PROGRESSIONS

A *geometric progression*, abbreviated G.P., is a sequence of numbers in which every term after the first is obtained by multiplying the preceding term by a fixed number. This fixed number is called the *common ratio*. Denoting the first term by a and the common ratio by r, a G.P. is defined by the sequence

$$a, ar, ar^2, ar^3, ar^4, \cdots,$$

each term of which contains r raised to a power that is one less than the number of the term. Hence, if we denote the nth term by L, we have the formula

(Eq. 1) $$L = ar^{n-1}.$$

To obtain a formula for S_n, the sum of the first n terms of the sequence, we first indicate this sum and then rewrite the sequence with *every* term multiplied by r. We next subtract the second expression from the first, observing that all terms cancel in pairs except the first term of the first indicated sum and the last term of the second indicated sum. These operations are performed as follows.

$$S_n = a + ar + ar^2 + ar^3 + \cdots + ar^{n-1}$$
$$rS_n = \phantom{a + {}} ar + ar^2 + ar^3 + \cdots + ar^{n-1} + ar^n$$
subtracting: $\overline{ S_n - rS_n = a - ar^n}$

and the resulting equation, solved for S_n, gives

(Eq. 2) $$S_n = \frac{a - ar^n}{1 - r} = a\,\frac{1 - r^n}{1 - r}, \qquad r \neq 1.$$

Note that Equation 2 is not valid for the special case $r = 1$; however, in such case each term of the G.P. is equal to the first term and we can write

(Eq. 3) $$S_n = na, \qquad r = 1.$$

Another formula which is often useful is obtained if we combine Equations 1 and 2 thus:

(Eq. 4) $$S_n = \frac{a - ar^{n-1}r}{1 - r} = \frac{a - rL}{1 - r},$$

where, just as in the case of an A.P., there are five quantities involved. They are connected by Equations 1 and 2: if any three of the five quantities are known, the remaining two can be determined.

Example. Find the eighth term and the sum of the first eight terms of the G.P.

$$3, -6, 12, -24, \cdots.$$

Solution: Here $a = 3$, and $n = 8$; also $ar = -6$. Therefore $r = -2$. Substituting the values of a, r, and n in Equation 1 we get

$$L = 3(-2)^{8-1} = 3(-2)^7 = 3(-128) = -384.$$

For S_8, we use Equation 2, getting $S_8 = 3 \cdot \dfrac{1 - (-2)^8}{1 - (-2)} = 3 \cdot \dfrac{1 - 256}{3} = -255.$

5   GEOMETRIC MEANS

The terms of a geometric progression between the first term and the last term are called the *geometric means* between these two terms. Thus, to insert k geometric means between any two numbers x and y, we need to consider a G.P. of $k + 2$ terms having $a = x$, $n = k + 2$, and $L = y$, and compute the common ratio r.

If x, y, and z are three consecutive terms of a G.P., then y is called the geometric mean between x and z. From the definition of a G.P., it follows that

$$\frac{y}{x} = \frac{z}{y}, \qquad y^2 = xz,$$

whence $$y = \pm\sqrt{xz},$$

which last equation shows that two real numbers must be either both positive or both negative to have a real geometric mean between them. Furthermore, if two numbers have one real geometric mean between them, they must have two, one positive and one negative.

Example.   Find the geometric mean between 2 and 32.

Solution: Let *y* be a geometric mean between 2 and 32. From our last equation we find the following:

$$y = \pm\sqrt{64} = \pm 8.$$

Example.   Insert three geometric means between 64 and 4.

Solution: We consider a G.P. of five terms with $a = 64$, $L = 4$, and $n = 5$; by Equation 1 of the last section we have

$$4 = 64r^4; \quad \text{thus } r^4 = \tfrac{1}{16} \quad \text{and} \quad r = \pm\tfrac{1}{2}.$$

We then obtain two sets of means, 32, 16, 8 and -32, $+16$, -8.

EXERCISES

Find L and S_n for each of the following geometric progressions.

1. 1, 2, 4, 8, $\cdots$, $(n = 10)$.
2. 81, -27, 9, -3, $\cdots$, $(n = 6)$.
3. 1, $\tfrac{1}{2}$, $\tfrac{1}{4}$, $\tfrac{1}{8}$, $\cdots$, $(n = 8)$.

4. 2, 6, 18, 54, $\cdots$, $(n = 8)$.
5. 8, -4, 2, -1, $\cdots$, $(n = 10)$.
6. 8, 12, 18, 27, $\cdots$, $(n = 6)$.

7. 1, (1.02), $(1.02)^2$, $(1.02)^3$, $\cdots$, $(n = 20)$. (*Hint:*   Use Table II.)
8. $(1.03)^{-1}$, $(1.03)^{-2}$, $(1.03)^{-3}$, $(1.03)^{-4}$, $\cdots$, $(n = 40)$.
9. 50, $50(1.04)$, $50(1.04)^2$, $50(1.04)^3$, $\cdots$, $(n = 24)$.

In each of the following geometric progressions find the quantities indicated.

10. Given $a = 2$, $r = \tfrac{1}{2}$, $L = \tfrac{1}{128}$, find n and S_n.
11. Given $a = 1$, $r = 0.02$, $n = 6$, find L and S_n.
12. Given $r = \tfrac{2}{3}$, $n = 5$, $S_n = 211$, find a and L.
13. Given $a = 256$, $n = 7$, $L = 4$, find r and S_n.
14. Insert two geometric means between 72 and $\tfrac{64}{3}$.
15. Insert five geometric means between 8 and 27.
16. Find the geometric means between 10 and 40.

6   GEOMETRIC SERIES

The indicated sum of the terms of a geometric progression is called a *geometric series*. If the G.P. has a last term, the series is called a *finite geometric series*. If the G.P. has no last term, the corresponding series is called an *infinite geometric series*.

By Equation 2 of Section 4, the sum of the first *n* terms of a G.P. is

$$S_n = \frac{a - ar^n}{1 - r} = \frac{a}{1 - r} - \frac{ar^n}{1 - r}.$$

If $|r| < 1$, then $\lim\limits_{n \to \infty} r^n = 0$; therefore,

$$\lim_{n \to \infty} S_n = \lim_{n \to \infty} \left(\frac{a}{1-r} - \frac{ar^n}{1-r} \right)$$

$$= \frac{a}{1-r}, \quad \text{if } |r| < 1.$$

Denoting this limit by S, we have the following formula:

$$S = \frac{a}{1-r}, \quad |r| < 1.$$

In such a case S is called the *sum* of the infinite series and the series is said to converge. It should be emphasized that we are using the word *sum* here in a completely different sense from that in which it is used for finite addition, that is, in the sense of the limit just defined.

Example. Find the sum of the infinite series

$$1 + \frac{1}{2} + \frac{1}{4} + \frac{1}{8} + \frac{1}{16} + \cdots + \frac{1}{2^{n-1}} + \cdots.$$

Solution: Here $r = \frac{1}{2}$, so the formula given above is valid:

$$S = \frac{1}{1 - \frac{1}{2}} = 2.$$

Decimals that repeat indefinitely a fixed sequence of digits are called *repeating decimals*. Some examples of repeating decimals are

$0.33333\cdots,$
$0.125125125\cdots,$
$1.636363\cdots.$

Since repeating decimals can be written as infinite geometric series with r numerically less than 1, it follows that every repeating decimal can be expressed exactly as a common fraction by the use of the above formula.

Example. Express as a common fraction the repeating decimal $0.636363\cdots$.

Solution: The given decimal can be written as the infinite geometric series

$$0.63 + 0.0063 + 0.000063 + 0.00000063 + \cdots.$$

Here $a = 0.63$ and $r = 0.01$; substituting into the formula, we have

$$S = \frac{0.63}{1 - 0.01} = \frac{0.63}{0.99} = \frac{7}{11}.$$

EXERCISES

Find the sum of each of the following finite series.

1. $1 + (1.05) + (1.05)^2 + \cdots + (1.05)^{19}$.

2. $1 + (1.03)^{-1} + (1.03)^{-2} + (1.03)^{-3} + \cdots + (1.03)^{-40}$.

3. $1 + (1.01)^2 + (1.01)^4 + \cdots + (1.01)^{20}$.

Find the sum of each of the following infinite geometric series.

4. $16 + 8 + 4 + 2 + \cdots + \dfrac{16}{2^{n-1}} + \cdots$.

5. $81 + 27 + 9 + 3 + \cdots + 81(\tfrac{1}{3})^{n-1} + \cdots$.

6. $0.5 + 0.05 + 0.005 + 0.0005 + \cdots + (0.5)(\tfrac{1}{10})^{n-1} + \cdots$.

7. $24 - 12 + 6 - 3 + \cdots + 24(-\tfrac{1}{2})^{n-1} + \cdots$.

8. $3 - 2 + \tfrac{4}{3} - \tfrac{8}{9} + \cdots + 3(-\tfrac{2}{3})^{n-1} + \cdots$.

Express each of the following repeating decimals as a common fraction and use division to check your answer in each case.

9. $0.666666 \cdots$.

10. $0.27272727 \cdots$.

11. $1.727272 \cdots$.

12. $0.388888 \cdots$.

13. $3.2545454 \cdots$.

14. $5.342342342 \cdots$.

15. A total of 250 raffle tickets was sold at all prices, from 1 cent to $2.50. Find the gross receipts.

16. Find the cost of drilling a well 100 feet deep if the cost for drilling the first foot is 35 cents, the second foot 40 cents, the third foot 45 cents, and so on.

17. A sum of $570 is divided among 10 men in such a way that the second receives $10 more than the first, the third receives $10 more than the second, and so on. Find how much the first person received and how much the tenth received.

18. A rubber ball is dropped from a height of 50 feet. Each time the ball hits the ground, it rebounds to a height half as great as that from which it fell. Find how far the ball has traveled when it hits the ground the sixth time. Find how far the ball travels before coming to rest.

19. A man piles 117 logs so that there are 3 logs in the top layer, 4 logs in the second layer, 5 logs in the third layer, and so on. How many layers must he have and how many logs in the bottom layer?

20. What is x when x, $2x + 1$, and $4x - 2$ are three successive terms of an A.P.? Of a G.P.?

21. What is x if $x - 7$, $x + 3$, and $4x - 3$ are three successive terms of a G.P.?

22. Bacteria in milk will, under favorable conditions, double in number every 3 hours. If, in a certain quantity of fresh milk, the bacteria count is 1000 per cubic centimeter, what will it be in 24 hours?

23. If it were possible for a man to save 1 cent the first day of April, 2 cents the second day of April, 4 cents the third day of April, and so on, each day after the first saving twice as much as he saved the preceding day, how much would he have saved at the end of the month?

24. Thirty watermelons are placed in a straight row on the ground at intervals of 10 feet. A truck is parked at the end of the row, 25 feet from the first watermelon. If a man begins at the truck, picks up the watermelons, and carries them one at a time to the truck, what total distance has he walked when he reaches the truck with the last melon?

25. A man's salary was $5000 for the first year. Each year thereafter his salary was increased 10% over what it was the preceding year. What was his salary the sixth year? What was his total salary for the first six years?

26. Find the sum of all the even integers lying between 125 and 475 that are not divisible by 6.

27. If we make 10 annual deposits of $100 each, beginning now, and these draw interest at 3%, converted annually, how much will there be to our credit 20 years from now?

28. Three numbers whose sum is 15 are in arithmetic progression. If 2 is added to the first number, 3 is added to the second number, and 8 is added to the third number, the three new numbers are in geometric progression. Find the original numbers. (*Hint:* Let $a - d$, a, $a + d$ be the original numbers.)

29. A clock strikes the hours from 1 to 12. How many strokes does it make in 24 hours?

30. In a certain school system a new teacher starts at an annual salary of $3000 and is given an annual increase of $100 until a maximum of $4800 is reached. Under this system, what total amount would a teacher be paid for 25 continuous years of service?

31. At the end of each fiscal year a house, which cost $15,000 originally, is depreciated by 10% of the value it had at the beginning of the year. If the house has stood for 10 years, what is its value now?

32. A 10-gallon vat is full of pure alcohol. Two gallons are removed and replaced by 2 gallons of water. The new mixture is stirred well, and again 2 gallons are removed and replaced by 2 gallons of water. If this process is repeated 5 times, how much alcohol remains in the vat?

33. A man owes $1200. He pays $40 on the principal at the end of every month and interest at 6% per year on the amount unpaid during the month. In how many months will his payments be completed and how much will he have paid out in principal and interest?

34. In rolling down a long hill, a ball traveled 10 feet the first second, 25 feet the second second, 40 feet the third second, and so on, until it reached the bottom. How far did it roll during the tenth second and how far in the first 10 seconds?

7 ANNUITIES DEFINED

One of the most common experiences in our daily life is that of paying for something on the installment plan. In fact, many of the things we buy today, such as cars, TV sets, radios, furniture, houses, etc., are bought by making a down payment and agreeing to pay the balance, with interest, in equal payments at regular intervals of time. Most such payments belong to a class of payments called *annuities*. Strictly speaking, the word "annuity" implies annual payments, but we wish to use it in the succeeding sections in a more general sense. We define an annuity as a set of equal payments made at equal intervals of time, regardless of whether the payments are made annually, quarterly, monthly, or otherwise. The important features of an annuity are that the payments are equal and that the payment intervals are of the same length. By the payment interval is meant the period between two successive payments.

8 TYPES OF ANNUITIES

Annuities, generally speaking, are divided into three classes, annuities certain, contingent annuities, and perpetuities.

An *annuity certain* is an annuity whose number of payments, date of first payment, and date of last payment are fixed.

A *contingent annuity* is one whose date of either the first or last payment depends upon some event the date of which cannot be foretold. For example, certain life insurance policies carry the option that, when the insured reaches a stated age, he may elect to receive equal monthly payments as long as he lives; here the date of the last payment depends upon when the insured dies.

A *perpetuity* is an annuity whose payments begin at a fixed date and continue forever. Dividends on preferred stock are an example of a perpetuity.

9   ANNUITIES CERTAIN

According to the definitions given in Sections 7 and 8, an annuity certain is a fixed number of equal payments made at equal intervals of time, the first payment of which is due on a given fixed date. An annuity certain is called a *simple annuity* if the interest period is the same as the payment interval. Hereafter, when the word "annuity" is used in this text, it will mean a simple annuity unless otherwise defined.

In Section 4 of Chapter 11 we established the fundamental principle: *If the value of an obligation on a specific date and the worth of money are known, the value of the obligation can be found on any other date desired.* Now, if we think of the *n* payments of a given annuity as *n* individual payments and use the principle just stated, we can find the value of each of these payments on any arbitrary date, assuming, of course, a mutual agreement as to the worth of money. If a date is selected and the value of each of the payments of an annuity is found on that date, the sum of these values is called the *value of the annuity* on that date. Stated a bit more precisely, *the value of a given annuity on any specific date is that single payment, payable on that date, which is equivalent to the annuity.*

Example.   John deposits $100 on the same date each year for 5 years in a savings account that earns 3% interest converted annually. How much does he have to his credit just after the fifth deposit?

Solution: These five $100 annual deposits form an annuity of 5 payments and the amount John has to his credit just after his fifth deposit is the value of the annuity on the day of the fifth deposit. Let us now determine this value. We observe that the first deposit draws interest for 4 years, the second for 3 years, the third for 2 years, and the fourth for 1 year. The fifth, being due on the day in question, draws no interest. Our calculations may be arranged as follows.

$$
\begin{aligned}
\text{Value of 1st deposit on day of 5th deposit} &= 100(1.03)^4 = \$112.55 \\
\text{Value of 2nd deposit on day of 5th deposit} &= 100(1.03)^3 = \$109.27 \\
\text{Value of 3rd deposit on day of 5th deposit} &= 100(1.03)^2 = \$106.09 \\
\text{Value of 4th deposit on day of 5th deposit} &= 100(1.03) = \$103.00 \\
\text{Value of 5th deposit on day of 5th deposit} & = \$100.00 \\
\hline
\text{Value of the annuity on day of 5th deposit} & = \$530.91
\end{aligned}
$$

Therefore John had $530.91 to his credit just after the fifth deposit.

The procedure used in this example obviously would become long and laborious if the number of payments in the given annuity were large. To shorten the task, let us derive a formula for finding the value of any annuity of n payments on the day of the nth payment. We shall use the following notation in all discussions and problems involving simple annuities.

$R =$ size of each equal payment.

$i =$ interest rate per payment interval.

$n =$ total number of payments in the annuity.

$_nV_k =$ the value of an annuity of n equal payments on the date the kth payment is due.

$_nV_{-k} =$ the value of an annuity of n equal payments on a date k interest periods before the date on which the first payment of the annuity is due.

For example: the symbol $_{10}V_1$ represents the value of an annuity of ten equal payments on the date the first payment is due; $_{10}V_{-1}$ is the value of an annuity of ten equal payments on the date one period before the first payment is due; $_{10}V_{10}$ is the value of an annuity of ten equal payments on the date the last, or tenth, payment is due.

Since the value of an annuity of n equal payments on the date the nth payment is due is denoted by $_nV_n$, our problem is to find a formula for $_nV_n$. We now set up an equation of value, using the day the nth payment is due as focal date. The first payment draws interest for $(n - 1)$ periods; hence its accumulated amount on the focal date is $R(1 + i)^{n-1}$. The second payment draws interest for $n - 2$ periods and its accumulated amount is $R(1 + i)^{n-2}$. Similarly, the third payment draws interest for $n - 3$ periods, the fourth for $n - 4$ periods, etc. The nth payment, being due on the focal date, draws no interest. Our equation of value is

$$_nV_n = R(1 + i)^{n-1} + R(1 + i)^{n-2} + R(1 + i)^{n-3}$$

(Eq. 1)
$$+ \cdots + R(1 + i) + R.$$

Factoring R out of each term in the right member and reversing the order of the terms, we can write this as

$$_nV_n = R[1 + (1 + i) + (1 + i)^2 + \cdots$$

(Eq. 2)
$$+ (1 + i)^{n-2} + (1 + i)^{n-1}],$$

where the terms inside the bracket from a geometric series of n terms with $a = 1$ and $r = (1 + i)$. Using the formula

$$S_n = a\frac{1 - r^n}{1 - r} = a\frac{r^n - 1}{r - 1},$$

for the sum of such a series, we obtain the formula

(Eq. 3)
$$_nV_n = R\frac{(1 + i)^n - 1}{1 + i - 1} = R\frac{(1 + i)^n - 1}{i}.$$

The value of an annuity of n payments on the day of the nth payment is called the *amount of the annuity*. It follows from our last equation that the amount of an annuity of n payments of \$1 each is $[(1 + i)^n - 1]/i$. This quantity has been calculated for various values of i and n, and the results have been made available in tabular form. A brief table of this type is Table VI. By using such a table, values of $_nV_n$ are readily determined without long laborious calculations.

For convenience in writing, let

(Eq. 4) $$s(n, i) = \frac{(1 + i)^n - 1}{i}.$$

Equation 3 can now be written as

(Eq. 5) $$_nV_n = Rs(n, i).$$

Example.   Find the value of an annuity of 40 annual payments of \$200 each on the day the fortieth payment is due, assuming money worth 5% converted annually.

Solution: Substituting into the formula, Equation 5, we have

$$_nV_n = 200s(40, 0.05).$$

From Table VI, $s(40, 0.05) = 120.79977$.
Hence $_nV_n = 200(120.79977) = \$24,159.95$.

EXERCISES

1. What is the value of an annuity, of 20 equal payments of \$50 each, on the day the twentieth payment is due if the payment interval is six months and the interest rate is 4% converted semiannually?
2. What is the amount of an annuity of \$500 per year for 12 years if money is worth 6%?
3. If, beginning in 1957, I deposit \$200 on December 31 of each year with a trust company that pays 3% interest converted annually, how much will be to my credit January 1, 1967?
4. If money is worth 4%, 10 annual payments of \$150 each are equivalent to what single payment due on the same day as the last \$150 payment is made?
5. To provide for the education of his daughter, a man deposits \$400 on each of her birthdays until she is 15 years old. If the deposits earn 3% interest compounded annually, find the amount of the fund just after the last deposit is made.

10   THE PRESENT VALUE OF AN ANNUITY

In the last section we derived a formula for finding the value of an annuity of n payments on the date of the last payment. In many problems involving the paying of an obligation by means of a series of equal periodic payments it is important to have a formula for finding the value of these payments on the date which is one period, or payment interval, before the date of the first payment. The value of an annuity of n payments one payment period before the date the first payment is due is called the *present value* of the annuity and is denoted by $_nV_{-1}$. We now find a formula for $_nV_{-1}$. Consider an annuity of n payments of R dollars each and money worth i per period or payment interval. Take as focal date the date one period before the first payment is due. The value on the focal date of the first payment is $R(1 + i)^{-1}$, the value of the second is $R(1 + i)^{-2}$, the value of the third is $R(1 + i)^{-3}$, etc. The value on the focal date of the nth payment is $R(1 + i)^{-n}$. Writing an equation of value, we have

$$_nV_{-1} = R(1 + i)^{-1} + R(1 + i)^{-2} + R(1 + i)^{-3} + \cdots + R(1 + i)^{-n}.$$

The right member of this equation is a geometric series of n terms with $a = R(1 + i)^{-1}$ and $r = 1(1 + i)^{-1}$. Now using the formula for the sum of a geometric series, we get

$$_nV_{-1} = R(1 + i)^{-1} \cdot \frac{1 - (1 + i)^{-n}}{1 - (1 + i)^{-1}} = \frac{R}{1 + i} \cdot \frac{1 - (1 + i)^{-n}}{1 - (1 + i)^{-1}}.$$

Multiplying the denominators of the product on the right, we have the following formula:

(Eq. 1) $$_nV_{-1} = R\left[\frac{1 - (1 + i)^{-n}}{1 + i - 1}\right] = R\left[\frac{1 - (1 + i)^{-n}}{i}\right],$$

where the quantity $[1 - (1 + i)^{-n}]/i$ is the present value of an annuity of n payments of \$1 each where money is worth i per period. For convenience, we denote this quantity by $a(n, i)$; thus,

(Eq. 2) $$a(n, i) = \frac{1 - (1 + i)^{-n}}{i}.$$

Our formula now becomes

(Eq. 3) $$_nV_{-1} = Ra(n, i).$$

The values of $a(n, i)$ has been tabulated for various values of i and successive values of n. Table VII is such a table. For values of i not in the table, logarithms can be employed in conjunction with Equation 3, to compute the value of $_nV_{-1}$.

The formula, Equation 3, involves the four quantities $_nV_{-1}$, R, n, and i, and if any three of these quantities are known the fourth can be determined.

Example. A house can be bought by paying \$2000 down and \$500 at the end of every six months for 10 years. What is the equivalent cash value of the house, assuming money worth 4% converted semiannually and the first \$500 payment is due six months after date of purchase?

Solution: The equivalent cash value of the house is the present value of the \$500 payments plus the \$2000 down payment. We use our last formula to find the present value of the $500 payments. Here $R = 500$, $n = 20$, $i = 0.02$; substituting these values into the formula, we get

$$_{20}V_{-1} = 500a(20, 0.02).$$

From Table VII, $a(20, 0.02) = 16.35143$; hence

$$_{20}V_{-1} = 500(16.35143) = \$8176,$$

rounding off the answer to the nearest dollar. Thus the equivalent cash value of house $= \$8176 + \$2000 = \$10,176$.

Example.   Mr. Smith buys a car, the cash price of which is $2375. He agrees to pay $750 down and the balance with interest at 6% converted quarterly in 8 equal quarterly payments, the first due three months after date of purchase. Find the size of the quarterly payment.

Solution: The balance after the down payment is $2375 − \$750 = \$1625$. This is the present value of the 8 quarterly payments. Thus, in the formula, $_nV_{-1} = 1625$, $n = 8$, and $i = 0.015$; substituting these values into the formula and solving for R, we find

$$R = \frac{1625}{a(8, 0.015)} = \frac{1625}{7.48592} = \$217.07.$$

Example.   A loan of $2500 with interest at 4% converted quarterly is to be repaid by equal quarterly payments of $100 each, the first due three months from the date of loan. Find the number of full $100 payments needed in paying the loan.

Solution: Here $_nV_{-1} = 2500$, $R = 100$, and $i = 0.01$; substituting these values into the formula, Equation 3, we have $2500 = 100a(n, 0.01)$.
Solving for $a(n, 0.01)$, we get $a(n, 0.01) = 25$.
We now find n by inspecting Table VII. The values of $a(n, 0.01)$ are found in the 1% column. The number 25 is not found, but the first entry less than 25 is 24.3164, and the corresponding value of n is 28. Hence, 28 full $100 payments plus a final smaller payment will be needed to repay the loan.

Returning again to the formula for $_nV_n$ (Section 9), namely $_nV_n = Rs(n, i)$, we observe that it likewise involves four quantities, $_nV_n$, R, n, and i; when any three of these quantities are known, the fourth also can be determined.

EXERCISES

1.   Find the present value of **(a)** $100 a year for 7 years at 6%, **(b)** $50 every half-year for 7 years at 6% converted semiannually, and **(c)** $25 every three months for 7 years at 6% converted quarterly.
2.   Find the equivalent cash price of a house that may be purchased for $2500 down and payments of $500 every six months for 10 years. Assume that money is worth 6% converted semiannually and the first $500 payment is to be made six months after the down payment.
3.   A life insurance company settles a $15,000 claim by making 20 semiannual

payments, the first due six months hence. What is the semiannual payment if money is worth 8% converted semiannually?

4. A loan of $2000, bearing interest at 4% converted quarterly, is to be paid by payments of $200 at the end of every three months. What is the number of $200 payments if the first $200 payment is due three months from the date of loan?

5. A fund is being created to pay a debt of $3000 due in 15 years. If the fund is invested at 6% converted semiannually, what is the semiannual payment to be made to the fund at the end of every six months?

6. What is the cash price of a lot which is equivalent to $50 down and payments of $75 at the end of every three months thereafter for 5 years, if money is worth 8% converted quarterly?

7. A man pays $150 at the end of every six months for 10 years to a building and loan association which pays 4% interest compounded semiannually. What will his stock be worth at the end of this time?

8. A certain bond, if bought now, will pay dividends of $2 every three months for 20 years and a final additional payment of $110 at the end of 20 years. Find the present value of this bond and dividends to a man who is able to invest money at 4% converted quarterly.

9. A man borrows $10,000 with interest at 7% converted quarterly. He agrees to pay equal installments of $500 each, beginning three months hence, every three months as long as necessary. How many full $500 installments must be paid?

10. If a man deposits $100 at the end of every three months in a savings account that earns 4% converted quarterly, how long will it take for him to have $3000 to his credit?

11   FINDING THE VALUE OF AN ANNUITY ON ANY DATE

We have already derived formulas for finding the value of an annuity on both the date the last payment is due and the date one period before the first payment is due. We wish now to show how we may use the two formulas we already have to obtain the value of an annuity on any date. To keep our discussion as simple as possible, we shall confine ourselves to dates that are an integral number of payment periods from either of the two dates on which our given formulas apply.

First let us represent by a line diagram an annuity of n payments and indicate the two dates on which our known formulas are valid. In Fig. 12.1, a cross mark indicates a payment date where a payment of R dollars is due, a dot indicates the end of a payment period but where no payment is due.

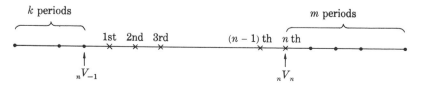

FIGURE 12.1

Suppose, for example, we wish the value of the annuity on a date that is m periods after the date the last payment is due. First we find the value on the date of the last payment and then accumulate the amount found for m more periods at the given interest rate. Since the value on the date of the nth payment is, as we have found (Section 9),

(Eq. 1) $$_nV_n = Rs(n, i),$$

the value m periods later, denoted by $_nV_{n+m}$, is found by multiplying $_nV_n$ by the accumulation factor $(1 + i)^m$. Thus

(Eq. 2) $$_nV_{n+m} = {_nV_n}(1 + i)^m.$$

Example. A contract calls for 10 annual payments of $200 each, the first due 1 year hence. If money is worth 5% converted annually, what single payment 15 years hence could replace this contract?

Solution: We first find the value of the contract on the date the last payment is due. Here $R = 200$, $n = 10$, $i = 0.05$; hence $_nV_n = 200s(10, 0.05)$.
From Table VI, $s(10, 0.05) = 12.577893$, so $_nV_n = 200(12.57789) = \$2515.58$.
From Equation 2, with $m = 5$, we have $_nV_{n+m} = 2515.58(1.05)^5 = \$3210.59$.

Suppose, next, that we wish to find the value of an annuity of n payments on the date the kth payment is due, where k is less than n. Our problem becomes very simple if we consider our annuity as two annuities, the first one consisting of the first k payments and the second consisting of the last $n - k$ payments. The value of the first annuity on the date the kth payment is due is $Rs(k, i)$. The value of the second annuity on this same date is $Ra(n - k, i)$. Hence the value $_nV_k$ of the original annuity on the date the kth payment is due is

$$_nV_k = Rs(k, i) + Ra(n - k, i),$$

(Eq. 3)   or $$_nV_k = R[s(k, i) + a(n - k, i)].$$

Example. A contract calls for 20 semiannual payments of $100 each. Find the single payment, due on the date the twelfth payment of the annuity is due, which is equivalent to the annuity if money is worth 4% converted semiannually.

Solution: We use Equation 3 with $R = 100$, $n = 20$, $k = 12$, $n - k = 8$, and $i = 0.02$:

(Eq. 4) $$_nV_k = 100[s(12, 0.02) + a(8, 0.02)].$$

From Tables VI and VII we find

$$s(12, 0.02) = 13.412090$$
and $$a(8, 0.02) = 7.325481$$
adding, $$s(12, 0.02) + a(8, 0.02) = 20.737571.$$

Therefore, $_nV_k = 100(20.73757) = \$2073.76$.

If, in Equation 3 we let $k = 1$, a formula for the value of an annuity on the date the first payment is due is obtained. Thus,

$$_nV_1 = R[s(1, i) + a(n - 1, i)].$$

But $s(1, i) = 1$ for all values of i; hence

(Eq. 5) $$_nV_1 = R[a(n - 1, i) + 1].$$

Finally, let us find the value $_nV_{-(k+1)}$ of an annuity of n payments on a date that is $k + 1$ periods before the date the first payment is due. We start by finding the value of the annuity one period before the date the first payment is due. This value is, as we have found (Section 10),

(Eq. 6) $$_nV_{-1} = Ra(n, i),$$

and so, to find $_nV_{-(k+1)}$, we simply need to discount $_nV_{-1}$ for k periods at the given interest rate. This is done by multiplying $_nV_{-1}$ by $(1 + i)^{-k}$:

(Eq. 7) $$_nV_{-(k+1)} = {}_nV_{-1}(1 + i)^{-k},$$

which can be combined with Equation 6 in a manner similar to the way we combined Equations 1 and 2 above. To do this, we proceed as follows: substituting the value of $_nV_{-1}$ in Equation 7, we obtain

$$_nV_{-(1+k)} = Ra(n, i)(1 + i)^{-k}.$$

Replacing $a(n, i)$ by its value, we have

$$_nV_{-(1+k)} = R\frac{1 - (1 + i)^{-n}}{i}(1 + i)^{-k},$$

or $$_nV_{-(1+k)} = R\frac{(1 + i)^{-k} - (1 + i)^{-n-k}}{i}.$$

Adding and subtracting 1 in the numerator of the right side of the last equation and rearranging, we obtain

$$_nV_{-(1+k)} = R\left[\frac{1 - (1 + i)^{-(n+k)}}{i} - \frac{1 - (1 + i)^{-k}}{i}\right]$$

(Eq. 8)   or $$_nV_{-(1+k)} = R[a(n + k, i) - a(k, i)].$$

Example.   What is the value now of an annuity of 10 annual payments of $500 each if the first payment is due 5 years hence and money is worth 6%?

Solution: Here $R = 500$, $n = 10$, $k = 4$, $i = 0.06$; substituting these values into Equation 8, we have the equation

$$_nV_{-(1+k)} = 500[a(14, 0.06) - a(4, 0.06)].$$

From Table VII we find

$$a(14, 0.06) = 9.294984$$
and
$$a(4, 0.06) = 3.465106$$
and subtracting, $$a(14, 0.06) - a(4, 0.06) = 5.829878.$$

Therefore, $_nV_{-(1+k)} = 500(5.829878) = \$2914.94$.

As a sort of summary of our annuity formulas, let us redraw our line diagram, indicating on it where each of our formulas applies: Fig. 12.2.

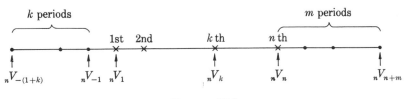

FIGURE 12.2

Each cross mark indicates where a payment of R dollars is due. A dot indicates the end of an interest period, but where no payment is due.

EXERCISES

1. A contract calls for 15 annual payments of $100 each, the first due 4 years hence. If money is worth 5%, this annuity may be equitably replaced by what single payment due **(a)** now, **(b)** 3 years hence, **(c)** 4 years hence, **(d)** 10 years hence, **(e)** 18 years hence, and **(f)** 19 years hence?

2. Since 1950 John has been depositing $200 in a savings account on January 1 of each year. If he continues this practice and his savings earn 3% converted annually, how much will he have to his credit December 31, 1960?

3. Mr. Smith owes $2000 which he wishes to pay in 20 equal quarterly installments, the first due at once. If he is permitted to do this and it is agreed that money is worth 4% converted quarterly, what is the size of the quarterly payments?

4. A man wishes to provide for his son's college education by investing some money now in a trust fund that earns 4% converted semiannually. If the son is 14 years old now, how much should his father invest to provide him with 8 semiannual payments of $1000 each, the first due when the son reaches 18 years of age, 4 years hence?

5. A house is leased for 5 years at $800 payable annually in advance. Find the cash equivalent of this lease if money is worth 6%.

6. A television set is bought at an installment price of $20 a month for eighteen months, the first payment due at the time of purchase. If interest at 12% converted monthly is charged, what should be the cash price of this set?

7. A sum of $1000 is deposited with a trust company that pays 4% interest converted quarterly. This is to provide a quarterly income of $50, the first due in 5 years. How long will the payments continue?

8. Instead of a cash settlement of $5000, the beneficiary of a life insurance policy elects to receive 40 equal quarterly payments, the first due three months hence. If the company allows 4% interest, converted quarterly, what will each payment be?

9. A young couple wishes to accumulate $4000 to use as a down payment, 5 years hence, on a house. How much should they deposit at the beginning of every six months for 5 years? Interest on the savings is 3% converted semiannually.

10. A contract calls for 20 quarterly payments of $200 each, the first due three months hence. If, instead of following this schedule, a single payment of $1000 is made 1 year hence and another single payment of $2000 is made 3 years hence, what final payment 5 years hence will close the transaction? Assume money worth 4% converted quarterly.

11. What equal quarterly payments, made each quarter for 10 years, will pay for a $10,000 house if the first payment is made on the day of purchase and interest is at 6% converted quarterly?

12. An annuity of $200 every two months, the first payment due January 1, 1958, is equivalent at 6% converted bimonthly to what single payment due (a) July 1, 1957, (b) November 1, 1957, (c) January 1, 1958, (d) January 1, 1960, and (e) January 1, 1968, if last payment is due January 1, 1960?

13. A county owes $100,000 which it wishes to pay in 5 equal annual payments, the first due 1 year hence. Find the annual payment if the debt bears 3% interest converted annually.

14. Mr. Jones owes a debt due in 5 years, the maturity value of which is $2000. He wishes to pay this debt in 10 equal semiannual installments, the first due in six months. If money is worth 6% converted semiannually, find the size of these semiannual payments.

12 AMORTIZATION OF A DEBT

By the *amortization* of an interest-bearing debt we shall mean the extinction of the debt, principal, and interest on outstanding principal, by a series of equal payments made at equal intervals. These periodic payments form an annuity whose present value is the principal of the debt. This method of extinguishing a debt is one of the most important applications of annuities.

One of the common problems in connection with the amortization of a debt is to find the periodic payment when the principal of the debt, the interest rate, and the number of payments are known. We shall illustrate by an example.

Example. A debt of $2000, bearing 4% interest converted quarterly, is to be amortized by 12 equal quarterly payments, the first due three months hence. Find the quarterly payment.

Solution: The 12 equal payments form an annuity whose present value is $2000; then $_nV_{-1} = 2000$, $n = 12$, and $i = 0.01$, and therefore $2000 = Ra(12, 0.01)$.

Solving for R, we have $R = \dfrac{2000}{a(12, 0.01)} = \dfrac{2000}{11.25508} = \$177.70.$

For accounting purposes each periodic payment is divided into two parts, a payment of interest on outstanding principal during the period and a reduction of the principal. Thus, another problem of importance is that of finding the outstanding principal for any period.

Example. What is the outstanding principal in the first example, above, just after the eighth payment? How much of the ninth payment is applied to payment of interest and how much to reduction of principal?

Solution: The outstanding principal just after the eighth payment obviously is the value on that date of the remaining 4 payments. This is simply the present value of the annuity formed by these 4 payments. Hence,

$$_4V_{-1} = 177.70a(4, 0.01) = 177.70(3.9020) = \$693.38.$$

This means that immediately after the eighth payment is made the debt could be canceled by payment of an additional $693.38. The interest on $693.38 for 1 period at 1% is $6.93. Thus $6.93 of the ninth payment applies to paying the interest for the ninth period; the remainder, $177.70 - \$6.93 = \$170.77$, is applied to the reduction of the principal.

Another type of problem that often arises is the following. A debtor can pay only a given amount periodically. How many such payments will be required to amortize the debt? This problem is equivalent to the problem of finding n when $_nV_{-1}$, R, and i are known. In general, it will be found that a certain number of full payments plus a smaller final payment will be needed. If such is the case, we shall assume that the final payment is due one period after the last full payment.

Example.   Suppose the debt in our first example is to be amortized by quarterly payments of $100 each, the first due in three months. Find **(a)** the number of full $100 payments, **(b)** the outstanding principal just after the last full payment is made, and **(c)** the concluding payment.

Solution: **a.**   Here $_nV_{-1} = 2000$, $R = 100$, and $i = 0.01$, and we are to find n; using the formula for $_nV_{-1}$, we have

$$2000 = 100a(n, 0.01),$$
$$a(n, 0.01) = 20.$$

From the 1% column of Table VII, we find

$$a(22, 0.01) = 19.660379 \quad \text{and} \quad a(23, 0.01) = 20.455821.$$

From this it follows that 22 payments of $100 each plus a final smaller payment will be needed.

b.   The method used in the second example above for finding the outstanding principal does not apply here, since the final payment is unknown as yet. However, the outstanding principal in this type problem can be found in the following way. Find the accumulated value of the original principal as if no payments had been made. In the particular problem at hand, this is

$$2000(1.01)^{22} = 2000(1.244716) = \$2489.43.$$

Next find the amount of an annuity of 22 payments of $100 each at 1% per period. We find $100s(22, 0.01) = 100(24.47159) = \$2447.16$.

The outstanding principal just after the twenty-second payment is $2489.43 - \$2447.16 = \$42.27$. Hence the concluding payment due one period later is $42.27 + (0.01)(42.27) = \$42.69$.

EXERCISES

1. A loan of $1000, with interest at 6% payable semiannually, is to be amortized by equal payments at the end of every six months for 4 years. What is the semiannual payment if the first payment is due six months after the date of loan?
2. In Exercise 1, what is the outstanding principal just after the fifth payment? How much of the sixth payment applies to interest and how much to reducing principal?
3. A $3000 loan, bearing 4% interest payable quarterly, is to be amortized by quarterly payments of $100 each. Find the number of full $100 payments, the first payment being made three months after date of loan.
4. Suppose the debtor in Exercise 3 omits the fourteenth, fifteenth, sixteenth, and seventeenth payments. (a) What should he pay on the day the eighteenth payment is due, including the eighteenth, to bring his payments up to schedule? (b) What is the outstanding principal just after the eighteenth payment?
5. A loan of $10,000 is to be repaid, principal and interest, in equal annual installments at the end of every year for 12 years, the first due 1 year after loan, with interest at 4%. Find the amount remaining unpaid just after the eighth payment. How much of the ninth payment is applied to interest and how much to reduction of principal?
6. A certain loan is to be amortized by 20 quarterly payments of $200 each, the first due 4 years hence, and a payment of $1000 due 9 years hence. What additional payment, along with the twelfth quarterly payment, would cancel the remainder of the debt? Interest is at 6% converted quarterly.
7. A small loan company lends $1000 at 12% payable monthly. It is to be repaid by 50 equal monthly payments, the first due one month after date of loan. (a) Find the size of the monthly payment. (b) What is the outstanding principal just after the thirtieth payment? (c) How much of the thirty-first payment applies to interest and how much to reduction of principal?
8. In Exercise 7, how much of the original principal will have been repaid just after the twentieth payment?
9. In Exercise 7, if the debtor omits the last 10 payments, how much would he owe on the day the fiftieth payment was originally due?
10. A debt of $2000, bearing 6% interest payable semiannually, is to be amortized by payments of $200 at the end of every six months, the first due now. Find the number of $200 payments and the concluding payment.
11. A $20,000 debt is to be amortized by equal annual payments for 20 years, the first due now. If interest is at 5% payable annually, what is the size of the annual payment? How much of the debt has been paid just after the tenth payment?
12. To repay a $3000 loan and 4% interest payable semiannually, Jones will pay $200 every six months for 3 years and $400 every six months after that. Find the number of $400 payments and the concluding payment if the first $200 payment is made six months after the date of loan.
13. A $2000 loan, bearing interest at 6% payable quarterly, is to be amortized by equal quarterly payments for 5 years, the first due three months after date of loan. Find the quarterly payment.

XIII

EXPONENTIAL AND LOGARITHMIC FUNCTIONS

1 INTRODUCTION

In Chapter XI we learned that money invested at compound interest is a growing quantity. Although the percentage rate remains constant, the total value of the investment grows faster and faster. In fact, the total rate of growth, measured in dollars per year, during any interest period, is a fixed percent of the amount accumulated at the beginning of that period. Thus, for the same nominal rate of interest, the greater the frequency of conversion, the greater is the total rate of growth of the investment.

For example, if money is invested at 6% converted annually, the total rate of growth of the investment (number of dollars per year) at any instant during the year is 6% of the value of the investment at the beginning of the year. If the interest is compounded semiannually, the total rate of growth of the investment at any instant will be 6% of the accumulation at the beginning of the half-year containing the instant in question. Similarly, if the conversion is monthly or daily or hourly or, in fact, of any frequency, the total rate of growth of the investment during any conversion period is 6% of the compound amount at the beginning of that conversion period. The total rate of growth in each of these cases may be considered the average total rate of growth over an interval, the interval being the conversion period in question. Hence, to obtain an instantaneous total rate of growth, we need to use a limiting process; that is, we need to find the limit approached by the average total rate of growth over a conversion period as the length of the conversion period is made to approach zero or, what is the same thing, as the frequency of conversion is increased indefinitely. The result of increasing the frequency indefinitely is called *compounding continuously*. We next consider the effect of compounding continuously.

2 COMPOUNDING CONTINUOUSLY

In Chapter XI, Section 7, we found that the compound amount of an original principal P at the end of t interest periods at the interest rate i per period is given by the formula $S = P(1 + i)^t$. Further, if r is the nominal rate of interest and k is the frequency of conversion, then $r = ki$. Hence the compound amount at the end of 1 year is

$$S = P\left(1 + \frac{r}{k}\right)^k.$$

Let us first consider the special case in which $P = 1$ and $r = 100\% = 1$. Our last equation then becomes

$$S = \left(1 + \frac{1}{k}\right)^k.$$

We are now concerned with two questions regarding this formula. First, does

$$\lim_{k \to \infty} \left(1 + \frac{1}{k}\right)^k$$

exist? Second, if so, what is this limit? We wish now to give some evidence in support of the contention that the limit does exist and also to obtain some notion of its value. Let us expand $(1 + 1/k)^k$, using the method for expanding a binomial given in Chapter III. We get

$$\left(1 + \frac{1}{k}\right)^k = 1^k + k(1^{k-1})\left(\frac{1}{k}\right) + \frac{k(k-1)}{2}(1^{k-2})\left(\frac{1}{k}\right)^2$$

$$+ \frac{k(k-1)(k-2)}{2\cdot 3}(1^{k-3})\left(\frac{1}{k}\right)^3 + \cdots$$

$$+ \frac{k(k-1)(k-2)\cdots[k-(k-1)]}{2\cdot 3\cdot 4 \cdots (k-2)(k-1)k}\left(\frac{1}{k}\right)^k,$$

whose right member we may simplify so that we have

$$\left(1 + \frac{1}{k}\right)^k = 2 + \frac{(1 - 1/k)}{2} + \frac{(1 - 1/k)(1 - 2/k)}{2\cdot 3} + \cdots$$

$$+ \frac{(1 - 1/k)(1 - 2/k)\cdots[1 - (k-1)/k]}{2\cdot 3\cdot 4 \cdots (k-2)(k-1)k}.$$

We observe from this equation that each term of the expansion is positive and increases with k; hence $(1 + 1/k)^k$ increases as k increases. Further, $(1 + 1/k)^k = 2$ when $k = 1$, and each of the factors $(1 - 1/k)$, $(1 - 2/k)$, $\cdots$, $[1 - (k - 1)/k]$ is positive and less than 1. Therefore, if we replace each factor by 1, we can write

$$\left(1 + \frac{1}{k}\right)^k < 2 + \frac{1}{2} + \left(\frac{1}{2}\right)\left(\frac{1}{3}\right) + \left(\frac{1}{2}\right)\left(\frac{1}{3}\right)\left(\frac{1}{4}\right) + \cdots$$
$$+ \left[\left(\frac{1}{2}\right)\left(\frac{1}{3}\right)\left(\frac{1}{4}\right) \cdots \left(\frac{1}{k}\right)\right],$$

whose right member is, in turn, less than the following sum

$$2 + \frac{1}{2} + \left(\frac{1}{2}\right)\left(\frac{1}{2}\right) + \left(\frac{1}{2}\right)\left(\frac{1}{2}\right)\left(\frac{1}{2}\right) + \cdots + \left[\left(\frac{1}{2}\right)\left(\frac{1}{2}\right)\left(\frac{1}{2}\right) \cdots \left(\frac{1}{2}\right)\right],$$

obtained by replacing each fractional factor of the inequality by $\frac{1}{2}$. This sum can be written

$$2 + \frac{1}{2} + \frac{1}{4} + \frac{1}{8} + \cdots + \frac{1}{2^{k-1}},$$

which shows it to be less than 3, no matter how large k may become. Hence, for k any positive integer,

$$\left(1 + \frac{1}{k}\right)^k < 3.$$

We have now shown the following three facts:

$(1 + 1/k)^k = 2$ when $k = 1$.
$(1 + 1/k)^k$ increases as k increases.
$(1 + 1/k)^k < 3$ for k any positive integer.

Therefore it seems reasonable to conclude that $\lim\limits_{k \to \infty} (1 + 1/k)^k$ does exist and that the value of the limit is a number greater than 2 and less than or equal to 3. It can be proved that this is indeed true. In fact, it can be shown that

(Eq. 1)
$$\lim_{k \to \infty} \left(1 + \frac{1}{k}\right)^k = e,$$

where e is an irrational number, whose value correct to five decimal places is

$$e = 2.71828,$$

and which, like the number π, plays an important role in mathematics. In our discussion of this limit, k was assumed to be a positive integer. This restriction is, however, not necessary. The same limit e exists if k is allowed to increase numerically through either positive or negative real values; in fact,

$$\lim_{|x| \to \infty} \left(1 + \frac{1}{x}\right)^x = e.$$

Returning to Equation 1 above, this means that \$1 invested at 100% interest compounded continuously will amount, at the end of 1 year, to $e = \$2.72$, rounded off to the nearest cent.

We wish now to find the amount at the end of t years of any original principal P invested at the nominal interest rate r compounded continuously. It is easily shown that the compound amount in t years of P dollars invested at the nominal rate r compounded k times per year is

(Eq. 2)
$$S = P\left(1 + \frac{r}{k}\right)^{kt},$$

and to find the amount when the interest is compounded continuously we need to find the limit

$$\lim_{k \to \infty} P\left(1 + \frac{r}{k}\right)^{kt}.$$

To do this, let $k = rx$; then $r/k = 1/x$ and $kt = rtx$. Therefore,

$$P\left(1 + \frac{r}{k}\right)^{kt} = P\left(1 + \frac{1}{x}\right)^{rtx} = P\left[\left(1 + \frac{1}{x}\right)^{x}\right]^{rt}.$$

Since r is to remain fixed, x must become infinite as k becomes infinite, and thus we have

$$\lim_{k \to \infty} P\left(1 + \frac{r}{k}\right)^{kt} = \lim_{x \to \infty} P\left[\left(1 + \frac{1}{x}\right)^{x}\right]^{rt} = P\left[\lim_{x \to \infty} \left(1 + \frac{1}{x}\right)^{x}\right]^{rt} = P(e)^{rt}.$$

That is,

(Eq. 3)
$$S = Pe^{rt}.$$

It is important to note that, since Equation 2 is strictly correct at the end of any conversion period, Equation 3 is correct for all values of t and not just for integral or rational values of t. This means that, if the interest is compounded continuously, the compound amount grows continuously, its value at any instant being given by Equation 3. Furthermore, the total rate of growth per year at any time within a conversion period, of an investment accumulating at a nominal interest rate r converted k times per year, is equal to r times the compound amount at the beginning of the interest period involved. It follows, therefore, that if the interest is compounded continuously the total rate of growth per year is at any instant equal to r times the compound amount at that instant. In other words, the total rate of growth per year in the case of interest compounded continuously is an instantaneous rate or, in the language of Chapter VII, it is the derivative of the amount S with respect to the time t. In symbols,

$$D_t S = rS;$$

thus, since
$$S = Pe^{rt},$$

(Eq. 4)

we have
$$D_t(Pe^{rt}) = rPe^{rt}.$$

Conversely, if any quantity increases with time in such a way that its rate of change per year (or per hour or per any convenient unit of time) is a constant percentage of the value of Q at that instant, then Q obeys a law of the form

$$(\text{Eq. 5}) \qquad\qquad Q = Q_0 e^{rt},$$

where Q_0 is the value of Q when $t = 0$, r is the constant percentage rate, and t is the time measured in some suitable units. If Q decreases at a constant percentage rate instead of increasing, Equation 5 still holds but r is then negative.

Obviously, one would never expect the bank or the building and loan association to convert one's interest continuously, but many quantities in nature do grow in just such a manner. Some examples are the number of bacteria in a culture, the number of cells in the body, the weight of a growing organism, or even the total human population, which actually increases almost continuously at a fairly steady percentage rate. In fact, the quantities in nature that grow in such a way are so numerous that Equation 5 is often referred to as the *law of growth*. It is also called the *compound interest law* or, abbreviated, "C.I.L."

Example.   The number of bacteria N in a culture increased at an instantaneous rate per hour, constantly equal to 30% of N. If at time $t = 0$, $N = 500$, what is the formula which gives N at any time t hours later?

Solution: Here we use Equation 5 with $Q = N$, $Q_0 = 500$, and $r = 0.3$; then

$$N = 500e^{0.3t}.$$

All radioactive substances disintegrate at a rate that is constantly equal to some percentage of the amount of the substance remaining; thus all such substances follow the law of growth also, but with r negative.

Example.   Radium decomposes at a time rate per 100 years which at any instant is about 4% of the amount remaining. Write a formula for the amount of the original 1000 milligrams remaining after t centuries.

Solution: Let Q milligrams be the amount remaining at time t; then $r = -0.04$ and $Q_0 = 1000$, and so $Q = 1000e^{-0.04t}$.

Note that the unit of time here is 100 years.

3   EXPONENTIAL FUNCTIONS

In the previous chapters we have discussed functions that could be expressed as a sum of terms of the type kx^n. Any term of this type is called *a power function*, which is characterized by the property that a variable base x is raised to a constant power n. The law of growth introduces a new kind of function, of the form e^x, called an *exponential function*. Here the base is a constant and the exponent is a variable. In general, an exponential function is a constant base, not necessarily e, raised to a variable power. Functions like e^x, 2^x, 3^{x^2}, a^t, 10^{2t}, etc. are exponential functions. For the present we shall restrict our discussion of exponential functions to the case in which the constant base is e. To solve problems involving exponential functions, we need to be able to evaluate these functions. Exponential functions play such an important role in mathematics that the values of e^x and e^{-x} have been computed for many values of x and made available in the form of a table, as was done for trigonometric functions, accumulation factors, and discount factors. Table IV gives the approximate values of e^x and e^{-x} for values of x from $x = 0$ to $x = 10$ for each successive hundredth. By interpolation this can be extended to each successive thousandth.

Example. Use Table IV to evaluate $e^{1.74}$ and $e^{-1.74}$.

Solution: Here $x = 1.74$. We find 1.74 in the x column and read the value of $e^{1.7}$ in the e^x column, and we find $e^{1.74} = 5.6973$.
Similarly, we find from the e^{-x} column that $e^{-1.74} = 0.17552$.

Example. In the first example of Section 2, find the number of bacteria in the culture at the end of 5 hours.

Solution: We found that the number of bacteria at the end of t hours was given by the formula $N = 500e^{0.3t}$; substituting $t = 5$, we get $N = 500e^{1.5}$.
From Table IV we find $e^{1.5} = 4.4817$, and hence $N = 500(4.4817) = 2241$, approximately.

EXERCISES

1. From Table IV find the approximate value of each of the following, using straight-line interpolation where necessary.

    a. $e^{0.07}$.   **c.** $e^{7.82}$.   **e.** $e^{-9.85}$.   **g.** $e^{-1.634}$.

    b. $e^{-0.05}$.   **d.** $e^{9.95}$.   **f.** $e^{2.345}$.

2. Assuming that the number of bacteria in a certain culture grows at a rate per hour that is constantly equal to 20% of the number then present, find a formula for the number present after t hours if $N = 1000$ when $t = 0$. Also find the number present when $t = 10$ and when $t = 20$.

3. **a.** Find a formula for the amount after t years of $2000 with interest at 6% converted continuously. How much is this after 10 years?

    b. What would the amount be after 10 years if the interest is at 6% converted semiannually?

4. Radium decomposes at a rate per century that is constantly equal to 3.8% of the quantity remaining at that time. How much will be left after 6000 years from an original 400 milligrams?

5. A certain house cost $20,000 to build. If it depreciates at an instantaneous rate per year that is constantly equal to 5% of the value V of the house at that instant, what is the value of the house at the end of 10 years?

6. The population of a certain city in 1930 was 100,000. Assuming that its total rate of growth per year is at each instant 5% of the population at that time, find the expected population in 1960; in 1970.

7. Given $D_t S = 0.03S$ and $S = 100$ when $t = 0$, write a formula for S in terms of t. What is S when $t = 75$?

8. An electric current dies out according to the law $D_t i = -100i$. Find i in terms of t if $i = 20$ when $t = 0$.

9. Given $D_x y = 2y$ and $y = 40$ when $x = 0$, express y as a function of x. Find the value of y when $x = 3$; when $x = -\frac{1}{2}$.

4 NATURAL LOGARITHMS DEFINED

Table IV suggests that there exists a value of e^x for each real value of x; we shall assume this to be true. Further, we shall assume that the exponential function e^x obeys the laws of exponents, as shown below.

The Laws of Exponents

LAW 1. $e^{x_1} e^{x_2} = e^{x_1 + x_2}$.

LAW 2. $e^{x_1} / e^{x_2} = e^{x_1 - x_2}$.

LAW 3. $(e^x)^n = e^{nx}$.

LAW 4. $e^{-x} = 1/e^x$.

LAW 5. $e^0 = 1$.

Since e itself is a positive number greater than 1, the number e^x is greater than zero for all real values of x, whether positive, negative, or zero.

We now wish to define the inverse function of e^x, which we shall call the natural logarithm of x and denote by $\ln x$.

The *natural logarithm* of x for all positive real values of x is defined as that number y such that $x = e^y$; that is,

$$\ln x = y \qquad \text{if and only if} \qquad x = e^y.$$

These last two equations shall be taken as equivalent statements. According to this definition, the natural logarithm of x is an exponent, namely the power to which the number e must be raised to produce x. For this reason e is said to be the base of natural logarithms. A little later we shall define logarithms to other bases.

We shall not concern ourselves here with how the value of $\ln x$ is calculated for a given value of x; however, the function $\ln x$ is of such importance that its values have been tabulated. Table V gives the natural logarithms of numbers from $x = 1.00$ to $x = 9.99$ correct to four places of decimals. With the use of Table V and interpolation, one can find N correct to four significant figures if $\ln N$ is known; for this reason the table is called a four-place table.

5 THE USE OF A NATURAL-LOGARITHM TABLE

If a number N is one of the numbers from 1.00 to 9.99, its natural logarithm can be read directly from Table V.

Example. Find ln 3.76.

Solution: In Table V look for 3.7 in the column headed N, then move across the table horizontally to the column headed 0.06. The number there is 1.3244. Thus ln 3.76 = 1.3244.

Example. Find ln 6.438.

Solution: Here we have to interpolate. We may arrange our work as follows.

$$
0.010 \left\{ 0.008 \left\{ \begin{array}{ll} 6.430 & 1.8610 \\ 6.438 & ? \\ 6.440 & 1.8625 \end{array} \right\} d \right\} 0.0015
$$

$$
\frac{d}{0.0015} = \frac{0.008}{0.010} = 0.8
$$

$$
d = 0.8(0.0015) = 0.00120.
$$

Hence ln 6.438 = 1.8610 + 0.0012 = 1.8622.

It is also important to be able to find N from the table if ln N is known. To do this, we simply reverse the procedure used above. We shall illustrate with examples.

Example. Given ln N = 1.4493, find N.

Solution: Here we look for 1.4493 in the body of the table. We find it in the column headed 0.06. We now move across horizontally and to the left, to the entry in the column headed N. The value found there is 4.2; that is, N = 4.26. The number 4.26 is called the *antilogarithm* of 1.4493. In other words, 4.26 is the number whose natural logarithm is 1.4493. So, to find N when its logarithm is given is to find the antilogarithm of the given logarithm.

Example. Given ln N = 1.6872, find N.

Solution: The number 1.6872 does not occur in the table, so we shall have to interpolate if we wish four-place accuracy. We look for the two numbers in the table nearest to 1.6872 and between which our number lies. Again we arrange our work in tabular form:

$$
0.010 \left\{ d \left\{ \begin{array}{ll} 5.400 & 1.6864 \\ ? & 1.6872 \\ 5.410 & 1.6882 \end{array} \right. \right\} 0.0008 \right\} 0.0018
$$

$$\frac{d}{0.010} = \frac{0.0008}{0.0018} = \frac{8}{18} = \frac{4}{9}$$

$d = \frac{4}{9}(0.010) = 0.004$, to three decimal places.

Therefore, $N = 5.400 + 0.004 = 5.404$.

EXERCISES

1. Find the natural logarithms of the following.
   - **a.** 3.06.
   - **b.** 5.72.
   - **c.** 7.88.
   - **d.** 6.734.
   - **e.** 4.006.
   - **f.** 8.296.
2. Find the numbers whose natural logarithms are:
   - **a.** 1.1725.
   - **b.** 1.5872.
   - **c.** 2.1883.
   - **d.** 1.5357.
   - **e.** 2.1662.
   - **f.** 1.8554.
3. By using natural logarithms, find the value of x for each of the following.
   - **a.** $e^x = 4.78$.
   - **b.** $e^{6x} = 7.84$.
   - **c.** $e^{0.05x} = 5.32$.
   - **d.** $e^{-x} = 3.75$. (*Hint:* $-x = \ln 3.75$.)
   - **e.** $e^{-0.06x} = 2.47$.
4. Solve for x in each of the following, after first solving for the exponential function.
   - **a.** $536 = 100e^{10x}$.
   - **b.** $476 = 200e^{0.6x}$.
   - **c.** $0.564 = 0.08e^{0.04x}$.
   - **d.** $748 = 125e^{-2x}$.

6 THE LAWS OF NATURAL LOGARITHMS

In working with natural logarithms it is convenient to have available the following laws, which are a direct consequence of the definition of a natural logarithm.

Law 1. *The natural logarithm of the product of two or more factors is equal to the sum of the natural logarithms of the factors; that is,*

$$\ln (MN \cdots Q) = \ln M + \ln N + \cdots + \ln Q.$$

Proof: Let $m = \ln M$, $n = \ln N$, $\cdots$, and $q = \ln Q$; in exponential form, these are $M = e^m$, $N = e^n$, $\cdots$, and $Q = e^q$.

Multiplication gives $MN \cdots Q = e^m \cdot e^n \cdots e^q = e^{m+n+\ldots+q}$.
By definition of a natural logarithm,

$$\ln (MN \cdots Q) = m + n + \cdots + q = \ln M + \ln N + \cdots + \ln Q.$$

Law 2. *The natural logarithm of a fraction is equal to the natural logarithm of the numerator minus the natural logarithm of the denominator; that is,*

$$\ln \frac{M}{N} = \ln M - \ln N.$$

Proof: Let $x = \ln M$ and $y = \ln N$; in exponential form this is written $M = e^x$ and $N = e^y$.

Division gives $M/N = \dfrac{e^x}{e^y} = e^{x-y}$.

By definition, $\ln(M/N) = x - y = \ln M - \ln N$.

Law 3. *The natural logarithm of the nth power of a number is equal to n times the natural logarithm of the number; that is,*

$$\ln M^n = n \ln M.$$

Proof: Let $x = \ln M$; then $M = e^x$.

Raise both sides to the nth power and get $M^n = (e^x)^n = e^{nx}$.

By definition, $\ln M^n = nx = n \ln M$.

By using Laws 1 and 3, we are able to find the natural logarithm of any four-digit number, regardless of whether it falls within our table or not. To do this, let us first note that any number can be expressed as the product of a number, lying on the interval 1 to 10, and the number 10 raised to some integral power. This integral power of 10 will be positive, zero, or negative, depending upon whether the given number is greater than 10, lies on the interval from 1 to 10, or is less than 1. For example,

$$475 = (4.75)(10^2), \qquad 0.8974 = (8.974)(10^{-1}),$$
$$0.0065 = (6.5)(10^{-3}), \qquad 350{,}000 = (3.5)(10^5).$$

Expressing a number in this form is called expressing the number in *scientific notation*.

Example. Find ln 284.

Solution: In scientific notation,

$$284 = (2.84)(10^2),$$

hence

$$\ln 284 = \ln (2.84)(10^2);$$

by Law 1,

$$= \ln 2.84 + \ln 10^2,$$

by Law 3,

$$= \ln 2.84 + 2 \ln 10,$$

and, from Table V,

$$= 1.0438 + 4.6052,$$

and, adding,

$$= 5.6490.$$

Example. Find ln 0.763.

Solution: Proceeding as in Example 1, we may write

$$\ln 0.763 = \ln (7.63)(10^{-1}),$$
$$= \ln 7.63 + \ln (10^{-1}),$$
$$= \ln 7.63 - \ln 10,$$
$$= 2.0321 - 2.3026,$$
$$= -0.2705.$$

Example. Given $\ln N = 9.0780$, find N.

Solution: The number 9.0780 is outside the range of Table V, since the largest logarithm occurring there is 2.3016. In such a case we subtract from $\ln N$ the smallest multiple of ln 10 that will give a number in the table. In this case, 3 ln 10 = 6.9078 subtracted from 9.0780 does give a number in our table, while 2 ln 10 = 4.6052 is too small. We proceed as follows:

$$\ln N - 3 \ln 10 = 9.0780 - 6.9078 = 2.1702,$$
$$\ln N - \ln 1000 = 2.1702,$$

$$\ln \frac{N}{1000} = 2.1702.$$

From Table V we find the antilogarithm of 2.1702 to be 8.76, and therefore

$$\frac{N}{1000} = 8.76, \quad \text{or} \quad N = 8760.$$

Example.   Given ln $N = -2.3183$, find N.

Solution: The number -2.3183, being negative, is not in our table of logarithms, so to obtain a number that falls within the table we add to ln N the smallest multiple of ln 10 necessary to produce a positive number as sum. In the case at hand, 2 ln 10 = ln 100 = 4.6052 will be sufficient. We proceed as follows:

$$\ln N + \ln 100 = -2.3183 + 4.6052,$$
$$\ln 100N = 2.2869.$$

To find the antilogarithm of 2.2869, we use Table V and interpolation. For convenience, let $x = 100N$:

$$
\begin{array}{cc}
x & \ln x \\
0.01 \left\{ d \left\{ \begin{array}{l} 9.84 \\ ? \\ 9.85 \end{array} \right. \right. & \left. \begin{array}{l} 2.2865 \\ 2.2869 \\ 2.2875 \end{array} \right\} 0.0004 \left. \right\} 0.0010
\end{array}
$$

$$\frac{d}{0.01} = \frac{0.0004}{0.0010} = \frac{4}{10},$$

$$d = 0.004$$
$$x = 9.84 + 0.004 = 9.844.$$

Therefore 100N = 9.844 and N = 0.09844.

EXERCISES

1. Find the natural logarithm of each of the following numbers: **(a)** 532, **(b)** 6740, **(c)** 0.485, **(d)** 0.0879, **(e)** 47,500, **(f)** 0.003864, **(g)** 962.7.
2. Find the numbers whose natural logarithms are the following: **(a)** 5.9296, **(b)** 9.7757, **(c)** 6.8748, **(d)** -0.2446, **(e)** -2.3820, **(f)** -1, **(g)** 5.
3. Find the value of x given $x = 476e^{1.3246}$. (*Hint:*   ln x = ln 476 + 1.3246.)
4. Compute the value of x given $x = 850e^{-1.4652}$.
5. Solve for x, given 682 = $394e^{10x}$. (*Hint:*   Show that $10x$ = ln 6.82 − ln 3.94.)
6. The number of bacteria in a certain culture increases at an instantaneous rate per hour that is equal at any instant to 15% of the number in the culture at that instant. Starting with an original number N_0, in how many hours will the number be doubled?

7. Use natural logarithms to evaluate each of the following.

a. $\dfrac{(47.3)(86.5)}{237}$.   **b.** $(2.78)^{4.2}$.   **c.** $\sqrt[5]{534}$.

8. Use natural logarithms to solve for x, given $(2.5)^x = 48$.

7 THE DERIVATIVE OF e^u AND $\ln u$

In Section 2 we found that if $S = Pe^{rt}$ then $D_t S = rPe^{rt}$; for the special case $P = 1$ and $r = 1$, these equations become

$$S = e^t \quad \text{and} \quad D_t S = e^t.$$

Thus the exponential function e^t has the interesting property that its instantaneous rate of change per unit change in t is always equal to the function itself; that is,

$$\text{if} \qquad y = e^t,$$
$$\text{then} \qquad D_t y = e^t$$
(Eq. 1) $\qquad\quad$ or $\qquad D_t(e^t) = e^t.$

We may now generalize the last formula in the following manner. Let

$$y = e^u,$$

where u is a differentiable function of t; then

and, with the chain rule, $\qquad \begin{aligned} D_u y &= e^u; \\ D_t y &= D_u y \cdot D_t u, \end{aligned}$
we obtain $\qquad\qquad\qquad D_t y = e^u D_t u$
(Eq. 2) $\qquad\quad$ or $\qquad\qquad\quad D_t(e^u) = e^u D_t u.$

In words, the derivative with respect to the independent variable of e to any power is equal to e to that same power times the derivative of the power with respect to the independent variable.

Example. Given $y = e^{3x^2}$, find $D_x y$.

Solution: Here $u = 3x^2$ and $D_x u = 6x$; therefore, $D_x y = (e^{3x^2})(6x) = 6xe^{3x^2}$.

Example. Find $D_x y$, given $y = x^2 e^{5x}$.

Solution: We need to recall the formula for the derivative of a product of two functions, namely $D_x(uv) = u\, D_x v + v\, D_x u$.
Differentiating, we find

$$D_x y = x^2\, D_x e^{5x} + e^{5x}\, D_x x^2 = x^2(e^{5x})(5) + e^{5x}(2x),$$
$$= 5x^2 e^{5x} + 2xe^{5x} = xe^{5x}(5x + 2).$$

To find a formula for the derivative of $\ln u$ we proceed as follows. Let

$$y = \ln u;$$

now, recalling the definition of $\ln u$, we may write this equation in the equivalent form

$$u = e^y$$

and, differentiating with respect to x, we get

$$D_x u = e^y D_x y$$

and, solving for $D_x y$, we obtain

$$D_x y = \frac{D_x u}{e^y} = \frac{D_x u}{u},$$

(Eq. 3)   or $D_x(\ln u) = \dfrac{D_x u}{u}.$

In words, the derivative of the natural logarithm of a quantity is equal to 1 divided by that quantity times the derivative of the quantity. In particular, if $u = x$, then

(Eq. 4) $D_x(\ln x) = 1/x.$

Example.   Find $D_x y$, given $y = \ln (x^2 + 1)$.

Solution: Substituting in the above formula and noting that here $u = x^2 + 1$, we get

$$D_x y = \frac{D_x(x^2 + 1)}{x^2 + 1} = \frac{2x}{x^2 + 1}.$$

Example.   Find $D_x y$, given $y = \ln \sqrt{\dfrac{x^2 - 1}{2x + 1}}.$

Solution: It is desirable in this case to use the laws of logarithms to simplify our function before differentiating. Using Law 3 first and then Law 2 (Section 6), we obtain

$$y = \tfrac{1}{2} \ln (x^2 - 1) - \tfrac{1}{2} \ln (2x + 1).$$

Differentiating, we get $D_x y = \dfrac{1}{2} \cdot \dfrac{2x}{x^2 - 1} - \dfrac{1}{2} \cdot \dfrac{2}{2x + 1} = \dfrac{x}{x^2 - 1} - \dfrac{1}{2x + 1}.$

8   THE INTEGRALS $\int e^u\, du$ AND $\int (du/u)$

In the last section we found that $D_u e^u = e^u$; it follows therefrom, and from the definition of an integral, that

(Eq. 1) $$\int e^u\, du = e^u + C.$$

Example.   Evaluate the integral $\int e^{5x}\, dx$.

Solution: Let $u = 5x$; then $du = 5\, dx$ or $dx = \tfrac{1}{5}\, du$.
Substituting in the given integral: $\int e^{5x}\, dx = \tfrac{1}{5} \int e^u\, du = \tfrac{1}{5} e^u + C = \tfrac{1}{5} e^{5x} + C.$

We have shown that $D_u(\ln u) = 1/u$; therefore,

(Eq. 2) $$\int \frac{du}{u} = \ln u + C, \quad \text{for } u \text{ positive.}$$

If u is negative, then $-u$ is positive, and we can write

(Eq. 3) $$\int \frac{du}{u} = \int \frac{-du}{(-u)} = \int \frac{d(-u)}{(-u)} = \ln(-u) + C, \quad \text{for } u \text{ negative.}$$

In Chapter III we defined the absolute value $|u|$ of a number u as follows: $|u| = u$ if u is positive or zero, and $|u| = -u$ if u is negative. With this absolute-value notation we can now combine the last two equations into the general formula

(Eq. 4) $$\int \frac{du}{u} = \ln |u| + C.$$

Example. Find the area bounded by the x axis, the curve $y = 1/x$, and the two ordinates $x = -10$ and $x = -2$.

Solution: Since our area is below the x axis, we use $A = -\int_a^b f(x)\, dx$, and obtain

$$A = -\int_{-10}^{-2} \frac{dx}{x} = -\ln |x| \Big]_{-10}^{-2} = -\ln |-2| + \ln |-10|$$

$$= -0.6931 + 2.3026 = 1.6095.$$

Example. Evaluate the integral $\int \dfrac{x\, dx}{x^2 + 1}$.

Solution: Let $u = x^2 + 1$; then

$$du = 2x\, dx, \quad \text{or} \quad x\, dx = \tfrac{1}{2} du.$$

Hence, $$\int \frac{x\, dx}{x^2 + 1} = \frac{1}{2} \int \frac{du}{u} = \frac{1}{2} \ln |u| + C = \frac{1}{2} \ln (x^2 + 1) + C.$$

We may leave the absolute-value signs off in this case, because $x^2 + 1$ is always positive.

EXERCISES

Find $D_x y$ in each of the following exercises.

1. $y = 5e^{2x}$.	**6.** $y = \ln (x^3)$.	**11.** $y = (\ln x)^2$.
2. $y = 10e^{-4x}$.	**7.** $y = e^x \ln x$.	**12.** $y = \ln (x^5)$.
3. $y = xe^x$.	**8.** $y = e^{x^3}$.	**13.** $y = \ln (x\sqrt{x^2 - 1})$.
4. $y = x^2 e^{-x}$.	**9.** $y = \ln (4x + 5)$.	**14.** $y = \ln (\ln x)$.
5. $y = \ln (3x)$.	**10.** $y = \ln 6x/(2x - 1)$.	**15.** $y = 5/e^{3x}$.

Evaluate each of the following integrals.

16. $\int e^{3x}\, dx.$

21. $\int \dfrac{dx}{x+1}.$

17. $\int xe^{x^2}\, dx.$

22. $\int \dfrac{3\, dx}{2x-1}.$

18. $\int \dfrac{2\, dx}{e^{5x}}.$

23. $\int \dfrac{e^x\, dx}{4+e^x}.$

19. $\int x^2 e^{-x^3}\, dx.$

24. $\int \dfrac{x\, dx}{4+x^2}.$

20. $\int \dfrac{2x^2+3x+5}{x}\, dx.$

25. $\int \dfrac{dx}{(x+1)^2}.$

26. Find the area above the x axis and under the curve $y = 10/x$, from $x = 1$ to $x = 8$.

27. Evaluate each definite integral: **(a)** $\displaystyle\int_{-7}^{-1} \dfrac{dx}{x-1},$ **(b)** $\displaystyle\int_0^2 e^{x/2}\, dx.$

9 LOGARITHMS TO ANY BASE

Let a be a positive number greater than 1 and let N be any positive number. We define the logarithm of N to the base a as the power to which a must be raised to produce N, and we write

(Eq. 1) $\qquad\qquad\qquad\qquad \log_a N = x,$

(Eq. 2) $\qquad\qquad\quad$ if $\qquad\quad N = a^x.$

By using the properties of a^x it can be shown that $\log_a N$ obeys laws analogous to those obeyed by $\ln N$; these are the following.

The Laws of Logarithms to Any Base a

LAW 1. $\log_a MN = \log_a M + \log_a N.$

LAW 2. $\log_a \dfrac{M}{N} = \log_a M - \log_a N.$

LAW 3. $\log_a M^n = n \log_a M.$

The precise meaning of the definition of $\log_a N$ may be clarified by the following examples.

Examples. $\log_5 25 = 2$ because $25 = 5^2.$
$\log_9 3 = \frac{1}{2}$ because $3 = 9^{1/2}.$
$\log_2 \frac{1}{4} = -2$ because $\frac{1}{4} = 2^{-2}.$
$\log_7 1 = 0$ because $1 = 7^0.$

The only bases of logarithms that are of any practical importance are $a = e$ and $a = 10$. Logarithms to the base 10 are useful for the purposes of computation because our number system uses the base 10; these logarithms are called *common logarithms*, and a complete discussion of them may be found in any college algebra textbook.

EXERCISES

Use the definition of $\log_a N$ to find the value of the following logarithms.

1. $\log_8 64$.

2. $\log_{25} 5$.

3. $\log_{10} 0.001$.

4. $\log_2 16$.

5. $\log_3 \frac{1}{27}$.

6. $\log_5 1$.

Solve each of the following problems for x.

7. $\log_3 81 = x$.

8. $\log_4 x = 3$.

9. $\log_x 32 = 5$.

10. $\log_x 16 = 4$.

11. $\log_5 x = -2$.

12. $\log_x 1000 = \frac{3}{4}$.

13. $\log_x 0.001 = -3$.

14. $\log_8 x = 0$.

15. $\log_8 x = -\frac{4}{3}$.

Write each of the following expressions as a single logarithm, assuming all logarithms to have the same base.

16. $\log P + \log Q + \log R$.

17. $\log a + 2 \log b$.

18. $2 \log x - \log y$.

19. $2 \log x + 3 \log y - 5 \log z$.

20. $\log x + \frac{1}{2} \log (x^2 + 1) - 2 \log (2x + 3)$.

21. $3 \log x + 2 \log y - \log z - \frac{1}{2} \log w$.

22. $\frac{1}{3}(\log x + \log y - 2 \log z)$.

XIV

PROBABILITY AND STATISTICS

1 INTRODUCTION

The word *probability* is used loosely in our everyday conversation, and we know only vaguely what it means. We talk of the chance that Tennessee will win a football game or that it will rain tomorrow. We are interested in a future event, of which the outcome is uncertain and about which we want to make a kind of prediction. In a mathematical discussion of probability we are more precise in that we try to present conditions under which we can make sensible numerical statements about uncertainties and to present methods of calculating numerical values of probabilities.

2 PROBABILITY

All mathematical probabilities are measured on a scale that extends from 0 to 1. The value 0 is assigned to any event that certainly will not occur; that is, the probability is 0 that the Earth and Mars will collide tomorrow. The value 1 is assigned to events that are certain to occur; that is, the probability is 1 that the sun will rise tomorrow. Events that may occur or may not occur are assigned fractional probabilities between 0 and 1.

Let us consider one of the simplest phenomena of chance, the outcome of the toss of a coin. Here there are two possible outcomes, a head or a tail. It is certain that a head or a tail will occur on any one toss of the coin. If it be agreed that these two outcomes are equally likely, the total probability of 1 must be equally divided between them. Thus we assign $\frac{1}{2}$ to each as its probability.

Another simple example is the roll of a die. An ideal die is a perfect cube with six faces having one to six dots. If we roll it once, the set of possible outcomes is $S = \{1, 2, 3, 4, 5, 6\}$. It is certain that one of these will occur, and if we agree to assign equal probabilities to the six numbers then each gets, as its equal share, $\frac{1}{6}$ of the total probability.

Many times we want the probability of an event E which consists of several elementary outcomes. Thus, the event "a die shows an even number of dots" corresponds to the subset $\{2, 4, 6\}$ of the original set S, and we naturally add the probabilities assigned to the elementary outcomes in the subset to obtain $\frac{3}{6}$ as the probability that the die will turn up even.

It should be noted that the set $S = \{1, 2, 3, 4, 5, 6\}$ of possible outcomes of the roll of a true die is not unique. We might, for instance, use the sets $S_1 = \{\text{odd number, even number}\}$ or $S_2 = \{\text{number is 2 or less, number is 3 or more}\}$. Each of these sets provides an *exhaustive* set of *mutually exclusive* outcomes for the experiment. The two outcomes in S_1 would be considered equally likely, and we would assign probability $\frac{1}{2}$ to each. For S_2, however, the outcomes are not equally likely, and it seems natural to assign the following probabilities:

$$Pr(\text{number is 2 or less}) = \tfrac{1}{3}$$
$$Pr(\text{number is 3 or more}) = \tfrac{2}{3}.$$

Definition 14.1. *If an event E can happen in m cases out of a total of n possible cases, which are all considered to be equally likely, then the* probability *of the event E is defined as m/n. The notation for this is $Pr(E) = m/n$.*

This definition is perfectly clear-cut and agrees with our intuitive notion of chance in the simplest situations. However, it is difficult or impossible to apply in more complicated situations, when we cannot make a simple enumeration of cases that are equally likely. In such situations we appeal to observational evidence for probabilities. Suppose, for example, that a coin is tossed a large number of times. The probability prediction is that heads will turn up one half of the time. That is, we can think of probability as predicting the relative frequency of occurrence of some event. It does not predict the outcome of any one trial or the order of the outcomes of several trials, but only what will happen in the long run or on the average, in a large number of trials. This leads us to assume that the relative frequency of occurrence of an event in an actual long-run series of trials will approximate the probability and that, the larger the number of trials, the better the approximation generally. For example, from mortality tables compiled in past years, we find that, of 100,000 new-born white American males, about 92,300 are alive at age 20. This allows us to estimate the probability that a new-born white American male will live to be 20 years old as 0.923. Insurance companies use such empirically determined relative frequencies in calculating life insurance premiums.

EXERCISES

1. What is the probability that a letter of the alphabet picked at random (by pure chance) will be a vowel?
2. If a card is drawn at random (by pure chance) from a pack of playing cards, what is the probability that it will be a heart? That it will be an honor card? That it will not be a diamond?
3. If two coins are tossed, what is the probability that both will show heads? That one will show heads and one tails?
4. Construct a table showing all the possible results when three coins are tossed. What is the probability of at least two heads? Of at most two heads?
5. In a roll of one die, what is the probability that the number of dots obtained will not exceed four? Will be at least four?
6. List the set of 36 equally likely, mutually exclusive, outcomes when two dice, one red and one green, are rolled.
   a. What is the probability of obtaining exactly one 6? Of not obtaining a 6? Of obtaining at least one 6?
   b. What is the probability that both dice show the same face?
7. Suppose you are only interested in the total number of dots that show when two dice are rolled. Use the material of Exercise 6 to compile a set of outcomes and probabilities pertinent to this problem.
   a. What is the probability of obtaining a total of 6 dots? Of a total of at most 6 dots?
   b. What total number of dots has the greatest probability?
8. The following mortality table shows the number of survivors, to various ages, among 100,000 new-born white American males.

Age x	Survivors to age x
0	100,000
10	93,601
20	92,293
30	90,092
40	86,880
50	80,521
60	67,787

   a. Estimate the probability that a new-born infant in this class will live to be 50 years old.
   b. Estimate the probability that a 20-year-old in this class will live to be 50 years old.
9. The probability that an individual will die from a particular operation is 0.01. A doctor has performed this operation 99 times in succession with no resulting deaths. Does this mean that the next such operation he performs will be fatal to the patient?

3 PERMUTATIONS AND COMBINATIONS

Many probability calculations involve questions similar to the following. If a coin is tossed n times (or if n separate coins are tossed), in how many distinguishable ways can we get exactly m heads and $n - m$ tails? If n is small, the question may be answered easily by listing all possible arrangements of n heads and tails, as in Exercises 3 and 4 of the last section, and then simply counting those arrangements that contain m heads and $n - m$ tails. When n is large, a complete listing of the possible arrangements becomes onerous to say the least. The answer to the question is obtainable without a listing, by means of a general formula for the number of arrangements of n objects that are not all distinct. Before we derive the formula, however, we shall consider some simpler problems in the enumeration of arrangements.

Permutations

We shall consider first the number of ways in which we can select and arrange two objects if we have five distinct objects from which to choose: If the objects are designated by the letters $A, B, C, D,$ and E, we have the following possibilities:

AB	BA	CA	DA	EA
AC	BC	CB	DB	EB
AD	BD	CD	DC	EC
AE	BE	CE	DE	ED

Here we consider AB and BA to be separate arrangements because the objects appear in different orders. Arrangements such as these, in which the order of the objects and the objects themselves are both distinguishing elements are called *permutations*. Specifically, we have enumerated all possible permutations of the five objects $A, B, C, D,$ and E, using exactly two at one time. The number of such permutations will be denoted by $P(5, 2)$, and here we see that $P(5, 2) = 20$. In general, $P(n, r)$ denotes the number of permutations which may be formed by using precisely r objects if n objects are available.

Observe in the example above that we have five choices for the first object and for each of these five choices there are four choices for the second object. Thus, in this example we have $P(5, 2) = 5 \cdot 4 = 20$.

In general, in the computation of $P(n, r)$ we have n choices for the first object. After the first object has been chosen there are $n - 1$ choices available for the second object, and each of these $n - 1$ choices may be associated with each of the n choices of the first object. Thus there are $n(n - 1)$ choices of the first two objects. There are $n - 2$ choices available for the third object, and each of these choices may be associated with each of the choices for the first two objects. Thus there are $n(n - 1)(n - 2)$ choices for the first three objects. This line of reasoning may be continued down to the $n - r + 1$ available choices for the rth object and to the final formula for the permutations of r objects when n are available:

$$P(n, r) = n(n - 1)(n - 2) \cdots (n - r + 1).$$

Expressions similar to this one will occur frequently in the remaining discussion; consequently, it will be convenient to have a more concise notation. We define n *factorial*, written $n!$, where n is a positive integer, to be the product of the first n positive integers:

$$1! = 1$$
$$2! = 1 \cdot 2$$
$$3! = 1 \cdot 2 \cdot 3$$
$$\cdot \quad \cdot \quad \cdot \quad \cdot \quad \cdot \quad \cdot$$
$$\cdot \quad \cdot \quad \cdot \quad \cdot \quad \cdot \quad \cdot$$
$$n! = 1 \cdot 2 \cdot 3 \cdots (n - 1)n.$$

Note: This list is completed with the special definition

$$0! = 1.$$

Now we may rewrite our formula by multiplying it by the fraction $(n - r)!/(n - r)!$, which puts it in a much more convenient form to remember:

$$P(n, r) = \frac{n(n - 1) \cdots (n - r + 1)(n - r) \cdots 2 \cdot 1}{(n - r)(n - r - 1) \cdots 2 \cdot 1} = \frac{n!}{(n - r)!}.$$

Example. How many different itineraries can be made out if each is to include 3 points of interest from a selected list of 9 points of interest? (Two itineraries that include the same points of interest will be considered different if they include these 3 points in a different order.)

Solution: Here $n = 9$ and $r = 3$. The order of arrangement is important, so the number of itineraries is the number of permutations:

$$P(9, 3) = \frac{9!}{(9 - 3)!} = \frac{9!}{6!} = \frac{9 \cdot 8 \cdot 7 \cdot \cancel{6} \cdot \cancel{5} \cdot \cancel{4} \cdot \cancel{3} \cdot \cancel{2} \cdot \cancel{1}}{\cancel{6} \cdot \cancel{5} \cdot \cancel{4} \cdot \cancel{3} \cdot \cancel{2} \cdot \cancel{1}} = 504.$$

In some instances one or more of the objects being arranged may be indistinguishable, and the interchanges of these objects may be discounted in the enumeration of the number of permutations.

Example. How many distinct 9-letter arrangements may be made from the letters of the word *Tennessee*?

Solution: There are 9 letters and all 9 are to be used, but it is not true that $9!$ distinguishable arrangements are possible. The 4 letters e may be interchanged without affecting the apparent arrangement. Since, for each apparent arrangement, there are $P(4, 4) = 24$ ways of interchanging the letters e without affecting anything else, the number $9!$ counts each arrangement of them 24 times. By the same argument, each of the pairs of letters n and s gives twice as many apparent arrangements as are exactly distinguishable. Thus, the number of distinct arrangements is

$$\frac{P(9, 9)}{P(4, 4)P(2, 2)P(2, 2)} = \frac{9!}{4!2!2!} = 3780.$$

In general, the formula for computing the number of distinguishable permutations of n objects of which a certain group, i in number, are alike and another group, j in number, are alike, and so on, is

$$\frac{n!}{i!j! \cdots}.$$

Combinations

Consider again our first example above. We might have requested the number of itineraries possible in which the only requirement was that the three points of interest were to be distinct. In this case the order in which the three points were visited would be of no importance; the distinguishing feature here is the specific choice of three points. We wish the number of combinations of nine points, three of which are to be chosen each time. We shall denote this by $C(9, 3)$. The distinction between permutations and combinations is a matter of order and of whether it makes any difference.

In counting permutations, two different arrangements of the same set of objects are considered to be different, as are two sets of objects some of which are different or all of which are different. In counting combinations, we distinguish only sets whose objects are some or all different. A rearrangement of the same set of objects does not produce a different combination. We determined that $P(9, 3) = 504$, but to determine $C(9, 3)$ we observe that for each combination of three things, all of which are to be used, there are $P(3, 3) = 6$ ways of permuting them. Hence we have

$$P(3, 3)C(9, 3) = P(9, 3)$$

or
$$C(9, 3) = \frac{P(9, 3)}{P(3, 3)};$$

thus
$$C(9, 3) = \frac{9!}{(9 - 3)!} \div \frac{3!}{(3 - 3)!},$$

or
$$C(9, 3) = \frac{9!}{6!3!} = 84.$$

In general, we observe in similar fashion that, if $C(n, r)$ is the number of combinations of n things, r of which are to be used each time, then

$$P(r, r)C(n, r) = P(n, r),$$

or
$$C(n, r) = \frac{P(n, r)}{P(r, r)},$$

and this reduces to

$$C(n, r) = \frac{n!}{(n - r)! r!}.$$

It should be noted that the formulas for $C(n, r)$ and for the number of permutations of n objects, of which r are indistinguishable from each other and the remaining $n - r$ are also indistinguishable from each other, are identical. The identity of the formulas does not identify the two concepts.

Example. Find the number of ways in which a committee of 4 can be chosen from a class of 11. (Here the order of choice makes no difference.)

Solution: $C(11, 4) = \dfrac{11!}{7! 4!} = \dfrac{11 \cdot 10 \cdot 9 \cdot 8 \cdot 7!}{7! \cdot 4 \cdot 3 \cdot 2 \cdot 1} = 330.$

Example. Suppose that the class in the example above is composed of 7 men and 4 women and that the committee is to be chosen by lot. What is the probability that the committee will be composed of 2 men and 2 women?

Solution: The total number n of committees possible is again 330. For the committee to be composed of 2 men and 2 women, we note that there are $C(7, 2) = 21$ ways of selecting the men and $C(4, 2) = 6$ ways of selecting the women. The favorable committee may then be chosen in $m = 21 \cdot 6 = 126$ ways. By the definition of the probability of an event, the probability required here is $126/330 = 21/55$.

Example. Five cards are to be dealt from the standard deck of 52 cards. What is the probability that all 5 are spades?

Solution: Since there are 13 spades, the number m of possible 5-card hands, all of which are spades, is $C(13, 5)$. Similarly, the number n of 5-card hands which can be dealt from the entire deck is $C(52, 5)$. Hence

$$Pr(E) = \frac{C(13, 5)}{C(52, 5)} = \frac{33}{66640}.$$

EXERCISES

Exercises 1 to 10 are problems in permutations.

1. Evaluate $P(5, 5)$ and $P(5, 3)$.
2. How many 7-letter arrangements may be formed from the letters in *Alabama?*
3. How many 4-letter arrangements may be formed from the letters in *New York?*
4. How many 11-letter arrangements may be formed from the letters in *Mississippi?*
5. How many 4-digit numbers with distinct digits can be written by use of the digits 1, 2, 3, 4, and 5 if the number is to be an even number?
6. How many 3-letter "words" are possible with our usual alphabet if the only requirement for a "word" is that it have at least 1 of the 5 vowels? How many such "words" are possible if none is to contain any single letter more than once?
7. A certain airline has 10 terminals. If a ticket shows only the terminals of

departure and destination, how many different tickets may be written for this airline?

8. If 1 each of the tickets of different types for the airline in Exercise 7 is placed in a hat and then one is drawn from the hat at random, what is the probability that a specific one of the 10 terminals will be named on that ticket?

9. In how many ways can 10 coins be arranged in a row so that 4 heads and 6 tails show up?

10. If 10 equally balanced coins are tossed, what is the probability of obtaining 4 heads and 6 tails?

11. Evaluate $C(9, 3)$ and $C(9, 6)$. How do these values compare? Why?

12. Prove that $C(n, r) = C(n, n - r)$ if n is a positive integer and r is a nonnegative integer. $(n > r)$

13. A committee of 3 men and 2 women is to be appointed from a group of 12 men and 10 women. How many distinct possibilities are there?

14. A certain military unit has 48 privates on the roster. How many different lists of 5 privates each can be made up for KP duty?

15. A baseball team has 18 men on the roster as follows: 2 catchers, 7 pitchers, 5 infielders other than pitcher or catcher, and 4 outfielders. How many different lineups, without regard to batting order, can be fielded? How many different batting orders are possible?

16. What is the probability that 2 cards drawn at random from a deck of 52 cards will both be black?

17. What is the probability that 4 cards drawn at random from a standard deck will be of the same suit?

18. A box contains 15 small plastic balls all alike except for color; 9 are white and the rest are red. If 3 balls are drawn simultaneously and at random, what is the probability that they will all be red? That there will be 1 red and 2 whites?

19. A purchaser agrees to buy a lot of 100 items if a careful examination of 10 of the items selected at random reveals no defects. If, unknown to the purchaser, the lot of 100 contains 2 defective items, what is the probability that he will buy the lot?

20. A box contains 50 good and 5 defective screws. If 10 screws are used, what is the probability that none is defective?

21. Suppose 3 bad light bulbs get mixed up with 12 good ones, and that you start testing the bulbs one by one. What is the probability that you will find 2 defective among the first 6 tested?

22. There are 3 roads between towns A and B, and a salesman wants to go from A to B and return. How many different routes are possible? Explain the conditions under which each of the following answers would be correct: 9, 6, 3.

4   THE BINOMIAL EXPANSION;
PROBABILITY RULES

The use of permutations enables us to establish the binomial expansion of $(a + b)^n$, where n is a positive integer; this expansion was introduced in Section 17 of Chapter III. We need notice only that in forming the product of n factors, each of which is $a + b$, we will choose either an a or a b from each factor, but not both. Thus the terms must be of the type

$$C \cdot a^r \cdot b^{n-r},$$

where r is an integer. The coefficient C is the number of distinguishable orders of arrangement of r factors a and $n - r$ factors b. The identity of the formula for this number of permutations and the formula for $C(n, r)$ has already been noted. It is customary to take advantage of that identity for purposes of a notation. Thus, the term that involves $a^r b^{n-r}$ will be written as

(Eq. 1)
$$C(n, r) \cdot a^r \cdot b^{n-r}.$$

The entire expansion is obtained by summing all such terms, r taking on the integral values from 0 to n inclusive. Thus

(Eq. 2)
$$(a + b)^n = C(n, n) \cdot a^n + C(n, n - 1) \cdot a^{n-1}b$$
$$+ C(n, n - 2) \cdot a^{n-2}b^2 + \cdots + C(n, 1) \cdot ab^{n-1} + C(n, 0) \cdot b^n.$$

Note that, since $C(n, r) = C(n, n - r)$, the coefficients in Equation 2 appear symmetrically from the ends of the expansion.

The student should review the examples and exercises on the binomial expansion given in Section 18 of Chapter III.

The binomial expansion finds application in probability theory in the calculation of the probabilities of repeated trials, such as in tossing a coin many times or tossing many equally balanced coins.

Example.   What is the probability that a random throw of n coins will show x heads and $n - x$ tails for any one of the possible values $x = 0, 1, 2, \cdots, n$?

Solution: There are 2 ways of throwing each coin and so 2^n ways of throwing the n coins. Out of these 2^n ways, the number of ways yielding x heads and $n - x$ tails is the number of permutations of x heads and $n - x$ tails. This number is equal in value to $C(n, x)$. Thus the required probability is

(Eq. 3)
$$\frac{C(n, x)}{2^n} = C(n, x) \left(\frac{1}{2}\right)^x \left(\frac{1}{2}\right)^{n-x}.$$

Notice that the right-hand side of Equation 3 is the special case of Equation 1 obtained by setting $a = b = \frac{1}{2}$ and $r = x$. The example displays a general principle in the calculation of probabilities for repeated trials.

Principle: If an experiment can lead to only two possible results, the success of an event E or the failure of that event, and if the probabilities that the event succeed or fail in a single trial of the experiment are p and $q = 1 - p$, respectively, then the probability that the event E will succeed in x and fail in $n - x$ trials out of n independent trials of the experiment is

(Eq. 4)
$$C(n, x) \cdot p^x \cdot q^{n-x}.$$

We have used implicitly three basic rules from probability theory in the discussion thus far. These will now be stated without proof.

Rule 1.   *If E and F denote events that are mutually exclusive (that is, that cannot occur simultaneously), then the probability that one of E or F*

will occur is the sum of the separate probabilities of E and F. In symbols, $Pr(E \text{ or } F) = Pr(E) + Pr(F)$.

Rule 2.   If E is any event and if "not E" denotes the failure of E to occur, then $Pr(E) = 1 - Pr(\text{not } E)$.

This rule is a corollary of the first one, since the events E and "not E" are mutually exclusive and one or the other is certain to occur.

Rule 3.   If E and F denote events that are independent of each other (that is, the occurrence of either one does not affect the probability of occurrence of the other), then the probability that E and F will both occur is the product of the probabilities Pr(E) and Pr(F) of the single events E and F, each calculated without reference to whether or not the other event has or has not occurred. In symbols, $Pr(E \text{ and } F) = Pr(E) \cdot Pr(F)$.

Example. The game of chuck-a-luck is often played at small carnivals. A player pays a nickel to play. Three dice are rolled. If any "sixes" appear up, the player gets his nickel back and as bonus he gets an extra nickel for each "six" that appears. What is the probability that a player will win one or more nickels?

Solution: There are 3 mutually exclusive outcomes of the roll of the dice that will win for the player: 3 "sixes," 2 "sixes" and anything else on the third die, and 1 "six" and anything else on the other 2 dice. To calculate the probabilities of these three cases, think of the dice as numbered: first die, second die, and third die. Let E, F, and G, respectively, denote the possible events described above.

For E to occur, all 3 dice must show "sixes." The probability of a six on any one die is $\frac{1}{6}$ and the dice are independent so, by Rule 3 $Pr(E) = (\frac{1}{6})^3 = \frac{1}{216}$.

The event F can occur in three mutually exclusive ways, to be denoted by F_1, F_2, and F_3, where the subscript denotes in each case the number of the die that does not show a "six." Again the probability of any one "six" is $\frac{1}{6}$, while the probability of not a "six" is $\frac{5}{6}$. By Rule 3,

$$Pr(F_1) = \frac{5}{6} \cdot \frac{1}{6} \cdot \frac{1}{6} = \frac{5}{216},$$

$$Pr(F_2) = \frac{1}{6} \cdot \frac{5}{6} \cdot \frac{1}{6} = \frac{5}{216},$$

$$Pr(F_3) = \frac{1}{6} \cdot \frac{1}{6} \cdot \frac{5}{6} = \frac{5}{216}.$$

By Rule 1, then, $Pr(F) = Pr(F_1) + Pr(F_2) + Pr(F_3) = \frac{15}{216}$.

In a similar way, the event G may be broken into three mutually exclusive cases, G_1, G_2, and G_3, where the subscript denotes in each case the number of the die that shows a "six." As above,

$$Pr(G_1) = \frac{1}{6} \cdot \frac{5}{6} \cdot \frac{5}{6} = \frac{25}{216},$$

$$Pr(G_2) = \frac{5}{6} \cdot \frac{1}{6} \cdot \frac{5}{6} = \frac{25}{216},$$

$$Pr(G_3) = \frac{5}{6} \cdot \frac{5}{6} \cdot \frac{1}{6} = \frac{25}{216},$$

and $$Pr(G) = Pr(G_1) + Pr(G_2) + Pr(G_3) = \frac{75}{216}.$$

Finally, by Rule 1, Pr(player wins) $= Pr(E) + Pr(F) + Pr(G) = \frac{91}{216}$.

The meaning of independence in Rule 3 is further illustrated by the following example, in which the trials are not independent.

Example.   A bag contains 15 marbles of the same size. Of these, 10 are white and 5 are red. Marbles are to be drawn at random from the bag one at a time until 3 have been withdrawn. What is the probability that the 3 marbles drawn will be red?

Solution: For the first marble drawn there are $n_1 = 15$ from which to draw and of these $m_1 = 5$ are red. Thus the probability that the first marble drawn will be red is $\frac{5}{15}$. After the first marble has been drawn, there remain $n_2 = 14$ marbles, of which $m_2 = 4$ are red for the second draw. Thus the probability that the second marble drawn will be red is $\frac{4}{14}$. Similarly, after the first 2 red marbles have been withdrawn, the probability that the third marble drawn will be red is $\frac{3}{13}$.

To obtain the probability that all three marbles will be red, we still multiply together the three single trial probabilities, just as in Rule 3 to get the result $\frac{1}{3} \cdot \frac{2}{7} \cdot \frac{3}{13} = \frac{2}{91}$. The departure from Rule 3 occurred in that the single trial probabilities were not calculated independently of each other.

Note that the same final result in this example could have been obtained by the use of a ratio of combinations, $C(5, 3)/C(15, 3) = 2/91$. Compare the last two examples of Section 3. Thus, this last method takes into account automatically the lack of independence of successive trials. It should not be used when trials are independent.

EXERCISES

1.   What is the probability that a 5-card hand containing 3 aces and 2 kings will be dealt from a standard 52-card deck?
2.   What is the probability that a penny will land with heads showing exactly 5 times if it is tossed 8 times?
3.   What is the probability that, if a pair of dice is thrown, the sum of the dots will be at least 7? Exactly 7?
4.   John has 3 white shirts and 4 colored shirts, while Joe has 2 white shirts and 6 colored shirts. What is the probability that both John and Joe wear white shirts the same day, assuming choices are random? What is the probability, assuming they each wear a clean shirt each day and have no 24-hour laundry service, that they both wear white shirts 2 days in succession?
5.   What is the probability that a "six" will appear exactly 3 times if a die is thrown 6 times?
6.   If it rains, on the average, 20% of the days in July, what is the probability that 3 randomly specified days in July will be dry?
7.   Eighty percent of a certain tribe are right-handed and 60 percent have brown

eyes. What is the probability that a randomly selected member of the tribe shall be left-handed and have brown eyes?

8. If 90% of the items manufactured by a certain company pass inspection, what is the probability that 8 chosen at random out of a shipment of 10 will pass inspection?

9. A case of 100 toy autos contains 10 defective ones. If 5 are selected at random and shipped to a store, what is the probability that the store will receive at least 1 defective toy?

10. Assume that on the average 1 telephone number out of 5 called between 4 and 5 P.M. on weekdays in a certain city is busy. What is the probability that, if 10 randomly selected telephone numbers are called during this hour, not more than 2 of them will be busy?

11. If 12 coins are tossed, what is the probability that at least 2 heads show?

12. Each of the 50 states has two senators. What is the probability that Tennessee will be represented on a committee of 50 chosen at random from the 100 senators?

13. Suppose there are 2 nickels and 2 dimes in each of 2 boxes. Find the probability of drawing 2 dimes when 1 coin is drawn at random from each box, and when all the coins are put in 1 box and then 2 coins are drawn at random.

14. An urn contains 4 white, 5 red, and 6 black balls. Another urn contains 5 white, 6 red, and 7 black balls. One ball is selected from each urn. What is the probability that they will be of the same color?

5   MATHEMATICAL EXPECTATION

In any experiment or game in which numerical values are attached to each of the mutually exclusive events in an exhaustive set, the sum, over that set of events, of the products of the values of the events and the probabilities of the events is called the *mathematical expectation* of the values (briefly, the "expectation" or the "expected value") of the experiment or game.

Example. In a toss of 3 coins, let the value of each possible outcome be the number x of heads that show on the coins. Find the expectation of a toss.

Solution: The possible values of x are 0, 1, 2, and 3, and these values may be used to denote also the mutually exclusive set of events in this case. Thus,

$$\text{Expectation} = 0 \cdot Pr(x = 0) + 1 \cdot Pr(x = 1) + 2 \cdot Pr(x = 2) + 3 \cdot Pr(x = 3)$$
$$= 0 \cdot (\tfrac{1}{2})^3 + 1 \cdot 3 \cdot (\tfrac{1}{2})^3 + 2 \cdot 3 \cdot (\tfrac{1}{2})^3 + 3 \cdot 1 \cdot (\tfrac{1}{2})^3$$
$$= \tfrac{12}{8} = 1.5.$$

In a gambling game, the attached values for which the expectation is desired are usually the amounts of money to be gained or lost (taken to be positive if there is a gain, negative if there is a loss, zero if there is neither gain nor loss) from the occurrence of the various outcomes of the game. A game is called a fair game if the player's expectation from the game is zero. By way of illustration, let us return to the second example of Section 4, in which the game chuck-a-luck was described.

Example. Is chuck-a-luck a fair game?

Solution: We found that the total probability that a player will win is 91/216. Thus, the probability of not winning is 125/216 and the value attached to this event is -5 since the player loses the nickel that he paid. The event E has the value 15, F has the value 10, and G has the value 5, since the player has gains of those amounts associated with those events. The player's expectation from the game is

$$15 \cdot Pr(E) + 10 \cdot Pr(F) + 5 \cdot Pr(G) - 5 \cdot Pr(\text{not winning})$$

$$= \frac{15}{216} + \frac{150}{216} + \frac{375}{216} - \frac{625}{216} = -\frac{85}{216}.$$

This is approximately -0.4 cent; the game is not a fair game.

Example. John and Joe frequently have their coffee breaks together. It is their habit to match pennies to see which one will pay for the coffee each time. Coffee costs them 10 cents per cup. Is this a fair game?

Solution: On those occasions that John matches Joe, the game and its results may be tabulated as follows:

John's coin	Joe's coin	Who pays
H	H	Joe
T	T	Joe
H	T	John
T	H	John

The probability that John will pay is $\frac{1}{2}$, and in this case he pays 20 cents and receives a 10-cent cup of coffee; the net value to him is -10. The probability that John will not pay is also $\frac{1}{2}$, and in this case he receives a free cup of coffee; the net value to him is 10. Thus his expectation from the game is zero. Clearly, the situation is the same if Joe matches John. This is a fair game for John. It is also a fair game for Joe.

The expectation of value of an experiment or game is interpretable physically as the average of the values obtained from the experiment or game from a long series of repeated runs of the experiment or plays of the game.

EXERCISES

1. Find the expected value of the sum of the number of dots that show up on the roll of a pair of dice.
2. A game is played on the basis of a roll of 1 die. The player receives 2 pennies for each dot that shows up on the die. What is a fair price to play this game?
3. A certain lottery has 100,000 tickets numbered serially. A ticket costs its buyer $2.00. The tickets numbered 500, 8325, and 92,350 pay off $10,000 each to their purchasers. What is a purchaser's expectation of value from a single ticket in this lottery?
4. If the probability of death from an airplane accident of any individual passen-

ger on a one-way air trip is 10^{-5}, what is a fair price for an individual one-way-air-trip accident-insurance policy for $25,000? Ignore the costs and profits of running the insurance company.

5. If 5000 lottery tickets are sold at $1 each on a $2000 car, what is the expected gain of a person who buys 1 ticket?

6. A bag contains 7 white and 5 red balls. Three are withdrawn successively without replacement. What is the expected number of red balls drawn?

7. One purse contains 10 pennies and 4 dimes. Another purse contains 5 pennies and 6 dimes. One coin is drawn at random for each purse. What is the expected total draw?

6 PROBABILITY DISTRIBUTIONS

It has been remarked earlier in the text that one of the roles of mathematics in applications is to provide models for observed relationships. The theory of probability provides models for the prediction of the relative frequencies of events arising from random experiments. In this section we will give examples of several widely used models.

Example.   This is an example from industrial quality control. Suppose that, under the well-controlled conditions of a modern assembly line, 10% of all finished items are defective, that is, that the probability of a defective item is 0.1. What is the probability of 0, 1, 2, 3 defectives in a sample of 3 items drawn at random for testing?

Solution: The experiment in this case consists of drawing one item at random from the production line and noting whether it is good (G) or defective (D). The experiment is performed 3 times. If we assume that the 3 trials are independent of each other and that $Pr(G) = 0.9$ and $Pr(D) = 0.1$ for each trial, then Equation 4 of Section 4 can be applied in finding the required probabilities. Thus, if x is the number of defectives in the sample of 3, then

$$Pr(x = x_i) = C(3, x_i)(0.1)^{x_i}(0.9)^{3-x_i} \qquad \{x_i\} = \{0, 1, 2, 3\}.$$

It is convenient to present the results in tabular form:

No. of defectives, x_i	0	1	2	3
$Pr(x = x_i)$	0.729	0.243	0.027	0.001

We have listed a mutually exclusive and exhaustive set of outcomes with associated probabilities. The ordered pairs $[x_i, Pr(x_i)]$ define a function called the probability function for this experiment; see Fig. 14.1.

Since the formula for the probability function is one term of a binomial expansion, we may say that we have an example of the *binomial probability distribution*. It serves as a model for many practical situations.

The physical interpretation in this example is that, if we were to draw a great many 3-item samples for testing, about 73% of the samples would contain no defective, 24% would contain 1 defective, and only 3% would contain

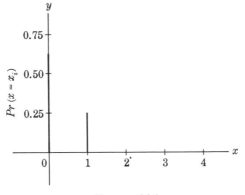

FIGURE 14.1

as many as 2 defectives. If we do obtain as improbable a result as a sample with 2 or 3 defectives, we reason that there may be some trouble in the control of the production process that has caused $Pr(D)$ to be larger than 0.1.

Thus far our discussion has been limited to cases in which the number of possible outcomes is finite. In many chance experiments the outcome is a measurement such as length, weight, or time, and the set of all possible outcomes is associated with a continuous variable. Our previous definition of probability then will not apply. We shall give an intuitive geometric approach to this type of problem (a rigorous treatment would require mathematical techniques that are beyond the scope of this text).

Example. Suppose a traffic signal has a 90-second cycle showing green for 50, amber for 10, and red for 30 seconds. What is the probability that a motorist will "hit" the green signal, assuming that he approaches the signal under chance conditions?

Solution: The time at which the motorist reaches the signal, measured from the start of the green signal, may be represented by the line interval of 0 to 90. The probability that he reaches the signal at some time in the cycle is 1 and will be

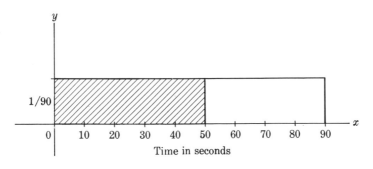

FIGURE 14.2

represented by a rectangle of height 1/90 and area 1, as shown in Fig. 14.2. The probability that he "hits" the green light is, then,

$$\frac{\text{area of shaded rectangle}}{\text{area of large rectangle}} = \frac{50/90}{90/90} = \frac{5}{9}.$$

Example.   Experience in a certain factory has shown that an exponential function is a satisfactory probability model for the times required to serve mechanics at a tool crib. To be specific, suppose that areas under the curve $y = e^{-x}$, where x is time in minutes, can be used to represent the probability that the service time is of a given duration. What is the probability that the service time will be 1 minute or less? That it will be 3 minutes or less?

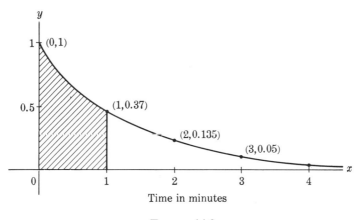

FIGURE 14.3

Solution: The graph of $y = e^{-x}$ is given in Fig. 14.3, in which are used several values from Table **IV** of the appendix. The probability that the service time will be 1 minute or less will be the ratio of the shaded area to the total area, or

$$\int_0^1 e^{-x}\, dx \Big/ \int_0^\infty e^{-x}\, dx.$$

We state without proof that the denominator is 1, so the required probability (see Section 8 of Chapter XII) is

$$\int_0^1 e^{-x}\, dx = -e^{-x}\Big]_0^1 = 1 - e^{-1} = 1 - 0.36788 = 0.63212.$$

Approximately 63 % of the time calls at the tool crib will require 1 minute or less, provided the probability model adequately describes the real situation.

We leave it to the reader to show that, in the example just given, about 95 % of all calls will require 3 minutes or less. Note that probability is represented by *area* under a curve and not by the height of y in each of the last two examples. In general, probabilities associated with a continuous variable x are defined in such a way that the probability that x takes on a value between a and b is the area under a curve over the interval a to b. Since the area over a single point is 0, the probability that a continuous chance variable x will take on a specific value is defined as 0.

The most important probability distribution is the *standard normal distribution* specified by the curve whose equation is

(Eq. 1)
$$y = \frac{1}{\sqrt{2\pi}} e^{-x^2/2}.$$

The table below gives the values of y for a few values of x. Further values could be computed by using the table of exponentials.

x	0.0	±0.5	±1.0	±1.5	±2.0	±2.5	±3.0	±3.5	±4.0
y	0.3989	0.3521	0.2420	0.1295	0.0540	0.0175	0.0044	0.0009	0.0001

If we plot these points and join them with a smooth curve, we obtain the well-known bell-shaped curve of Fig. 14.4. This curve has the following

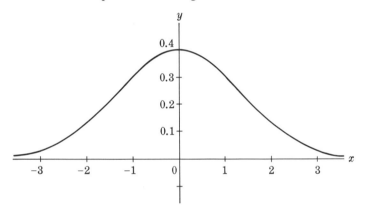

FIGURE 14.4

properties, some of which are obvious and some of which require advanced calculus for proof:

1. It is symmetric about the y axis.
2. It is always above the x axis, extends indefinitely to the left and to the right, and approaches the x axis as its distance from the y axis increases.
3. The area bounded by the curve and the x axis is 1.
4. The area under the curve between $x = a$ and $x = b$ can be interpreted as the probability that a value of x selected at random from a set of numbers which has this distribution will have a value between a and b.

The area under the standard normal curve over the interval $x = a$ to $x = b$ can be obtained by evaluating the integral

(Eq. 2)
$$\frac{1}{\sqrt{2\pi}} \int_a^b e^{-x^2/2} \, dx,$$

although, unfortunately, this integral is one that cannot be evaluated by ordinary means. We shall, however, give a table of values for the integral $I(a)$, the area from $x = 0$ to $x = a$,

(Eq. 3) $$I(a) = \frac{1}{\sqrt{2\pi}} \int_0^a e^{-x^2/2} \, dx,$$

and from the table we will be able to evaluate Equation 2 for any values of a and b. To do this, we note that

(Eq. 4) $$\frac{1}{\sqrt{2\pi}} \int_a^b e^{-x^2/2} \, dx = \frac{1}{\sqrt{2\pi}} \int_0^b e^{-x^2/2} \, dx - \frac{1}{\sqrt{2\pi}} \int_0^a e^{-x^2/2} \, dx$$

and

(Eq. 5) $$\frac{1}{\sqrt{2\pi}} \int_{-a}^0 e^{-x^2/2} \, dx = \frac{1}{\sqrt{2\pi}} \int_0^a e^{-x^2/2} \, dx.$$

The table, accompanying, gives the values of $I(a)$ for values of a from 0 to 4. Since the curve is so very close to the x axis at $x = 4$ and continues to approach the x axis, the area to the right of $x = 4$ is negligible.

Areas Under the Standard Normal Curve

a	$I(a)$	a	$I(a)$	a	$I(a)$
.0	.0000	1.4	.4192	2.8	.4974
.1	.0398	1.5	.4332	2.9	.4981
.2	.0793	1.6	.4452	3.0	.4987
.3	.1179	1.7	.4554	3.1	.4990
.4	.1554	1.8	.4641	3.2	.4993
.5	.1915	1.9	.4713	3.3	.4995
.6	.2257	2.0	.4772	3.4	.4997
.7	.2580	2.1	.4821	3.5	.4998
.8	.2881	2.2	.4861	3.6	.4998
.9	.3159	2.3	.4893	3.7	.4999
1.0	.3413	2.4	.4918	3.8	.4999
1.1	.3643	2.5	.4938	3.9	.5000
1.2	.3849	2.6	.4953	4.0	.5000
1.3	.4032	2.7	.4965		

Example. Given a set of numbers that has the standard normal distribution, find the probability that an element selected at random has a value between -0.4 and $+1.2$.

Solution: This probability is the area under the curve from $x = -0.4$ to $x = 1.2$, or the area from $x = -0.4$ to $x = 0$ plus the area from $x = 0$ to $x = 1.2$. By symmetry, the area from $x = -0.4$ to $x = 0$ is equal to the area from $x = 0$ to $x = 0.4$. Therefore, the area is

$$I(0.4) + I(1.2) = 0.1554 + 0.3849 = 0.5403$$

and so the required probability is 0.5403. Alternatively, using Equations 4 and 5 we obtain

$$\frac{1}{\sqrt{2\pi}} \int_{-0.4}^{1.2} e^{-x^2/2}\, dx = \frac{1}{\sqrt{2\pi}} \int_{0}^{1.2} e^{-x^2/2}\, dx - \frac{1}{\sqrt{2\pi}} \int_{0}^{-0.4} e^{-x^2/2}\, dx,$$

$$= \frac{1}{\sqrt{2\pi}} \int_{0}^{1.2} e^{-x^2/2}\, dx + \frac{1}{\sqrt{2\pi}} \int_{-0.4}^{0} e^{-x^2/2}\, dx,$$

$$= \frac{1}{\sqrt{2\pi}} \int_{0}^{1.2} e^{-x^2/2}\, dx + \frac{1}{\sqrt{2\pi}} \int_{0}^{0.4} e^{-x^2/2}\, dx,$$

$$= 0.3849 + 0.1554 = 0.5403.$$

Example.   Given a set of numbers that has the standard normal distribution, find the probability that an element selected at random has a value between $x = 0.8$ and $x = 2.2$.

Solution: This probability is the area under the curve from $x = 0.8$ to $x = 2.2$, or the area under the curve from $x = 0$ to $x = 2.2$ minus the area under the curve from $x = 0$ to $x = 0.8$. Hence, the required probability is

$$I(2.2) - I(0.8) = 0.4861 - 0.2881 = 0.1980.$$

This distribution is a satisfactory model for a wide variety of practical situations. For example, heights of men, intelligence test scores, and diameters of bolts often have approximately normal distributions. We shall discuss some of these applications in Section 9, but first it will be necessary to develop some additional theory.

EXERCISES

1. A certain machine produces 5% defective items in the long run. What is the probability distribution of x, the number of defectives in random samples of 2 items each. Exhibit your answer as a table and as a formula.

2. Evaluate $\dfrac{1}{\sqrt{2\pi}} \displaystyle\int_{-2.3}^{1.8} e^{-x^2/2}\, dx.$

4. Evaluate $\dfrac{1}{\sqrt{2\pi}} \displaystyle\int_{3.2}^{4.0} e^{-x^2/2}\, dx.$

3. Evaluate $\dfrac{1}{\sqrt{2\pi}} \displaystyle\int_{1.1}^{2.1} e^{-x^2/2}\, dx.$

5. Evaluate $\dfrac{1}{\sqrt{2\pi}} \displaystyle\int_{3.5}^{1,000,000} e^{-x^2/2}\, dx.$

7 MEAN VALUE, VARIANCE, AND STANDARD DEVIATION

It is often useful to have measures that summarize the information in a probability distribution. The three most useful measures are the mean value (which we have studied in Section 5 as mathematical expectation), the variance, and the standard deviation. We shall give definitions for the case of distributions in which the variable takes only a finite number of values; generalizations require material from the integral calculus, beyond the scope of this text.

Definition 14.2. *If an experiment can result in the set of numbers* $\{x_i\} = \{x_1, x_2, \cdots, x_n\}$ *with probabilities* $Pr(x_i)$, *respectively, then the* expected value *of* x *is*

(Eq. 1) $$E(x) = x_1 Pr(x_1) + x_2 Pr(x_2) + \cdots + x_n Pr(x_n).$$

In the special case in which each of the x_i has probability $1/n$ we obtain the usual formula for the arithmetic mean

(Eq. 2) $$E(x) = \frac{x_1 + x_2 + \cdots + x_n}{n}.$$

$E(x)$ is often denoted by the symbol μ (the Greek letter for m, the first letter of the word "mean"). We now state some theorems about expected values. The theorems hold in general, but we shall limit the discussion in this section to the simple case in which $Pr(x_i) = 1/n$ for all x_i.

Theorem 14.1. *If the set* $\{x_i - a\}$ *is formed from the set* $\{x_i\}$ *by the subtraction of* a *from each element, then* $E(x - a) = E(x) - a$.

    Proof: $E(x - a) = \dfrac{(x_1 - a) + (x_2 - a) + \cdots + (x_n - a)}{n}$,

$$= \frac{x_1 + x_2 + \cdots + x_n - na}{n},$$

$$= \frac{x_1 + x_2 + \cdots + x_n}{n} - \frac{na}{n},$$

$$= E(x) - a.$$

Theorem 14.2. *If the set* $\{cx_i\}$ *is formed from the set* $\{x_i\}$ *by the multiplication of each element by* c, *then* $E(cx) = cE(x)$.

    Proof: $E(cx) = \dfrac{cx_1 + cx_2 + \cdots + cx_n}{n}$,

$$= c\frac{x_1 + x_2 + \cdots + x_n}{n} = cE(x).$$

These two theorems are sometimes useful in reducing the amount of arithmetic required for calculating mean values.

    Example. Find the arithmetic mean of the set

$$\{x_i\} = \{245, 251, 248, 253, 255\}.$$

Solution 1:   By definition,

$$E(x) = \frac{245 + 251 + 248 + 253 + 255}{5},$$

$$= \frac{1252}{5} = 250.4.$$

Solution 2:   Subtract 250 from each element to obtain the set $\{-5, 1, -2, 3, 5\}$ whose mean is $2/5 = 0.4$. By Theorem 14.1,

$$E(x - 250) = E(x) - 250,$$
$$E(x) = E(x - 250) + 250 = 250.4.$$

Example.   Find the arithmetic mean of the set $\{x_i\} = \{0.04, 0.07, 0.08, 0.05\}$.

Solution: Multiply each element of the set by 100 to obtain the set $\{4, 7, 8, 5\}$, whose mean is $24/4 = 6$. By Theorem 14.2,

$$E(100x) = 100E(x)$$

$$E(x) = \frac{E(100x)}{100} = \frac{6}{100} = 0.06.$$

Note that the mean value of a set is not necessarily an element of the set. The "usefulness" of the mean value of a set of numbers is generally greater if the numbers of the set do not deviate a great deal from the mean. The variance can be used as a measure of this deviation.

Definition 14.3.   *The variance $V(x)$ of the set $\{x_i\}$ with mean value $E(x) = \mu$ is the* expected value *of the set $\{(x_i - \mu)^2\}$ whose elements are the squares of the differences between the corresponding elements of the original set and the mean of that set. Thus,*

(Eq. 3) $$V(x) = (x_1 - \mu)^2 Pr(x_1) + (x_2 - \mu)^2 Pr(x_2) \\ + \cdots + (x_n - \mu)^2 Pr(x_n).$$

If $Pr(x_i) = 1/n$ for each x_i, this reduces to

(Eq. 4) $$V(x) = \frac{(x_1 - \mu)^2 + (x_2 - \mu)^2 + \cdots + (x_n - \mu)^2}{n}.$$

Note that the variance is nonnegative. If all the x_i are equal and hence equal to μ, the variance is zero. If the x_i do not differ much from μ, the variance will be small but, if the deviations $x_i - \mu$ are large, then the variance will be large.

Example.   Compute the variance of the set $\{x_i\} = \{2, 4, 0, 3, -1\}$.

Solution: $\mu = 8/5 = 1.6$. We have $\{x_i - \mu\} = \{0.4, 2.4, -1.6, 1.4, -2.6\}$. Hence the variance is the arithmetic mean of the set

$$\{(x_i - \mu)^2\} = \{0.16, 5.76, 2.56, 1.96, 6.76\},$$
$$V(x) = 17.20/5 = 3.44.$$

The variance has several interesting properties, which are stated in the following theorems.

Theorem 14.3.   *If μ and $V(x)$ are the mean and variance, respectively, of the set $\{x_i\}$ and if $E(x^2)$ is the mean of the set $\{x_i^2\}$, then $V(x) = E(x^2) - \mu^2$.*

Proof: $V(x) = \dfrac{(x_1 - \mu)^2 + (x_2 - \mu)^2 + \cdots + (x_n - \mu)^2}{n},$

$$= \frac{x_1^2 + x_2^2 + \cdots + x_n^2 - 2\mu(x_1 + x_2 + \cdots + x_n) + n\mu^2}{n};$$

but $\dfrac{x_1^2 + x_2^2 + \cdots + x_n^2}{n} = E(x^2)$

and $\dfrac{x_1 + x_2 + \cdots + x_n}{n} = \mu,$ by definition.

Therefore, $V(x) = E(x^2) - 2\mu \cdot \mu + \mu^2 = E(x^2) - \mu^2$.

Thus, the variance of a set of numbers may be calculated by taking the mean of the squares minus the square of the mean of the numbers. This method is usually simpler.

Example.   Compute the variance of the set $\{x_i\}$ of the last example by the method given above.

Solution: Given the set $\{x_i\} = \{2, 4, 0, 3, -1\}$, the set $\{x_i^2\} = \{4, 16, 0, 9, 1\}$ and $E(x^2) = \frac{30}{5} = 6$. Moreover, $\mu = 1.6$, and so

$$V(x) = E(x^2) - \mu^2 = 6 - (1.6)^2 = 6 - 2.56 = 3.44,$$

as before.

Theorem 14.4.   *If the set $\{cx_i\}$ is formed from the set $\{x_i\}$ by multiplying each element of the set by the constant c, then $V(cx) = c^2V(x)$.*

Proof: By the preceding theorem, we know that

$$V(cx) = E(c^2x^2) - [E(cx)]^2.$$

But, by Theorem 14.2, we have

$$V(cx) = c^2E(x^2) - [cE(x)]^2,$$
$$= c^2[E(x^2) - \mu^2],$$
$$= c^2V(x).$$

The arithmetic mean of a set and deviations from the mean are measured in the same units as the elements of the set, but the variance is measured in square units. Thus, if the elements of a set are measurements in inches, the mean will be given in inches but the variance will be in inches squared. To obtain a measure of variability measured in original units, it is natural to take the square root of the variance.

Definition 14.4. *The standard deviation of a set* $\{x_i\}$, *denoted by* $\sigma(x)$ *(read "sigma of x"), is the positive square root of the variance of the set. Thus,* $\sigma(x) = \sqrt{V(x)}$.

The standard deviation is frequently called the "root mean square," since it is the square root of the mean of the squares of the deviations from the mean.

We are now ready to show how to construct a standard set, a concept which will be required in the last section of the chapter when we deal with some practical applications of the normal distribution.

Definition 14.5. *A set will be called a* standard set *if the mean of the set is zero and the standard deviation is* 1.

Theorem 14.5. *If the set* $\{x_i\}$ *has mean* μ *and standard deviation* $\sigma \neq 0$, *then the set* $\{(x_i - \mu)/\sigma\}$ *is a standard set.*

Proof: By Theorems 14.1 and 14.2,

$$E\left(\frac{x - \mu}{\sigma}\right) = E\left(\frac{x}{\sigma} - \frac{\mu}{\sigma}\right) = E\left(\frac{x}{\sigma}\right) - \frac{\mu}{\sigma},$$

$$= \frac{1}{\sigma} E(x) - \frac{\mu}{\sigma} = \frac{\mu}{\sigma} - \frac{\mu}{\sigma} = 0.$$

By Theorem 14.3,

$$V\left(\frac{x - \mu}{\sigma}\right) = E\left(\frac{x - \mu}{\sigma}\right)^2 - \left[E\left(\frac{x - \mu}{\sigma}\right)\right]^2.$$

By Theorem 14.4,

$$E\left(\frac{x - \mu}{\sigma}\right)^2 = \frac{1}{\sigma^2} E(x - \mu)^2$$

$$V\left(\frac{x - \mu}{\sigma}\right) = \frac{1}{\sigma^2} E(x - \mu)^2 - 0 = \frac{1}{\sigma^2} \cdot \sigma^2 = 1.$$

It follows that the standard deviation of the set $\{(x_i - \mu)/\sigma\}$ is also 1. Thus, a standard set may be constructed from any set by subtracting the mean from each element and dividing the differences by the standard deviation.

Example. Construct a standard set from the set $\{4, 0, 3, 4, 1, 6\}$.

Solution: We first calculate $E(x) = \mu = \frac{18}{6} = 3$ and $E(x^2) = \frac{78}{6} = 13$, so that

$$V(x) = E(x^2) - \mu^2 = 13 - 9 = 4, \qquad \text{by Theorem 14.3.}$$

We also have $\sigma(x) = \sqrt{V(x)} = 2$. Now construct the set $\{x - \mu\} = \{1, -3, 0, 1, -2, 3\}$ whose mean is 0. Finally, construct the set

$$\{(x - \mu)/\sigma\} = \{\tfrac{1}{2}, -\tfrac{3}{2}, 0, \tfrac{1}{2}, -1, \tfrac{3}{2}\} = \{0.5, -1.5, 0, 0.5, -1, 1.5\}.$$

This is the required standard set.

Check: The mean of this set is 0 and the variance is

$$\frac{0.25 + 2.25 + 0 + 0.25 + 1 + 2.25}{6} = 1.$$

Therefore the standard deviation is also 1.

EXERCISES

Find the mean, variance, and standard deviation of each of the following sets.

1. $\{4, 4.2, 5, 5.6, 7, 9\}$.
2. $\{7, 3, 5, 4, 1, 9, 8, 7, 5, 4\}$.
3. $\{6, 6, 6, 6, 6, 6, 6, 7\}$.
4. $\{9, 10, 10, 10, 10, 10, 10, 11\}$.
5. Obtain a standard set corresponding to $\{4, 6, 7, 5, 2, 6, 6, 4, 4, 6\}$. Check your result.
6. Obtain a standard set corresponding to $\{5, 10, 13, 7, 17, 8\}$. Check your result.

8   POPULATIONS AND SAMPLES

The observations that are recorded when an experiment is performed usually will be only a subset of all the possible observations under the given conditions. We say that we have a *sample* from a given *population*. In the theory of statistics it is assumed that the population can be adequately described by some probability distribution and that the data of the sample, when properly drawn, can be used to make inferences about the characteristics of this distribution, such as its form, mean, and standard deviation.

Since the data in a sample represent only a subset of the population, it is necessary to introduce some new notation for the measures calculated from the sample data. Suppose that an experiment yields a sample of n observations with values $x_1, x_2, \cdots, x_k$ and respective frequencies $f_1, f_2, \cdots, f_k$. Of course, $f_1 + f_2 + \cdots + f_k = n$, and the relative frequency of occurrence of any x_i is f_i/n. The information in the sample may be summarized by the *sample mean* $\bar{x}$, the *sample variance* s^2, and the *sample standard deviation* s. Formulas for these three quantities are

(Eq. 1) $\bar{x} = \dfrac{x_1 f_1 + x_2 f_2 + \cdots + x_k f_k}{n}$

(Eq. 2) $s^2 = \dfrac{(x_1 - \bar{x})^2 f_1 + (x_2 - \bar{x})^2 f_2 + \cdots + (x_k - \bar{x})^2 f_k}{n}$

(Eq. 3) $s = \sqrt{\text{sample variance } s^2}$.

When the respective frequencies f_i are all equal to unity, the Equations 1 and 2 simplify to

(Eq. 1b) $\bar{x} = \dfrac{x_1 + x_2 + \cdots + x_n}{n}$

(Eq. 2b) $s^2 = \dfrac{(x_1 - \bar{x})^2 + (x_2 - \bar{x})^2 + \cdots + (x_n - \bar{x})^2}{n}$.

A convenient computing formula, algebraically equivalent to Equation 2, is

(Eq. 2c) $s^2 = \dfrac{x_1^2 f_1 + x_2^2 f_2 + \cdots + x_k^2 f_k}{n} - \bar{x}^2$.

Note that we are here using n to denote the number of observations in the sample, not the total number of possible outcomes. Theorems 14.1 to 14.5 may be restated in terms of $\bar{x}$, s^2, and s with only a change of notation, and are not repeated here.

We have already remarked the relationship between relative frequency and probability when n is large. It is also true that, for large samples drawn at random, $\bar{x}$, s^2, and s will usually be good approximations of $E(x) = \mu$, $\sigma^2(x)$, and $\sigma(x)$, respectively.

Example. Three pennies were tossed 100 times, with the following results:

No. of heads, x_i	0	1	2	3
Frequency, f_i	19	31	41	9

Calculate the relative frequencies, the mean, the variance, and the standard deviation for the sample data. Compare the results with the corresponding quantities for the theoretical frequency distribution.

Solution: The necessary calculations are presented below in tabular form, in order to display the analogies between the distribution of the sample data and the probability distribution which serves as the population model.

Sample Data

x_i	f_i	f_i/n	$x_i f_i$	$x_i - \bar{x}$	$(x_i - \bar{x})^2$	$(x_i - \bar{x})^2 f_i$
0	19	.19	0	-1.4	1.96	37.24
1	31	.31	31	$-.4$	.16	4.96
2	41	.41	82	.6	.36	14.76
3	9	.09	27	1.6	2.56	23.04
	$n = 100$ 1.00		140			80.00

$\bar{x} = 140/100 = 1.4,$ $s^2 = 80/100 = 0.8,$ $s = 0.894$

Probability Distribution

x_i	$Pr(x_i)$	$x_iPr(x_i)$	$x_i - \mu$	$(x_i - \mu)^2$	$(x_i - \mu)^2Pr(x_i)$
0	.125	0	−1.5	2.25	.28125
1	.375	.375	− .5	.25	.09375
2	.375	.750	.5	.25	.09375
3	.125	.375	1.5	2.25	.28125
	1.000	$\mu = 1.500$			$\sigma^2 = .75000$
					$\sigma = .866$

EXERCISES

1. Compute s^2 and σ^2 in the example of this section, using the computing formulas for these quantities.
2. Prove that the following equation holds for the simple case in which $f_i = 1$ for all i. Start with Equation 2 of this section.

$$s^2 = \frac{x_1^2 + x_2^2 + \cdots + x_n^2}{n} - \bar{x}^2$$

3. **a.** Roll a die 100 times and record your results as a frequency distribution. Compute the mean, variance, and standard deviation for your data.
   b. Find the expected value, variance, and standard deviation of the probability distribution associated with the roll of a true die. Compare these results with the experimental results just obtained.

9 NORMAL PROBABILITY DISTRIBUTIONS

Large sets of observations arising in a wide variety of fields of study often can be described by the probability distribution drawn in Fig. 14.5. This

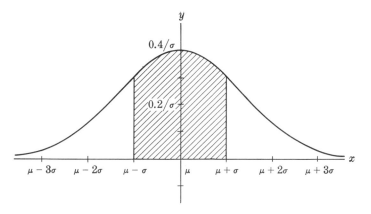

FIGURE 14.5

is called the normal probability distribution with mean μ and standard deviation σ. Actually, there are infinitely many normal distributions, because there are infinitely many possible values of μ and σ. The specific normal distribution that we studied in Section 6 is called the standard normal distribution because its mean is 0 and its standard deviation is 1. Fortunately, questions about any normal distribution can be reduced to questions about the standard normal distribution by the standardization technique described in Section 7. Consider the points $\mu - 2\sigma$, $\mu - \sigma$, μ, $\mu + \sigma$, and $\mu + 2\sigma$ on the x axis, which are labeled in the figure. These would become the elements -2, -1, 0, 1, 2 of the standard set $\{(x - \mu)/\sigma\}$ and, since $\sigma = 1$ for this set, Fig. 14.5 would become Fig. 14.4 (Section 6) by a mere relabeling of the axes. Thus, the table of the same section can be used to find probabilities for any normal distribution.

Example. Given a set of numbers that is normally distributed with mean μ and standard deviation σ, what is the probability that an element of the set has a value between $\mu - \sigma$ and $\mu + \sigma$?

Solution: We have remarked that $\mu - \sigma$ and $\mu + \sigma$ correspond to the elements -1 and $+1$ of the standard set; then the required probability is the shaded area in Fig. 14.5 or the corresponding area under the standard normal curve (Fig. 14.4). This is

$$\frac{1}{\sqrt{2\pi}} \int_{-1}^{1} e^{-x^2/2}\, dx = 2I(1) = 2 \cdot 0.3413 = 0.6826.$$

Thus, for any normal distribution, approximately 68% of the values will deviate from the mean by 1 standard deviation or less. Similarly, it can be shown that approximately 95% of the numbers will have values within 2 standard deviations of the mean.

Example. Measurements of 400 metal rods selected at random from the output of a certain production process gave the following distribution for the rod diameters, measured to the nearest hundredth of an inch; present the data of this sample graphically.

Diameter	.33	.34	.35	.36	.37	.38	.39	.40	.41
Frequency	1	0	4	54	139	146	50	4	2

Solution: Since the diameters are measured to the nearest hundredth of an inch, a reading of 0.33 may represent a true value anywhere between 0.325 and 0.335. The one observation at 0.33 is therefore pictured as a rectangle, its base running from 0.325 to 0.335 and its height being 1. The other frequencies are treated similarly. The resulting graph is called a *histogram* and is the usual method of graphing such data; see Fig. 14.6.

Here we have used areas of rectangles to correspond to frequencies just as we used areas under curves to represent probabilities. The shape of the

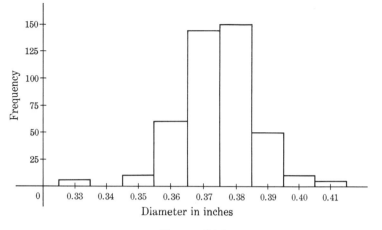

FIGURE 14.6

histogram of the sample data helps us to select an appropriate model for the population distribution. In this case it seems reasonable to assume that the diameters of all rods manufactured by this process will be normally distributed.

Example. Assuming that the variation in the diameters of the rods in the example above is normally distributed and that the sample mean and standard deviation, $\bar{x}$ and s respectively, are good approximations of μ and σ (a reasonable assumption, since the sample is large), what is the probability that a given rod has a diameter of at least 0.355 inch? How many rods should be purchased to obtain at least 1000 rods with diameters of 0.355 inch or more?

Solution: Calculations in which the formulas of Section 8 are used give a mean of 0.375 inch and a standard deviation of 0.01 inch for the 400 diameters. Therefore, the deviation in which we are interested, namely $0.355 - 0.375 = -0.02$ inch, is equal to -2 standard deviations. The required probability is the area to the right of -2 under the standard normal curve, or $I(2) + 0.5000 = 0.4772 + 0.5000 = 0.9772$. In other words, we would expect 97.72% of the rods to have a diameter at least as large as 0.355 inch. Hence, out of N rods we would expect $0.9772N$ rods of the desired size. Since we want at least 1000, we must have $0.9772N \geq 1000$. This requires that $N \geq 1023.3$, or 1024 rods.

Example. A manufacturer of light bulbs would like to claim that 90% of bulbs of a certain type will have a life of at least T hours when used under standard conditions. Five hundred of these bulbs were selected at random and burned until all failed. The distribution of the times to failure, rounded to the nearest 50 hours, is given in the following table. Use these data to estimate the time T which the manufacturer can use in his claim.

Time to failure in hours	150	200	250	300	350	400	450	500	550
Number of bulbs	1	4	67	153	184	83	6	0	2

Solution: It will first be necessary to calculate the mean and variance of the data. The calculations are arranged below in the usual tabular form. In the column headed f place the number of bulbs having the life given in the column headed x. In the third column place $f_i x_i$, the number in the f column multiplied by the corresponding number in the x column. In the fourth column place $f_i x_i^2$, the number in the fx column multiplied by the corresponding number in the x column. The totals of the f, fx, and fx^2 columns provide the necessary sums for computing the mean and variance by Equations 1 and 2c of the preceding section.

f	x	fx	fx^2
1	150	150	22,500
4	200	800	160,000
67	250	16,750	4,187,500
153	300	45,900	13,770,000
184	350	64,400	22,540,000
83	400	33,200	13,280,000
6	450	2,700	1,215,000
0	500	0	0
2	550	1,100	605,000
500		165,000	55,780,000

$$\bar{x} = \frac{165,000}{500} = 330 \text{ hours.}$$

$$s^2 = \frac{55,780,000}{500} - (330)^2 = 111,560 - 108,900,$$

$$= 2660 \text{ (hour)}^2.$$

$$s = \sqrt{2660} = 51.6 \text{ hours.}$$

We are now ready to solve the problem of the estimation of T. We shall assume that the distribution of the lives (x) of all bulbs of the special type is normal and that μ and σ are approximated closely by $\bar{x} = 330$ and $s = 51.6$, respectively. We require the value $x = T$ such that the probability of a value of x greater than T is 0.90. This is equivalent to asking for that value c of the standard normal distribution which has 90% of the area to the right of it. It is clear that c is negative and such that

$$\frac{1}{\sqrt{2\pi}} \int_c^\infty e^{-x^2/2} \, dx = \frac{1}{\sqrt{2\pi}} \int_c^0 e^{-x^2/2} \, dx + 0.5 = 0.90,$$

$$\frac{1}{\sqrt{2\pi}} \int_c^0 e^{-x^2/2} \, dx = 0.4.$$

Reference to the table in Section 6 shows that c is between -1.2 and -1.3, and interpolation yields the more accurate value $c = -1.28$. Thus, the required value T deviates from the mean by -1.28 standard deviations, or $(T - 330)/51.6 = -1.28$ and $T = 264$ hours.

The last two examples are illustrations of statistical inference. In each we have used the incomplete information contained in a sample to make predictions about a larger set, the population. There are, of course, risks of error in such procedures, but modern statistical methods based upon a firm foundation of probability theory enable us to make useful estimates and decisions and to assess the reliability of the results. The usefulness of the methods is indicated by their widespread acceptance in such fields as agriculture, medicine, psychology, the physical sciences, marketing, economics, and management science.

EXERCISES

1. Given a set of numbers that is normally distributed, with mean 50 and standard deviation 4, find the probability that an element selected at random from the set will have a value between 48 and 54; will have a value less than 56.

2. Scores on a certain college entrance test can be assumed to be normally distributed, with mean 200 and standard deviation 75.
   a. What percentage of the scores are between 50 and 350? What percentage greater than 275?
   b. College A will admit any applicant who makes a score of at least 125 on the test. How many will be expected to be admitted out of 600 applicants?
   c. College B will admit any applicant who makes a score in the upper 40%. Find the minimum score necessary for admission to this college.

3. Consider the data on rod diameters given in the second example of the text.
   a. Show that $\bar{x} = 0.375$ inch and $s = 0.01$ inch.
   b. Suppose that rods with diameters between 0.355 inch and 0.395 inch can be sold at a profit of 5¢ each. Rods under 0.355 inch in diameter must be scrapped, with a resulting loss of 2¢ per rod. Rods over 0.395 inch in diameter can be reworked to specifications and then sold for a profit of 3¢ each. Estimate the expected profit per rod, based on this sample of 400 rods.

4. A group of men was measured for height; the following table records the results.

Height in inches	62	63	64	65	66	67	68	69
Number of men with that height	1	2	0	3	6	15	70	130

Height in inches	70	71	72	73	74	75	76	77
Number of men with that height	360	410	250	110	35	10	7	1

Assuming the population to be normal, what is the probability that a man picked at random will be between 68 and 70 inches tall?

5. Ten coins were tossed 1000 times, and the following results were obtained.

Number of heads	0	1	2	3	4	5	6	7	8	9	10
Number of occurrences	2	10	44	107	209	252	211	110	47	7	1

Assuming the population distribution to be normal, what is the probability that at least 8 coins will be alike on a given throw?

6. A company manufactures steel plates. A random sample was tested for thickness with the following results.

Thickness in inches	1.97	1.98	1.99	2.00	2.01	2.02	2.03
Number of plates	2	23	212	571	253	36	3

A customer wants 2000 plates but specifies that the thickness must be at least 1.98 inches and not more than 2.02 inches. How many plates should be shipped to satisfy the requirements?

TABULAR
APPENDIX

0°

′	Sin	Tan	Ctn	Cos	′
0	.00000	.00000	—	1.0000	60
1	.00029	.00029	3437.7	1.0000	59
2	.00058	.00058	1718.9	1.0000	58
3	.00087	.00087	1145.9	1.0000	57
4	.00116	.00116	859.44	1.0000	56
5	.00145	.00145	687.55	1.0000	55
6	.00175	.00175	572.96	1.0000	54
7	.00204	.00204	491.11	1.0000	53
8	.00233	.00233	429.72	1.0000	52
9	.00262	.00262	381.97	1.0000	51
10	.00291	.00291	343.77	1.0000	50
11	.00320	.00320	312.52	.99999	49
12	.00349	.00349	286.48	.99999	48
13	.00378	.00378	264.44	.99999	47
14	.00407	.00407	245.55	.99999	46
15	.00436	.00436	229.18	.99999	45
16	.00465	.00465	214.86	.99999	44
17	.00495	.00495	202.22	.99999	43
18	.00524	.00524	190.98	.99999	42
19	.00553	.00553	180.93	.99998	41
20	.00582	.00582	171.89	.99998	40
21	.00611	.00611	163.70	.99998	39
22	.00640	.00640	156.26	.99998	38
23	.00669	.00669	149.47	.99998	37
24	.00698	.00698	143.24	.99998	36
25	.00727	.00727	137.51	.99997	35
26	.00756	.00756	132.22	.99997	34
27	.00785	.00785	127.32	.99997	33
28	.00814	.00815	122.77	.99997	32
29	.00844	.00844	118.54	.99996	31
30	.00873	.00873	114.59	.99996	30
31	.00902	.00902	110.89	.99996	29
32	.00931	.00931	107.43	.99996	28
33	.00960	.00960	104.17	.99995	27
34	.00989	.00989	101.11	.99995	26
35	.01018	.01018	98.218	.99995	25
36	.01047	.01047	95.489	.99995	24
37	.01076	.01076	92.908	.99994	23
38	.01105	.01105	90.463	.99994	22
39	.01134	.01135	88.144	.99994	21
40	.01164	.01164	85.940	.99993	20
41	.01193	.01193	83.844	.99993	19
42	.01222	.01222	81.847	.99993	18
43	.01251	.01251	79.943	.99992	17
44	.01280	.01280	78.126	.99992	16
45	.01309	.01309	76.390	.99991	15
46	.01338	.01338	74.729	.99991	14
47	.01367	.01367	73.139	.99991	13
48	.01396	.01396	71.615	.99990	12
49	.01425	.01425	70.153	.99990	11
50	.01454	.01455	68.750	.99989	10
51	.01483	.01484	67.402	.99989	9
52	.01513	.01513	66.105	.99989	8
53	.01542	.01542	64.858	.99988	7
54	.01571	.01571	63.657	.99988	6
55	.01600	.01600	62.499	.99987	5
56	.01629	.01629	61.383	.99987	4
57	.01658	.01658	60.306	.99986	3
58	.01687	.01687	59.266	.99986	2
59	.01716	.01716	58.261	.99985	1
60	.01745	.01746	57.290	.99985	0
′	Cos	Ctn	Tan	Sin	′

89°

1°

′	Sin	Tan	Ctn	Cos	′
0	.01745	.01746	57.290	.99985	60
1	.01774	.01775	56.351	.99984	59
2	.01803	.01804	55.442	.99984	58
3	.01832	.01833	54.561	.99983	57
4	.01862	.01862	53.709	.99983	56
5	.01891	.01891	52.882	.99982	55
6	.01920	.01920	52.081	.99982	54
7	.01949	.01949	51.303	.99981	53
8	.01978	.01978	50.549	.99980	52
9	.02007	.02007	49.816	.99980	51
10	.02036	.02036	49.104	.99979	50
11	.02065	.02066	48.412	.99979	49
12	.02094	.02095	47.740	.99978	48
13	.02123	.02124	47.085	.99977	47
14	.02152	.02153	46.449	.99977	46
15	.02181	.02182	45.829	.99976	45
16	.02211	.02211	45.226	.99976	44
17	.02240	.02240	44.639	.99975	43
18	.02269	.02269	44.066	.99974	42
19	.02298	.02298	43.508	.99974	41
20	.02327	.02328	42.964	.99973	40
21	.02356	.02357	42.433	.99972	39
22	.02385	.02386	41.916	.99972	38
23	.02414	.02415	41.411	.99971	37
24	.02443	.02444	40.917	.99970	36
25	.02472	.02473	40.436	.99969	35
26	.02501	.02502	39.965	.99969	34
27	.02530	.02531	39.506	.99968	33
28	.02560	.02560	39.057	.99967	32
29	.02589	.02589	38.618	.99966	31
30	.02618	.02619	38.188	.99966	30
31	.02647	.02648	37.769	.99965	29
32	.02676	.02677	37.358	.99963	28
33	.02705	.02706	36.956	.99963	27
34	.02734	.02735	36.563	.99963	26
35	.02763	.02764	36.178	.99962	25
36	.02792	.02793	35.801	.99961	24
37	.02821	.02822	35.431	.99960	23
38	.02850	.02851	35.070	.99959	22
39	.02879	.02881	34.715	.99959	21
40	.02908	.02910	34.368	.99958	20
41	.02938	.02939	34.027	.99957	19
42	.02967	.02968	33.694	.99956	18
43	.02996	.02997	33.366	.99955	17
44	.03025	.03026	33.045	.99954	16
45	.03054	.03055	32.730	.99953	15
46	.03083	.03084	32.421	.99952	14
47	.03112	.03114	32.118	.99952	13
48	.03141	.03143	31.821	.99951	12
49	.03170	.03172	31.528	.99950	11
50	.03199	.03201	31.242	.99949	10
51	.03228	.03230	30.960	.99948	9
52	.03257	.03259	30.683	.99947	8
53	.03286	.03288	30.412	.99946	7
54	.03316	.03317	30.145	.99945	6
55	.03345	.03346	29.882	.99944	5
56	.03374	.03376	29.624	.99943	4
57	.03403	.03405	29.371	.99942	3
58	.03432	.03434	29.122	.99941	2
59	.03461	.03463	28.877	.99940	1
60	.03490	.03492	28.636	.99939	0
′	Cos	Ctn	Tan	Sin	′

88°

TABLE I. NATURAL TRIGONOMETRIC FUNCTIONS   463

2°

′	Sin	Tan	Ctn	Cos	′
0	.03490	.03492	28.636	.99939	60
1	.03519	.03521	28.399	.99938	59
2	.03548	.03550	28.166	.99937	58
3	.03577	.03579	27.937	.99936	57
4	.03606	.03609	27.712	.99935	56
5	.03635	.03638	27.490	.99934	55
6	.03664	.03667	27.271	.99933	54
7	.03693	.03696	27.057	.99932	53
8	.03723	.03725	26.845	.99931	52
9	.03752	.03754	26.637	.99930	51
10	.03781	.03783	26.432	.99929	50
11	.03810	.03812	26.230	.99927	49
12	.03839	.03842	26.031	.99926	48
13	.03868	.03871	25.835	.99925	47
14	.03897	.03900	25.642	.99924	46
15	.03926	.03929	25.452	.99923	45
16	.03955	.03958	25.264	.99922	44
17	.03984	.03987	25.080	.99921	43
18	.04013	.04016	24.898	.99919	42
19	.04042	.04046	24.719	.99918	41
20	.04071	.04075	24.542	.99917	40
21	.04100,	.04104	24.368	.99916	39
22	.04129	.04133	24.196	.99915	38
23	.04159	.04162	24.026	.99913	37
24	.04188	.04191	23.859	.99912	36
25	.04217	.04220	23.695	.99911	35
26	.04246	.04250	23.532	.99910	34
27	.04275	.04279	23.372	.99909	33
28	.04304	.04308	23.214	.99907	32
29	.04333	.04337	23.058	.99906	31
30	.04362	.04366	22.904	.99905	30
31	.04391	.04395	22.752	.99904	29
32	.04420	.04424	22.602	.99902	28
33	.04449	.04454	22.454	.99901	27
34	.04478	.04483	22.308	.99900	26
35	.04507	.04512	22.164	.99898	25
36	.04536	.04541	22.022	.99897	24
37	.04565	.04570	21.881	.99896	23
38	.04594	.04599	21.743	.99894	22
39	.04623	.04628	21.606	.99893	21
40	.04653	.04658	21.470	.99892	20
41	.04682	.04687	21.337	.99890	19
42	.04711	.04716	21.205	.99889	18
43	.04740	.04745	21.075	.99888	17
44	.04769	.04774	20.946	.99886	16
45	.04798	.04803	20.819	.99885	15
46	.04827	.04833	20.693	.99883	14
47	.04856	.04862	20.569	.99882	13
48	.04885	.04891	20.446	.99881	12
49	.04914	.04920	20.325	.99879	11
50	.04943	.04949	20.206	.99878	10
51	.04972	.04978	20.087	.99876	9
52	.05001	.05007	19.970	.99875	8
53	.05030	.05037	19.855	.99873	7
54	.05059	.05066	19.740	.99872	6
55	.05088	.05095	19.627	.99870	5
56	.05117	.05124	19.516	.99869	4
57	.05146	.05153	19.405	.99867	3
58	.05175	.05182	19.296	.99866	2
59	.05205	.05212	19.188	.99864	1
60	.05234	.05241	19.081	.99863	0
′	Cos	Ctn	Tan	Sin	′

87°

3°

′	Sin	Tan	Ctn	Cos	′
0	.05234	.05241	19.081	.99863	60
1	.05263	.05270	18.976	.99861	59
2	.05292	.05299	18.871	.99860	58
3	.05321	.05328	18.768	.99858	57
4	.05350	.05357	18.666	.99857	56
5	.05379	.05387	18.564	.99855	55
6	.05408	.05416	18.464	.99854	54
7	.05437	.05445	18.366	.99852	53
8	.05466	.05474	18.268	.99851	52
9	.05495	.05503	18.171	.99849	51
10	.05524	.05533	18.075	.99847	50
11	.05553	.05562	17.980	.99846	49
12	.05582	.05591	17.886	.99844	48
13	.05611	.05620	17.793	.99842	47
14	.05640	.05649	17.702	.99841	46
15	.05669	.05678	17.611	.99839	45
16	.05698	.05708	17.521	.99838	44
17	.05727	.05737	17.431	.99836	43
18	.05756	.05766	17.343	.99834	42
19	.05785	.05795	17.256	.99833	41
20	.05814	.05824	17.169	.99831	40
21	.05844	.05854	17.084	.99829	39
22	.05873	.05883	16.999	.99827	38
23	.05902	.05912	16.915	.99826	37
24	.05931	.05941	16.832	.99824	36
25	.05960	.05970	16.750	.99822	35
26	.05989	.05999	16.668	.99821	34
27	.06018	.06029	16.587	.99819	33
28	.06047	.06058	16.507	.99817	32
29	.06076	.06087	16.428	.99815	31
30	.06105	.06116	16.350	.99813	30
31	.06134	.06145	16.272	.99812	29
32	.06163	.06175	16.195	.99810	28
33	.06192	.06204	16.119	.99808	27
34	.06221	.06233	16.043	.99806	26
35	.06250	.06262	15.969	.99804	25
36	.06279	.06291	15.895	.99803	24
37	.06308	.06321	15.821	.99801	23
38	.06337	.06350	15.748	.99799	22
39	.06366	.06379	15.676	.99797	21
40	.06395	.06408	15.605	.99795	20
41	.06424	.06438	15.534	.99793	19
42	.06453	.06467	15.464	.99792	18
43	.06482	.06496	15.394	.99790	17
44	.06511	.06525	15.325	.99788	16
45	.06540	.06554	15.257	.99786	15
46	.06569	.06584	15.189	.99784	14
47	.06598	.06613	15.122	.99782	13
48	.06627	.06642	15.056	.99780	12
49	.06656	.06671	14.990	.99778	11
50	.06685	.06700	14.924	.99776	10
51	.06714	.06730	14.860	.99774	9
52	.06743	.06759	14.795	.99772	8
53	.06773	.06788	14.732	.99770	7
54	.06802	.06817	14.669	.99768	6
55	.06831	.06847	14.606	.99766	5
56	.06860	.06876	14.544	.99764	4
57	.06889	.06905	14.482	.99762	3
58	.06918	.06934	14.421	.99760	2
59	.06947	.06963	14.361	.99758	1
60	.06976	.06993	14.301	.99756	0
′	Cos	Ctn	Tan	Sin	′

86°

4°

′	Sin	Tan	Ctn	Cos	′
0	.06976	.06993	14.301	.99756	60
1	.07005	.07022	14.241	.99754	59
2	.07034	.07051	14.182	.99752	58
3	.07063	.07080	14.124	.99750	57
4	.07092	.07110	14.065	.99748	56
5	.07121	.07139	14.008	.99746	55
6	.07150	.07168	13.951	.99744	54
7	.07179	.07197	13.894	.99742	53
8	.07208	.07227	13.838	.99740	52
9	.07237	.07256	13.782	.99738	51
10	.07266	.07285	13.727	.99736	50
11	.07295	.07314	13.672	.99734	49
12	.07324	.07344	13.617	.99731	48
13	.07353	.07373	13.563	.99729	47
14	.07382	.07402	13.510	.99727	46
15	.07411	.07431	13.457	.99725	45
16	.07440	.07461	13.404	.99723	44
17	.07469	.07490	13.352	.99721	43
18	.07498	.07519	13.300	.99719	42
19	.07527	.07548	13.248	.99716	41
20	.07556	.07578	13.197	.99714	40
21	.07585	.07607	13.146	.99712	39
22	.07614	.07636	13.096	.99710	38
23	.07643	.07665	13.046	.99708	37
24	.07672	.07695	12.996	.99705	36
25	.07701	.07724	12.947	.99703	35
26	.07730	.07753	12.898	.99701	34
27	.07759	.07782	12.850	.99699	33
28	.07788	.07812	12.801	.99696	32
29	.07817	.07841	12.754	.99694	31
30	.07846	.07870	12.706	.99692	30
31	.07875	.07899	12.659	.99689	29
32	.07904	.07929	12.612	.99687	28
33	.07933	.07958	12.566	.99685	27
34	.07962	.07987	12.520	.99683	26
35	.07991	.08017	12.474	.99680	25
36	.08020	.08046	12.429	.99678	24
37	.08049	.08075	12.384	.99676	23
38	.08078	.08104	12.339	.99673	22
39	.08107	.08134	12.295	.99671	21
40	.08136	.08163	12.251	.99668	20
41	.08165	.08192	12.207	.99666	19
42	.08194	.08221	12.163	.99664	18
43	.08223	.08251	12.120	.99661	17
44	.08252	.08280	12.077	.99659	16
45	.08281	.08309	12.035	.99657	15
46	.08310	.08339	11.992	.99654	14
47	.08339	.08368	11.950	.99652	13
48	.08368	.08397	11.909	.99649	12
49	.08397	.08427	11.867	.99647	11
50	.08426	.08456	11.826	.99644	10
51	.08455	.08485	11.785	.99642	9
52	.08484	.08514	11.745	.99639	8
53	.08513	.08544	11.705	.99637	7
54	.08542	.08573	11.664	.99635	6
55	.08571	.08602	11.625	.99632	5
56	.08600	.08632	11.585	.99630	4
57	.08629	.08661	11.546	.99627	3
58	.08658	.08690	11.507	.99625	2
59	.08687	.08720	11.468	.99622	1
60	.08716	.08749	11.430	.99619	0
′	Cos	Ctn	Tan	Sin	′

85°

5°

′	Sin	Tan	Ctn	Cos	′
0	.08716	.08749	11.430	.99619	60
1	.08745	.08778	11.392	.99617	59
2	.08774	.08807	11.354	.99614	58
3	.08803	.08837	11.316	.99612	57
4	.08831	.08866	11.279	.99609	56
5	.08860	.08895	11.242	.99607	55
6	.08889	.08925	11.205	.99604	54
7	.08918	.08954	11.168	.99602	53
8	.08947	.08983	11.132	.99599	52
9	.08976	.09013	11.095	.99596	51
10	.09005	.09042	11.059	.99594	50
11	.09034	.09071	11.024	.99591	49
12	.09063	.09101	10.988	.99588	48
13	.09092	.09130	10.953	.99586	47
14	.09121	.09159	10.918	.99583	46
15	.09150	.09189	10.883	.99580	45
16	.09179	.09218	10.848	.99578	44
17	.09208	.09247	10.814	.99575	43
18	.09237	.09277	10.780	.99572	42
19	.09266	.09306	10.746	.99570	41
20	.09295	.09335	10.712	.99567	40
21	.09324	.09365	10.678	.99564	39
22	.09353	.09394	10.645	.99562	38
23	.09382	.09423	10.612	.99559	37
24	.09411	.09453	10.579	.99556	36
25	.09440	.09482	10.546	.99553	35
26	.09469	.09511	10.514	.99551	34
27	.09498	.09541	10.481	.99548	33
28	.09527	.09570	10.449	.99545	32
29	.09556	.09600	10.417	.99542	31
30	.09585	.09629	10.385	.99540	30
31	.09614	.09658	10.354	.99537	29
32	.09642	.09688	10.322	.99534	28
33	.09671	.09717	10.291	.99531	27
34	.09700	.09746	10.260	.99528	26
35	.09729	.09776	10.229	.99526	25
36	.09758	.09805	10.199	.99523	24
37	.09787	.09834	10.168	.99520	23
38	.09816	.09864	10.138	.99517	22
39	.09845	.09893	10.108	.99514	21
40	.09874	.09923	10.078	.99511	20
41	.09903	.09952	10.048	.99508	19
42	.09932	.09981	10.019	.99506	18
43	.09961	.10011	9.9893	.99503	17
44	.09990	.10040	9.9601	.99500	16
45	.10019	.10069	9.9310	.99497	15
46	.10048	.10099	9.9021	.99494	14
47	.10077	.10128	9.8734	.99491	13
48	.10106	.10158	9.8448	.99488	12
49	.10135	.10187	9.8164	.99485	11
50	.10164	.10216	9.7882	.99482	10
51	.10192	.10246	9.7601	.99479	9
52	.10221	.10275	9.7322	.99476	8
53	.10250	.10305	9.7044	.99473	7
54	.10279	.10334	9.6768	.99470	6
55	.10308	.10363	9.6493	.99467	5
56	.10337	.10393	9.6220	.99464	4
57	.10366	.10422	9.5949	.99461	3
58	.10395	.10452	9.5679	.99458	2
59	.10424	.10481	9.5411	.99455	1
60	.10453	.10510	9.5144	.99452	0
′	Cos	Ctn	Tan	Sin	′

84°

TABLE I. NATURAL TRIGONOMETRIC FUNCTIONS   465

6°

′	Sin	Tan	Ctn	Cos	′
0	.10453	.10510	9.5144	.99452	60
1	.10482	.10540	9.4878	.99449	59
2	.10511	.10569	9.4614	.99446	58
3	.10540	.10599	9.4352	.99443	57
4	.10569	.10628	9.4090	.99440	56
5	.10597	.10657	9.3831	.99437	55
6	.10626	.10687	9.3572	.99434	54
7	.10655	.10716	9.3315	.99431	53
8	.10684	.10746	9.3060	.99428	52
9	.10713	.10775	9.2806	.99424	51
10	.10742	.10805	9.2553	.99421	50
11	.10771	.10834	9.2302	.99418	49
12	.10800	.10863	9.2052	.99415	48
13	.10829	.10893	9.1803	.99412	47
14	.10858	.10922	9.1555	.99409	46
15	.10887	.10952	9.1309	.99406	45
16	.10916	.10981	9.1065	.99402	44
17	.10945	.11011	9.0821	.99399	43
18	.10973	.11040	9.0579	.99396	42
19	.11002	.11070	9.0338	.99393	41
20	.11031	.11099	9.0098	.99390	40
21	.11060	.11128	8.9860	.99386	39
22	.11089	.11158	8.9623	.99383	38
23	.11118	.11187	8.9387	.99380	37
24	.11147	.11217	8.9152	.99377	36
25	.11176	.11246	8.8919	.99374	35
26	.11205	.11276	8.8686	.99370	34
27	.11234	.11305	8.8455	.99367	33
28	.11263	.11335	8.8225	.99364	32
29	.11291	.11364	8.7996	.99360	31
30	.11320	.11394	8.7769	.99357	30
31	.11349	.11423	8.7542	.99354	29
32	.11378	.11452	8.7317	.99351	28
33	.11407	.11482	8.7093	.99347	27
34	.11436	.11511	8.6870	.99344	26
35	.11465	.11541	8.6648	.99341	25
36	.11494	.11570	8.6427	.99337	24
37	.11523	.11600	8.6208	.99334	23
38	.11552	.11629	8.5989	.99331	22
39	.11580	.11659	8.5772	.99327	21
40	.11609	.11688	8.5555	.99324	20
41	.11638	.11718	8.5340	.99320	19
42	.11667	.11747	8.5126	.99317	18
43	.11696	.11777	8.4913	.99314	17
44	.11725	.11806	8.4701	.99310	16
45	.11754	.11836	8.4490	.99307	15
46	.11783	.11865	8.4280	.99303	14
47	.11812	.11895	8.4071	.99300	13
48	.11840	.11924	8.3863	.99297	12
49	.11869	.11954	8.3656	.99293	11
50	.11898	.11983	8.3450	.99290	10
51	.11927	.12013	8.3245	.99286	9
52	.11956	.12042	8.3041	.99283	8
53	.11985	.12072	8.2838	.99279	7
54	.12014	.12101	8.2636	.99276	6
55	.12043	.12131	8.2434	.99272	5
56	.12071	.12160	8.2234	.99269	4
57	.12100	.12190	8.2035	.99265	3
58	.12129	.12219	8.1837	.99262	2
59	.12158	.12249	8.1640	.99258	1
60	.12187	.12278	8.1443	.99255	0
′	Cos	Ctn	Tan	Sin	′

83°

7°

′	Sin	Tan	Ctn	Cos	′
0	.12187	.12278	8.1443	.99255	60
1	.12216	.12308	8.1248	.99251	59
2	.12245	.12338	8.1054	.99248	58
3	.12274	.12367	8.0860	.99244	57
4	.12302	.12397	8.0667	.99240	56
5	.12331	.12426	8.0476	.99237	55
6	.12360	.12456	8.0285	.99233	54
7	.12389	.12485	8.0095	.99230	53
8	.12418	.12515	7.9906	.99226	52
9	.12447	.12544	7.9718	.99222	51
10	.12476	.12574	7.9530	.99219	50
11	.12504	.12603	7.9344	.99215	49
12	.12533	.12633	7.9158	.99211	48
13	.12562	.12662	7.8973	.99208	47
14	.12591	.12692	7.8789	.99204	46
15	.12620	.12722	7.8606	.99200	45
16	.12649	.12751	7.8424	.99197	44
17	.12678	.12781	7.8243	.99193	43
18	.12706	.12810	7.8062	.99189	42
19	.12735	.12840	7.7882	.99186	41
20	.12764	.12869	7.7704	.99182	40
21	.12793	.12899	7.7525	.99178	39
22	.12822	.12929	7.7348	.99175	38
23	.12851	.12958	7.7171	.99171	37
24	.12880	.12988	7.6996	.99167	36
25	.12908	.13017	7.6821	.99163	35
26	.12937	.13047	7.6647	.99160	34
27	.12966	.13076	7.6473	.99156	33
28	.12995	.13106	7.6301	.99152	32
29	.13024	.13136	7.6129	.99148	31
30	.13053	.13165	7.5958	.99144	30
31	.13081	.13195	7.5787	.99141	29
32	.13110	.13224	7.5618	.99137	28
33	.13139	.13254	7.5449	.99133	27
34	.13168	.13284	7.5281	.99129	26
35	.13197	.13313	7.5113	.99125	25
36	.13226	.13343	7.4947	.99122	24
37	.13254	.13372	7.4781	.99118	23
38	.13283	.13402	7.4615	.99114	22
39	.13312	.13432	7.4451	.99110	21
40	.13341	.13461	7.4287	.99106	20
41	.13370	.13491	7.4124	.99102	19
42	.13399	.13521	7.3962	.99098	18
43	.13427	.13550	7.3800	.99094	17
44	.13456	.13580	7.3639	.99091	16
45	.13485	.13609	7.3479	.99087	15
46	.13514	.13639	7.3319	.99083	14
47	.13543	.13669	7.3160	.99079	13
48	.13572	.13698	7.3002	.99075	12
49	.13600	.13728	7.2844	.99071	11
50	.13629	.13758	7.2687	.99067	10
51	.13658	.13787	7.2531	.99063	9
52	.13687	.13817	7.2375	.99059	8
53	.13716	.13846	7.2220	.99055	7
54	.13744	.13876	7.2066	.99051	6
55	.13773	.13906	7.1912	.99047	5
56	.13802	.13935	7.1759	.99043	4
57	.13831	.13965	7.1607	.99039	3
58	.13860	.13995	7.1455	.99035	2
59	.13889	.14024	7.1304	.99031	1
60	.13917	.14054	7.1154	.99027	0
′	Cos	Ctn	Tan	Sin	′

82°

8°

′	Sin	Tan	Ctn	Cos	′
0	.13917	.14054	7.1154	.99027	**60**
1	.13946	.14084	7.1004	.99023	59
2	.13975	.14113	7.0855	.99019	58
3	.14004	.14143	7.0706	.99015	57
4	.14033	.14173	7.0558	.99011	56
5	.14061	.14202	7.0410	.99006	**55**
6	.14090	.14232	7.0264	.99002	54
7	.14119	.14262	7.0117	.98998	53
8	.14148	.14291	6.9972	.98994	52
9	.14177	.14321	6.9827	.98990	51
10	.14205	.14351	6.9682	.98986	**50**
11	.14234	.14381	6.9538	.98982	49
12	.14263	.14410	6.9395	.98978	48
13	.14292	.14440	6.9252	.98973	47
14	.14320	.14470	6.9110	.98969	46
15	.14349	.14499	6.8969	.98965	**45**
16	.14378	.14529	6.8828	.98961	44
17	.14407	.14559	6.8687	.98957	43
18	.14436	.14588	6.8548	.98953	42
19	.14464	.14618	6.8408	.98948	41
20	.14493	.14648	6.8269	.98944	**40**
21	.14522	.14678	6.8131	.98940	39
22	.14551	.14707	6.7994	.98936	38
23	.14580	.14737	6.7856	.98931	37
24	.14608	.14767	6.7720	.98927	36
25	.14637	.14796	6.7584	.98923	**35**
26	.14666	.14826	6.7448	.98919	34
27	.14695	.14856	6.7313	.98914	33
28	.14723	.14886	6.7179	.98910	32
29	.14752	.14915	6.7045	.98906	31
30	.14781	.14945	6.6912	.98902	**30**
31	.14810	.14975	6.6779	.98897	29
32	.14838	.15005	6.6646	.98893	28
33	.14867	.15034	6.6514	.98889	27
34	.14896	.15064	6.6383	.98884	26
35	.14925	.15094	6.6252	.98880	**25**
36	.14954	.15124	6.6122	.98876	24
37	.14982	.15153	6.5992	.98871	23
38	.15011	.15183	6.5863	.98867	22
39	.15040	.15213	6.5734	.98863	21
40	.15069	.15243	6.5606	.98858	**20**
41	.15097	.15272	6.5478	.98854	19
42	.15126	.15302	6.5350	.98849	18
43	.15155	.15332	6.5223	.98845	17
44	.15184	.15362	6.5097	.98841	16
45	.15212	.15391	6.4971	.98836	**15**
46	.15241	.15421	6.4846	.98832	14
47	.15270	.15451	6.4721	.98827	13
48	.15299	.15481	6.4596	.98823	12
49	.15327	.15511	6.4472	.98818	11
50	.15356	.15540	6.4348	.98814	**10**
51	.15385	.15570	6.4225	.98809	9
52	.15414	.15600	6.4103	.98805	8
53	.15442	.15630	6.3980	.98800	7
54	.15471	.15660	6.3859	.98796	6
55	.15500	.15689	6.3737	.98791	**5**
56	.15529	.15719	6.3617	.98787	4
57	.15557	.15749	6.3496	.98782	3
58	.15586	.15779	6.3376	.98778	2
59	.15615	.15809	6.3257	.98773	1
60	.15643	.15838	6.3138	.98769	**0**
′	Cos	Ctn	Tan	Sin	′

81°

9°

′	Sin	Tan	Ctn	Cos	′
0	.15643	.15838	6.3138	.98769	**60**
1	.15672	.15868	6.3019	.98764	59
2	.15701	.15898	6.2901	.98760	58
3	.15730	.15928	6.2783	.98755	57
4	.15758	.15958	6.2666	.98751	56
5	.15787	.15988	6.2549	.98746	**55**
6	.15816	.16017	6.2432	.98741	54
7	.15845	.16047	6.2316	.98737	53
8	.15873	.16077	6.2200	.98732	52
9	.15902	.16107	6.2085	.98728	51
10	.15931	.16137	6.1970	.98723	**50**
11	.15959	.16167	6.1856	.98718	49
12	.15988	.16196	6.1742	.98714	48
13	.16017	.16226	6.1628	.98709	47
14	.16046	.16256	6.1515	.98704	46
15	.16074	.16286	6.1402	.98700	**45**
16	.16103	.16316	6.1290	.98695	44
17	.16132	.16346	6.1178	.98690	43
18	.16160	.16376	6.1066	.98686	42
19	.16189	.16405	6.0955	.98681	41
20	.16218	.16435	6.0844	.98676	**40**
21	.16246	.16465	6.0734	.98671	39
22	.16275	.16495	6.0624	.98667	38
23	.16304	.16525	6.0514	.98662	37
24	.16333	.16555	6.0405	.98657	36
25	.16361	.16585	6.0296	.98652	**35**
26	.16390	.16615	6.0188	.98648	34
27	.16419	.16645	6.0080	.98643	33
28	.16447	.16674	5.9972	.98638	32
29	.16476	.16704	5.9865	.98633	31
30	.16505	.16734	5.9758	.98629	**30**
31	.16533	.16764	5.9651	.98624	29
32	.16562	.16794	5.9545	.98619	28
33	.16591	.16824	5.9439	.98614	27
34	.16620	.16854	5.9333	.98609	26
35	.16648	.16884	5.9228	.98604	**25**
36	.16677	.16914	5.9124	.98600	24
37	.16706	.16944	5.9019	.98595	23
38	.16734	.16974	5.8915	.98590	22
39	.16763	.17004	5.8811	.98585	21
40	.16792	.17033	5.8708	.98580	**20**
41	.16820	.17063	5.8605	.98576	19
42	.16849	.17093	5.8502	.98570	18
43	.16878	.17123	5.8400	.98565	17
44	.16906	.17153	5.8298	.98561	16
45	.16935	.17183	5.8197	.98556	**15**
46	.16964	.17213	5.8095	.98551	14
47	.16992	.17243	5.7994	.98546	13
48	.17021	.17273	5.7894	.98541	12
49	.17050	.17303	5.7794	.98536	11
50	.17078	.17333	5.7694	.98531	**10**
51	.17107	.17363	5.7594	.98526	9
52	.17136	.17393	5.7495	.98521	8
53	.17164	.17423	5.7396	.98516	7
54	.17193	.17453	5.7297	.98511	6
55	.17222	.17483	5.7199	.98506	**5**
56	.17250	.17513	5.7101	.98501	4
57	.17279	.17543	5.7004	.98496	3
58	.17308	.17573	5.6906	.98491	2
59	.17336	.17603	5.6809	.98486	1
60	.17365	.17633	5.6713	.98481	**0**
′	Cos	Ctn	Tan	Sin	′

80°

TABLE I. NATURAL TRIGONOMETRIC FUNCTIONS   467

10°

′	Sin	Tan	Ctn	Cos	′
0	.17365	.17633	5.6713	.98481	60
1	.17393	.17663	5.6617	.98476	59
2	.17422	.17693	5.6521	.98471	58
3	.17451	.17723	5.6425	.98466	57
4	.17479	.17753	5.6329	.98461	56
5	.17508	.17783	5.6234	.98455	55
6	.17537	.17813	5.6140	.98450	54
7	.17565	.17843	5.6045	.98445	53
8	.17594	.17873	5.5951	.98440	52
9	.17623	.17903	5.5857	.98435	51
10	.17651	17933	5.5764	.98430	50
11	.17680	.17963	5.5671	.98425	49
12	.17708	.17993	5.5578	.98420	48
13	.17737	.18023	5.5485	.98414	47
14	.17766	.18053	5.5393	.98409	46
15	.17794	.18083	5.5301	.98404	45
16	.17823	.18113	5.5209	.98399	44
17	.17852	.18143	5.5118	.98394	43
18	.17880	.18173	5.5026	.98389	42
19	.17909	.18203	5.4936	.98383	41
20	.17937	.18233	5.4845	.98378	40
21	.17966	.18263	5.4755	.98373	39
22	.17995	.18293	5.4665	.98368	38
23	.18023	.18323	5.4575	.98362	37
24	.18052	.18353	5.4486	.98357	36
25	.18081	.18384	5.4397	.98352	35
26	.18109	.18414	5.4308	.98347	34
27	.18138	.18444	5.4219	.98341	33
28	.18166	.18474	5.4131	.98336	32
29	.18195	.18504	5.4043	.98331	31
30	.18224	.18534	5.3955	.98325	30
31	.18252	.18564	5.3868	.98320	29
32	.18281	.18594	5.3781	.98315	28
33	.18309	.18624	5.3694	.98310	27
34	.18338	.18654	5.3607	.98304	26
35	.18367	.18684	5.3521	.98299	25
36	.18395	.18714	5.3435	.98294	24
37	.18424	.18745	5.3349	.98288	23
38	.18452	.18775	5.3263	.98283	22
39	.18481	.18805	5.3178	.98277	21
40	.18509	.18835	5.3093	.98272	20
41	.18538	.18865	5.3008	.98267	19
42	.18567	.18895	5.2924	.98261	18
43	.18595	.18925	5.2839	.98256	17
44	.18624	.18955	5.2755	.98250	16
45	.18652	.18986	5.2672	.98245	15
46	.18681	.19016	5.2588	.98240	14
47	.18710	.19046	5.2505	.98234	13
48	.18738	.19076	5.2422	.98229	12
49	.18767	.19106	5.2339	.98223	11
50	.18795	.19136	5.2257	.93218	10
51	.18824	.19166	5.2174	.98212	9
52	.18852	.19197	5.2092	.98207	8
53	.18881	.19227	5.2011	.98201	7
54	.18910	.19257	5.1929	.98196	6
55	.18938	.19287	5.1848	.98190	5
56	.18967	.19317	5.1767	.98185	4
57	.18995	.19347	5.1686	.98179	3
58	.19024	.19378	5.1606	.98174	2
59	.19052	.19408	5.1526	.98168	1
60	.19081	.19438	5.1446	.98163	0
′	Cos	Ctn	Tan	Sin	′

79°

11°

′	Sin	Tan	Ctn	Cos	′
0	.19081	.19438	5.1446	.98163	60
1	.19109	.19468	5.1366	.98157	59
2	.19138	.19498	5.1286	.98152	58
3	.19167	.19529	5.1207	.98146	57
4	.19195	.19559	5.1128	.98140	56
5	.19224	.19589	5.1049	.98135	55
6	.19252	.19619	5.0970	.98129	54
7	.19281	.19649	5.0892	.98124	53
8	.19309	.19680	5.0814	.98118	52
9	.19338	.19710	5.0736	.98112	51
10	.19366	.19740	5.0658	.98107	50
11	.19395	.19770	5.0581	.98101	49
12	.19423	.19801	5.0504	.98096	48
13	.19452	.19831	5.0427	.98090	47
14	.19481	.19861	5.0350	.98084	46
15	.19509	.19891	5.0273	.98079	45
16	.19538	.19921	5.0197	.98073	44
17	.19566	.19952	5.0121	.98067	43
18	.19595	.19982	5.0045	.98061	42
19	.19623	.20012	4.9969	.98056	41
20	.19652	.20042	4.9894	.98050	40
21	.19680	.20073	4.9819	.98044	39
22	.19709	.20103	4.9744	.98039	38
23	.19737	.20133	4.9669	.98033	37
24	.19766	.20164	4.9594	.98027	36
25	.19794	.20194	4.9520	.98021	35
26	.19823	.20224	4.9446	.98016	34
27	.19851	.20254	4.9372	.98010	33
28	.19880	.20285	4.9298	.98004	32
29	.19908	.20315	4.9225	.97998	31
30	.19937	.20345	4.9152	.97992	30
31	.19965	.20376	4.9078	.97987	29
32	.19994	.20406	4.9006	.97981	28
33	.20022	.20436	4.8933	.97975	27
34	.20051	.20466	4.8860	.97969	26
35	.20079	.20497	4.8788	.97963	25
36	.20108	.20527	4.8716	.97958	24
37	.20136	.20557	4.8644	.97952	23
38	.20165	.20588	4.8573	.97946	22
39	.20193	.20618	4.8501	.97940	21
40	.20222	.20648	4.8430	.97934	20
41	.20250	.20679	4.8359	.97928	19
42	.20279	.20709	4.8288	.97922	18
43	.20307	.20739	4.8218	.97916	17
44	.20336	.20770	4.8147	.97910	16
45	.20364	.20800	4.8077	.97905	15
46	.20393	.20830	4.8007	.97899	14
47	.20421	.20861	4.7937	.97893	13
48	.20450	.20891	4.7867	.97887	12
49	.20478	.20921	4.7798	.97881	11
50	.20507	.20952	4.7729	.97875	10
51	.20535	.20982	4.7659	.97869	9
52	.20563	.21013	4.7591	.97863	8
53	.20592	.21043	4.7522	.97857	7
54	.20620	.21073	4.7453	.97851	6
55	.20649	.21104	4.7385	.97845	5
56	.20677	.21134	4.7317	.97839	4
57	.20706	.21164	4.7249	.97833	3
58	.20734	.21195	4.7181	.97827	2
59	.20763	.21225	4.7114	.97821	1
60	.20791	.21256	4.7046	.97815	0
′	Cos	Ctn	Tan	Sin	′

78°

12°

′	Sin	Tan	Ctn	Cos	′
0	.20791	.21256	4.7046	.97815	**60**
1	.20820	.21286	4.6979	.97809	59
2	.20848	.21316	4.6912	.97803	58
3	.20877	.21347	4.6845	.97797	57
4	.20905	.21377	4.6779	.97791	56
5	.20933	.21408	4.6712	.97784	**55**
6	.20962	.21438	4.6646	.97778	54
7	.20990	.21469	4.6580	.97772	53
8	.21019	.21499	4.6514	.97766	52
9	.21047	.21529	4.6448	.97760	51
10	.21076	.21560	4.6382	.97754	**50**
11	.21104	.21590	4.6317	.97748	49
12	.21132	.21621	4.6252	.97742	48
13	.21161	.21651	4.6187	.97735	47
14	.21189	.21682	4.6122	.97729	46
15	.21218	.21712	4.6057	.97723	**45**
16	.21246	.21743	4.5993	.97717	44
17	.21275	.21773	4.5928	.97711	43
18	.21303	.21804	4.5864	.97705	42
19	.21331	.21834	4.5800	.97698	41
20	.21360	.21864	4.5736	.97692	**40**
21	.21388	.21895	4.5673	.97686	39
22	.21417	.21925	4.5609	.97680	38
23	.21445	.21956	4.5546	.97673	37
24	.21474	.21986	4.5483	.97667	36
25	.21502	.22017	4.5420	.97661	**35**
26	.21530	.22047	4.5357	.97655	34
27	.21559	.22078	4.5294	.97648	33
28	.21587	.22108	4.5232	.97642	32
29	.21616	.22139	4.5169	.97636	31
30	.21644	.22169	4.5107	.97630	**30**
31	.21672	.22200	4.5045	.97623	29
32	.21701	.22231	4.4983	.97617	28
33	.21729	.22261	4.4922	.97611	27
34	.21758	.22292	4.4860	.97604	26
35	.21786	.22322	4.4799	.97598	**25**
36	.21814	.22353	4.4737	.97592	24
37	.21843	.22383	4.4676	.97585	23
38	.21871	.22414	4.4615	.97579	22
39	.21899	.22444	4.4555	.97573	21
40	.21928	.22475	4.4494	.97566	**20**
41	.21956	.22505	4.4434	.97560	19
42	.21985	.22536	4.4373	.97553	18
43	.22013	.22567	4.4313	.97547	17
44	.22041	.22597	4.4253	.97541	16
45	.22070	.22628	4.4194	.97534	**15**
46	.22098	.22658	4.4134	.97528	14
47	.22126	.22689	4.4075	.97521	13
48	.22155	.22719	4.4015	.97515	12
49	.22183	.22750	4.3956	.97508	11
50	.22212	.22781	4.3897	.97502	**10**
51	.22240	.22811	4.3838	.97496	9
52	.22268	.22842	4.3779	.97489	8
53	.22297	.22872	4.3721	.97483	7
54	.22325	.22903	4.3662	.97476	6
55	.22353	.22934	4.3604	.97470	**5**
56	.22382	.22964	4.3546	.97463	4
57	.22410	.22995	4.3488	.97457	3
58	.22438	.23026	4.3430	.97450	2
59	.22467	.23056	4.3372	.97444	1
60	.22495	.23087	4.3315	.97437	**0**
′	Cos	Ctn	Tan	Sin	′

13°

′	Sin	Tan	Ctn	Cos	′
0	.22495	.23087	4.3315	.97437	**60**
1	.22523	.23117	4.3267	.97430	59
2	.22552	.23148	4.3200	.97424	58
3	.22580	.23179	4.3143	.97417	57
4	.22608	.23209	4.3086	.97411	56
5	.22637	.23240	4.3029	.97404	**55**
6	.22665	.23271	4.2972	.97398	54
7	.22693	.23301	4.2916	.97391	53
8	.22722	.23332	4.2859	.97384	52
9	.22750	.23363	4.2803	.97378	51
10	.22778	.23393	4.2747	.97371	**50**
11	.22807	.23424	4.2691	.97365	49
12	.22835	.23455	4.2635	.97358	48
13	.22863	.23485	4.2580	.97351	47
14	.22892	.23516	4.2524	.97345	46
15	.22920	.23547	4.2468	.97338	**45**
16	.22948	.23578	4.2413	.97331	44
17	.22977	.23608	4.2358	.97325	43
18	.23005	.23639	4.2303	.97318	42
19	.23033	.23670	4.2248	.97311	41
20	.23062	.23700	4.2193	.97304	**40**
21	.23090	.23731	4.2139	.97298	39
22	.23118	.23762	4.2084	.97291	38
23	.23146	.23793	4.2030	.97284	37
24	.23175	.23823	4.1976	.97278	36
25	.23203	.23854	4.1922	.97271	**35**
26	.23231	.23885	4.1868	.97264	34
27	.23260	.23916	4.1814	.97257	33
28	.23288	.23946	4.1760	.97251	32
29	.23316	.23977	4.1706	.97244	31
30	.23345	.24008	4.1653	.97237	**30**
31	.23373	.24039	4.1600	.97230	29
32	.23401	.24069	4.1547	.97223	28
33	.23429	.24100	4.1493	.97217	27
34	.23458	.24131	4.1441	.97210	26
35	.23486	.24162	4.1388	.97203	**25**
36	.23514	.24193	4.1335	.97196	24
37	.23542	.24223	4.1282	.97189	23
38	.23571	.24254	4.1230	.97182	22
39	.23599	.24285	4.1178	.97176	21
40	.23627	.24316	4.1126	.97169	**20**
41	.23656	.24347	4.1074	.97162	19
42	.23684	.24377	4.1022	.97155	18
43	.23712	.24408	4.0970	.97148	17
44	.23740	.24439	4.0918	.97141	16
45	.23769	.24470	4.0867	.97134	**15**
46	.23797	.24501	4.0815	.97127	14
47	.23825	.24532	4.0764	.97120	13
48	.23853	.24562	4.0713	.97113	12
49	.23882	.24593	4.0662	.97106	11
50	.23910	.24624	4.0611	.97100	**10**
51	.23938	.24655	4.0560	.97093	9
52	.23966	.24686	4.0509	.97086	8
53	.23995	.24717	4.0459	.97079	7
54	.24023	.24747	4.0408	.97072	6
55	.24051	.24778	4.0358	.97065	**5**
56	.24079	.24809	4.0308	.97058	4
57	.24108	.24840	4.0257	.97051	3
58	.24136	.24871	4.0207	.97044	2
59	.24164	.24902	4.0158	.97037	1
60	.24192	.24933	4.0108	.97030	**0**
′	Cos	Ctn	Tan	Sin	′

77°

76°

TABLE I. NATURAL TRIGONOMETRIC FUNCTIONS   469

14°

′	Sin	Tan	Ctn	Cos	′
0	.24192	.24933	4.0108	.97030	60
1	.24220	.24964	4.0058	.97023	59
2	.24249	.24995	4.0009	.97015	58
3	.24277	.25026	3.9959	.97008	57
4	.24305	.25056	3.9910	.97001	56
5	.24333	.25087	3.9861	.96994	55
6	.24362	.25118	3.9812	.96987	54
7	.24390	.25149	3.9763	.96980	53
8	.24418	.25180	3.9714	.96973	52
9	.24446	.25211	3.9665	.96966	51
10	.24474	.25242	3.9617	.96959	50
11	.24503	.25273	3.9568	.96952	49
12	.24531	.25304	3.9520	.96945	48
13	.24559	.25335	3.9471	.96937	47
14	.24587	.25366	3.9423	.96930	46
15	.24615	.25397	3.9375	.96923	45
16	.24644	.25428	3.9327	.96916	44
17	.24672	.25459	3.9279	.96909	43
18	.24700	.25490	3.9232	.96902	42
19	.24728	.25521	3.9184	.96894	41
20	.24756	.25552	3.9136	.96887	40
21	.24784	.25583	3.9089	.96880	39
22	.24813	.25614	3.9042	.96873	38
23	.24841	.25645	3.8995	.96866	37
24	.24869	.25676	3.8947	.96858	36
25	.24897	.25707	3.8900	.96851	35
26	.24925	.25738	3.8854	.96844	34
27	.24954	.25769	3.8807	.96837	33
28	.24982	.25800	3.8760	.96829	32
29	.25010	.25831	3.8714	.96822	31
30	.25038	.25862	3.8667	.96815	30
31	.25066	.25893	3.8621	.96807	29
32	.25094	.25924	3.8575	.96800	28
33	.25122	.25955	3.8528	.96793	27
34	.25151	.25986	3.8482	.96786	26
35	.25179	.26017	3.8436	.96778	25
36	.25207	.26048	3.8391	.96771	24
37	.25235	.26079	3.8345	.96764	23
38	.25263	.26110	3.8299	.96756	22
39	.25291	.26141	3.8254	.96749	21
40	.25320	.26172	3.8208	.96742	20
41	.25348	.26203	3.8163	.96734	19
42	.25376	.26235	3.8118	.96727	18
43	.25404	.26266	3.8073	.96719	17
44	.25432	.26297	3.8028	.96712	16
45	.25460	.26328	3.7983	.96705	15
46	.25488	.26359	3.7938	.96697	14
47	.25516	.26390	3.7893	.96690	13
48	.25545	.26421	3.7848	.96682	12
49	.25573	.26452	3.7804	.96675	11
50	.25601	.26483	3.7760	.96667	10
51	.25629	.26515	3.7715	.96660	9
52	.25657	.26546	3.7671	.96653	8
53	.25685	.26577	3.7627	.96645	7
54	.25713	.26608	3.7583	.96638	6
55	.25741	.26639	3.7539	.96630	5
56	.25769	.26670	3.7495	.96623	4
57	.25798	.26701	3.7451	.96615	3
58	.25826	.26733	3.7408	.96608	2
59	.25854	.26764	3.7364	.96600	1
60	.25882	.26795	3.7321	.96593	0
′	Cos	Ctn	Tan	Sin	′

75°

15°

′	Sin	Tan	Ctn	Cos	′
0	.25882	.26795	3.7321	.96593	60
1	.25910	.26826	3.7277	.96585	59
2	.25938	.26857	3.7234	.96578	58
3	.25966	.26888	3.7191	.96570	57
4	.25994	.26920	3.7148	.96562	56
5	.26022	.26951	3.7105	.96555	55
6	.26050	.26982	3.7062	.96547	54
7	.26079	.27013	3.7019	.96540	53
8	.26107	.27044	3.6976	.96532	52′
9	.26135	.27076	3.6933	.96524	51
10	.26163	.27107	3.6891	.96517	50
11	.26191	.27138	3.6848	.96509	49
12	.26219	.27169	3.6806	.96502	48
13	.26247	.27201	3.6764	.96494	47
14	.26275	.27232	3.6722	.96486	46
15	.26303	.27263	3.6680	.96479	45
16	.26331	.27294	3.6638	.96471	44
17	.26359	.27326	3.6596	.96463	43
18	.26387	.27357	3.6554	.96456	42
19	.26415	.27388	3.6512	.96448	41
20	.26443	.27419	3.6470	.96440	40
21	.26471	.27451	3.6429	.96433	39
22	.26500	.27482	3.6387	.96425	38
23	.26528	.27513	3.6346	.96417	37
24	.26556	.27545	3.6305	.96410	36
25	.26584	.27576	3.6264	.96402	35
26	.26612	.27607	3.6222	.96394	34
27	.26640	.27638	3.6181	.96386	33
28	.26668	.27670	3.6140	.96379	32
29	.26696	.27701	3.6100	.96371	31
30	.26724	.27732	3.6059	.96363	30
31	.26752	.27764	3.6018	.96355	29
32	.26780	.27795	3.5978	.96347	28
33	.26808	.27826	3.5937	.96340	27
34	.26836	.27858	3.5897	.96332	26
35	.26864	.27889	3.5856	.96324	25
36	.26892	.27921	3.5816	.96316	24
37	.26920	.27952	3.5776	.96308	23
38	.26948	.27983	3.5736	.96301	22
39	.26976	.28015	3.5696	.96293	21
40	.27004	.28046	3.5656	.96285	20
41	.27032	.28077	3.5616	.96277	19
42	.27060	.28109	3.5576	.96269	18
43	.27088	.28140	3.5536	.96261	17
44	.27116	.28172	3.5497	.96253	16
45	.27144	.28203	3.5457	.96246	15
46	.27172	.28234	3.5418	.96238	14
47	.27200	.28266	3.5379	.96230	13
48	.27228	.28297	3.5339	.96222	12
49	.27256	.28329	3.5300	.96214	11
50	.27284	.28360	3.5261	.96206	10
51	.27312	.28391	3.5222	.96198	9
52	.27340	.28423	3.5183	.96190	8
53	.27368	.28454	3.5144	.96182	7
54	.27396	.28486	3.5105	.96174	6
55	.27424	.28517	3.5067	.96166	5
56	.27452	.28549	3.5028	.96158	4
57	.27480	.28580	3.4989	.96150	3
58	.27508	.28612	3.4951	.96142	2
59	.27536	.28643	3.4912	.96134	1
60	.27564	.28675	3.4874	.96126	0
′	Cos	Ctn	Tan	Sin	′

74°

16°

′	Sin	Tan	Ctn	Cos	′
0	.27564	.28675	3.4874	.96126	60
1	.27592	.28706	3.4836	.96118	59
2	.27620	.28738	3.4798	.96110	58
3	.27648	.28769	3.4760	.96102	57
4	.27676	.28801	3.4722	.96094	56
5	.27704	.28832	3.4684	.96086	55
6	.27731	.28864	3.4646	.96078	54
7	.27759	.28895	3.4608	.96070	53
8	.27787	.28927	3.4570	.96062	52
9	.27815	.28958	3.4533	.96054	51
10	.27843	.28990	3.4495	.96046	50
11	.27871	.29021	3.4458	.96037	49
12	.27899	.29053	3.4420	.96029	48
13	.27927	.29084	3.4383	.96021	47
14	.27955	.29116	3.4346	.96013	46
15	.27983	.29147	3.4308	.96005	45
16	.28011	.29179	3.4271	.95997	44
17	.28039	.29210	3.4234	.95989	43
18	.28067	.29242	3.4197	.95981	42
19	.28095	.29274	3.4160	.95972	41
20	.28123	.29305	3.4124	.95964	40
21	.28150	.29337	3.4087	.95956	39
22	.28178	.29368	3.4050	.95948	38
23	.28206	.29400	3.4014	.95940	37
24	.28234	.29432	3.3977	.95931	36
25	.28262	.29463	3.3941	.95923	35
26	.28290	.29495	3.3904	.95915	34
27	.28318	.29526	3.3868	.95907	33
28	.28346	.29558	3.3832	.95898	32
29	.28374	.29590	3.3796	.95890	31
30	.28402	.29621	3.3759	.95882	30
31	.28429	.29653	3.3723	.95874	29
32	.28457	.29685	3.3687	.95865	28
33	.28485	.29716	3.3652	.95857	27
34	.28513	.29748	3.3616	.95849	26
35	.28541	.29780	3.3580	.95841	25
36	.28569	.29811	3.3544	.95832	24
37	.28597	.29843	3.3509	.95824	23
38	.28625	.29875	3.3473	.95816	22
39	.28652	.29906	3.3438	.95807	21
40	.28680	.29938	3.3402	.95799	20
41	.28708	.29970	3.3367	.95791	19
42	.28736	.30001	3.3332	.95782	18
43	.28764	.30033	3.3297	.95774	17
44	.28792	.30065	3.3261	.95766	16
45	.28820	.30097	3.3226	.95757	15
46	.28847	.30128	3.3191	.95749	14
47	.28875	.30160	3.3156	.95740	13
48	.28903	.30192	3.3122	.95732	12
49	.28931	.30224	3.3087	.95724	11
50	.28959	.30255	3.3052	.95715	10
51	.28987	.30287	3.3017	.95707	9
52	.29015	.30319	3.2983	.95698	8
53	.29042	.30351	3.2948	.95690	7
54	.29070	.30382	3.2914	.95681	6
55	.29098	.30414	3.2879	.95673	5
56	.29126	.30446	3.2845	.95664	4
57	.29154	.30478	3.2811	.95656	3
58	.29182	.30509	3.2777	.95647	2
59	.29209	.30541	3.2743	.95639	1
60	.29237	.30573	3.2709	.95630	0
′	Cos	Ctn	Tan	Sin	′

73°

17°

′	Sin	Tan	Ctn	Cos	′
0	.29237	.30573	3.2709	.95630	60
1	.29265	.30605	3.2675	.95622	59
2	.29293	.30637	3.2641	.95613	58
3	.29321	.30669	3.2607	.95605	57
4	.29348	.30700	3.2573	.95596	56
5	.29376	.30732	3.2539	.95588	55
6	.29404	.30764	3.2506	.95579	54
7	.29432	.30796	3.2472	.95571	53
8	.29460	.30828	3.2438	.95562	52
9	.29487	.30860	3.2405	.95554	51
10	.29515	.30891	3.2371	.95545	50
11	.29543	.30923	3.2338	.95536	49
12	.29571	.30955	3.2305	.95528	48
13	.29599	.30987	3.2272	.95519	47
14	.29626	.31019	3.2238	.95511	46
15	.29654	.31051	3.2205	.95502	45
16	.29682	.31083	3.2172	.95493	44
17	.29710	.31115	3.2139	.95485	43
18	.29737	.31147	3.2106	.95476	42
19	.29765	.31178	3.2073	.95467	41
20	.29793	.31210	3.2041	.95459	40
21	.29821	.31242	3.2008	.95450	39
22	.29849	.31274	3.1975	.95441	38
23	.29876	.31306	3.1943	.95433	37
24	.29904	.31338	3.1910	.95424	36
25	.29932	.31370	3.1878	.95415	35
26	.29960	.31402	3.1845	.95407	34
27	.29987	.31434	3.1813	.95398	33
28	.30015	.31466	3.1780	.95389	32
29	.30043	.31498	3.1748	.95380	31
30	.30071	.31530	3.1716	.95372	30
31	.30098	.31562	3.1684	.95363	29
32	.30126	.31594	3.1652	.95354	28
33	.30154	.31626	3.1620	.95345	27
34	.30182	.31658	3.1588	.95337	26
35	.30209	.31690	3.1556	.95328	25
36	.30237	.31722	3.1524	.95319	24
37	.30265	.31754	3.1492	.95310	23
38	.30292	.31786	3.1460	.95301	22
39	.30320	.31818	3.1429	.95293	21
40	.30348	.31850	3.1397	.95284	20
41	.30376	.31882	3.1366	.95275	19
42	.30403	.31914	3.1334	.95266	18
43	.30431	.31946	3.1303	.95257	17
44	.30459	.31978	3.1271	.95248	16
45	.30486	.32010	3.1240	.95240	15
46	.30514	.32042	3.1209	.95231	14
47	.30542	.32074	3.1178	.95222	13
48	.30570	.32106	3.1146	.95213	12
49	.30597	.32139	3.1115	.95204	11
50	.30625	.32171	3.1084	.95195	10
51	.30653	.32203	3.1053	.95186	9
52	.30680	.32235	3.1022	.95177	8
53	.30708	.32267	3.0991	.95168	7
54	.30736	.32299	3.0961	.95159	6
55	.30763	.32331	3.0930	.95150	5
56	.30791	.32363	3.0899	.95142	4
57	.30819	.32396	3.0868	.95133	3
58	.30846	.32428	3.0838	.95124	2
59	.30874	.32460	3.0807	.95115	1
60	.30902	.32492	3.0777	.95106	0
′	Cos	Ctn	Tan	Sin	′

72°

TABLE I. NATURAL TRIGONOMETRIC FUNCTIONS   471

18°

′	Sin	Tan	Ctn	Cos	′
0	.30902	.32492	3.0777	.95106	60
1	.30929	.32524	3.0746	.95097	59
2	.30957	.32556	3.0716	.95088	58
3	.30985	.32588	3.0686	.95079	57
4	.31012	.32621	3.0655	.95070	56
5	.31040	.32653	3.0625	.95061	55
6	.31068	.32685	3.0595	.95052	54
7	.31095	.32717	3.0565	.95043	53
8	.31123	.32749	3.0535	.95033	52
9	.31151	.32782	3.0505	.95024	51
10	.31178	.32814	3.0475	.95015	50
11	.31206	.32846	3.0445	.95006	49
12	.31233	.32878	3.0415	.94997	48
13	.31261	.32911	3.0385	.94988	47
14	.31289	.32943	3.0356	.94979	46
15	.31316	.32975	3.0326	.94970	45
16	.31344	.33007	3.0296	.94961	44
17	.31372	.33040	3.0267	.94952	43
18	.31399	.33072	3.0237	.94943	42
19	.31427	.33104	3.0208	.94933	41
20	.31454	.33136	3.0178	.94924	40
21	.31482	.33169	3.0149	.94915	39
22	.31510	.33201	3.0120	.94906	38
23	.31537	.33233	3.0090	.94897	37
24	.31565	.33266	3.0061	.94888	36
25	.31593	.33298	3.0032	.94878	35
26	.31620	.33330	3.0003	.94869	34
27	.31648	.33363	2.9974	.94860	33
28	.31675	.33395	2.9945	.94851	32
29	.31703	.33427	2.9916	.94842	31
30	.31730	.33460	2.9887	.94832	30
31	.31758	.33492	2.9858	.94823	29
32	.31786	.33524	2.9829	.94814	28
33	.31813	.33557	2.9800	.94805	27
34	.31841	.33589	2.9772	.94795	26
35	.31868	.33621	2.9743	.94786	25
36	.31896	.33654	2.9714	.94777	24
37	.31923	.33686	2.9686	.94768	23
38	.31951	.33718	2.9657	.94758	22
39	.31979	.33751	2.9629	.94749	21
40	.32006	.33783	2.9600	.94740	20
41	.32034	.33816	2.9572	.94730	19
42	.32061	.33848	2.9544	.94721	18
43	.32089	.33881	2.9515	.94712	17
44	.32116	.33913	2.9487	.94702	16
45	.32144	.33945	2.9459	.94693	15
46	.32171	.33978	2.9431	.94684	14
47	.32199	.34010	2.9403	.94674	13
48	.32227	.34043	2.9375	.94665	12
49	.32254	.34075	2.9347	.94656	11
50	.32282	.34108	2.9319	.94646	10
51	.32309	.34140	2.9291	.94637	9
52	.32337	.34173	2.9263	.94627	8
53	.32364	.34205	2.9235	.94618	7
54	.32392	.34238	2.9208	.94609	6
55	.32419	.34270	2.9180	.94599	5
56	.32447	.34303	2.9152	.94590	4
57	.32474	.34335	2.9125	.94580	3
58	.32502	.34368	2.9097	.94571	2
59	.32529	.34400	2.9070	.94561	1
60	.32557	.34433	2.9042	.94552	0
′	Cos	Ctn	Tan	Sin	′

71°

19°

′	Sin	Tan	Ctn	Cos	′
0	.32557	.34433	2.9042	.94552	60
1	.32584	.34465	2.9015	.94542	59
2	.32612	.34498	2.8987	.94533	58
3	.32639	.34530	2.8960	.94523	57
4	.32667	.34563	2.8933	.94514	56
5	.32694	.34596	2.8905	.94504	55
6	.32722	.34628	2.8878	.94495	54
7	.32749	.34661	2.8851	.94485	53
8	.32777	.34693	2.8824	.94476	52
9	.32804	.34726	2.8797	.94466	51
10	.32832	.34758	2.8770	.94457	50
11	.32859	.34791	2.8743	.94447	49
12	.32887	.34824	2.8716	.94438	48
13	.32914	.34856	2.8689	.94428	47
14	.32942	.34889	2.8662	.94418	46
15	.32969	.34922	2.8636	.94409	45
16	.32997	.34954	2.8609	.94399	44
17	.33024	.34987	2.8582	.94390	43
18	.33051	.35020	2.8556	.94380	42
19	.33079	.35052	2.8529	.94370	41
20	.33106	.35085	2.8502	.94361	40
21	.33134	.35118	2.8476	.94351	39
22	.33161	.35150	2.8449	.94342	38
23	.33189	.35183	2.8423	.94332	37
24	.33216	.35216	2.8397	.94322	36
25	.33244	.35248	2.8370	.94313	35
26	.33271	.35281	2.8344	.94303	34
27	.33298	.35314	2.8318	.94293	33
28	.33326	.35346	2.8291	.94284	32
29	.33353	.35379	2.8265	.94274	31
30	.33381	.35412	2.8239	.94264	30
31	.33408	.35445	2.8213	.94254	29
32	.33436	.35477	2.8187	.94245	28
33	.33463	.35510	2.8161	.94235	27
34	.33490	.35543	2.8135	.94225	26
35	.33518	.35576	2.8109	.94215	25
36	.33545	.35608	2.8083	.94206	24
37	.33573	.35641	2.8057	.94196	23
38	.33600	.35674	2.8032	.94186	22
39	.33627	.35707	2.8006	.94176	21
40	.33655	.35740	2.7980	.94167	20
41	.33682	.35772	2.7955	.94157	19
42	.33710	.35805	2.7929	.94147	18
43	.33737	.35838	2.7903	.94137	17
44	.33764	.35871	2.7878	.94127	16
45	.33792	.35904	2.7852	.94118	15
46	.33819	.35937	2.7827	.94108	14
47	.33846	.35969	2.7801	.94098	13
48	.33874	.36002	2.7776	.94088	12
49	.33901	.36035	2.7751	.94078	11
50	.33929	.36068	2.7725	.94068	10
51	.33956	.36101	2.7700	.94058	9
52	.33983	.36134	2.7675	.94049	8
53	.34011	.36167	2.7650	.94039	7
54	.34038	.36199	2.7625	.94029	6
55	.34065	.36232	2.7600	.94019	5
56	.34093	.36265	2.7575	.94009	4
57	.34120	.36298	2.7550	.93999	3
58	.34147	.36331	2.7525	.93989	2
59	.34175	.36364	2.7500	.93979	1
60	.34202	.36397	2.7475	.93969	0
′	Cos	Ctn	Tan	Sin	′

70°

20°

′	Sin	Tan	Ctn	Cos	′
0	.34202	.36397	2.7475	.93969	60
1	.34229	.36430	2.7450	.93959	59
2	.34257	.36463	2.7425	.93949	58
3	.34284	.36496	2.7400	.93939	57
4	.34311	.36529	2.7376	.93929	56
5	.34339	.36562	2.7351	.93919	55
6	.34366	.36595	2.7326	.93909	54
7	.34393	.36628	2.7302	.93899	53
8	.34421	.36661	2.7277	.93889	52
9	.34448	.36694	2.7253	.93879	51
10	.34475	.36727	2.7228	.93869	50
11	.34503	.36760	2.7204	.93859	49
12	.34530	.36793	2.7179	.93849	48
13	.34557	.36826	2.7155	.93839	47
14	.34584	.36859	2.7130	.93829	46
15	.34612	.36892	2.7106	.93819	45
16	.34639	.36925	2.7082	.93809	44
17	.34666	.36958	2.7058	.93799	43
18	.34694	.36991	2.7034	.93789	42
19	.34721	.37024	2.7009	.93779	41
20	.34748	.37057	2.6985	.93769	40
21	.34775	.37090	2.6961	.93759	39
22	.34803	.37123	2.6937	.93748	38
23	.34830	.37157	2.6913	.93738	37
24	.34857	.37190	2.6889	.93728	36
25	.34884	.37223	2.6865	.93718	35
26	.34912	.37256	2.6841	.93708	34
27	.34939	.37289	2.6818	.93698	33
28	.34966	.37322	2.6794	.93688	32
29	.34993	.37355	2.6770	.93677	31
30	.35021	.37388	2.6746	.93667	30
31	.35048	.37422	2.6723	.93657	29
32	.35075	.37455	2.6699	.93647	28
33	.35102	.37488	2.6675	.93637	27
34	.35130	.37521	2.6652	.93626	26
35	.35157	.37554	2.6628	.93616	25
36	.35184	.37588	2.6605	.93606	24
37	.35211	.37621	2.6581	.93596	23
38	.35239	.37654	2.6558	.93585	22
39	.35266	.37687	2.6534	.93575	21
40	.35293	.37720	2.6511	.93565	20
41	.35320	.37754	2.6488	.93555	19
42	.35347	.37787	2.6464	.93544	18
43	.35375	.37820	2.6441	.93534	17
44	.35402	.37853	2.6418	.93524	16
45	.35429	.37887	2.6395	.93514	15
46	.35456	.37920	2.6371	.93503	14
47	.35484	.37953	2.6348	.93493	13
48	.35511	.37986	2.6325	.93483	12
49	.35538	.38020	2.6302	.93472	11
50	.35565	.38053	2.6279	.93462	10
51	.35592	.38086	2.6256	.93452	9
52	.35619	.38120	2.6233	.93441	8
53	.35647	.38153	2.6210	.93431	7
54	.35674	.38186	2.6187	.93420	6
55	.35701	.38220	2.6165	.93410	5
56	.35728	.38253	2.6142	.93400	4
57	.35755	.38286	2.6119	.93389	3
58	.35782	.38320	2.6096	.93379	2
59	.35810	.38353	2.6074	.93368	1
60	.35837	.38386	2.6051	.93358	0
′	Cos	Ctn	Tan	Sin	′

69°

21°

′	Sin	Tan	Ctn	Cos	′
0	.35837	.38386	2.6051	.93358	60
1	.35864	.38420	2.6028	.93348	59
2	.35891	.38453	2.6006	.93337	58
3	.35918	.38487	2.5983	.93327	57
4	.35945	.38520	2.5961	.93316	56
5	.35973	.38553	2.5938	.93306	55
6	.36000	.38587	2.5916	.93295	54
7	.36027	.38620	2.5893	.93285	53
8	.36054	.38654	2.5871	.93274	52
9	.36081	.38687	2.5848	.93264	51
10	.36108	.38721	2.5826	.93253	50
11	.36135	.38754	2.5804	.93243	49
12	.36162	.38787	2.5782	.93232	48
13	.36190	.38821	2.5759	.93222	47
14	.36217	.38854	2.5737	.93211	46
15	.36244	.38888	2.5715	.93201	45
16	.36271	.38921	2.5693	.93190	44
17	.36298	.38955	2.5671	.93180	43
18	.36325	.38988	2.5649	.93169	42
19	.36352	.39022	2.5627	.93159	41
20	.36379	.39055	2.5605	.93148	40
21	.36406	.39089	2.5583	.93137	39
22	.36434	.39122	2.5561	.93127	38
23	.36461	.39156	2.5539	.93116	37
24	.36488	.39190	2.5517	.93106	36
25	.36515	.39223	2.5495	.93095	35
26	.36542	.39257	2.5473	.93084	34
27	.36569	.39290	2.5452	.93074	33
28	.36596	.39324	2.5430	.93063	32
29	.36623	.39357	2.5408	.93052	31
30	.36650	.39391	2.5386	.93042	30
31	.36677	.39425	2.5365	.93031	29
32	.36704	.39458	2.5343	.93020	28
33	.36731	.39492	2.5322	.93010	27
34	.36758	.39526	2.5300	.92999	26
35	.36785	.39559	2.5279	.92988	25
36	.36812	.39593	2.5257	.92978	24
37	.36839	.39626	2.5236	.92967	23
38	.36867	.39660	2.5214	.92956	22
39	.36894	.39694	2.5193	.92945	21
40	.36921	.39727	2.5172	.92935	20
41	.36948	.39761	2.5150	.92924	19
42	.36975	.39795	2.5129	.92913	18
43	.37002	.39829	2.5108	.92902	17
44	.37029	.39862	2.5086	.92892	16
45	.37056	.39896	2.5065	.92881	15
46	.37083	.39930	2.5044	.92870	14
47	.37110	.39963	2.5023	.92859	13
48	.37137	.39997	2.5002	.92849	12
49	.37164	.40031	2.4981	.92838	11
50	.37191	.40065	2.4960	.92827	10
51	.37218	.40098	2.4939	.92816	9
52	.37245	.40132	2.4918	.92805	8
53	.37272	.40166	2.4897	.92794	7
54	.37299	.40200	2.4876	.92784	6
55	.37326	.40234	2.4855	.92773	5
56	.37353	.40267	2.4834	.92762	4
57	.37380	.40301	2.4813	.92751	3
58	.37407	.40335	2.4792	.92740	2
59	.37434	.40369	2.4772	.92729	1
60	.37461	.40403	2.4751	.92718	0
′	Cos	Ctn	Tan	Sin	′

68°

TABLE I. NATURAL TRIGONOMETRIC FUNCTIONS 473

22°

′	Sin	Tan	Ctn	Cos	′
0	.37461	.40403	2.4751	.92718	60
1	.37488	.40436	2.4730	.92707	59
2	.37515	.40470	2.4709	.92697	58
3	.37542	.40504	2.4689	.92686	57
4	.37569	.40538	2.4668	.92675	56
5	.37595	.40572	2.4648	.92664	55
6	.37622	.40606	2.4627	.92653	54
7	.37649	.40640	2.4606	.92642	53
8	.37676	.40674	2.4586	.92631	52
9	.37703	.40707	2.4566	.92620	51
10	.37730	.40741	2.4545	.92609	50
11	.37757	.40775	2.4525	.92598	49
12	.37784	.40809	2.4504	.92587	48
13	.37811	.40843	2.4484	.92576	47
14	.37838	.40877	2.4464	.92565	46
15	.37865	.40911	2.4443	.92554	45
16	.37892	.40945	2.4423	.92543	44
17	.37919	.40979	2.4403	.92532	43
18	.37946	.41013	2.4383	.92521	42
19	.37973	.41047	2.4362	.92510	41
20	.37999	.41081	2.4342	.92499	40
21	.38026	.41115	2.4322	.92488	39
22	.38053	.41149	2.4302	.92477	38
23	.38080	.41183	2.4282	.92466	37
24	.38107	.41217	2.4262	.92455	36
25	.38134	.41251	2.4242	.92444	35
26	.38161	.41285	2.4222	.92432	34
27	.38188	.41319	2.4202	.92421	33
28	.38215	.41353	2.4182	.92410	32
29	.38241	.41387	2.4162	.92399	31
30	.38268	.41421	2.4142	.92388	30
31	.38295	.41455	2.4122	.92377	29
32	.38322	.41490	2.4102	.92366	28
33	.38349	.41524	2.4083	.92355	27
34	.38376	.41558	2.4063	.92343	26
35	.38403	.41592	2.4043	.92332	25
36	.38430	.41626	2.4023	.92321	24
37	.38456	.41660	2.4004	.92310	23
38	.38483	.41694	2.3984	.92299	22
39	.38510	.41728	2.3964	.92287	21
40	.38537	.41763	2.3945	.92276	20
41	.38564	.41797	2.3925	.92265	19
42	.38591	.41831	2.3906	.92254	18
43	.38617	.41865	2.3886	.92243	17
44	.38644	.41899	2.3867	.92231	16
45	.38671	.41933	2.3847	.92220	15
46	.38698	.41968	2.3828	.92209	14
47	.38725	.42002	2.3808	.92198	13
48	.38752	.42036	2.3789	.92186	12
49	.38778	.42070	2.3770	.92175	11
50	.38805	.42105	2.3750	.92164	10
51	.38832	.42139	2.3731	.92152	9
52	.38859	.42173	2.3712	.92141	8
53	.38886	.42207	2.3693	.92130	7
54	.38912	.42242	2.3673	.92119	6
55	.38939	.42276	2.3654	.92107	5
56	.38966	.42310	2.3635	.92096	4
57	.38993	.42345	2.3616	.92085	3
58	.39020	.42379	2.3597	.92073	2
59	.39046	.42413	2.3578	.92062	1
60	.39073	.42447	2.3559	.92050	0
′	Cos	Ctn	Tan	Sin	′

67°

23°

′	Sin	Tan	Ctn	Cos	′
0	.39073	.42447	2.3559	.92050	60
1	.39100	.42482	2.3539	.92039	59
2	.39127	.42516	2.3520	.92028	58
3	.39153	.42551	2.3501	.92016	57
4	.39180	.42585	2.3483	.92005	56
5	.39207	.42619	2.3464	.91994	55
6	.39234	.42654	2.3445	.91982	54
7	.39260	.42688	2.3426	.91971	53
8	.39287	.42722	2.3407	.91959	52
9	.39314	.42757	2.3388	.91948	51
10	.39341	.42791	2.3369	.91936	50
11	.39367	.42826	2.3351	.91925	49
12	.39394	.42860	2.3332	.91914	48
13	.39421	.42894	2.3313	.91902	47
14	.39448	.42929	2.3294	.91891	46
15	.39474	.42963	2.3276	.91879	45
16	.39501	.42998	2.3257	.91868	44
17	.39528	.43032	2.3238	.91856	43
18	.39555	.43067	2.3220	.91845	42
19	.39581	.43101	2.3201	.91833	41
20	.39608	.43136	2.3183	.91822	40
21	.39635	.43170	2.3164	.91810	39
22	.39661	.43205	2.3146	.91799	38
23	.39688	.43239	2.3127	.91787	37
24	.39715	.43274	2.3109	.91775	36
25	.39741	.43308	2.3090	.91764	35
26	.39768	.43343	2.3072	.91752	34
27	.39795	.43378	2.3053	.91741	33
28	.39822	.43412	2.3035	.91729	32
29	.39848	.43447	2.3017	.91718	31
30	.39875	.43481	2.2998	.91706	30
31	.39902	.43516	2.2980	.91694	29
32	.39928	.43550	2.2962	.91683	28
33	.39955	.43585	2.2944	.91671	27
34	.39982	.43620	2.2925	.91660	26
35	.40008	.43654	2.2907	.91648	25
36	.40035	.43689	2.2889	.91636	24
37	.40062	.43724	2.2871	.91625	23
38	.40088	.43758	2.2853	.91613	22
39	.40115	.43793	2.2835	.91601	21
40	.40141	.43828	2.2817	.91590	20
41	.40168	.43862	2.2799	.91578	19
42	.40195	.43897	2.2781	.91566	18
43	.40221	.43932	2.2763	.91555	17
44	.40248	.43966	2.2745	.91543	16
45	.40275	.44001	2.2727	.91531	15
46	.40301	.44036	2.2709	.91519	14
47	.40328	.44071	2.2691	.91508	13
48	.40355	.44105	2.2673	.91496	12
49	.40381	.44140	2.2655	.91484	11
50	.40408	.44175	2.2637	.91472	10
51	.40434	.44210	2.2620	.91461	9
52	.40461	.44244	2.2602	.91449	8
53	.40488	.44279	2.2584	.91437	7
54	.40514	.44314	2.2566	.91425	6
55	.40541	.44349	2.2549	.91414	5
56	.40567	.44384	2.2531	.91402	4
57	.40594	.44418	2.2513	.91390	3
58	.40621	.44453	2.2496	.91378	2
59	.40647	.44488	2.2478	.91366	1
60	.40674	.44523	2.2460	.91355	0
′	Cos	Ctn	Tan	Sin	′

66°

24°

′	Sin	Tan	Ctn	Cos	′
0	.40674	.44523	2.2460	.91355	**60**
1	.40700	.44558	2.2443	.91343	59
2	.40727	.44593	2.2425	.91331	58
3	.40753	.44627	2.2408	.91319	57
4	.40780	.44662	2.2390	.91307	56
5	.40806	.44697	2.2373	.91295	**55**
6	.40833	.44732	2.2355	.91283	54
7	.40860	.44767	2.2338	.91272	53
8	.40886	.44802	2.2320	.91260	52
9	.40913	.44837	2.2303	.91248	51
10	.40939	.44872	2.2286	.91236	**50**
11	.40966	.44907	2.2268	.91224	49
12	.40992	.44942	2.2251	.91212	48
13	.41019	.44977	2.2234	.91200	47
14	.41045	.45012	2.2216	.91188	46
15	.41072	.45047	2.2199	.91176	**45**
16	.41098	.45082	2.2182	.91164	44
17	.41125	.45117	2.2165	.91152	43
18	.41151	.45152	2.2148	.91140	42
19	.41178	.45187	2.2130	91128	41
20	.41204	.45222	2.2113	.91116	**40**
21	.41231	.45257	2.2096	.91104	39
22	.41257	.45292	2.2079	.91092	38
23	.41284	.45327	2.2062	.91080	37
24	.41310	.45362	2.2045	.91068	36
25	.41337	.45397	2.2028	.91056	**35**
26	.41363	.45432	2.2011	.91044	34
27	.41390	.45467	2.1994	.91032	33
28	.41416	.45502	2.1977	.91020	32
29	.41443	.45538	2.1960	.91008	31
30	.41469	.45573	2.1943	.90996	**30**
31	.41496	.45608	2.1926	.90984	29
32	.41522	.45643	2.1909	.90972	28
33	.41549	.45678	2.1892	.90960	27
34	.41575	.45713	2.1876	.90948	26
35	.41602	.45748	2.1859	.90936	**25**
36	.41628	.45784	2.1842	.90924	24
37	.41655	.45819	2.1825	.90911	23
38	.41681	.45854	2.1808	.90899	22
39	.41707	.45889	2.1792	.90887	21
40	.41734	.45924	2.1775	.90875	**20**
41	.41760	.45960	2.1758	.90863	19
42	.41787	.45995	2.1742	.90851	18
43	.41813	.46030	2.1725	.90839	17
44	.41840	.46065	2.1708	.90826	16
45	.41866	.46101	2.1692	.90814	**15**
46	.41892	.46136	2.1675	.90802	14
47	.41919	.46171	2.1659	.90790	13
48	.41945	.46206	2.1642	.90778	12
49	.41972	.46242	2.1625	.90766	11
50	.41998	.46277	2.1609	.90753	**10**
51	.42024	.46312	2.1592	.90741	9
52	.42051	.46348	2.1576	.90729	8
53	.42077	.46383	2.1560	.90717	7
54	.42104	.46418	2.1543	.90704	6
55	.42130	.46454	2.1527	.90692	**5**
56	.42156	.46489	2.1510	.90680	4
57	.42183	.46525	2.1494	.90668	3
58	.42209	.46560	2.1478	.90655	2
59	.42235	.46595	2.1461	.90643	1
60	.42262	.46631	2.1445	.90631	**0**
′	Cos	Ctn	Tan	Sin	′

25°

′	Sin	Tan	Ctn	Cos	′
0	.42262	.46631	2.1445	.90631	**60**
1	.42288	.46666	2.1429	.90618	59
2	.42315	.46702	2.1413	.90606	58
3	.42341	.46737	2.1396	.90594	57
4	.42367	.46772	2.1380	.90582	56
5	.42394	.46808	2.1364	.90569	**55**
6	.42420	.46843	2.1348	.90557	54
7	.42446	.46879	2.1332	.90545	53
8	.42473	.46914	2.1315	.90532	52
9	.42499	.46950	2.1299	.90520	51
10	.42525	.46985	2.1283	.90507	**50**
11	.42552	.47021	2.1267	.90495	49
12	.42578	.47056	2.1251	.90483	48
13	.42604	.47092	2.1235	.90470	47
14	.42631	.47128	2.1219	.90458	46
15	.42657	.47163	2.1203	.90446	**45**
16	.42683	.47199	2.1187	.90433	44
17	.42709	.47234	2.1171	.90421	43
18	.42736	.47270	2.1155	.90408	42
19	.42762	.47305	2.1139	.90396	41
20	.42788	.47341	2.1123	.90383	**40**
21	.42815	.47377	2.1107	.90371	39
22	.42841	.47412	2.1092	.90358	38
23	.42867	.47448	2.1076	.90346	37
24	.42894	.47483	2.1060	.90334	36
25	.42920	.47519	2.1044	.90321	**35**
26	.42946	.47555	2.1028	.90309	34
27	.42972	.47590	2.1013	.90296	33
28	.42999	.47626	2.0997	.90284	32
29	.43025	.47662	2.0981	.90271	31
30	.43051	.47698	2.0965	.90259	**30**
31	.43077	.47733	2.0950	.90246	29
32	.43104	.47769	2.0934	.90233	28
33	.43130	.47805	2.0918	.90221	27
34	.43156	.47840	2.0903	.90208	26
35	.43182	.47876	2.0887	.90196	**25**
36	.43209	.47912	2.0872	.90183	24
37	.43235	.47948	2.0856	.90171	23
38	.43261	.47984	2.0840	.90158	22
39	.43287	.48019	2.0825	.90146	21
40	.43313	.48055	2.0809	.90133	**20**
41	.43340	.48091	2.0794	.90120	19
42	.43366	.48127	2.0778	.90108	18
43	.43392	.48163	2.0763	.90095	17
44	.43418	.48198	2.0748	.90082	16
45	.43445	.48234	2.0732	.90070	**15**
46	.43471	.48270	2.0717	.90057	14
47	.43497	.48306	2.0701	.90045	13
48	.43523	.48342	2.0686	.90032	12
49	.43549	.48378	2.0671	.90019	11
50	.43575	.48414	2.0655	.90007	**10**
51	.43602	.48450	2.0640	.89994	9
52	.43628	.48486	2.0625	.89981	8
53	.43654	.48521	2.0609	.89968	7
54	.43680	.48557	2.0594	.89956	6
55	.43706	.48593	2.0579	.89943	**5**
56	.43733	.48629	2.0564	.89930	4
57	.43759	.48665	2.0549	.89918	3
58	.43785	.48701	2.0533	.89905	2
59	.43811	.48737	2.0518	.89892	1
60	.43837	.48773	2.0503	.89879	**0**
′	Cos	Ctn	Tan	Sin	′

65°   **64°**

TABLE I. NATURAL TRIGONOMETRIC FUNCTIONS   475

26°

′	Sin	Tan	Ctn	Cos	′
0	.43837	.48773	2.0503	.89879	60
1	.43863	.48809	2.0488	.89867	59
2	.43889	.48845	2.0473	.89854	58
3	.43916	.48881	2.0458	.89841	57
4	.43942	.48917	2.0443	.89828	56
5	.43968	.48953	2.0428	.89816	55
6	.43994	.48989	2.0413	.89803	54
7	.44020	.49026	2.0398	.89790	53
8	.44046	.49062	2.0383	.89777	52
9	.44072	.49098	2.0368	.89764	51
10	.44098	.49134	2.0353	.89752	50
11	.44124	.49170	2.0338	.89739	49
12	.44151	.49206	2.0323	.89726	48
13	.44177	.49242	2.0308	.89713	47
14	.44203	.49278	2.0293	.89700	46
15	.44229	.49315	2.0278	.89687	45
16	.44255	.49351	2.0263	.89674	44
17	.44281	.49387	2.0248	.89662	43
18	.44307	.49423	2.0233	.89649	42
19	.44333	.49459	2.0219	.89636	41
20	.44359	.49495	2.0204	.89623	40
21	.44385	.49532	2.0189	.89610	39
22	.44411	.49568	2.0174	.89597	38
23	.44437	.49604	2.0160	.89584	37
24	.44464	.49640	2.0145	.89571	36
25	.44490	.49677	2.0130	.89558	35
26	.44516	.49713	2.0115	.89545	34
27	.44542	.49749	2 0101	.89532	33
28	.44568	.49786	2.0086	.89519	32
29	.44594	.49822	2.0072	.89506	31
30	.44620	.49858	2.0057	.89493	30
31	.44646	.49894	2.0042	.89480	29
32	.44672	.49931	2.0028	.89467	28
33	.44698	.49967	2.0013	.89454	27
34	.44724	.50004	1.9999	.89441	26
35	.44750	.50040	1.9984	.89428	25
36	.44776	.50076	1.9970	.89415	24
37	.44802	.50113	1.9955	.89402	23
38	.44828	.50149	1.9941	.89389	22
39	.44854	.50185	1.9926	.89376	21
40	.44880	.50222	1.9912	.89363	20
41	.44906	.50258	1.9897	.89350	19
42	.44932	.50295	1 9883	.89337	18
43	.44958	.50331	1.9868	.89324	17
44	.44984	.50368	1.9854	.89311	16
45	.45010	.50404	1.9840	.89298	15
46	.45036	.50441	1.9825	.89285	14
47	.45062	.50477	1.9811	.89272	13
48	.45088	.50514	1.9797	.89259	12
49	.45114	.50550	1.9782	.89245	11
50	.45140	.50587	1.9768	.89232	10
51	.45166	.50623	1.9754	.89219	9
52	.45192	.50660	1.9740	.89206	8
53	.45218	.50696	1.9725	.89193	7
54	.45243	.50733	1.9711	.89180	6
55	.45269	.50769	1.9697	.89167	5
56	.45295	.50806	1.9683	.89153	4
57	.45321	.50843	1.9669	.89140	3
58	.45347	.50879	1.9654	.89127	2
59	.45373	.50916	1.9640	.89114	1
60	.45399	.50953	1.9626	.89101	0
′	Cos	Ctn	Tan	Sin	′

63°

27°

′	Sin	Tan	Ctn	Cos	′
0	.45399	.50953	1.9626	.89101	60
1	.45425	.50989	1.9612	.89087	59
2	.45451	.51026	1.9598	.89074	58
3	.45477	.51063	1.9584	.89061	57
4	.45503	.51099	1.9570	.89048	56
5	.45529	.51136	1.9556	.89035	55
6	.45554	.51173	1.9542	.89021	54
7	.45580	.51209	1.9528	.89008	53
8	.45606	.51246	1.9514	.88995	52
9	.45632	.51283	1.9500	.88981	51
10	.45658	.51319	1.9486	.88968	50
11	.45684	.51356	1.9472	.88955	49
12	.45710	.51393	1.9458	.88942	48
13	.45736	.51430	1.9444	.88928	47
14	.45762	.51467	1.9430	.88915	46
15	.45787	.51503	1.9416	.88902	45
16	.45813	.51540	1.9402	.88888	44
17	.45839	.51577	1.9388	.88875	43
18	.45865	.51614	1.9375	.88862	42
19	.45891	.51651	1.9361	.88848	41
20	.45917	.51688	1.9347	.88835	40
21	.45942	.51724	1.9333	.88822	39
22	.45968	.51761	1.9319	.88808	38
23	.45994	.51798	1.9306	.88795	37
24	.46020	.51835	1.9292	.88782	36
25	.46046	.51872	1.9278	.88768	35
26	.46072	.51909	1.9265	.88755	34
27	.46097	.51946	1.9251	.88741	33
28	.46123	.51983	1.9237	.88728	32
29	.46149	.52020	1.9223	.88715	31
30	.46175	.52057	1.9210	.88701	30
31	.46201	.52094	1.9196	.88688	29
32	.46226	.52131	1.9183	.88674	28
33	.46252	.52168	1.9169	.88661	27
34	.46278	.52205	1.9155	.88647	26
35	.46304	.52242	1.9142	.88634	25
36	.46330	.52279	1.9128	.88620	24
37	.46355	.52316	1.9115	.88607	23
38	.46381	.52353	1.9101	.88593	22
39	.46407	.52390	1.9088	.88580	21
40	.46433	.52427	1.9074	.88566	20
41	.46458	.52464	1.9061	.88553	19
42	.46484	.52501	1.9047	.88539	18
43	.46510	.52538	1.9034	.88526	17
44	.46536	.52575	1.9020	.88512	16
45	.46561	.52613	1.9007	.88499	15
46	.46587	.52650	1.8993	.88485	14
47	.46613	.52687	1.8980	.88472	13
48	.46639	.52724	1.8967	.88458	12
49	.46664	.52761	1.8953	.88445	11
50	.46690	.52798	1.8940	.88431	10
51	.46716	.52836	1.8927	.88417	9
52	.46742	.52873	1.8913	.88404	8
53	.46767	.52910	1.8900	.88390	7
54	.46793	.52947	1.8887	.88377	6
55	.46819	.52985	1.8873	.88363	5
56	.46844	.53022	1.8860	.88349	4
57	.46870	.53059	1.8847	.88336	3
58	.46896	.53096	1.8834	.88322	2
59	.46921	.53134	1.8820	.88308	1
60	.46947	.53171	1.8807	.88295	0
′	Cos	Ctn	Tan	Sin	′

62°

28°

′	Sin	Tan	Ctn	Cos	′
0	.46947	.53171	1.8807	.88295	**60**
1	.46973	.53208	1.8794	.88281	59
2	.46999	.53246	1.8781	.88267	58
3	.47024	.53283	1.8768	.88254	57
4	.47050	.53320	1.8755	.88240	56
5	.47076	.53358	1.8741	.88226	**55**
6	.47101	.53395	1.8728	.88213	54
7	.47127	.53432	1.8715	.88199	53
8	.47153	.53470	1.8702	.88185	52
9	.47178	.53507	1.8689	.88172	51
10	.47204	.53545	1.8676	.88158	**50**
11	.47229	.53582	1.8663	.88144	49
12	.47255	.53620	1.8650	.88130	48
13	.47281	.53657	1.8637	.88117	47
14	.47306	.53694	1.8624	.88103	46
15	.47332	.53732	1.8611	.88089	**45**
16	.47358	.53769	1.8598	.88075	44
17	.47383	.53807	1.8585	.88062	43
18	.47409	.53844	1.8572	.88048	42
19	.47434	.53882	1.8559	.88034	41
20	.47460	.53920	1.8546	.88020	**40**
21	.47486	.53957	1.8533	.88006	39
22	.47511	.53995	1.8520	.87993	38
23	.47537	.54032	1.8507	.87979	37
24	.47562	.54070	1.8495	.87965	36
25	.47588	.54107	1.8482	.87951	**35**
26	.47614	.54145	1.8469	.87937	34
27	.47639	.54183	1.8456	.87923	33
28	.47665	.54220	1.8443	.87909	32
29	.47690	.54258	1.8430	.87896	31
30	.47716	.54296	1.8418	.87882	**30**
31	.47741	.54333	1.8405	.87868	29
32	.47767	.54371	1.8392	.87854	28
33	.47793	.54409	1.8379	.87840	27
34	.47818	.54446	1.8367	.87826	26
35	.47844	.54484	1.8354	.87812	**25**
36	.47869	.54522	1.8341	.87798	24
37	.47895	.54560	1.8329	.87784	23
38	.47920	.54597	1.8316	.87770	22
39	.47946	.54635	1.8303	.87756	21
40	.47971	.54673	1.8291	.87743	**20**
41	.47997	.54711	1.8278	.87729	19
42	.48022	.54748	1.8265	.87715	18
43	.48048	.54786	1.8253	.87701	17
44	.48073	.54824	1.8240	.87687	16
45	.48099	.54862	1.8228	.87673	**15**
46	.48124	.54900	1.8215	.87659	14
47	.48150	.54938	1.8202	.87645	13
48	.48175	.54975	1.8190	.87631	12
49	.48201	.55013	1.8177	.87617	11
50	.48226	.55051	1.8165	.87603	**10**
51	.48252	.55089	1.8152	.87589	9
52	.48277	.55127	1.8140	.87575	8
53	.48303	.55165	1.8127	.87561	7
54	.48328	.55203	1.8115	.87546	6
55	.48354	.55241	1.8103	.87532	**5**
56	.48379	.55279	1.8090	.87518	4
57	.48405	.55317	1.8078	.87504	3
58	.48430	.55355	1.8065	.87490	2
59	.48456	.55393	1.8053	.87476	1
60	.48481	.55431	1.8040	.87462	**0**
′	Cos	Ctn	Tan	Sin	′

61°

29°

′	Sin	Tan	Ctn	Cos	′
0	.48481	.55431	1.8040	.87462	**60**
1	.48506	.55469	1.8028	.87448	59
2	.48532	.55507	1.8016	.87434	58
3	.48557	.55545	1.8003	.87420	57
4	.48583	.55583	1.7991	.87406	56
5	.48608	.55621	1.7979	.87391	**55**
6	.48634	.55659	1.7966	.87377	54
7	.48659	.55697	1.7954	.87363	53
8	.48684	.55736	1.7942	.87349	52
9	.48710	.55774	1.7930	.87335	51
10	.48735	.55812	1.7917	.87321	**50**
11	.48761	.55850	1.7905	.87306	49
12	.48786	.55888	1.7893	.87292	48
13	.48811	.55926	1.7881	.87278	47
14	.48837	.55964	1.7868	.87264	46
15	.48862	.56003	1.7856	.87250	**45**
16	.48888	.56041	1.7844	.87235	44
17	.48913	.56079	1.7832	.87221	43
18	.48938	.56117	1.7820	.87207	42
19	.48964	.56156	1.7808	.87193	41
20	.48989	.56194	1.7796	.87178	**40**
21	.49014	.56232	1.7783	.87164	39
22	.49040	.56270	1.7771	.87150	38
23	.49065	.56309	1.7759	.87136	37
24	.49090	.56347	1.7747	.87121	36
25	.49116	.56385	1.7735	.87107	**35**
26	.49141	.56424	1.7723	.87093	34
27	.49166	.56462	1.7711	.87079	33
28	.49192	.56501	1.7699	.87064	32
29	.49217	.56539	1.7687	.87050	31
30	.49242	.56577	1.7675	.87036	**30**
31	.49268	.56616	1.7663	.87021	29
32	.49293	.56654	1.7651	.87007	28
33	.49318	.56693	1.7639	.86993	27
34	.49344	.56731	1.7627	.86978	26
35	.49369	.56769	1.7615	.86964	**25**
36	.49394	.56808	1.7603	.86949	24
37	.49419	.56846	1.7591	.86935	23
38	.49445	.56885	1.7579	.86921	22
39	.49470	.56923	1.7567	.86906	21
40	.49495	.56962	1.7556	.86892	**20**
41	.49521	.57000	1.7544	.86878	19
42	.49546	.57039	1.7532	.86863	18
43	.49571	.57078	1.7520	.86849	17
44	.49596	.57116	1.7508	.86834	16
45	.49622	.57155	1.7496	.86820	**15**
46	.49647	.57193	1.7485	.86805	14
47	.49672	.57232	1.7473	.86791	13
48	.49697	.57271	1.7461	.86777	12
49	.49723	.57309	1.7449	.86762	11
50	.49748	.57348	1.7437	.86748	**10**
51	.49773	.57386	1.7426	.86733	9
52	.49798	.57425	1.7414	.86719	8
53	.49824	.57464	1.7402	.86704	7
54	.49849	.57503	1.7391	.86690	6
55	.49874	.57541	1.7379	.86675	**5**
56	.49899	.57580	1.7367	.86661	4
57	.49924	.57619	1.7355	.86646	3
58	.49950	.57657	1.7344	.86632	2
59	.49975	.57696	1.7332	.86617	1
60	.50000	.57735	1.7321	.86603	**0**
′	Cos	Ctn	Tan	Sin	′

60°

TABLE I. NATURAL TRIGONOMETRIC FUNCTIONS   477

30°

′	Sin	Tan	Ctn	Cos	′
0	.50000	.57735	1.7321	.86603	**60**
1	.50025	.57774	1.7309	.86588	59
2	.50050	.57813	1.7297	.86573	58
3	.50076	.57851	1.7286	.86559	57
4	.50101	.57890	1.7274	.86544	56
5	.50126	.57929	1.7262	.86530	**55**
6	.50151	.57968	1.7251	.86515	54
7	.50176	.58007	1.7239	.86501	53
8	.50201	.58046	1.7228	.86486	52
9	.50227	.58085	1.7216	.86471	51
10	.50252	.58124	1.7205	.86457	**50**
11	.50277	.58162	1.7193	.86442	49
12	.50302	.58201	1.7182	.86427	48
13	.50327	.58240	1.7170	.86413	47
14	.50352	.58279	1.7159	.86398	46
15	.50377	.58318	1.7147	.86384	**45**
16	.50403	.58357	1.7136	.86369	44
17	.50428	.58396	1.7124	.86354	43
18	.50453	.58435	1.7113	.86340	42
19	.50478	.58474	1.7102	.86325	41
20	.50503	.58513	1.7090	.86310	**40**
21	.50528	.58552	1.7079	.86295	39
22	.50553	.58591	1.7067	.86281	38
23	.50578	.58631	1.7056	.86266	37
24	.50603	.58670	1.7045	.86251	36
25	.50628	.58709	1.7033	.86237	**35**
26	.50654	.58748	1.7022	.86222	34
27	.50679	.58787	1.7011	.86207	33
28	.50704	.58826	1.6999	.86192	32
29	.50729	.58865	1.6988	.86178	31
30	.50754	.58905	1.6977	.86163	**30**
31	.50779	.58944	1.6965	.86148	29
32	.50804	.58983	1.6954	.86133	28
33	.50829	.59022	1.6943	.86119	27
34	.50854	.59061	1.6932	.86104	26
35	.50879	.59101	1.6920	.86089	**25**
36	.50904	.59140	1.6909	.86074	24
37	.50929	.59179	1.6898	.86059	23
38	.50954	.59218	1.6887	.86045	22
39	.50979	.59258	1.6875	.86030	21
40	.51004	.59297	1.6864	.86015	**20**
41	.51029	.59336	1.6853	.86000	19
42	.51054	.59376	1.6842	.85985	18
43	.51079	.59415	1.6831	.85970	17
44	.51104	.59454	1.6820	.85956	16
45	.51129	.59494	1.6808	.85941	**15**
46	.51154	.59533	1.6797	.85926	14
47	.51179	.59573	1.6786	.85911	13
48	.51204	.59612	1.6775	.85896	12
49	.51229	.59651	1.6764	.85881	11
50	.51254	.59691	1.6753	.85866	**10**
51	.51279	.59730	1.6742	.85851	9
52	.51304	.59770	1.6731	.85836	8
53	.51329	.59809	1.6720	.85821	7
54	.51354	.59849	1.6709	.85806	6
55	.51379	.59888	1.6698	.85792	**5**
56	.51404	.59928	1.6687	.85777	4
57	.51429	.59967	1.6676	.85762	3
58	.51454	.60007	1.6665	.85747	2
59	.51479	.60046	1.6654	.85732	1
60	.51504	.60086	1.6643	.85717	**0**
′	Cos	Ctn	Tan	Sin	′

59°

31°

′	Sin	Tan	Ctn	Cos	′
0	.51504	.60086	1.6643	.85717	**60**
1	.51529	.60126	1.6632	.85702	59
2	.51554	.60165	1.6621	.85687	58
3	.51579	.60205	1.6610	.85672	57
4	.51604	.60245	1.6599	.85657	56
5	.51628	.60284	1.6588	.85642	**55**
6	.51653	.60324	1.6577	.85627	54
7	.51678	.60364	1.6566	.85612	53
8	.51703	.60403	1.6555	.85597	52
9	.51728	.60443	1.6545	.85582	51
10	.51753	.60483	1.6534	.85567	**50**
11	.51778	.60522	1.6523	.85551	49
12	.51803	.60562	1.6512	.85536	48
13	.51828	.60602	1.6501	.85521	47
14	.51852	.60642	1.6490	.85506	46
15	.51877	.60681	1.6479	.85491	**45**
16	.51902	.60721	1.6469	.85476	44
17	.51927	.60761	1.6458	.85461	43
18	.51952	.60801	1.6447	.85446	42
19	.51977	.60841	1.6436	.85431	41
20	.52002	.60881	1.6426	.85416	**40**
21	.52026	.60921	1.6415	.85401	39
22	.52051	.60960	1.6404	.85385	38
23	.52076	.61000	1.6393	.85370	37
24	.52101	.61040	1.6383	.85355	36
25	.52126	.61080	1.6372	.85340	**35**
26	.52151	.61120	1.6361	.85325	34
27	.52175	.61160	1.6351	.85310	33
28	.52200	.61200	1.6340	.85294	32
29	.52225	.61240	1.6329	.85279	31
30	.52250	.61280	1.6319	.85264	**30**
31	.52275	.61320	1.6308	.85249	29
32	.52299	.61360	1.6297	.85234	28
33	.52324	.61400	1.6287	.85218	27
34	.52349	.61440	1.6276	.85203	26
35	.52374	.61480	1.6265	.85188	**25**
36	.52399	.61520	1.6255	.85173	24
37	.52423	.61561	1.6244	.85157	23
38	.52448	.61601	1.6234	.85142	22
39	.52473	.61641	1.6223	.85127	21
40	.52498	.61681	1.6212	.85112	**20**
41	.52522	.61721	1.6202	.85096	19
42	.52547	.61761	1.6191	.85081	18
43	.52572	.61801	1.6181	.85066	17
44	.52597	.61842	1.6170	.85051	16
45	.52621	.61882	1.6160	.85035	**15**
46	.52646	.61922	1.6149	.85020	14
47	.52671	.61962	1.6139	.85005	13
48	.52696	.62003	1.6128	.84989	12
49	.52720	.62043	1.6118	.84974	11
50	.52745	.62083	1.6107	.84959	**10**
51	.52770	.62124	1.6097	.84943	9
52	.52794	.62164	1.6087	.84928	8
53	.52819	.62204	1.6076	.84913	7
54	.52844	.62245	1.6066	.84897	6
55	.52869	.62285	1.6055	.84882	**5**
56	.52893	.62325	1.6045	.84866	4
57	.52918	.62366	1.6034	.84851	3
58	.52943	.62406	1.6024	.84836	2
59	.52967	.62446	1.6014	.84820	1
60	.52992	.62487	1.6003	.84805	**0**
′	Cos	Ctn	Tan	Sin	′

58°

32°

′	Sin	Tan	Ctn	Cos	′
0	.52992	.62487	1.6003	.84805	60
1	.53017	.62527	1.5993	.84789	59
2	.53041	.62568	1.5983	.84774	58
3	.53066	.62608	1.5972	.84759	57
4	.53091	.62649	1.5962	.84743	56
5	.53115	.62689	1.5952	.84728	55
6	.53140	.62730	1.5941	.84712	54
7	.53164	.62770	1.5931	.84697	53
8	.53189	.62811	1.5921	.84681	52
9	.53214	.62852	1.5911	.84666	51
10	.53238	.62892	1.5900	.84650	50
11	.53263	.62933	1.5890	.84635	49
12	.53288	.62973	1.5880	.84619	48
13	.53312	.63014	1.5869	.84604	47
14	.53337	.63055	1.5859	.84588	46
15	.53361	.63095	1.5849	.84573	45
16	.53386	.63136	1.5839	.84557	44
17	.53411	.63177	1.5829	.84542	43
18	.53435	.63217	1.5818	.84526	42
19	.53460	.63258	1.5808	.84511	41
20	.53484	.63299	1.5798	.84495	40
21	.53509	.63340	1.5788	.84480	39
22	.53534	.63380	1.5778	.84464	38
23	.53558	.63421	1.5768	.84448	37
24	.53583	.63462	1.5757	.84433	36
25	.53607	.63503	1.5747	.84417	35
26	.53632	.63544	1.5737	.84402	34
27	.53656	.63584	1.5727	.84386	33
28	.53681	.63625	1.5717	.84370	32
29	.53705	.63666	1.5707	.84355	31
30	.53730	.63707	1.5697	.84339	30
31	.53754	.63748	1.5687	.84324	29
32	.53779	.63789	1.5677	.84308	28
33	.53804	.63830	1.5667	.84292	27
34	.53828	.63871	1.5657	.84277	26
35	.53853	.63912	1.5647	.84261	25
36	.53877	.63953	1.5637	.84245	24
37	.53902	.63994	1.5627	.84230	23
38	.53926	.64035	1.5617	.84214	22
39	.53951	.64076	1.5607	.84198	21
40	.53975	.64117	1.5597	.84182	20
41	.54000	.64158	1.5587	.84167	19
42	.54024	.64199	1.5577	.84151	18
43	.54049	.64240	1.5567	.84135	17
44	.54073	.64281	1.5557	.84120	16
45	.54097	.64322	1.5547	.84104	15
46	.54122	.64363	1.5537	.84088	14
47	.54146	.64404	1.5527	.84072	13
48	.54171	.64446	1.5517	.84057	12
49	.54195	.64487	1.5507	.84041	11
50	.54220	.64528	1.5497	.84025	10
51	.54244	.64569	1.5487	.84009	9
52	.54269	.64610	1.5477	.83994	8
53	.54293	.64652	1.5468	.83978	7
54	.54317	.64693	1.5458	.83962	6
55	.54342	.64734	1.5448	.83946	5
56	.54366	.64775	1.5438	.83930	4
57	.54391	.64817	1.5428	.83915	3
58	.54415	.64858	1.5418	.83899	2
59	.54440	.64899	1.5408	.83883	1
60	.54464	.64941	1.5399	.83867	0
′	Cos	Ctn	Tan	Sin	′

57°

33°

′	Sin	Tan	Ctn	Cos	′
0	.54464	.64941	1.5399	.83867	60
1	.54488	.64982	1.5389	.83851	59
2	.54513	.65024	1.5379	.83835	58
3	.54537	.65065	1.5369	.83819	57
4	.54561	.65106	1.5359	.83804	56
5	.54586	.65148	1.5350	.83788	55
6	.54610	.65189	1.5340	.83772	54
7	.54635	.65231	1.5330	.83756	53
8	.54659	.65272	1.5320	.83740	52
9	.54683	.65314	1.5311	.83724	51
10	.54708	.65355	1.5301	.83708	50
11	.54732	.65397	1.5291	.83692	49
12	.54756	.65438	1.5282	.83676	48
13	.54781	.65480	1.5272	.83660	47
14	.54805	.65521	1.5262	.83645	46
15	.54829	.65563	1.5253	.83629	45
16	.54854	.65604	1.5243	.83613	44
17	.54878	.65646	1.5233	.83597	43
18	.54902	.65688	1.5224	.83581	42
19	.54927	.65729	1.5214	.83565	41
20	.54951	.65771	1.5204	.83549	40
21	.54975	.65813	1.5195	.83533	39
22	.54999	.65854	1.5185	.83517	38
23	.55024	.65896	1.5175	.83501	37
24	.55048	.65938	1.5166	.83485	36
25	.55072	.65980	1.5156	.83469	35
26	.55097	.66021	1.5147	.83453	34
27	.55121	.66063	1.5137	.83437	33
28	.55145	.66105	1.5127	.83421	32
29	.55169	.66147	1.5118	.83405	31
30	.55194	.66189	1.5108	.83389	30
31	.55218	.66230	1.5099	.83373	29
32	.55242	.66272	1.5089	.83356	28
33	.55266	.66314	1.5080	.83340	27
34	.55291	.66356	1.5070	.83324	26
35	.55315	.66398	1.5061	.83308	25
36	.55339	.66440	1.5051	.83292	24
37	.55363	.66482	1.5042	.83276	23
38	.55388	.66524	1.5032	.83260	22
39	.55412	.66566	1.5023	.83244	21
40	.55436	.66608	1.5013	.83228	20
41	.55460	.66650	1.5004	.83212	19
42	.55484	.66692	1.4994	.83195	18
43	.55509	.66734	1.4985	.83179	17
44	.55533	.66776	1.4975	.83163	16
45	.55557	.66818	1.4966	.83147	15
46	.55581	.66860	1.4957	.83131	14
47	.55605	.66902	1.4947	.83115	13
48	.55630	.66944	1.4938	.83098	12
49	.55654	.66986	1.4928	.83082	11
50	.55678	.67028	1.4919	.83066	10
51	.55702	.67071	1.4910	.83050	9
52	.55726	.67113	1.4900	.83034	8
53	.55750	.67155	1.4891	.83017	7
54	.55775	.67197	1.4882	.83001	6
55	.55799	.67239	1.4872	.82985	5
56	.55823	.67282	1.4863	.82969	4
57	.55847	.67324	1.4854	.82953	3
58	.55871	.67366	1.4844	.82936	2
59	.55895	.67409	1.4835	.82920	1
60	.55919	.67451	1.4826	.82904	0
′	Cos	Ctn	Tan	Sin	′

56°

TABLE I. NATURAL TRIGONOMETRIC FUNCTIONS   479

34°

'	Sin	Tan	Ctn	Cos	'
0	.55919	.67451	1.4826	.82904	60
1	.55943	.67493	1.4816	.82887	59
2	.55968	.67536	1.4807	.82871	58
3	.55992	.67578	1.4798	.82855	57
4	.56016	.67620	1.4788	.82839	56
5	.56040	.67663	1.4779	.82822	55
6	.56064	.67705	1.4770	.82806	54
7	.56088	.67748	1.4761	.82790	53
8	.56112	.67790	1.4751	.82773	52
9	.56136	.67832	1.4742	.82757	51
10	.56160	.67875	1.4733	.82741	50
11	.56184	.67917	1.4724	.82724	49
12	.56208	.67960	1.4715	.82708	48
13	.56232	.68002	1.4705	.82692	47
14	.56256	.68045	1.4696	.82675	46
15	.56280	.68088	1.4687	.82659	45
16	.56305	.68130	1.4678	.82643	44
17	.56329	.68173	1.4669	.82626	43
18	.56353	.68215	1.4659	.82610	42
19	.56377	.68258	1.4650	.82593	41
20	.56401	.68301	1.4641	.82577	40
21	.56425	.68343	1.4632	.82561	39
22	.56449	.68386	1.4623	.82544	38
23	.56473	.68429	1.4614	.82528	37
24	.56497	.68471	1.4605	.82511	36
25	.56521	.68514	1.4596	.82495	35
26	.56545	.68557	1.4586	.82478	34
27	.56569	.68600	1.4577	.82462	33
28	.56593	.68642	1.4568	.82446	32
29	.56617	.68685	1.4559	.82429	31
30	.56641	.68728	1.4550	.82413	30
31	.56665	.68771	1.4541	.82396	29
32	.56689	.68814	1.4532	.82380	28
33	.56713	.68857	1.4523	.82363	27
34	.56736	.68900	1.4514	.82347	26
35	.56760	.68942	1.4505	.82330	25
36	.56784	.68985	1.4496	.82314	24
37	.56808	.69028	1.4487	.82297	23
38	.56832	.69071	1.4478	.82281	22
39	.56856	.69114	1.4469	.82264	21
40	.56880	.69157	1.4460	.82248	20
41	.56904	.69200	1.4451	.82231	19
42	.56928	.69243	1.4442	.82214	18
43	.56952	.69286	1.4433	.82198	17
44	.56976	.69329	1.4424	.82181	16
45	.57000	.69372	1.4415	.82165	15
46	.57024	.69416	1.4406	.82148	14
47	.57047	.69459	1.4397	.82132	13
48	.57071	.69502	1.4388	.82115	12
49	.57095	.69545	1.4379	.82098	11
50	.57119	.69588	1.4370	.82082	10
51	.57143	.69631	1.4361	.82065	9
52	.57167	.69675	1.4352	.82048	8
53	.57191	.69718	1.4344	.82032	7
54	.57215	.69761	1.4335	.82015	6
55	.57238	.69804	1.4326	.81999	5
56	.57262	.69847	1.4317	.81982	4
57	.57286	.69891	1.4308	.81965	3
58	.57310	.69934	1.4299	.81949	2
59	.57334	.69977	1.4290	.81932	1
60	.57358	.70021	1.4281	.81915	0
'	Cos	Ctn	Tan	Sin	'

55°

35°

'	Sin	Tan	Ctn	Cos	'
0	.57358	.70021	1.4281	.81915	60
1	.57381	.70064	1.4273	.81899	59
2	.57405	.70107	1.4264	.81882	58
3	.57429	.70151	1.4255	.81865	57
4	.57453	.70194	1.4246	.81848	56
5	.57477	.70238	1.4237	.81832	55
6	.57501	.70281	1.4229	.81815	54
7	.57524	.70325	1.4220	.81798	53
8	.57548	.70368	1.4211	.81782	52
9	.57572	.70412	1.4202	.81765	51
10	.57596	.70455	1.4193	.81748	50
11	.57619	.70499	1.4185	.81731	49
12	.57643	.70542	1.4176	.81714	48
13	.57667	.70586	1.4167	.81698	47
14	.57691	.70629	1.4158	.81681	46
15	.57715	.70673	1.4150	.81664	45
16	.57738	.70717	1.4141	.81647	44
17	.57762	.70760	1.4132	.81631	43
18	.57786	.70804	1.4124	.81614	42
19	.57810	.70848	1.4115	.81597	41
20	.57833	.70891	1.4106	.81580	40
21	.57857	.70935	1.4097	.81563	39
22	.57881	.70979	1.4089	.81546	38
23	.57904	.71023	1.4080	.81530	37
24	.57928	.71066	1.4071	.81513	36
25	.57952	.71110	1.4063	.81496	35
26	.57976	.71154	1.4054	.81479	34
27	.57999	.71198	1.4045	.81462	33
28	.58023	.71242	1.4037	.81445	32
29	.58047	.71285	1.4028	.81428	31
30	.58070	.71329	1.4019	.81412	30
31	.58094	.71373	1.4011	.81395	29
32	.58118	.71417	1.4002	.81378	28
33	.58141	.71461	1.3994	.81361	27
34	.58165	.71505	1.3985	.81344	26
35	.58189	.71549	1.3976	.81327	25
36	.58212	.71593	1.3968	.81310	24
37	.58236	.71637	1.3959	.81293	23
38	.58260	.71681	1.3951	.81276	22
39	.58283	.71725	1.3942	.81259	21
40	.58307	.71769	1.3934	.81242	20
41	.58330	.71813	1.3925	.81225	19
42	.58354	.71857	1.3916	.81208	18
43	.58378	.71901	1.3908	.81191	17
44	.58401	.71946	1.3899	.81174	16
45	.58425	.71990	1.3891	.81157	15
46	.58449	.72034	1.3882	.81140	14
47	.58472	.72078	1.3874	.81123	13
48	.58496	.72122	1.3865	.81106	12
49	.58519	.72167	1.3857	.81089	11
50	.58543	.72211	1.3848	.81072	10
51	.58567	.72255	1.3840	.81055	9
52	.58590	.72299	1.3831	.81038	8
53	.58614	.72344	1.3823	.81021	7
54	.58637	.72388	1.3814	.81004	6
55	.58661	.72432	1.3806	.80987	5
56	.58684	.72477	1.3798	.80970	4
57	.58708	.72521	1.3789	.80953	3
58	.58731	.72565	1.3781	.80936	2
59	.58755	.72610	1.3772	.80919	1
60	.58779	.72654	1.3764	.80902	0
'	Cos	Ctn	Tan	Sin	'

54°

36°

′	Sin	Tan	Ctn	Cos	′
0	.58779	.72654	1.3764	.80902	60
1	.58802	.72699	1.3755	.80885	59
2	.58826	.72743	1.3747	.80867	58
3	.58849	.72788	1.3739	.80850	57
4	.58873	.72832	1.3730	.80833	56
5	.58896	.72877	1.3722	.80816	55
6	.58920	.72921	1.3713	.80799	54
7	.58943	.72966	1.3705	.80782	53
8	.58967	.73010	1.3697	.80765	52
9	.58990	.73055	1.3688	.80748	51
10	.59014	.73100	1.3680	.80730	50
11	.59037	.73144	1.3672	.80713	49
12	.59061	.73189	1.3663	.80696	48
13	.59084	.73234	1.3655	.80679	47
14	.59108	.73278	1.3647	.80662	46
15	.59131	.73323	1.3638	.80644	45
16	.59154	.73368	1.3630	.80627	44
17	.59178	.73413	1.3622	.80610	43
18	.59201	.73457	1.3613	.80593	42
19	.59225	.73502	1.3605	.80576	41
20	.59248	.73547	1.3597	.80558	40
21	.59272	.73592	1.3588	.80541	39
22	.59295	.73637	1.3580	.80524	38
23	.59318	.73681	1.3572	.80507	37
24	.59342	.73726	1.3564	.80489	36
25	.59365	.73771	1.3555	.80472	35
26	.59389	.73816	1.3547	.80455	34
27	.59412	.73861	1.3539	.80438	33
28	.59436	.73906	1.3531	.80420	32
29	.59459	.73951	1.3522	.80403	31
30	.59482	.73996	1.3514	.80386	30
31	.59506	.74041	1.3506	.80368	29
32	.59529	.74086	1.3498	.80351	28
33	.59552	.74131	1.3490	.80334	27
34	.59576	.74176	1.3481	.80316	26
35	.59599	.74221	1.3473	.80299	25
36	.59622	.74267	1.3465	.80282	24
37	.59646	.74312	1.3457	.80264	23
38	.59669	.74357	1.3449	.80247	22
39	.59693	.74402	1.3440	.80230	21
40	.59716	.74447	1.3432	.80212	20
41	.59739	.74492	1.3424	.80195	19
42	.59763	.74538	1.3416	.80178	18
43	.59786	.74583	1.3408	.80160	17
44	.59809	.74628	1.3400	.80143	16
45	.59832	.74674	1.3392	.80125	15
46	.59856	.74719	1.3384	.80108	14
47	.59879	.74764	1.3375	.80091	13
48	.59902	.74810	1.3367	.80073	12
49	.59926	.74855	1.3359	.80056	11
50	.59949	.74900	1.3351	.80038	10
51	.59972	.74946	1.3343	.80021	9
52	.59995	.74991	1.3335	.80003	8
53	.60019	.75037	1.3327	.79986	7
54	.60042	.75082	1.3319	.79968	6
55	.60065	.75128	1.3311	.79951	5
56	.60089	.75173	1.3303	.79934	4
57	.60112	.75219	1.3295	.79916	3
58	.60135	.75264	1.3287	.79899	2
59	.60158	.75310	1.3278	.79881	1
60	.60182	.75355	1.3270	.79864	0
′	Cos	Ctn	Tan	Sin	′

53°

37°

′	Sin	Tan	Ctn	Cos	′
0	.60182	.75355	1.3270	.79864	60
1	.60205	.75401	1.3262	.79846	59
2	.60228	.75447	1.3254	.79829	58
3	.60251	.75492	1.3246	.79811	57
4	.60274	.75538	1.3238	.79793	56
5	.60298	.75584	1.3230	.79776	55
6	.60321	.75629	1.3222	.79758	54
7	.60344	.75675	1.3214	.79741	53
8	.60367	.75721	1.3206	.79723	52
9	.60390	.75767	1.3198	.79706	51
10	.60414	.75812	1.3190	.79688	50
11	.60437	.75858	1.3182	.79671	49
12	.60460	.75904	1.3175	.79653	48
13	.60483	.75950	1.3167	.79635	47
14	.60506	.75996	1.3159	.79618	46
15	.60529	.76042	1.3151	.79600	45
16	.60553	.76088	1.3143	.79583	44
17	.60576	.76134	1.3135	.79565	43
18	.60599	.76180	1.3127	.79547	42
19	.60622	.76226	1.3119	.79530	41
20	.60645	.76272	1.3111	.79512	40
21	.60668	.76318	1.3103	.79494	39
22	.60691	.76364	1.3095	.79477	38
23	.60714	.76410	1.3087	.79459	37
24	.60738	.76456	1.3079	.79441	36
25	.60761	.76502	1.3072	.79424	35
26	.60784	.76548	1.3064	.79406	34
27	.60807	.76594	1.3056	.79388	33
28	.60830	.76640	1.3048	.79371	32
29	.60853	.76686	1.3040	.79353	31
30	.60876	.76733	1.3032	.79335	30
31	.60899	.76779	1.3024	.79318	29
32	.60922	.76825	1.3017	.79300	28
33	.60945	.76871	1.3009	.79282	27
34	.60968	.76918	1.3001	.79264	26
35	.60991	.76964	1.2993	.79247	25
36	.61015	.77010	1.2985	.79229	24
37	.61038	.77057	1.2977	.79211	23
38	.61061	.77103	1.2970	.79193	22
39	.61084	.77149	1.2962	.79176	21
40	.61107	.77196	1.2954	.79158	20
41	.61130	.77242	1.2946	.79140	19
42	.61153	.77289	1.2938	.79122	18
43	.61176	.77335	1.2931	.79105	17
44	.61199	.77382	1.2923	.79087	16
45	.61222	.77428	1.2915	.79069	15
46	.61245	.77475	1.2907	.79051	14
47	.61268	.77521	1.2900	.79033	13
48	.61291	.77568	1.2892	.79016	12
49	.61314	.77615	1.2884	.78998	11
50	.61337	.77661	1.2876	.78980	10
51	.61360	.77708	1.2869	.78962	9
52	.61383	.77754	1.2861	.78944	8
53	.61406	.77801	1.2853	.78926	7
54	.61429	.77848	1.2846	.78908	6
55	.61451	.77895	1.2838	.78891	5
56	.61474	.77941	1.2830	.78873	4
57	.61497	.77988	1.2822	.78855	3
58	.61520	.78035	1.2815	.78837	2
59	.61543	.78082	1.2807	.78819	1
60	.61566	.78129	1.2799	.78801	0
′	Cos	Ctn	Tan	Sin	′

52°

TABLE I. NATURAL TRIGONOMETRIC FUNCTIONS 481

38°

′	Sin	Tan	Ctn	Cos	′
0	.61566	.78129	1.2799	.78801	60
1	.61589	.78175	1.2792	.78783	59
2	.61612	.78222	1.2784	.78765	58
3	.61635	.78269	1.2776	.78747	57
4	.61658	.78316	1.2769	.78729	56
5	.61681	.78363	1.2761	.78711	55
6	.61704	.78410	1.2753	.78694	54
7	.61726	.78457	1.2746	.78676	53
8	.61749	.78504	1.2738	.78658	52
9	.61772	.78551	1.2731	.78640	51
10	.61795	.78598	1.2723	.78622	50
11	.61818	.78645	1.2715	.78604	49
12	.61841	.78692	1.2708	.78586	48
13	.61864	.78739	1.2700	.78568	47
14	.61887	.78786	1.2693	.78550	46
15	.61909	.78834	1.2685	.78532	45
16	.61932	.78881	1.2677	.78514	44
17	.61955	.78928	1.2670	.78496	43
18	.61978	.78975	1.2662	.78478	42
19	.62001	.79022	1.2655	.78460	41
20	.62024	.79070	1.2647	.78442	40
21	.62046	.79117	1.2640	.78424	39
22	.62069	.79164	1.2632	.78405	38
23	.62092	.79212	1.2624	.78387	37
24	.62115	.79259	1.2617	.78369	36
25	.62138	.79306	1.2609	.78351	35
26	.62160	.79354	1.2602	.78333	34
27	.62183	.79401	1.2594	.78315	33
28	.62206	.79449	1.2587	.78297	32
29	.62229	.79496	1.2579	.78279	31
30	.62251	.79544	1.2572	.78261	30
31	.62274	.79591	1.2564	.78243	29
32	.62297	.79639	1.2557	.78225	28
33	.62320	.79686	1.2549	.78206	27
34	.62342	.79734	1.2542	.78188	26
35	.62365	.79781	1.2534	.78170	25
36	.62388	.79829	1.2527	.78152	24
37	.62411	.79877	1.2519	.78134	23
38	.62433	.79924	1.2512	.78116	22
39	.62456	.79972	1.2504	.78098	21
40	.62479	.80020	1.2497	.78079	20
41	.62502	.80067	1.2489	.78061	19
42	.62524	.80115	1.2482	.78043	18
43	.62547	.80163	1.2475	.78025	17
44	.62570	.80211	1.2467	.78007	16
45	.62592	.80258	1.2460	.77988	15
46	.62615	.80306	1.2452	.77970	14
47	.62638	.80354	1.2445	.77952	13
48	.62660	.80402	1.2437	.77934	12
49	.62683	.80450	1.2430	.77916	11
50	.62706	.80498	1.2423	.77897	10
51	.62728	.80546	1.2415	.77879	9
52	.62751	.80594	1.2408	.77861	8
53	.62774	.80642	1.2401	.77843	7
54	.62796	.80690	1.2393	.77824	6
55	.62819	.80738	1.2386	.77806	5
56	.62842	.80786	1.2378	.77788	4
57	.62864	.80834	1.2371	.77769	3
58	.62887	.80882	1.2364	.77751	2
59	.62909	.80930	1.2356	.77733	1
60	.62932	.80978	1.2349	.77715	0
′	Cos	Ctn	Tan	Sin	′

51°

39°

′	Sin	Tan	Ctn	Cos	′
0	.62932	.80978	1.2349	.77715	60
1	.62955	.81027	1.2342	.77696	59
2	.62977	.81075	1.2334	.77678	58
3	.63000	.81123	1.2327	.77660	57
4	.63022	.81171	1.2320	.77641	56
5	.63045	.81220	1.2312	.77623	55
6	.63068	.81268	1.2305	.77605	54
7	.63090	.81316	1.2298	.77586	53
8	.63113	.81364	1.2290	.77568	52
9	.63135	.81413	1.2283	.77550	51
10	.63158	.81461	1.2276	.77531	50
11	.63180	.81510	1.2268	.77513	49
12	.63203	.81558	1.2261	.77494	48
13	.63225	.81606	1.2254	.77476	47
14	.63248	.81655	1.2247	.77458	46
15	.63271	.81703	1.2239	.77439	45
16	.63293	.81752	1.2232	.77421	44
17	.63316	.81800	1.2225	.77402	43
18	.63338	.81849	1.2218	.77384	42
19	.63361	.81898	1.2210	.77366	41
20	.63383	.81946	1.2203	.77347	40
21	.63406	.81995	1.2196	.77329	39
22	.63428	.82044	1.2189	.77310	38
23	.63451	.82092	1.2181	.77292	37
24	.63473	.82141	1.2174	.77273	36
25	.63496	.82190	1.2167	.77255	35
26	.63518	.82238	1.2160	.77236	34
27	.63540	.82287	1.2153	.77218	33
28	.63563	.82336	1.2145	.77199	32
29	.63585	.82385	1.2138	.77181	31
30	.63608	.82434	1.2131	.77162	30
31	.63630	.82483	1.2124	.77144	29
32	.63653	.82531	1.2117	.77125	28
33	.63675	.82580	1.2109	.77107	27
34	.63698	.82629	1.2102	.77088	26
35	.63720	.82678	1.2095	.77070	25
36	.63742	.82727	1.2088	.77051	24
37	.63765	.82776	1.2081	.77033	23
38	.63787	.82825	1.2074	.77014	22
39	.63810	.82874	1.2066	.76996	21
40	.63832	.82923	1.2059	.76977	20
41	.63854	.82972	1.2052	.76959	19
42	.63877	.83022	1.2045	.76940	18
43	.63899	.83071	1.2038	.76921	17
44	.63922	.83120	1.2031	.76903	16
45	.63944	.83169	1.2024	.76884	15
46	.63966	.83218	1.2017	.76866	14
47	.63989	.83268	1.2009	.76847	13
48	.64011	.83317	1.2002	.76828	12
49	.64033	.83366	1.1995	.76810	11
50	.64056	.83415	1.1988	.76791	10
51	.64078	.83465	1.1981	.76772	9
52	.64100	.83514	1.1974	.76754	8
53	.64123	.83564	1.1967	.76735	7
54	.64145	.83613	1.1960	.76717	6
55	.64167	.83662	1.1953	.76698	5
56	.64190	.83712	1.1946	.76679	4
57	.64212	.83761	1.1939	.76661	3
58	.64234	.83811	1.1932	.76642	2
59	.64256	.83860	1.1925	.76623	1
60	.64279	.83910	1.1918	.76604	0
′	Cos	Ctn	Tan	Sin	′

50°

40°

'	Sin	Tan	Ctn	Cos	'
0	.64279	.83910	1.1918	.76604	60
1	.64301	.83960	1.1910	.76586	59
2	.64323	.84009	1.1903	.76567	58
3	.64346	.84059	1.1896	.76548	57
4	.64368	.84108	1.1889	.76530	56
5	.64390	.84158	1.1882	.76511	55
6	.64412	.84208	1.1875	.76492	54
7	.64435	.84258	1.1868	.76473	53
8	.64457	.84307	1.1861	.76455	52
9	.64479	.84357	1.1854	.76436	51
10	.64501	.84407	1.1847	.76417	50
11	.64524	.84457	1.1840	.76398	49
12	.64546	.84507	1.1833	.76380	48
13	.64568	.84556	1.1826	.76361	47
14	.64590	.84606	1.1819	.76342	46
15	.64612	.84656	1.1812	.76323	45
16	.64635	.84706	1.1806	.76304	44
17	.64657	.84756	1.1799	.76286	43
18	.64679	.84806	1.1792	.76267	42
19	.64701	.84856	1.1785	.76248	41
20	.64723	.84906	1.1778	.76229	40
21	.64746	.84956	1.1771	.76210	39
22	.64768	.85006	1.1764	.76192	38
23	.64790	.85057	1.1757	.76173	37
24	.64812	.85107	1.1750	.76154	36
25	.64834	.85157	1.1743	.76135	35
26	.64856	.85207	1.1736	.76116	34
27	.64878	.85257	1.1729	.76097	33
28	.64901	.85308	1.1722	.76078	32
29	.64923	.85358	1.1715	.76059	31
30	.64945	.85408	1.1708	.76041	30
31	.64967	.85458	1.1702	.76022	29
32	.64989	.85509	1.1695	.76003	28
33	.65011	.85559	1.1688	.75984	27
34	.65033	.85609	1.1681	.75965	26
35	.65055	.85660	1.1674	.75946	25
36	.65077	.85710	1.1667	.75927	24
37	.65100	.85761	1.1660	.75908	23
38	.65122	.85811	1.1653	.75889	22
39	.65144	.85862	1.1647	.75870	21
40	.65166	.85912	1.1640	.75851	20
41	.65188	.85963	1.1633	.75832	19
42	.65210	.86014	1.1626	.75813	18
43	.65232	.86064	1.1619	.75794	17
44	.65254	.86115	1.1612	.75775	16
45	.65276	.86166	1.1606	.75756	15
46	.65298	.86216	1.1599	.75738	14
47	.65320	.86267	1.1592	.75719	13
48	.65342	.86318	1.1585	.75700	12
49	.65364	.86368	1.1578	.75680	11
50	.65386	.86419	1.1571	.75661	10
51	.65408	.86470	1.1565	.75642	9
52	.65430	.86521	1.1558	.75623	8
53	.65452	.86572	1.1551	.75604	7
54	.65474	.86623	1.1544	.75585	6
55	.65496	86674	1.1538	.75566	5
56	.65518	.86725	1.1531	.75547	4
57	.65540	.86776	1.1524	.75528	3
58	.65562	.86827	1.1517	.75509	2
59	.65584	.86878	1.1510	.75490	1
60	.65606	.86929	1.1504	.75471	0
'	Cos	Ctn	Tan	Sin	'

49°

41°

'	Sin	Tan	Ctn	Cos	'
0	.65606	.86929	1.1504	.75471	60
1	.65628	.86980	1.1497	.75452	59
2	.65650	.87031	1.1490	.75433	58
3	.65672	.87082	1.1483	.75414	57
4	.65694	.87133	1.1477	.75395	56
5	.65716	.87184	1.1470	.75375	55
6	.65738	.87236	1.1463	.75356	54
7	.65759	.87287	1.1456	.75337	53
8	.65781	.87338	1.1450	.75318	52
9	.65803	.87389	1.1443	.75299	51
10	.65825	.87441	1.1436	.75280	50
11	.65847	.87492	1.1430	.75261	49
12	.65869	.87543	1.1423	.75241	48
13	.65891	.87595	1.1416	.75222	47
14	.65913	.87646	1.1410	.75203	46
15	.65935	.87698	1.1403	.75184	45
16	.65956	.87749	1.1396	.75165	44
17	.65978	.87801	1.1389	.75146	43
18	.66000	.87852	1.1383	.75126	42
19	.66022	.87904	1.1376	.75107	41
20	.66044	.87955	1.1369	.75088	40
21	.66066	.88007	1.1363	.75069	39
22	.66088	.88059	1.1356	.75050	38
23	.66109	.88110	1.1349	.75030	37
24	.66131	.88162	1.1343	.75011	36
25	.66153	.88214	1.1336	.74992	35
26	.66175	.88265	1.1329	.74973	34
27	.66197	.88317	1.1323	.74953	33
28	.66218	.88369	1.1316	.74934	32
29	.66240	.88421	1.1310	.74915	31
30	.66262	.88473	1.1303	.74896	30
31	.66284	.88524	1.1296	.74876	29
32	.66306	.88576	1.1290	.74857	28
33	.66327	.88628	1.1283	.74838	27
34	.66349	.88680	1.1276	.74818	26
35	.66371	.88732	1.1270	.74799	25
36	.66393	.88784	1.1263	.74780	24
37	.66414	.88836	1.1257	.74760	23
38	.66436	.88888	1.1250	.74741	22
39	.66458	.88940	1.1243	.74722	21
40	.66480	.88992	1.1237	.74703	20
41	.66501	.89045	1.1230	.74683	19
42	.66523	.89097	1.1224	.74664	18
43	.66545	.89149	1.1217	.74644	17
44	.66566	.89201	1.1211	.74625	16
45	.66588	.89253	1.1204	.74606	15
46	.66610	.89306	1.1197	.74586	14
47	.66632	.89358	1.1191	.74567	13
48	.66653	.89410	1.1184	.74548	12
49	.66675	.89463	1.1178	.74528	11
50	.66697	.89515	1.1171	.74509	10
51	.66718	.89567	1.1165	.74489	9
52	.66740	.89620	1.1158	.74470	8
53	.66762	.89672	1.1152	.74451	7
54	.66783	.89725	1.1145	.74431	6
55	.66805	.89777	1.1139	.74412	5
56	.66827	.89830	1.1132	.74392	4
57	.66848	.89883	1.1126	.74373	3
58	.66870	.89935	1.1119	.74353	2
59	.66891	.89988	1.1113	.74334	1
60	.66913	.90040	1.1106	.74314	0
'	Cos	Ctn	Tan	Sin	'

48°

TABLE I. NATURAL TRIGONOMETRIC FUNCTIONS   483

42°

′	Sin	Tan	Ctn	Cos	′
0	.66913	.90040	1.1106	.74314	60
1	.66935	.90093	1.1100	.74295	59
2	.66956	.90146	1.1093	.74276	58
3	.66978	.90199	1.1087	.74256	57
4	.66999	.90251	1.1080	.74237	56
5	.67021	.90304	1.1074	.74217	55
6	.67043	.90357	1.1067	.74198	54
7	.67064	.90410	1.1061	.74178	53
8	.67086	.90463	1.1054	.74159	52
9	.67107	.90516	1.1048	.74139	51
10	.67129	.90569	1.1041	.74120	50
11	.67151	.90621	1.1035	.74100	49
12	.67172	.90674	1.1028	.74080	48
13	.67194	.90727	1.1022	.74061	47
14	.67215	.90781	1.1016	.74041	46
15	.67237	.90834	1.1009	.74022	45
16	.67258	.90887	1.1003	.74002	44
17	.67280	.90940	1.0996	.73983	43
18	.67301	.90993	1.0990	.73963	42
19	.67323	.91046	1.0983	.73944	41
20	.67344	.91099	1.0977	.73924	40
21	.67366	.91153	1.0971	.73904	39
22	.67387	.91206	1.0964	.73885	38
23	.67409	.91259	1.0958	.73865	37
24	.67430	.91313	1.0951	.73846	36
25	.67452	.91366	1.0945	.73826	35
26	.67473	.91419	1.0939	.73806	34
27	.67495	.91473	1.0932	.73787	33
28	.67516	.91526	1.0926	.73767	32
29	.67538	.91580	1.0919	.73747	31
30	.67559	.91633	1.0913	.73728	30
31	.67580	.91687	1.0907	.73708	29
32	.67602	.91740	1.0900	.73688	28
33	.67623	.91794	1.0894	.73669	27
34	.67645	.91847	1.0888	.73649	26
35	.67666	.91901	1.0881	.73629	25
36	.67688	.91955	1.0875	.73610	24
37	.67709	.92008	1.0869	.73590	23
38	.67730	.92062	1.0862	.73570	22
39	.67752	.92116	1.0856	.73551	21
40	.67773	.92170	1.0850	.73531	20
41	.67795	.92224	1.0843	.73511	19
42	.67816	.92277	1.0837	.73491	18
43	.67837	.92331	1.0831	.73472	17
44	.67859	.92385	1.0824	.73452	16
45	.67880	.92439	1.0818	.73432	15
46	.67901	.92493	1.0812	.73413	14
47	.67923	.92547	1.0805	.73393	13
48	.67944	.92601	1.0799	.73373	12
49	.67965	.92655	1.0793	.73353	11
50	.67987	.92709	1.0786	.73333	10
51	.68008	.92763	1.0780	.73314	9
52	.68029	.92817	1.0774	.73294	8
53	.68051	.92872	1.0768	.73274	7
54	.68072	.92926	1.0761	.73254	6
55	68093	.92980	1.0755	.73234	5
56	.68115	.93034	1.0749	.73215	4
57	.68136	.93088	1.0742	.73195	3
58	.68157	.93143	1.0736	.73175	2
59	.68179	.93197	1.0730	.73155	1
60	.68200	.93252	1.0724	.73135	0
′	Cos	Ctn	Tan	Sin	′

47°

43°

′	Sin	Tan	Ctn	Cos	′
0	.68200	.93252	1.0724	.73135	60
1	.68221	.93306	1.0717	.73116	59
2	.68242	.93360	1.0711	.73096	58
3	.68264	.93415	1.0705	.73076	57
4	.68285	.93469	1.0699	.73056	56
5	.68306	.93524	1.0692	.73036	55
6	.68327	.93578	1.0686	.73016	54
7	.68349	.93633	1.0680	.72996	53
8	.68370	.93688	1.0674	.72976	52
9	.68391	.93742	1.0668	.72957	51
10	.68412	.93797	1.0661	.72937	50
11	.68434	.93852	1.0655	.72917	49
12	.68455	.93906	1.0649	.72897	48
13	.68476	.93961	1.0643	.72877	47
14	.68497	.94016	1.0637	.72857	46
15	.68518	.94071	1.0630	.72837	45
16	.68539	.94125	1.0624	.72817	44
17	.68561	.94180	1.0618	.72797	43
18	.68582	.94235	1.0612	.72777	42
19	.68603	.94290	1.0606	.72757	41
20	.68624	.94345	1.0599	.72737	40
21	.68645	.94400	1.0593	.72717	39
22	.68666	.94455	1.0587	.72697	38
23	.68688	.94510	1.0581	.72677	37
24	.68709	.94565	1.0575	.72657	36
25	.68730	.94620	1.0569	.72637	35
26	.68751	.94676	1.0562	.72617	34
27	.68772	.94731	1.0556	.72597	33
28	.68793	.94786	1.0550	.72577	32
29	.68814	.94841	1.0544	.72557	31
30	.68835	.94896	1.0538	.72537	30
31	.68857	.94952	1.0532	.72517	29
32	.68878	.95007	1.0526	.72497	28
33	.68899	.95062	1.0519	.72477	27
34	.68920	.95118	1.0513	.72457	26
35	.68941	.95173	1.0507	.72437	25
36	.68962	.95229	1.0501	.72417	24
37	.68983	.95284	1.0495	.72397	23
38	.69004	.95340	1.0489	.72377	22
39	.69025	.95395	1.0483	.72357	21
40	.69046	.95451	1.0477	.72337	20
41	.69067	.95506	1.0470	.72317	19
42	.69088	.95562	1.0464	.72297	18
43	.69109	.95618	1.0458	.72277	17
44	.69130	.95673	1.0452	.72257	16
45	.69151	.95729	1.0446	.72236	15
46	.69172	.95785	1.0440	.72216	14
47	.69193	.95841	1.0434	.72196	13
48	.69214	.95897	1.0428	.72176	12
49	.69235	.95952	1.0422	.72156	11
50	.69256	.96008	1.0416	.72136	10
51	.69277	.96064	1.0410	.72116	9
52	.69298	.96120	1.0404	.72095	8
53	.69319	.96176	1.0398	.72075	7
54	.69340	.96232	1.0392	.72055	6
55	.69361	.96288	1.0385	.72035	5
56	.69382	.96344	1.0379	.72015	4
57	.69403	.96400	1.0373	.71995	3
58	.69424	.96457	1.0367	.71974	2
59	.69445	.96513	1.0361	.71954	1
60	.69466	.96569	1.0355	.71934	0
′	Cos	Ctn	Tan	Sin	′

46°

44°

′	Sin	Tan	Ctn	Cos	′
0	.69466	.96569	1.0355	.71934	**60**
1	.69487	.96625	1.0349	.71914	59
2	.69508	.96681	1.0343	.71894	58
3	.69529	.96738	1.0337	.71873	57
4	.69549	.96794	1.0331	.71853	56
5	.69570	.96850	1.0325	.71833	**55**
6	.69591	.96907	1.0319	.71813	54
7	.69612	.96963	1.0313	.71792	53
8	.69633	.97020	1.0307	.71772	52
9	.69654	.97076	1.0301	.71752	51
10	.69675	.97133	1.0295	.71732	**50**
11	.69696	.97189	1.0289	.71711	49
12	.69717	.97246	1.0283	.71691	48
13	.69737	.97302	1.0277	.71671	47
14	.69758	.97359	1.0271	.71650	46
15	.69779	.97416	1.0265	.71630	**45**
16	.69800	.97472	1.0259	.71610	44
17	.69821	.97529	1.0253	.71590	43
18	.69842	.97586	1.0247	.71569	42
19	.69862	.97643	1.0241	.71549	41
20	.69883	.97700	1.0235	.71529	**40**
21	.69904	.97756	1.0230	.71508	39
22	.69925	.97813	1.0224	.71488	38
23	.69946	.97870	1.0218	.71468	37
24	.69966	.97927	1.0212	.71447	36
25	.69987	.97984	1.0206	.71427	**35**
26	.70008	.98041	1.0200	.71407	34
27	.70029	.98098	1.0194	.71386	33
28	.70049	.98155	1.0188	.71366	32
29	.70070	.98213	1.0182	.71345	31
30	.70091	.98270	1.0176	.71325	**30**
31	.70112	.98327	1.0170	.71305	29
32	.70132	.98384	1.0164	.71284	28
33	.70153	.98441	1.0158	.71264	27
34	.70174	.98499	1.0152	.71243	26
35	.70195	.98556	1.0147	.71223	**25**
36	.70215	.98613	1.0141	.71203	24
37	.70236	.98671	1.0135	.71182	23
38	.70257	.98728	1.0129	.71162	22
39	.70277	.98786	1.0123	.71141	21
40	.70298	.98843	1.0117	.71121	**20**
41	.70319	.98901	1.0111	.71100	19
42	.70339	.98958	1.0105	.71080	18
43	.70360	.99016	1.0099	.71059	17
44	.70381	.99073	1.0094	.71039	16
45	.70401	.99131	1.0088	.71019	**15**
46	.70422	.99189	1.0082	.70998	14
47	.70443	.99247	1.0076	.70978	13
48	.70463	.99304	1.0070	.70957	12
49	.70484	.99362	1.0064	.70937	11
50	.70505	.99420	1.0058	.70916	**10**
51	.70525	.99478	1.0052	.70896	9
52	.70546	.99536	1.0047	.70875	8
53	.70567	.99594	1.0041	.70855	7
54	.70587	.99652	1.0035	.70834	6
55	.70608	.99710	1.0029	.70813	**5**
56	.70628	.99768	1.0023	.70793	4
57	.70649	.99826	1.0017	.70772	3
58	.70670	.99884	1.0012	.70752	2
59	.70690	.99942	1.0006	.70731	1
60	.70711	1.0000	1.0000	.70711	**0**
′	Cos	Ctn	Tan	Sin	′

45°

TABLE II. COMPOUND AMOUNT   485

$$(1 + r)^n$$

n	$\frac{5}{12}\%$	$\frac{1}{2}\%$	$\frac{7}{12}\%$	$\frac{3}{4}\%$	1%
1	1.004 167	1.005 000	1.005 833	1.007 500	1.010 000
2	1.008 351	1.010 025	1.011 701	1.015 056	1.020 100
3	1.012 552	1.015 075	1.017 602	1.022 669	1.030 301
4	1.016 771	1.020 151	1.023 538	1.030 339	1.040 604
5	1.021 008	1.025 251	1.029 509	1.038 067	1.051 010
6	1.025 262	1.030 378	1.035 514	1.045 852	1.061 520
7	1.029 534	1.035 529	1.041 555	1.053 696	1.072 135
8	1.033 824	1.040 707	1.047 631	1.061 599	1.082 857
9	1.038 131	1.045 911	1.053 742	1.069 561	1.093 685
10	1.042 457	1.051 140	1.059 889	1.077 583	1.104 622
11	1.046 800	1.056 396	1.066 071	1.085 664	1.115 668
12	1.051 162	1.061 678	1.072 290	1.093 807	1.126 825
13	1.055 542	1.066 986	1.078 545	1.102 010	1.138 093
14	1.059 940	1.072 321	1.084 837	1.110 276	1.149 474
15	1.064 356	1.077 683	1.091 165	1.118 603	1.160 969
16	1.068 791	1.083 071	1.097 530	1.126 992	1.172 579
17	1.073 244	1.088 487	1.103 932	1.135 445	1.184 304
18	1.077 716	1.093 929	1.110 372	1.143 960	1.196 147
19	1.082 207	1.099 399	1.116 849	1.152 540	1.208 109
20	1.086 716	1.104 896	1.123 364	1.161 184	1.220 190
21	1.091 244	1.110 420	1.129 917	1.169 893	1.232 392
22	1.095 791	1.115 972	1.136 508	1.178 667	1.244 716
23	1.100 357	1.121 552	1.143 138	1.187 507	1.257 163
24	1.104 941	1.127 160	1.149 806	1.196 414	1.269 735
25	1.109 545	1.132 796	1.156 513	1.205 387	1.282 432
26	1.114 168	1.138 460	1.163 260	1.214 427	1.295 256
27	1.118 811	1.144 152	1.170 045	1.223 535	1.308 209
28	1.123 472	1.149 873	1.176 870	1.232 712	1.321 291
29	1.128 154	1.155 622	1.183 736	1.241 957	1.334 504
30	1.132 854	1.161 400	1.190 641	1.251 272	1.347 849
31	1.137 574	1.167 207	1.197 586	1.260 656	1.361 327
32	1.142 314	1.173 043	1.204 572	1.270 111	1.374 941
33	1.147 074	1.178 908	1.211 599	1.279 637	1.388 690
34	1.151 853	1.184 803	1.218 666	1.289 234	1.402 577
35	1.156 653	1.190 727	1.225 775	1.298 904	1.416 603
36	1.161 472	1.196 681	1.232 926	1.308 645	1.430 769
37	1.166 312	1.202 664	1.240 118	1.318 460	1.445 076
38	1.171 171	1.208 677	1.247 352	1.328 349	1.459 527
39	1.176 051	1.214 721	1.254 628	1.338 311	1.474 123
40	1.180 951	1.220 794	1.261 947	1.348 349	1.488 864
41	1.185 872	1.226 898	1.269 308	1.358 461	1.503 752
42	1.190 813	1.233 033	1.276 712	1.368 650	1.518 790
43	1.195 775	1.239 198	1.284 160	1.378 915	1.533 978
44	1.200 757	1.245 394	1.291 651	1.389 256	1.549 318
45	1.205 760	1.251 621	1.299 185	1.399 676	1.564 811
46	1.210 784	1.257 879	1.306 764	1.410 173	1.580 459
47	1.215 829	1.264 168	1.314 387	1.420 750	1.596 263
48	1.220 895	1.270 489	1.322 054	1.431 405	1.612 226
49	1.225 982	1.276 842	1.329 766	1.442 141	1.628 348
50	1.231 091	1.283 226	1.337 523	1.452 957	1.644 632

$$(1 + r)^n$$

n	$\frac{5}{12}\%$	$\frac{1}{2}\%$	$\frac{7}{12}\%$	$\frac{3}{4}\%$	1%
51	1.236 220	1.289 642	1.345 325	1.463 854	1.661 078
52	1.241 371	1.296 090	1.353 173	1.474 833	1.677 689
53	1.246 544	1.302 571	1.361 066	1.485 894	1.694 466
54	1.251 737	1.309 083	1.369 006	1.497 038	1.711 410
55	1.256 953	1.315 629	1.376 992	1.508 266	1.728 525
56	1.262 190	1.322 207	1.385 024	1.519 578	1.745 810
57	1.267 449	1.328 818	1.393 103	1.530 975	1.763 268
58	1.272 730	1.335 462	1.401 230	1.542 457	1.780 901
59	1.278 034	1.342 139	1.409 404	1.554 026	1.798 710
60	1.283 359	1.348 850	1.417 625	1.565 681	1.816 697
61	1.288 706	1.355 594	1.425 895	1.577 424	1.834 864
62	1.294 076	1.362 372	1.434 212	1.589 254	1.853 212
63	1.299 468	1.369 184	1.442 579	1.601 174	1.871 744
64	1.304 882	1.376 030	1.450 994	1.613 183	1.890 462
65	1.310 319	1.382 910	1.459 458	1.625 281	1.909 366
66	1.315 779	1.389 825	1.467 971	1.637 471	1.928 460
67	1.321 261	1.396 774	1.476 535	1.649 752	1.947 745
68	1.326 766	1.403 758	1.485 148	1.662 125	1.967 222
69	1.332 295	1.410 777	1.493 811	1.674 591	1.986 894
70	1.337 846	1.417 831	1.502 525	1.687 151	2.006 763
71	1.343 420	1.424 920	1.511 290	1.699 804	2.026 831
72	1.349 018	1.432 044	1.520 106	1.712 553	2.047 099
73	1.354 639	1.439 204	1.528 973	1.725 397	2.067 570
74	1.360 283	1.446 401	1.537 892	1.738 337	2.088 246
75	1.365 951	1.453 633	1.546 863	1.751 375	2.109 128
76	1.371 642	1.460 901	1.555 886	1.764 510	2.130 220
77	1.377 357	1.468 205	1.564 962	1.777 744	2.151 522
78	1.383 096	1.475 546	1.574 091	1.791 077	2.173 037
79	1.388 859	1.482 924	1.583 273	1.804 510	2.194 768
80	1.394 646	1.490 339	1.592 509	1.818 044	2.216 715
81	1.400 457	1.497 790	1.601 799	1.831 679	2.238 882
82	1.406 293	1.505 279	1.611 143	1.845 417	2.261 271
83	1.412 152	1.512 806	1.620 541	1.859 258	2.283 884
84	1.418 036	1.520 370	1.629 994	1.873 202	2.306 723
85	1.423 945	1.527 971	1.639 502	1.887 251	2.329 790
86	1.429 878	1.535 611	1.649 066	1.901 405	2.353 088
87	1.435 835	1.543 289	1.658 686	1.915 666	2.376 619
88	1.441 818	1.551 006	1.668 361	1.930 033	2.400 385
89	1.447 826	1.558 761	1.678 093	1.944 509	2.424 389
90	1.453 858	1.566 555	1.687 882	1.959 092	2.448 633
91	1.459 916	1.574 387	1.697 728	1.973 786	2.473 119
92	1.465 999	1.582 259	1.707 632	1.988 589	2.497 850
93	1.472 107	1.590 171	1.717 593	2.003 503	2.522 829
94	1.478 241	1.598 122	1.727 612	2.018 530	2.548 057
95	1.484 400	1.606 112	1.737 690	2.033 669	2.573 538
96	1.490 585	1.614 143	1.747 826	2.048 921	2.599 273
97	1.496 796	1.622 213	1.758 022	2.064 288	2.625 266
98	1.503 033	1.630 324	1.768 277	2.079 770	2.651 518
99	1.509 296	1.638 776	1.778 592	2.095 369	2.678 033
100	1.515 584	1.646 668	1.788 967	2.111 084	2.704 814

TABLE II. COMPOUND AMOUNT   487

$$(1 + r)^n$$

n	$1\frac{1}{8}\%$	$1\frac{1}{4}\%$	$1\frac{1}{2}\%$	$1\frac{3}{4}\%$	2%
1	1.011 250	1.012 500	1.015 000	1.017 500	1.020 000
2	1.022 627	1.025 156	1.030 225	1.035 306	1.040 400
3	1.034 131	1.037 971	1.045 678	1.053 424	1.061 208
4	1.045 765	1.050 945	1.061 364	1.071 859	1.082 432
5	1.057 530	1.064 082	1.077 284	1.090 617	1.104 081
6	1.069 427	1.077 383	1.093 443	1.109 702	1.126 162
7	1.081 458	1.090 850	1.109 845	1.129 122	1.148 686
8	1.093 625	1.104 486	1.126 493	1.148 882	1.171 659
9	1.105 928	1.118 292	1.143 390	1.168 987	1.195 093
10	1.118 370	1.132 271	1 160 541	1.189 444	1.218 994
11	1.130 951	1.146 424	1.177 949	1.210 260	1.243 374
12	1.143 674	1.160 755	1.195 618	1.231 439	1.268 242
13	1.156 541	1.175 264	1.213 552	1.252 990	1.293 607
14	1.169 552	1.189 955	1.231 756	1.274 917	1.319 479
15	1.182 709	1.204 829	1.250 232	1.297 228	1.345 868
16	1.196 015	1.219 890	1.268 986	1.319 929	1.372 786
17	1.209 470	1.235 138	1.288 020	1.343 028	1.400 241
18	1.223 077	1.250 577	1.307 341	1.366 531	1.428 246
19	1.236 836	1.266 210	1.326 951	1.390 445	1.456 811
20	1.250 751	1.282 037	1.346 855	1.414 778	1.485 947
21	1.264 821	1.298 063	1.367 058	1.439 537	1.515 666
22	1.279 051	1.314 288	1.387 564	1.464 729	1.545 980
23	1.293 440	1.330 717	1.408 377	1.490 361	1.576 899
24	1.307 991	1.347 351	1.429 503	1.516 443	1.608 437
25	1.322 706	1.364 193	1.450 945	1.542 981	1.640 606
26	1.337 587	1.381 245	1.472 710	1.569 983	1.673 418
27	1.352 634	1.398 511	1.494 800	1.597 457	1.706 886
28	1.367 852	1.415 992	1.517 222	1.625 413	1.741 024
29	1.383 240	1.433 692	1.539 981	1.653 858	1.775 845
30	1.398 801	1.451 613	1.563 080	1.682 800	1.811 362
31	1.414 538	1.469 759	1.586 526	1.712 249	1.847 589
32	1.430 451	1.488 131	1.610 324	1.742 213	1.884 541
33	1.446 544	1.506 732	1.634 479	1.772 702	1.922 231
34	1.462 818	1.525 566	1.658 996	1.803 725	1.960 676
35	1.479 274	1.544 636	1.683 881	1.835 290	1.999 890
36	1.495 916	1.563 944	1.709 140	1.867 407	2.039 887
37	1.512 745	1.583 493	1.734 777	1.900 087	2.080 685
38	1.529 764	1.603 287	1.760 798	1.933 338	2.122 299
39	1.546 973	1.623 328	1.787 210	1.967 172	2.164 745
40	1.564 377	1.643 619	1.814 018	2.001 597	2.208 040
41	1.581 976	1.664 165	1.841 229	2.036 625	2.252 200
42	1.599 773	1.684 967	1.868 847	2.072 266	2.297 244
43	1.617 771	1.706 029	1.896 880	2.108 531	2.343 189
44	1.635 971	1.727 354	1.925 333	2.145 430	2.390 053
45	1.654 375	1.748 946	1.954 213	2.182 975	2.437 854
46	1.672 987	1.770 808	1.983 526	2.221 177	2.486 611
47	1.691 808	1.792 943	2.013 279	2.260 048	2.536 344
48	1.710 841	1.815 355	2.043 478	2.299 599	2.587 070
49	1.730 088	1.838 047	2.074 130	2.339 842	2.638 812
50	1.749 552	1.861 022	2.105 242	2.380 789	2.691 588

$$(1 + r)^n$$

n	$1\frac{1}{8}\%$	$1\frac{1}{4}\%$	$1\frac{1}{2}\%$	$1\frac{3}{4}\%$	2%
51	1.769 234	1.884 285	2.136 821	2.422 453	2.745 420
52	1.789 138	1.907 839	2.168 873	2.464 846	2.800 328
53	1.809 266	1.931 687	2.201 406	2.507 980	2.856 335
54	1.829 620	1.955 833	2.234 428	2.551 870	2.913 461
55	1.850 203	1.980 281	2.267 944	2.596 528	2.971 731
56	1.871 018	2.005 034	2.301 963	2.641 967	3.031 165
57	1.892 067	2.030 097	2.336 493	2.688 202	3.091 789
58	1.913 353	2.055 473	2.371 540	2.735 245	3.153 624
59	1.934 878	2.081 167	2.407 113	2.783 112	3.216 697
60	1.956 645	2.107 181	2.443 220	2.831 816	3.281 031
61	1.978 657	2.133 521	2.479 868	2.881 373	3.346 651
62	2.000 917	2.160 190	2.517 066	2.931 797	3.413 584
63	2.023 428	2.187 193	2.554 822	2.983 104	3.481 856
64	2.046 191	2.214 532	2.593 144	3.035 308	3.551 493
65	2.069 211	2.242 214	2.632 042	3.088 426	3.622 523
66	2.092 489	2.270 242	2.671 522	3.142 473	3.694 974
67	2.116 030	2.298 620	2.711 595	3.197 466	3.768 873
68	2.139 835	2.327 353	2.752 269	3.253 422	3.844 251
69	2.163 908	2.356 444	2.793 553	3.310 357	3.921 136
70	2.188 252	2.385 900	2.835 456	3.368 288	3.999 558
71	2.212 870	2.415 724	2.877 988	3.427 233	4.079 549
72	2.237 765	2.445 920	2.921 158	3.487 210	4.161 140
73	2.262 940	2.476 494	2.964 975	3.548 236	4.244 363
74	2.288 398	2.507 450	3.009 450	3.610 330	4.329 250
75	2.314 142	2.538 794	3.054 592	3.673 511	4.415 835
76	2.340 177	2.570 529	3.100 411	3.737 797	4.504 152
77	2.366 504	2.602 660	3.146 917	3.803 209	4.594 235
78	2.393 127	2.635 193	3.194 120	3.869 765	4.686 120
79	2.420 049	2.668 133	3.242 032	3.937 486	4.779 842
80	2.447 275	2.701 485	3.290 663	4.006 392	4.875 439
81	2.474 807	2.735 254	3.340 023	4.076 504	4.972 948
82	2.502 648	2.769 444	3.390 123	4.147 843	5.072 407
83	2.530 803	2.804 062	3.440 975	4.220 430	5.173 855
84	2.559 275	2.839 113	3.492 590	4.294 287	5.277 332
85	2.588 067	2.874 602	3.544 978	4.369 437	5.382 879
86	2.617 182	2.910 534	3.598 153	4.445 903	5.490 536
87	2.646 626	2.946 916	3.652 125	4.523 706	5.600 347
88	2.676 400	2.983 753	3.706 907	4.602 871	5.712 354
89	2.706 510	3.021 049	3.762 511	4.683 421	5.826 601
90	2.736 958	3.058 813	3.818 949	4.765 381	5.943 133
91	2.767 749	3.097 048	3.876 233	4.848 775	6.061 996
92	2.798 886	3.135 761	3.934 376	4.933 629	6.183 236
93	2.830 373	3.174 958	3.993 392	5.019 967	6.306 900
94	2.862 215	3.214 645	4.053 293	5.107 816	6.433 038
95	2.894 415	3.254 828	4.114 092	5.197 203	6.561 699
96	2.926 977	3.295 513	4.175 804	5.288 154	6.692 933
97	2.959 906	3.336 707	4.238 441	5.380 697	6.826 792
98	2.993 205	3.378 416	4.302 017	5.474 859	6.963 328
99	3.026 878	3.420 646	4.366 547	5.570 669	7.102 594
100	3.060 930	3.463 404	4.432 046	5.668 156	7.244 646

TABLE II. COMPOUND AMOUNT   489

$$(1 + r)^n$$

n	3%	4%	5%	6%	7%
1	1.030 000	1.040 000	1.050 000	1.060 000	1.070 000
2	1.060 900	1.081 600	1.102 500	1.123 600	1.144 900
3	1.092 727	1.124 864	1.157 625	1.191 016	1.225 043
4	1.125 509	1.169 859	1.215 506	1.262 477	1.310 796
5	1.159 274	1.216 653	1.276 282	1.338 226	1.402 552
6	1.194 052	1.265 319	1.340 096	1.418 519	1.500 730
7	1.229 874	1.315 932	1.407 100	1.503 630	1.605 781
8	1.266 770	1.368 569	1.477 455	1.593 848	1.718 186
9	1.304 773	1.423 312	1.551 328	1.689 479	1.838 459
10	1.343 916	1.480 244	1.628 895	1.790 848	1.967 151
11	1.384 234	1.539 454	1.710 339	1.898 299	2.104 852
12	1.425 761	1.601 032	1.795 856	2.012 196	2.252 192
13	1.468 534	1.665 074	1.885 649	2.132 928	2.409 845
14	1.512 590	1.731 676	1.979 932	2.260 904	2.578 534
15	1.557 967	1.800 944	2.078 928	2.396 558	2.759 032
16	1.604 706	1.872 981	2.182 875	2.540 352	2.952 164
17	1.652 848	1.947 900	2.292 018	2.692 773	3.158 815
18	1.702 433	2.025 817	2.406 619	2.854 339	3.379 932
19	1.753 506	2.106 849	2.526 950	3.025 600	3.616 528
20	1.806 111	2.191 123	2.653 298	3.207 135	3.869 684
21	1.860 295	2.278 768	2.785 963	3.399 564	4.140 562
22	1.916 103	2.369 919	2.925 261	3.603 537	4.430 402
23	1.973 587	2.464 716	3.071 524	3.819 750	4.740 530
24	2.032 794	2.563 304	3.225 100	4.048 935	5.072 367
25	2.093 778	2.665 836	3.386 355	4.291 871	5.427 433
26	2.156 591	2.772 470	3.555 673	4.549 383	5 807 353
27	2.221 289	2.883 369	3.733 456	4.822 346	6.213 868
28	2.287 928	2.998 703	3.920 129	5.111 687	6.648 838
29	2.356 566	3.118 651	4.116 136	5.418 388	7.114 257
30	2.427 262	3.243 398	4.321 942	5.743 491	7.612 255
31	2.500 080	3.373 133	4.538 039	6.088 101	8.145 113
32	2.575 083	3.508 059	4.764 941	6.453 387	8 715 271
33	2.652 335	3.648 381	5 003 189	6.840 590	9 325 340
34	2.731 905	3.794 316	5.253 348	7.251 025	9.978 114
35	2.813 862	3.946 089	5 516 015	7.686 087	10 676 581
36	2.898 278	4.103 933	5.791 816	8.147 252	11.423 942
37	2.985 227	4.268 090	6.081 407	8.636 087	12 223 618
38	3.074 783	4.438 813	6.385 477	9.154 252	13.079 271
39	3.167 027	4.616 366	6.704 751	9.703 507	13.994 820
40	3.262 038	4.801 021	7.039 989	10.285 718	14.974 458
41	3.359 899	4.993 061	7.391 988	10.902 861	16.022 670
42	3.460 696	5.192 784	7.761 588	11.557 033	17.144 257
43	3.564 517	5.400 495	8.149 667	12.250 455	18.344 355
44	3.671 452	5.616 515	8.557 150	12.985 482	19.628 460
45	3.781 596	5.841 176	8.985 008	13.764 611	21 002 452
46	3.895 044	6.074 823	9.434 258	14 590 487	22.472 623
47	4.011 895	6.317 816	9.905 971	15.465 917	24.045 707
48	4.132 252	6.570 528	10.401 270	16.393 872	25.728 907
49	4.256 219	6.833 349	10.921 333	17.377 504	27.529 930
50	4.383 906	7.106 683	11.467 400	18.420 154	29.457 025

$$(1 + r)^n$$

n	3%	4%	5%	6%	7%
51	4.515 423	7.390 951	12.040 770	19.525 364	31.519 017
52	4.650 886	7.686 589	12.642 808	20.696 885	33.725 348
53	4.790 412	7.994 052	13.274 949	21.938 698	36.086 122
54	4.934 125	8.313 814	13.938 696	23.255 020	38.612 151
55	5.082 149	8.646 367	14.635 631	24.650 322	41.315 001
56	5.234 613	8.992 222	15.367 412	26.129 341	44.207 052
57	5.391 651	9.351 910	16.135 783	27.697 101	47.301 545
58	5.553 401	9.725 987	16.942 572	29.358 927	50.612 653
59	5.720 003	10.115 026	17.789 701	31.120 463	54.155 539
60	5.891 603	10.519 627	18.679 186	32.987 691	57.946 427
61	6.068 351	10.940 413	19.613 145	34.966 952	62.002 677
62	6.250 402	11.378 029	20.593 802	37.064 969	66.342 864
63	6.437 914	11.833 150	21.623 493	39.288 868	70.986 865
64	6.631 051	12.306 476	22.704 667	41.646 200	75.955 945
65	6.829 983	12.798 735	23.839 901	44.144 972	81.272 861
66	7.034 882	13.310 685	25.031 896	46.793 670	86.961 962
67	7.245 929	13.843 112	26.283 490	49.601 290	93.049 299
68	7.463 307	14.396 836	27.597 665	52.577 368	99.562 750
69	7.687 206	14.972 710	28.977 548	55.732 010	106.532 142
70	7.917 822	15.571 618	30.426 426	59.075 930	113.989 392
71	8.155 357	16.194 483	31.947 747	62.620 486	121.968 650
72	8.400 017	16.842 262	33.545 134	66.377 715	130.506 455
73	8.652 018	17.515 953	35.222 391	70.360 378	139.641 907
74	8.911 578	18.216 591	36.983 510	74.582 001	149.416 840
75	9.178 926	18.945 255	38.832 686	79.056 921	159.876 019
76	9.454 293	19.703 065	40.774 320	83.800 336	171.067 341
77	9.737 922	20.491 187	42.813 036	88.828 356	183.042 055
78	10.030 060	21.310 835	44.953 688	94.158 058	195.854 998
79	10.330 962	22.163 268	47.201 372	99.807 541	209.564 848
80	10.640 891	23.049 799	49.561 441	105.795 993	224.234 388
81	10.960 117	23.971 791	52.039 531	112.143 753	239.930 795
82	11.288 921	24.930 663	54.641 489	118.872 378	256.725 950
83	11.627 588	25.927 889	57.373 563	126.004 721	274.696 767
84	11.976 416	26.965 005	60.242 241	133.565 004	293.925 541
85	12.335 709	28.043 605	63.254 353	141.578 904	314.500 328
86	12.705 780	29.165 349	66.417 071	150.073 639	336.515 351
87	13.086 953	30.331 963	69.737 925	159.078 057	360.071 426
88	13.479 562	31.545 242	73.224 821	168.622 741	385.276 426
89	13.883 949	32.807 051	76.886 062	178.740 105	412.245 776
90	14.300 467	34.119 333	80.730 365	189.464 511	441.102 980
91	14.729 481	35.484 107	84.766 883	200.832 382	471.980 188
92	15.171 366	36.903 471	89.005 227	212.882 325	505.018 802
93	15.626 507	38.379 610	93.455 489	225.655 264	540.370 118
94	16.095 302	39.914 794	98.128 263	239.194 580	578.196 026
95	16.578 161	41.511 386	103.034 676	253.546 255	618.669 748
96	17.075 506	43.171 841	108.186 410	268.759 030	661.976 630
97	17.587 771	44.898 715	113.595 731	284.884 572	708.314 994
98	18.115 404	46.694 664	119.275 517	301.977 646	757.897 044
99	18.658 866	48.562 450	125.239 293	320.096 305	810.949 837
100	19.218 632	50.504 948	131.501 258	339.302 084	867.716 326

TABLE III. PRESENT VALUE 491

$$(1 + r)^{-n}$$

n	$\frac{5}{12}\%$	$\frac{1}{2}\%$	$\frac{7}{12}\%$	$\frac{3}{4}\%$	1%
1	0.995 851	0.995 025	0.994 200	0.992 556	0.990 099
2	0.991 718	0.990 075	0.984 435	0.985 167	0.980 296
3	0 987 603	0.985 149	0.982 702	0 977 833	0.970 590
4	0.983 506	0.980 248	0.977 003	0.970 554	0.960 980
5	0.979 425	0.975 371	0.971 337	0.963 329	0.951 466
6	0.975 361	0.970 518	0.965 704	0 956 158	0.942 045
7	0.971 313	0.965 690	0.960 103	0.949 040	0.932 718
8	0.967 283	0.960 885	0.954 535	0.941 975	0.923 483
9	0.963 269	0.956 105	0.948 999	0.934 963	0.914 340
10	0.959 272	0.951 348	0.943 495	0.928 003	0.905 287
11	0.955 292	0.946 615	0.938 024	0 921 095	0 896 324
12	0.951 328	0.941 905	0.932 583	0 914 238	0.887 449
13	0.947 381	0.937 219	0.927 175	0.907 432	0 878 663
14	0.943 450	0.932 556	0.921 798	0.900 677	0.869 963
15	0.939 535	0.927 917	0.916 452	0.893 973	0.861 349
16	0.935 637	0.923 300	0.911 137	0.887 318	0.852 821
17	0.931 754	0.918 707	0.905 853	0 880 712	0.844 377
18	0.927 888	0.914 136	0.900 599	0.874 156	0 836 017
19	0.924 038	0.909 588	0.895 376	0.867 649	0.827 740
20	0.920 204	0.905 063	0.890 183	0.861 190	0.819 544
21	0.916 385	0.900 560	0.885 021	0.854 779	0 811 430
22	0.912 583	0.896 080	0.879 888	0.848 416	0.803 396
23	0 908 796	0.891 622	0.874 785	0.842 100	0 795 442
24	0.905 025	0 887 186	0.869 712	0.835 831	0 787 566
25	0 901 270	0.882 772	0.864 668	0.829 609	0.779 768
26	0.897 530	0.878 380	0.859 053	0.823 434	0 772 048
27	0.893 806	0.874 010	0.854 668	0.817 304	0.764 404
28	0.890 097	0.869 662	0.849 711	0.811 220	0.756 836
29	0.886 404	0.865 335	0.844 783	0.805 181	0.749 342
30	0.882 726	0.861 030	0.839 884	0.799 187	0.741 923
31	0.879 063	0.856 746	0.835 013	0.793 238	0 734 577
32	0.875 416	0.852 484	0.830 170	0.787 333	0.727 304
33	0.871 783	0.848 242	0.825 356	0.781 472	0.720 103
34	0.868 166	0.844 022	0.820 569	0.775 654	0.712 973
35	0.864 564	0.839 823	0.815 810	0.769 880	0 705 914
36	0.860 976	0.835 645	0.811 079	0.764 149	0.698 925
37	0.857 404	0.831 487	0.806 375	0.758 461	0.692 005
38	0.853 846	0.827 351	0.801 699	0.752 814	0 685 153
39	0.850 303	0.823 235	0.797 049	0.747 210	0.678 370
40	0.846 775	0.819 139	0.792 427	0.741 648	0.671 653
41	0.843 261	0.815 064	0.787 831	0.736 127	0.665 003
42	0.839 762	0.811 009	0.783 262	0.730 647	0.658 419
43	0.836 278	0.806 974	0.778 719	0.725 208	0.651 900
44	0.832 808	0.802 959	0.774 203	0.719 810	0.645 445
45	0.829 352	0.798 964	0.769 713	0.714 451	0.639 055
46	0.825 911	0.794 989	0.765 249	0.709 133	0.632 728
47	0.822 484	0.791 034	0.760 811	0.703 854	0.626 463
48	0.819 071	0.787 098	0.756 399	0.698 614	0.620 260
49	0.815 672	0.783 182	0.752 012	0.693 414	0.614 119
50	0.812 288	0.779 286	0.747 651	0.688 252	0.608 039

$$(1 + r)^{-n}$$

n	$\dfrac{5}{12}\%$	$\dfrac{1}{2}\%$	$\dfrac{7}{12}\%$	$\dfrac{3}{4}\%$	1%
51	0.808 917	0.775 409	0.743 315	0.683 128	0.602 019
52	0.805 561	0.771 551	0.739 004	0.678 043	0.596 058
53	0 802 218	0.767 713	0.734 718	0.672 995	0.590 156
54	0.798 890	0.763 893	0.730 457	0.667 986	0.584 313
55	0.795 575	0.760 093	0.726 221	0.663 013	0.578 528
56	0.792 274	0.756 311	0.722 009	0.658 077	0.572 800
57	0.788 986	0.752 548	0.717 822	0.653 178	0.567 129
58	0.785 712	0.748 804	0.713 659	0.648 316	0.561 514
59	0.782 452	0.745 079	0.709 520	0.643 490	0.555 954
60	0.779 205	0.741 372	0.705 405	0.638 700	0.550 450
61	0.775 972	0.737 684	0.701 314	0.633 945	0.545 000
62	0.772 752	0.734 014	0.697 247	0.629 226	0.539 604
63	0 769 546	0.730 362	0.693 203	0.624 542	0.534 261
64	0.766 353	0.726 728	0.689 183	0.619 893	0.528 971
65	0.763 173	0.723 113	0.685 186	0.615 278	0.523 734
66	0 760 006	0.719 515	0.681 212	0.610 698	0.518 548
67	0.756 853	0.715 935	0.677 262	0.606 152	0.513 414
68	0 753 712	0.712 374	0.673 334	0.601 639	0.508 331
69	0.750 585	0.708 829	0.669 429	0.597 161	0.503 298
70	0.747 470	0.705 303	0.665 546	0.592 715	0.498 315
71	0.744 369	0.701 794	0.661 687	0.588 303	0.493 381
72	0.741 280	0.698 302	0.657 849	0.583 924	0.488 496
73	0 738 204	0.694 828	0.654 034	0.579 577	0.483 659
74	0 735 141	0.691 371	0.650 241	0.575 262	0.478 871
75	0.732 091	0.687 932	0.646 470	0.570 980	0.474 129
76	0 729 053	0.684 509	0.642 721	0.566 730	0.469 435
77	0 726 028	0.681 104	0.638 993	0.562 511	0.464 787
78	0 723 015	0.677 715	0.635 287	0.558 323	0.460 185
79	0 720 015	0.674 343	0.631 603	0.554 167	0.455 629
80	0.717 028	0.670 988	0.627 940	0.550 042	0.451 118
81	0 714 052	0.667 650	0.624 298	0.545 947	0.446 651
82	0 711 090	0.664 329	0.620 678	0.541 883	0.442 229
83	0 708 139	0.661 023	0 617 078	0.537 849	0.437 851
84	0 705 201	0.657 735	0.613 499	0.533 845	0.433 515
85	0 702 275	0.654 462	0.609 941	0.529 871	0.429 223
86	0.699 361	0 651 206	0.606 404	0.525 927	0.424 974
87	0.696 459	0.647 967	0.602 887	0.522 012	0.420 766
88	0.693 569	0.644 743	0.599 391	0.518 126	0.416 600
89	0.690 691	0.641 535	0.595 914	0.514 269	0.412 475
90	0.687 825	0.638 344	0.592 458	0.510 440	0.408 391
91	0.684 971	0.635 168	0.589 022	0.506 641	0.404 348
92	0.682 129	0.632 008	0.585 606	0.502 869	0.400 344
93	0.679 298	0.628 863	0.582 210	0.499 126	0.396 380
94	0.676 480	0.625 735	0.578 834	0.495 410	0.392 456
95	0 673 673	0.622 622	0.575 477	0.491 722	0.388 570
96	0 670 877	0.619 524	0.572 139	0.488 062	0.384 723
97	0 668 094	0.616 442	0.568 821	0.484 428	0.380 914
98	0 665 321	0.613 375	0.565 522	0.480 822	0.377 142
99	0 662 561	0.610 323	0.562 242	0.477 243	0.373 408
100	0.659 812	0.607 287	0.558 982	0.473 690	0.369 711

TABLE III. PRESENT VALUE   493

$$(1 + r)^{-n}$$

n	$1\frac{1}{8}\%$	$1\frac{1}{4}\%$	$1\frac{1}{2}\%$	$1\frac{3}{4}\%$	2%
1	0.988 875	0.987 654	0.985 222	0.982 801	0.980 392
2	0.977 874	0.975 461	0.970 662	0.965 898	0.961 169
3	0.966 995	0.963 418	0.956 317	0.949 285	0.942 322
4	0.956 238	0.951 524	0.942 184	0.932 959	0.923 845
5	0.945 600	0.939 777	0.928 260	0.916 913	0.905 731
6	0.935 080	0.928 175	0.914 542	0.901 143	0.887 971
7	0.924 677	0.916 716	0.901 027	0.885 644	0.870 560
8	0.914 391	0.905 398	0.887 711	0.870 412	0.853 490
9	0.904 218	0.894 221	0.874 592	0.855 441	0.836 755
10	0.894 159	0.883 181	0.861 667	0.840 729	0.820 348
11	0.884 211	0.872 277	0.848 933	0.826 269	0.804 263
12	0.874 375	0.861 509	0.836 387	0.812 058	0.788 493
13	0.864 647	0.850 873	0.824 027	0.798 091	0.773 033
14	0.855 028	0.840 368	0.811 849	0.784 365	0.757 875
15	0.845 516	0.829 993	0.799 852	0.770 875	0.743 015
16	0.836 110	0.819 746	0.788 031	0.757 616	0.728 446
17	0.826 808	0.809 626	0.776 385	0.744 586	0.714 163
18	0.817 610	0.799 631	0.764 912	0.731 780	0.700 159
19	0.808 515	0.789 759	0.753 607	0.719 194	0.686 431
20	0.799 520	0.780 009	0.742 470	0.706 825	0.672 971
21	0.790 625	0.770 379	0.731 498	0.694 668	0.659 776
22	0.781 830	0.760 868	0.720 688	0.682 720	0.646 839
23	0.773 132	0.751 475	0.710 037	0.670 978	0.634 156
24	0.764 531	0.742 197	0.699 544	0.659 438	0.621 721
25	0.756 026	0.733 034	0.689 206	0.648 096	0.609 531
26	0.747 615	0.723 984	0.679 021	0.636 950	0.597 579
27	0.739 298	0.715 046	0.668 986	0.625 995	0.585 862
28	0.731 073	0.706 219	0.659 099	0.615 228	0.574 375
29	0.722 940	0.697 500	0.649 359	0.604 647	0.563 112
30	0.714 898	0.688 889	0.639 762	0.594 248	0.552 071
31	0.706 945	0.680 384	0.630 308	0.584 027	0.541 246
32	0.699 080	0.671 984	0.620 993	0.573 982	0.530 633
33	0.691 303	0.663 688	0.611 816	0.564 111	0.520 229
34	0.683 612	0.655 494	0.602 774	0.554 408	0.510 028
35	0.676 007	0.647 402	0.593 866	0.544 873	0.500 028
36	0.668 487	0.639 409	0.585 090	0.535 502	0.490 223
37	0.661 050	0.631 515	0.576 443	0.526 292	0.480 611
38	0.653 696	0.623 719	0.567 924	0.517 240	0.471 187
39	0.646 424	0.616 019	0.559 531	0.508 344	0.461 948
40	0.639 232	0.608 413	0.551 262	0.499 601	0.452 890
41	0.632 121	0.600 902	0.543 116	0.491 008	0.444 010
42	0.625 089	0.593 484	0.535 089	0.482 563	0.435 304
43	0.618 135	0.586 157	0.527 182	0.474 264	0.426 769
44	0.611 258	0.578 920	0.519 391	0.466 107	0.418 401
45	0.604 458	0.571 773	0.511 715	0.458 090	0.410 197
46	0.597 733	0.564 714	0.504 153	0.450 212	0.402 154
47	0.591 084	0.557 742	0.496 702	0.442 469	0.394 268
48	0.584 508	0.550 856	0.489 362	0.434 858	0.386 538
49	0.578 005	0.544 056	0.482 130	0.427 379	0.378 958
50	0.571 575	0.537 339	0.475 005	0.420 029	0.371 528

$$(1 + r)^{-n}$$

n	$1\frac{1}{8}\%$	$1\frac{1}{4}\%$	$1\frac{1}{2}\%$	$1\frac{3}{4}\%$	2%
51	0.565 216	0.530 705	0.467 985	0.412 805	0.364 243
52	0.558 928	0.524 153	0.461 069	0.405 705	0.357 101
53	0.552 710	0.517 682	0.454 255	0.398 727	0.350 099
54	0.546 562	0.511 291	0.447 542	0.391 869	0.343 234
55	0.540 481	0.504 979	0.440 928	0.385 130	0.336 504
56	0.534 468	0.498 745	0.434 412	0.378 506	0.329 906
57	0.528 523	0.492 587	0.427 992	0.371 996	0.323 437
58	0.522 643	0.486 506	0.421 667	0.365 598	0.317 095
59	0.516 829	0.480 500	0.415 435	0.359 310	0.310 878
60	0.511 079	0.474 568	0.409 296	0.353 130	0.304 782
61	0.505 393	0.468 709	0.403 247	0.347 057	0.298 806
62	0.499 771	0.462 922	0.397 288	0.341 088	0.292 947
63	0.494 211	0.457 207	0.391 417	0.335 221	0.287 203
64	0.488 713	0.451 563	0.385 632	0.329 456	0.281 572
65	0.483 276	0.445 988	0.379 933	0.323 790	0.276 051
66	0.477 900	0.440 482	0.374 318	0.318 221	0.270 638
67	0.472 583	0.435 044	0.368 787	0.312 748	0.265 331
68	0.467 326	0.429 673	0.363 337	0.307 369	0.260 129
69	0.462 127	0.424 368	0.357 967	0.302 082	0.255 028
70	0.456 986	0.419 129	0.352 677	0.296 887	0.250 028
71	0.451 902	0.413 955	0.347 465	0.291 781	0.245 125
72	0.446 874	0.408 844	0.342 330	0.286 762	0.240 319
73	0.441 903	0.403 797	0.337 271	0.281 830	0.235 607
74	0.436 987	0.398 811	0.332 287	0.276 983	0.230 987
75	0.432 126	0.393 888	0.327 376	0.272 219	0.226 458
76	0.427 318	0.389 025	0.322 538	0.267 537	0.222 017
77	0.422 564	0.384 222	0.317 771	0.262 936	0.217 664
78	0.417 863	0.379 479	0.313 075	0.258 414	0.213 396
79	0.413 215	0.374 794	0.308 448	0.253 969	0.209 212
80	0.408 618	0.370 167	0.303 890	0.249 601	0.205 110
81	0.404 072	0.365 597	0.299 399	0.245 308	0.201 088
82	0.399 577	0.361 083	0.294 975	0.241 089	0.197 145
83	0.395 131	0.356 625	0.290 615	0.236 943	0.193 279
84	0.390 736	0.352 223	0.286 321	0.232 868	0.189 490
85	0.386 389	0.347 874	0.282 089	0.228 862	0.185 774
86	0.382 090	0.343 580	0.277 920	0.224 926	0.182 132
87	0.377 840	0.339 338	0.273 813	0.221 058	0.178 560
88	0.373 636	0.335 148	0.269 767	0.217 256	0.175 059
89	0.369 480	0.331 011	0.265 780	0.213 519	0.171 627
90	0.365 369	0.326 924	0.261 852	0.209 847	0.168 261
91	0.361 304	0.322 888	0.257 982	0.206 238	0.164 962
92	0.357 285	0.318 902	0.254 170	0.202 691	0.161 728
93	0.353 310	0.314 965	0.250 414	0.199 204	0.158 556
94	0.349 380	0.311 076	0.246 713	0.195 778	0.155 448
95	0.345 493	0.307 236	0.243 067	0.192 411	0.152 400
96	0.341 649	0.303 443	0.239 475	0.189 102	0.149 411
97	0.337 849	0.299 697	0.235 936	0.185 850	0.146 482
98	0.334 090	0.295 997	0.232 449	0.182 653	0.143 609
99	0.330 373	0.292 342	0.229 014	0.179 512	0.140 794
100	0.326 698	0.288 733	0.225 629	0.176 424	0.138 033

TABLE III. PRESENT VALUE   495

$$(1 + r)^{-n}$$

n	3%	4%	5%	6%	7%
1	0.970 874	0.961 538	0.952 381	0.943 396	0.934 579
2	0.942 596	0.924 556	0.907 029	0.889 996	0.873 439
3	0.915 142	0.888 996	0.863 838	0.839 619	0.816 298
4	0.888 487	0.854 804	0.822 702	0.792 094	0.762 895
5	0.862 609	0.821 927	0.783 526	0.747 258	0.712 986
6	0.837 484	0.790 315	0.746 215	0.704 961	0.666 342
7	0.813 092	0.759 918	0.710 681	0.665 057	0.622 750
8	0 789 409	0.730 690	0.676 839	0.627 412	0.582 009
9	0.766 417	0.702 587	0.644 609	0.591 898	0.543 934
10	0.744 094	0.675 564	0.613 913	0.558 395	0.508 349
11	0.722 421	0.649 581	0.584 679	0.526 788	0.475 093
12	0.701 380	0.624 597	0.556 837	0.496 969	0.444 012
13	0.680 951	0.600 574	0.530 321	0.468 839	0.414 964
14	0.661 118	0.577 475	0.505 068	0.442 301	0.387 817
15	0.641 862	0.555 265	0.481 017	0.417 265	0.362 446
16	0.623 167	0.533 908	0.458 112	0.393 646	0.338 735
17	0.605 016	0.513 373	0.436 297	0.371 364	0.316 574
18	0.587 395	0.493 628	0.415 521	0.350 344	0.295 864
19	0.570 286	0.474 642	0.395 734	0.330 513	0.276 508
20	0.553 676	0.456 387	0.376 889	0.311 805	0.258 419
21	0.537 549	0.438 834	0.358 942	0.294 155	0.241 513
22	0.521 893	0.421 955	0.341 850	0.277 505	0.225 713
23	0.506 692	0.405 726	0.325 571	0.261 797	0.210 947
24	0.491 934	0.390 121	0.310 068	0.246 979	0.197 147
25	0.477 606	0.375 117	0.295 303	0.232 999	0.184 249
26	0.463 695	0.360 689	0.281 241	0.219 810	0.172 195
27	0.450 189	0.346 817	0.267 848	0.207 368	0.160 930
28	0.437 077	0.333 477	0.255 094	0.195 630	0.150 402
29	0.424 346	0.320 651	0.242 946	0.184 557	0.140 563
30	0.411 987	0.308 319	0.231 377	0.174 110	0.131 367
31	0.399 987	0.296 460	0.220 359	0.164 255	0.122 773
32	0.388 337	0.285 058	0.209 866	0.154 957	0.114 741
33	0.377 026	0.274 094	0.199 873	0.146 186	0.107 235
34	0.366 045	0.263 552	0.190 355	0.137 912	0.100 219
35	0.355 383	0.253 415	0.181 291	0.130 105	0.093 663
36	0.345 032	0.243 669	0.172 657	0.122 741	0.087 535
37	0.334 983	0.234 297	0.164 436	0.115 793	0.081 809
38	0.325 226	0.225 285	0.156 605	0.109 239	0.076 457
39	0.315 754	0.216 621	0.149 148	0.103 056	0.071 455
40	0.306 557	0.208 289	0.142 046	0.097 222	0.066 780
41	0.297 628	0.200 278	0.135 282	0.091 719	0.062 412
42	0.288 959	0.192 575	0.128 840	0.086 527	0.058 329
43	0.280 543	0.185 168	0.122 704	0.081 630	0.054 513
44	0.272 372	0.178 046	0.116 861	0.077 009	0.050 946
45	0.264 439	0.171 198	0.111 297	0.072 650	0.047 613
46	0.256 737	0.164 614	0.105 997	0.068 538	0.044 499
47	0.249 259	0.158 283	0.100 949	0.064 658	0.041 587
48	0.241 999	0.152 195	0.096 142	0.060 998	0.038 867
49	0.234 950	0.146 341	0.091 564	0.057 546	0.036 324
50	0.228 107	0.140 713	0.087 204	0.054 288	0.033 945

$$(1 + r)^{-n}$$

n	3%	4%	5%	6%	7%
51	0.221 463	0.135 301	0.083 051	0.051 215	0.031 727
52	0.215 013	0.130 097	0.079 096	0.048 316	0.029 651
53	0.208 750	0.125 093	0.075 330	0.045 582	0.027 711
54	0.202 670	0.120 282	0.071 743	0.043 001	0.025 899
55	0.196 767	0.115 656	0.068 326	0.040 567	0.024 204
56	0.191 036	0.111 207	0.065 073	0.038 271	0.022 621
57	0.185 472	0.106 930	0.061 974	0.036 105	0.021 141
58	0.180 070	0.102 817	0.059 023	0.034 061	0.019 758
59	0.174 825	0.098 863	0.056 212	0.032 133	0.018 465
60	0.169 733	0.095 060	0.053 536	0.030 314	0.017 257
61	0.164 789	0.091 404	0.050 986	0.028 598	0.016 128
62	0.159 990	0.087 889	0.048 558	0.026 980	0.015 073
63	0.155 330	0.084 508	0.046 246	0.025 453	0.014 087
64	0.150 806	0.081 258	0.044 044	0.024 012	0.013 166
65	0.146 413	0.078 133	0.041 946	0.022 653	0.012 304
66	0.142 149	0.075 128	0.039 949	0.021 370	0.011 499
67	0.138 009	0.072 238	0.038 047	0.020 161	0.010 747
68	0.133 989	0.069 460	0.036 235	0.019 020	0.010 044
69	0.130 086	0.066 788	0.034 509	0.017 943	0.009 387
70	0.126 297	0.064 219	0.032 866	0.016 927	0.008 773
71	0.122 619	0.061 749	0.031 301	0.015 969	0.008 199
72	0.119 047	0.059 374	0.029 811	0.015 065	0.007 662
73	0.115 580	0.057 091	0.028 391	0.014 213	0.007 161
74	0.112 214	0.054 895	0.027 039	0.013 408	0.006 693
75	0.108 945	0.052 784	0.025 752	0.012 649	0.006 255
76	0.105 772	0.050 754	0.024 525	0.011 933	0.005 846
77	0.102 691	0.048 801	0.023 357	0.011 258	0.005 463
78	0.099 700	0.046 924	0.022 245	0.010 620	0.005 106
79	0.096 796	0.045 120	0.021 186	0.010 019	0.004 772
80	0.093 977	0.043 384	0.020 177	0.009 452	0.004 460
81	0.091 240	0.041 716	0.019 216	0.008 917	0.004 168
82	0.088 582	0.040 111	0.018 301	0.008 412	0.003 895
83	0.086 002	0.038 569	0.017 430	0.007 936	0.003 640
84	0.083 497	0.037 085	0.016 600	0.007 487	0.003 402
85	0.081 065	0.035 659	0.015 809	0.007 063	0.003 180
86	0.078 704	0.034 287	0.015 056	0.006 663	0.002 972
87	0 076 412	0.032 969	0.014 339	0.006 286	0 002 777
88	0.074 186	0.031 701	0.013 657	0.005 930	0.002 596
89	0.072 026	0.030 481	0 013 006	0.005 595	0.002 426
90	0.069 928	0.029 309	0.012 387	0.005 278	0.002 267
91	0.067 891	0.028 182	0.011 797	0.004 979	0.002 119
92	0.065 914	0.027 098	0.011 235	0.004 697	0.001 980
93	0.063 994	0.026 056	0.010 700	0.004 432	0.001 851
94	0.062 130	0.025 053	0.010 191	0.004 181	0.001 730
95	0.060 320	0.024 090	0.009 705	0.003 944	0.001 616
96	0.058 563	0.023 163	0.009 243	0.003 721	0.001 511
97	0.056 858	0.022 272	0.008 803	0.003 510	0.001 412
98	0.055 202	0.021 416	0.008 384	0 003 312	0.001 319
99	0.053 594	0.020 592	0.007 985	0.003 124	0.001 233
100	0.052 033	0.019 800	0.007 604	0.002 947	0.001 152

TABLE IV. EXPONENTIAL FUNCTIONS   497

x	e^x	$\text{Log}_{10}\, e^x$	e^{-x}	x	e^x	$\text{Log}_{10}\, e^x$	e^{-x}
0.00	1.0000	.00 000	1.00 000	**0.50**	1.6487	.21 715	.60 653
0.01	1.0101	.00 434	0.99 005	0.51	1.6653	.22 149	.60 050
0.02	1.0202	.00 869	.98 020	0.52	1.6820	.22 583	.59 452
0.03	1.0305	.01 303	.97 045	0.53	1.6989	.23 018	.58 860
0.04	1.0408	.01 737	.96 079	0.54	1.7160	.23 452	.58 275
0.05	1.0513	.02 171	.95 123	**0.55**	1.7333	.23 886	.57 695
0.06	1.0618	.02 606	.94 176	0.56	1.7507	.24 320	.57 121
0.07	1.0725	.03 040	.93 239	0.57	1.7683	.24 755	.56 553
0.08	1.0833	.03 474	.92 312	0.58	1.7860	.25 189	.55 990
0.09	1.0942	.03 909	.91 393	0.59	1.8040	.25 623	.55 433
0.10	1.1052	.04 343	.90 484	**0.60**	1.8221	.26 058	.54 881
0.11	1.1163	.04 777	.89 583	0.61	1.8404	.26 492	.54 335
0.12	1.1275	.05 212	.88 692	0.62	1.8589	.26 926	.53 794
0.13	1.1388	.05 646	.87 810	0.63	1.8776	.27 361	.53 259
0.14	1.1503	.06 080	.86 936	0.64	1.8965	.27 795	.52 729
0.15	1.1618	.06 514	.86 071	**0.65**	1.9155	.28 229	.52 205
0.16	1.1735	.06 949	.85 214	0.66	1.9348	.28 663	.51 685
0.17	1.1853	.07 383	.84 366	0.67	1.9542	.29 098	.51 171
0.18	1.1972	.07 817	.83 527	0.68	1.9739	.29 532	.50 662
0.19	1.2092	.08 252	.82 696	0.69	1.9937	.29 966	.50 158
0.20	1.2214	.08 686	.81 873	**0.70**	2.0138	.30 401	.49 659
0.21	1.2337	.09 120	.81 058	0.71	2.0340	.30 835	.49 164
0.22	1.2461	.09 554	.80 252	0.72	2.0544	.31 269	.48 675
0.23	1.2586	.09 989	.79 453	0.73	2.0751	.31 703	.48 191
0.24	1.2712	.10 423	.78 663	0.74	2.0959	.32 138	.47 711
0.25	1.2840	.10 857	.77 880	**0.75**	2.1170	.32 572	.47 237
0.26	1.2969	.11 292	.77 105	0.76	2.1383	.33 006	.46 767
0.27	1.3100	.11 726	.76 338	0.77	2.1598	.33 441	.46 301
0.28	1.3231	.12 160	.75 578	0.78	2.1815	.33 875	.45 841
0.29	1.3364	.12 595	.74 826	0.79	2.2034	.34 309	.45 384
0.30	1.3499	.13 029	.74 082	**0.80**	2.2255	.34 744	.44 933
0.31	1.3634	.13 463	.73 345	0.81	2.2479	.35 178	.44 486
0.32	1.3771	.13 897	.72 615	0.82	2.2705	.35 612	.44 043
0.33	1.3910	.14 332	.71 892	0.83	2.2933	.36 046	.43 605
0.34	1.4049	.14 766	.71 177	0.84	2.3164	.36 481	.43 171
0.35	1.4191	.15 200	.70 469	**0.85**	2.3396	.36 915	.42 741
0.36	1.4333	.15 635	.69 768	0.86	2.3632	.37 349	.42 316
0.37	1.4477	.16 069	.69 073	0.87	2.3869	.37 784	.41 895
0.38	1.4623	.16 503	.68 386	0.88	2.4109	.38 218	.41 478
0.39	1.4770	.16 937	.67 706	0.89	2.4351	.38 652	.41 066
0.40	1.4918	.17 372	.67 032	**0.90**	2.4596	.39 087	.40 657
0.41	1.5068	.17 806	.66 365	0.91	2.4843	.39 521	.40 252
0.42	1.5220	.18 240	.65 705	0.92	2.5093	.39 955	.39 852
0.43	1.5373	.18 675	.65 051	0.93	2.5345	.40 389	.39 455
0.44	1.5527	.19 109	.64 404	0.94	2.5600	.40 824	.39 063
0.45	1.5683	.19 543	.63 763	**0.95**	2.5857	.41 258	.38 674
0.46	1.5841	.19 978	.63 128	0.96	2.6117	.41 692	.38 289
0.47	1.6000	.20 412	.62 500	0.97	2.6379	.42 127	.37 908
0.48	1.6161	.20 846	.61 878	0.98	2.6645	.42 561	.37 531
0.49	1.6323	.21 280	**.61 263**	0.99	2.6912	.42 995	.37 158
0.50	1.6487	.21 715	.60 653	**1.00**	2.7183	.43 429	.36 788
x	e^x	$\text{Log}_{10}\, e^x$	e^{-x}	x	e^x	$\text{Log}_{10}\, e^x$	e^{-x}

x	e^x	$Log_{10}\, e^x$	e^{-x}	x	e^x	$Log_{10}\, e^x$	e^{-x}
1.00	2.7183	.43 429	.36 788	**1.50**	4.4817	.65 144	.22 313
1.01	2.7456	.43 864	.36 422	1.51	4.5267	.65 578	.22 091
1.02	2.7732	.44 298	.36 059	1.52	4.5722	.66 013	.21 871
1.03	2.8011	.44 732	.35 701	1.53	4.6182	.66 447	.21 654
1.04	2.8292	.45 167	.35 345	1.54	4.6646	.66 881	.21 438
1.05	2.8577	.45 601	.34 994	**1.55**	4.7115	.67 316	.21 225
1.06	2.8864	.46 035	.34 646	1.56	4.7588	.67 750	.21 014
1.07	2.9154	.46 470	.34 301	1.57	4.8066	.68 184	.20 805
1.08	2.9447	.46 904	.33 960	1.58	4.8550	.68 619	.20 598
1.09	2.9743	.47 338	.33 622	1.59	4.9037	.69 053	.20 393
1.10	3.0042	.47 772	.33 287	**1.60**	4.9530	.69 487	.20 190
1.11	3.0344	.48 207	.32 956	1.61	5.0028	.69 921	.19 989
1.12	3.0649	.48 641	.32 628	1.62	5.0531	.70 356	.19 790
1.13	3.0957	.49 075	.32 303	1.63	5.1039	.70 790	.19 593
1.14	3.1268	.49 510	.31 982	1.64	5.1552	.71 224	.19 398
1.15	3.1582	.49 944	.31 664	**1.65**	5.2070	.71 659	.19 205
1.16	3.1899	.50 378	.31 349	1.66	5.2593	.72 093	.19 014
1.17	3.2220	.50 812	.31 037	1.67	5.3122	.72 527	.18 825
1.18	3.2544	.51 247	.30 728	1.68	5.3656	.72 961	.18 637
1.19	3.2871	.51 681	.30 422	1.69	5.4195	.73 396	.18 452
1.20	3.3201	.52 115	.30 119	**1.70**	5.4739	.73 830	.18 268
1.21	3.3535	.52 550	.29 820	1.71	5.5290	.74 264	.18 087
1.22	3.3872	.52 984	.29 523	1.72	5.5845	.74 699	.17 907
1.23	3.4212	.53 418	.29 229	1.73	5.6407	.75 133	.17 728
1.24	3.4556	.53 853	.28 938	1.74	5.6973	.75 567	.17 552
1.25	3.4903	.54 287	.28 650	**1.75**	5.7546	.76 002	.17 377
1.26	3.5254	.54 721	.28 365	1.76	5.8124	.76 436	.17 204
1.27	3.5609	.55 155	.28 083	1.77	5.8709	.76 870	.17 033
1.28	3.5966	.55 590	.27 804	1.78	5.9299	.77 304	.16 864
1.29	3.6328	.56 024	.27 527	1.79	5.9895	.77 739	.16 696
1.30	3.6693	.56 458	.27 253	**1.80**	6.0496	.78 173	.16 530
1.31	3.7062	.56 893	.26 982	1.81	6.1104	.78 607	.16 365
1.32	3.7434	.57 327	.26 714	1.82	6.1719	.79 042	.16 203
1.33	3.7810	.57 761	.26 448	1.83	6.2339	.79 476	.16 041
1.34	3.8190	.58 195	.26 185	1.84	6.2965	.79 910	.15 882
1.35	3.8574	.58 630	.25 924	**1.85**	6.3598	.80 344	.15 724
1.36	3.8962	.59 064	.25 666	1.86	6.4237	.80 779	.15 567
1.37	3.9354	.59 498	.25 411	1.87	6.4883	.81 213	.15 412
1.38	3.9749	.59 933	.25 158	1.88	6.5535	.81 647	.15 259
1.39	4.0149	.60 367	.24 908	1.89	6.6194	.82 082	.15 107
1.40	4.0552	.60 801	.24 660	**1.90**	6.6859	.82 516	.14 957
1.41	4.0960	.61 236	.24 414	1.91	6.7531	.82 950	.14 808
1.42	4.1371	.61 670	.24 171	1.92	6.8210	.83 385	.14 661
1.43	4.1787	.62 104	.23 931	1.93	6.8895	.83 819	.14 515
1.44	4.2207	.62 538	.23 693	1.94	6.9588	.84 253	.14 370
1.45	4.2631	.62 973	.23 457	**1.95**	7.0287	.84 687	.14 227
1.46	4.3060	.63 407	.23 224	1.96	7.0993	.85 122	.14 086
1.47	4.3492	.63 841	.22 993	1.97	7.1707	.85 556	.13 946
1.48	4.3929	.64 276	.22 764	1.98	7.2427	.85 990	.13 807
1.49	4.4371	.64 710	.22 537	1.99	7.3155	.86 425	.13 670
1.50	4.4817	.65 144	.22 313	**2.00**	7.3891	.86 859	.13 534
x	e^x	$Log_{10}\, e^x$	e^{-x}	x	e^x	$Log_{10}\, e^x$	e^{-x}

TABLE IV. EXPONENTIAL FUNCTIONS   499

x	e^x	$Log_{10} e^x$	e^{-x}	x	e^x	$Log_{10} e^x$	e^{-x}
2.00	7.3891	.86 859	.13 534	**2.50**	12.182	1.08 574	.082 085
2.01	7.4633	.87 293	.13 399	2.51	12.305	1.09 008	.081 268
2.02	7.5383	.87 727	.13 266	2.52	12.429	1.09 442	.080 460
2.03	7.6141	.88 162	.13 134	2.53	12.554	1.09 877	.079 659
2.04	7.6906	.88 596	.13 003	2.54	12.680	1.10 311	.078 866
2.05	7.7679	.89 030	.12 873	**2.55**	12.807	1.10 745	.078 082
2.06	7.8460	.89 465	.12 745	2.56	12.936	1.11 179	.077 305
2.07	7.9248	.89 899	.12 619	2.57	13.066	1.11 614	.076 536
2.08	8.0045	.90 333	.12 493	2.58	13.197	1.12 048	.075 774
2.09	8.0849	.90 768	.12 369	2.59	13.330	1.12 482	.075 020
2.10	8.1662	.91 202	.12 246	**2.60**	13.464	1.12 917	.074 274
2.11	8.2482	.91 636	.12 124	2.61	13.599	1.13 351	.073 535
2.12	8.3311	.92 070	.12 003	2.62	13.736	1.13 785	.072 803
2.13	8.4149	.92 505	.11 884	2.63	13.874	1.14 219	.072 078
2.14	8.4994	.92 939	.11 765	2.64	14.013	1.14 654	.071 361
2.15	8.5849	.93 373	.11 648	**2.65**	14.154	1.15 088	.070 651
2.16	8.6711	.93 808	.11 533	2.66	14.296	1.15 522	.069 948
2.17	8.7583	.94 242	.11 418	2.67	14.440	1.15 957	.069 252
2.18	8.8463	.94 676	.11 304	2.68	14.585	1.16 391	.068 563
2.19	8.9352	.95 110	.11 192	2.69	14.732	1.16 825	.067 881
2.20	9.0250	95 545	.11 080	**2.70**	14.880	1.17 260	.067 206
2.21	9.1157	.95 979	.10 970	2.71	15.029	1.17 694	.066 537
2.22	9.2073	.96 413	.10 861	2.72	15.180	1.18 128	.065 875
2.23	9.2999	.96 848	.10 753	2.73	15.333	1.18 562	.065 219
2.24	9.3933	.97 282	.10 646	2.74	15.487	1.18 997	.064 570
2.25	9.4877	.97 716	.10 540	**2.75**	15.643	1.19 431	.063 928
2.26	9.5831	.98 151	.10 435	2.76	15.800	1.19 865	.063 292
2.27	9.6794	.98 585	.10 331	2.77	15.959	1.20 300	.062 662
2.28	9.7767	.99 019	.10 228	2.78	16.119	1.20 734	.062 039
2.29	9.8749	.99 453	.10 127	2.79	16.281	1.21 168	.061 421
2.30	9.9742	.99 888	.10 026	**2.80**	16.445	1.21 602	.060 810
2.31	10.074	1.00 322	.09 9261	2.81	16.610	1.22 037	.060 205
2.32	10.176	1.00 756	.09 8274	2.82	16.777	1.22 471	.059 606
2.33	10.278	1.01 191	.09 7296	2.83	16.945	1.22 905	.059 013
2.34	10.381	1.01 625	.09 6328	2.84	17.116	1.23 340	.058 426
2.35	10.486	1.02 059	.09 5369	**2.85**	17.288	1.23 774	.057 844
2.36	10.591	1.02 493	.09 4420	2.86	17.462	1.24 208	.057 269
2.37	10.697	1.02 928	.09 3481	2.87	17.637	1.24 643	.056 699
2.38	10.805	1.03 362	.09 2551	2.88	17.814	1.25 077	.056 135
2.39	10.913	1.03 796	.09 1630	2.89	17.993	1.25 511	.055 576
2.40	11.023	1.04 231	.09 0718	**2.90**	18.174	1.25 945	.055 023
2.41	11.134	1.04 665	.08 9815	2.91	18.357	1.26 380	.054 476
2.42	11.246	1.05 099	.08 8922	2.92	18.541	1.26 814	.053 934
2.43	11.359	1.05 534	.08 8037	2.93	18.728	1.27 248	.053 397
2.44	11.473	1.05 968	.08 7161	2.94	18.916	1.27 683	.052 866
2.45	11.588	1.06 402	.08 6294	**2.95**	19.106	1.28 117	.052 340
2.46	11.705	1.06 836	.08 5435	2.96	19.298	1.28 551	.051 819
2.47	11.822	1.07 271	.08 4585	2.97	19.492	1.28 985	.051 303
2.48	11.941	1.07 705	.08 3743	2.98	19.688	1.29 420	.050 793
2.49	12.061	1.08 139	.08 2910	2.99	19.886	1.29 854	.050 287
2.50	12.182	1.08 574	.08 2085	**3.00**	20.086	1.30 288	.049 787
x	e^x	$Log_{10} e^x$	e^{-x}	x	e^x	$Log_{10} e^x$	e^{-x}

x	e^x	$\text{Log}_{10}\, e^x$	e^{-x}	x	e^x	$\text{Log}_{10}\, e^x$	e^{-x}
3.00	20.086	1.30 288	.04 9787	**3.50**	33.115	1.52 003	.030 197
3.01	20.287	1.30 723	.04 9292	3.51	33.448	1.52 437	.029 897
3.02	20.491	1.31 157	.04 8801	3.52	33.784	1.52 872	.029 599
3.03	20.697	1.31 591	.04 8316	3.53	34.124	1.53 306	.029 305
3.04	20.905	1.32 026	.04 7835	3.54	34.467	1.53 740	.029 013
3.05	21.115	1.32 460	.04 7359	**3.55**	34.813	1.54 175	.028 725
3.06	21.328	1.32 894	.04 6888	3.56	35.163	1.54 609	.028 439
3.07	21.542	1.33 328	.04 6421	3.57	35.517	1.55 043	.028 156
3.08	21.758	1.33 763	.04 5959	3.58	35.874	1.55 477	.027 876
3.09	21.977	1.34 197	.04 5502	3.59	36.234	1.55 912	.027 598
3.10	22.198	1.34 631	.04 5049	**3.60**	36.598	1.56 346	.027 324
3.11	22.421	1.35 066	.04 4601	3.61	36.966	1.56 780	.027 052
3.12	22.646	1.35 500	.04 4157	3.62	37.338	1.57 215	.026 783
3.13	22.874	1.35 934	.04 3718	3.63	37.713	1.57 649	.026 516
3.14	23.104	1.36 368	.04 3283	3.64	38.092	1.58 083	.026 252
3.15	23.336	1.36 803	.04 2852	**3.65**	38.475	1.58 517	.025 991
3.16	23.571	1.37 237	.04 2426	3.66	38.861	1.58 952	.025 733
3.17	23.807	1.37 671	.04 2004	3.67	39.252	1.59 386	.025 476
3.18	24.047	1.38 106	.04 1586	3.68	39.646	1.59 820	.025 223
3.19	24.288	1.38 540	.04 1172	3.69	40.045	1.60 255	.024 972
3.20	24.533	1.38 974	.04 0762	**3.70**	40.447	1.60 689	.024 724
3.21	24.779	1.39 409	.04 0357	3.71	40.854	1.61 123	.024 478
3.22	25.028	1.39 843	.03 9955	3.72	41.264	1.61 558	.024 234
3.23	25.280	1.40 277	.03 9557	3.73	41.679	1.61 992	.023 993
3.24	25.534	1.40 711	.03 9164	3.74	42.098	1.62 426	.023 754
3.25	25.790	1.41 146	.03 8774	**3.75**	42.521	1.62 860	.023 518
3.26	26.050	1.41 580	.03 8388	3.76	42.948	1.63 295	.023 284
3.27	26.311	1.42 014	.03 8006	3.77	43.380	1.63 729	.023 052
3.28	26.576	1.42 449	.03 7628	3.78	43.816	1.64 163	.022 823
3.29	26.843	1.42 883	.03 7254	3.79	44.256	1.64 598	.022 596
3.30	27.113	1.43 317	.03 6883	**3.80**	44.701	1.65 032	.022 371
3.31	27.385	1.43 751	.03 6516	3.81	45.150	1.65 466	.022 148
3.32	27.660	1.44 186	.03 6153	3.82	45.604	1.65 900	.021 928
3.33	27.938	1.44 620	.03 5793	3.83	46.063	1.66 335	.021 710
3.34	28.219	1.45 054	.03 5437	3.84	46.525	1.66 769	.021 494
3.35	28.503	1.45 489	.03 5084	**3.85**	46.993	1.67 203	.021 280
3.36	28.789	1.45 923	.03 4735	3.86	47.465	1.67 638	.021 068
3.37	29.079	1.46 357	.03 4390	3.87	47.942	1.68 072	.020 858
3.38	29.371	1.46 792	.03 4047	3.88	48.424	1.68 506	.020 651
3.39	29.666	1.47 226	.03 3709	3.89	48.911	1.68 941	.020 445
3.40	29.964	1.47 660	.03 3373	**3.90**	49.402	1.69 375	.020 242
3.41	30.265	1.48 094	.03 3041	3.91	49.899	1.69 809	.020 041
3.42	30.569	1.48 529	.03 2712	3.92	50.400	1.70 243	.019 841
3.43	30.877	1.48 963	.03 2387	3.93	50.907	1.70 678	.019 644
3.44	31.187	1.49 397	.03 2065	3.94	51.419	1.71 112	.019 448
3.45	31.500	1.49 832	.03 1746	**3.95**	51.935	1.71 546	.019 255
3.46	31.817	1.50 266	.03 1430	3.96	52.457	1.71 981	.019 063
3.47	32.137	1.50 700	.03 1117	3.97	52.985	1.72 415	.018 873
3.48	32.460	1.51 134	.03 0807	3.98	53.517	1.72 849	.018 686
3.49	32.786	1.51 569	.03 0501	3.99	54.055	1.73 283	.018 500
3.50	33.115	1.52 003	.03 0197	**4.00**	54.598	1.73 718	.018 316
x	e^x	$\text{Log}_{10}\, e^x$	e^{-x}	x	e^x	$\text{Log}_{10}\, e^x$	e^{-x}

TABLE IV. EXPONENTIAL FUNCTIONS   501

x	e^x	$Log_{10}\,e^x$	e^{-x}	x	e^x	$Log_{10}\,e^x$	e^{-x}
4.00	54.598	1.73 718	.01 8316	**4.50**	90.017	1.95 433	.011 109
4.01	55.147	1.74 152	.01 8133	4.51	90.922	1.95 867	.010 998
4.02	55.701	1.74 586	.01 7953	4.52	91.836	1.96 301	.010 889
4.03	56.261	1.75 021	.01 7774	4.53	92.759	1.96 735	.010 781
4.04	56.826	1.75 455	.01 7597	4.54	93.691	1.97 170	.010 673
4.05	57.397	1.75 889	.01 7422	**4.55**	94.632	1 97 604	.010 567
4.06	57.974	1.76 324	.01 7249	4.56	95.583	1.98 038	.010 462
4.07	58.557	1.76 758	.01 7077	4.57	96.544	1.98 473	.010 358
4.08	59.145	1.77 192	.01 6907	4.58	97.514	1.98 907	.010 255
4.09	59.740	1.77 626	.01 6739	4.59	98.494	1.99 341	.010 153
4.10	60.340	1.78 061	.01 6573	**4.60**	99.484	1.99 775	.010 052
4.11	60.947	1.78 495	.01 6408	4.61	100.48	2.00 210	.009 9518
4.12	61.559	1.78 929	.01 6245	4.62	101.49	2.00 644	.009 8528
4.13	62.178	1.79 364	.01 6083	4.63	102.51	2.01 078	.009 7548
4.14	62.803	1.79 798	.01 5923	4.64	103.54	2.01 513	.009 6577
4.15	63.434	1.80 232	.01 5764	**4.65**	104.58	2.01 947	.009 5616
4.16	64.072	1.80 667	.01 5608	4.66	105.64	2.02 381	.009 4665
4.17	64.715	1.81 101	.01 5452	4.67	106.70	2.02 816	.009 3723
4.18	65.366	1.81 535	.01 5299	4.68	107.77	2.03 250	.009 2790
4.19	66.023	1.81 969	.01 5146	4.69	108.85	2.03 684	.009 1867
4.20	66.686	1.82 404	.01 4996	**4.70**	109.95	2.04 118	.009 0953
4.21	67.357	1.82 838	.01 4846	4.71	111.05	2.04 553	.009 0048
4.22	68.033	1.83 272	.01 4699	4.72	112.17	2.04 987	.008 9152
4.23	68.717	1.83 707	.01 4552	4.73	113.30	2.05 421	.008 8265
4.24	69.408	1.84 141	.01 4408	4.74	114.43	2.05 8⁻6	.008 7386
4.25	70.105	1.84 575	.01 4264	**4.75**	115.58	2.06 290	.008 6517
4.26	70.810	1.85 009	.01 4122	4.76	116.75	2.06 724	.008 5656
4.27	71.522	1.85 444	.01 3982	4.77	117.92	2.07 158	.008 4804
4.28	72.240	1.85 878	.01 3843	4.78	119.10	2.07 593	.008 3960
4.29	72.966	1.86 312	.01 3705	4.79	120.30	2.08 027	.008 3125
4.30	73.700	1.86 747	.01 3569	**4.80**	121.51	2.08 461	.008 2297
4.31	74.440	1.87 181	.01 3434	4.81	122.73	2.08 896	.008 1479
4.32	75.189	1.87 615	.01 3300	4.82	123.97	2.09 330	.008 0668
4.33	75.944	1.88 050	.01 3168	4.83	125.21	2.09 764	.007 9865
4.34	76.708	1.88 484	.01 3037	4.84	126.47	2.10 199	.007 9071
4.35	77.478	1.88 918	.01 2907	**4.85**	127.74	2.10 633	.007 8284
4.36	78.257	1.89 352	.01 2778	4.86	129.02	2.11 067	.007 7505
4.37	79.044	1.89 787	.01 2651	4.87	130.32	2.11 501	.007 6734
4.38	79.838	1.90 221	.01 2525	4.88	131.63	2.11 936	.007 5970
4.39	80.640	1.90 655	.01 2401	4.89	132.95	2.12 370	.007 5214
4.40	81.451	1.91 090	.01 2277	**4.90**	134.29	2.12 804	.007 4466
4.41	82.269	1.91 524	.01 2155	4.91	135.64	2.13 239	.007 3725
4.42	83.096	1.91 958	.01 2034	4.92	137.00	2.13 673	.007 2991
4.43	83.931	1.92 392	.01 1914	4.93	138.38	2.14 107	.007 2265
4.44	84.775	1.92 827	.01 1796	4.94	139.77	2.14 541	.007 1546
4.45	85.627	1.93 261	.01 1679	**4.95**	141.17	2.14 976	.007 0834
4.46	86.488	1.93 695	.01 1562	4.96	142.59	2.15 410	.007 0129
4.47	87.357	1.94 130	.01 1447	4.97	144.03	2.15 844	.006 9431
4.48	88.235	1.94 564	.01 1333	4.98	145.47	2.16 279	.006 8741
4.49	89.121	1.94 998	.01 1221	4.99	146.94	2.16 713	.006 8057
4.50	90.017	1.95 433	.01 1109	**5.00**	148.41	2.17 147	.006 7379

x	e^x	$Log_{10}\,e^x$	e^{-x}	x	e^x	$Log_{10}\,e^x$	e^{-x}

x	e^x	$\text{Log}_{10}\, e^x$	e^{-x}	x	e^x	$\text{Log}_{10}\, e^x$	e^{-x}
5.00	148.41	2.17 147	.00 67379	**7.50**	1 808.0	3.25 721	.000 5531
5.05	156.02	2.19 319	.00 64093	7.55	1 900.7	3.27 892	.000 5261
5.10	164.02	2.21 490	.00 60967	7.60	1 998.2	3.30 064	.000 5005
5.15	172.43	2.23 662	.00 57994	7.65	2 100.6	3.32 235	.000 4760
5.20	181.27	2.25 833	.00 55166	7.70	2 208.3	3.34 407	.000 4528
5.25	190.57	2.28 005	.00 52475	**7.75**	2 321.6	3.36 578	.000 4307
5.30	200.34	2.30 176	.00 49916	7.80	2 440.6	3.38 750	.000 4097
5.35	210.61	2.32 348	.00 47482	7.85	2 565.7	3.40 921	.000 3898
5.40	221.41	2.34 519	.00 45166	7.90	2 697.3	3.43 093	.000 3707
5.45	232.76	2.36 690	.00 42963	7.95	2 835.6	3.45 264	.000 3527
5.50	244.69	2.38 862	.00 40868	**8.00**	2 981.0	3.47 436	.000 3355
5.55	257.24	2.41 033	.00 38875	8.05	3 133.8	3.49 607	.000 3191
5.60	270.43	2.43 205	.00 36979	8.10	3 294.5	3.51 779	.000 3035
5.65	284.29	2.45 376	.00 35175	8.15	3 463.4	3.53 950	.000 2887
5.70	298.87	2.47 548	.00 33460	8.20	3 641.0	3.56 121	.000 2747
5.75	314.19	2.49 719	.00 31828	**8.25**	3 827.6	3.58 293	.000 2613
5.80	330.30	2.51 891	.00 30276	8.30	4 023.9	3.60 464	.000 2485
5.85	347.23	2.54 062	.00 28799	8.35	4 230.2	3.62 636	.000 2364
5.90	365.04	2.56 234	.00 27394	8.40	4 447.1	3.64 807	.000 2249
5.95	383.75	2.58 405	.00 26058	8.45	4 675.1	3.66 979	.000 2139
6.00	403.43	2.60 577	.00 24788	**8.50**	4 914.8	3.69 150	.000 2035
6.05	424.11	2.62 748	.00 23579	8.55	5 166.8	3.71 322	.000 1935
6.10	445.86	2.64 920	.00 22429	8.60	5 431.7	3.73 493	.000 1841
6.15	468.72	2.67 091	.00 21335	8.65	5 710.1	3.75 665	.000 1751
6.20	492.75	2.69 263	.00 20294	8.70	6 002.9	3.77 836	.000 1666
6.25	518.01	2.71 434	.00 19305	**8.75**	6 310.7	3.80 008	.000 1585
6.30	544.57	2.73 606	.00 18363	8.80	6 634.2	3.82 179	.000 1507
6.35	572.49	2.75 777	.00 17467	8.85	6 974.4	3.84 351	.000 1434
6.40	601.85	2.77 948	.00 16616	8.90	7 332.0	3.86 522	.000 1364
6.45	632.70	2.80 120	.00 15805	8.95	7 707.9	3.88 694	.000 1297
6.50	665.14	2.82 291	.00 15034	**9.00**	8 103.1	3.90 865	.000 1234
6.55	699.24	2.84 463	.00 14301	9.05	8 518.5	3.93 037	.000 1174
6.60	735.10	2.86 634	.00 13604	9.10	8 955.3	3.95 208	.000 1117
6.65	772.78	2.88 806	.00 12940	9.15	9 414.4	3.97 379	.000 1062
6.70	812.41	2.90 977	.00 12309	9.20	9 897.1	3.99 551	.000 1010
6.75	854.06	2.93 149	.00 11709	**9.25**	10 405	4.01 722	.000 0961
6.80	897.85	2.95 320	.00 11138	9.30	10 938	4.03 894	.000 0914
6.85	943.88	2.97 492	.00 10595	9.35	11 499	4.06 065	.000 0870
6.90	992.27	2.99 663	.00 10078	9.40	12 088	4.08 237	.000 0827
6.95	1 043.1	3.01 835	.00 09586	9.45	12 708	4.10 408	.000 0787
7.00	1 096.6	3.04 006	.00 09119	**9.50**	13 360	4.12 580	.000 0749
7.05	1 152.9	3.06 178	.00 08674	9.55	14 045	4.14 751	.000 0712
7.10	1 212.0	3.08 349	.00 08251	9.60	14 765	4.16 923	.000 0677
7.15	1 274.1	3.10 521	.00 07849	9.65	15 522	4.19 094	.000 0644
7.20	1 339.4	3.12 692	.00 07466	9.70	16 318	4.21 266	.000 0613
7.25	1 408.1	3.14 863	.00 07102	**9.75**	17 154	4.23 437	.000 0583
7.30	1 480.3	3.17 035	.00 06755	9.80	18 034	4.25 609	.000 0555
7.35	1 556.2	3.19 206	.00 06426	9.85	18 958	4.27 780	.000 0527
7.40	1 636.0	3.21 378	.00 06113	9.90	19 930	4.29 952	.000 0502
7.45	1 719.9	3.23 549	.00 05814	9.95	20 952	4.32 123	.000 0477
7.50	1 808.0	3.25 721	.00 05531	**10.00**	22 026	4.34 294	.000 0454
x	e^x	$\text{Log}_{10}\, e^x$	e^{-x}	x	e^x	$\text{Log}_{10}\, e^x$	e^{-x}

TABLE V. NATURAL LOGARITHMS   503

	.00	.01	.02	.03	.04	.05	.06	.07	.08	.09
1.0	0.0000	0.0100	0.0198	0.0296	0.0392	0.0488	0.0583	0.0677	0.0770	0.0862
1.1	.0953	.1044	.1133	.1222	.1310	.1398	.1484	.1570	.1655	.1740
1.2	.1823	.1906	.1989	.2070	.2151	.2231	.2311	.2390	.2469	.2546
1.3	.2624	.2700	.2776	.2852	.2927	.3001	.3075	.3148	.3221	.3293
1.4	.3365	.3436	.3507	.3577	.3646	.3716	.3784	.3853	.3920	.3988
1.5	.4055	.4121	.4187	.4253	.4318	.4383	.4447	.4511	.4574	.4637
1.6	.4700	.4762	.4824	.4886	.4947	.5008	.5068	.5128	.5188	.5247
1.7	.5306	.5365	.5423	.5481	.5539	.5596	.5653	.5710	.5766	.5822
1.8	.5878	.5933	.5988	.6043	.6098	.6152	.6206	.6259	.6313	.6366
1.9	.6419	.6471	.6523	.6575	.6627	.6678	.6729	.6780	.6831	.6881
2.0	.6932	.6981	.7031	.7080	.7130	.7178	.7227	.7276	.7324	.7372
2.1	.7419	.7467	.7514	.7561	.7608	.7655	.7701	.7747	.7793	.7839
2.2	.7885	.7930	.7975	.8020	.8065	.8109	.8154	.8198	.8242	.8286
2.3	.8329	.8373	.8416	.8459	.8502	.8544	.8587	.8629	.8671	.8713
2.4	.8755	.8796	.8838	.8879	.8920	.8961	.9002	.9042	.9083	.9123
2.5	.9163	.9203	.9243	.9282	.9322	.9361	.9400	.9439	.9478	.9517
2.6	.9555	.9594	0.9632	0.9670	0.9708	0.9746	0.9783	0.9821	0.9858	0.9895
2.7	0.9933	0.9970	1.0006	1.0043	1.0080	1.0116	1.0152	1.0189	1.0225	1.0260
2.8	1.0296	1.0332	.0367	.0403	.0438	.0473	.0508	1.0543	.0578	.0613
2.9	.0647	.0682	.0716	.0750	.0784	.0818	.0852	1.0886	.0919	.0953
3.0	.0986	.1019	.1053	.1086	.1119	.1151	.1184	.1217	.1249	.1282
3.1	.1314	.1346	.1378	.1410	.1442	.1474	.1506	.1537	.1569	.1600
3.2	.1632	.1663	.1694	.1725	.1756	.1787	.1817	.1848	.1878	.1909
3.3	.1939	.1970	.2000	.2030	.2060	.2090	.2119	.2149	.2179	.2208
3.4	.2238	.2267	.2296	.2326	.2355	.2384	.2413	.2442	.2470	.2499
3.5	.2528	.2556	.2585	.2613	.2641	.2670	.2698	.2726	.2754	.2782
3.6	.2809	.2837	.2865	.2892	.2920	.2947	.2975	.3002	.3029	.3056
3.7	.3083	.3110	.3137	.3164	.3191	.3218	.3244	.3271	.3297	.3324
3.8	.3350	.3376	.3403	.3429	.3455	.3481	.3507	.3533	.3558	.3584
3.9	.3610	.3635	.3661	.3686	.3712	.3737	.3762	.3788	.3813	.3838
4.0	.3863	.3888	.3913	.3938	.3962	.3987	.4012	.4036	.4061	.4085
4.1	.4110	.4134	.4159	.4183	.4207	.4231	.4255	.4279	.4303	.4327
4.2	.4351	.4375	.4398	.4422	.4446	.4469	.4493	.4516	.4540	.4563
4.3	.4586	.4609	.4633	.4656	.4679	.4702	.4725	.4748	.4771	.4793
4.4	.4816	.4839	.4861	.4884	.4907	.4929	.4952	.4974	.4996	.5019
4.5	.5041	.5063	.5085	.5107	.5129	.5151	.5173	.5195	.5217	.5239
4.6	.5261	.5282	.5304	.5326	.5347	.5369	.5390	.5412	.5433	.5454
4.7	.5476	.5497	.5518	.5539	.5560	.5581	.5603	.5624	.5644	.5665
4.8	.5686	.5707	.5728	.5749	.5769	.5790	.5810	.5831	.5852	.5872
4.9	.5892	.5913	.5933	.5953	.5974	.5994	.6014	.6034	.6054	.6074
5.0	.6094	.6114	.6134	.6154	.6174	.6194	.6214	.6233	.6253	.6273
5.1	.6292	.6312	.6332	.6351	.6371	.6390	.6409	.6429	.6448	.6467
5.2	.6487	.6506	.6525	.6544	.6563	.6582	.6601	.6620	.6639	.6658
5.3	.6677	.6696	.6715	.6734	.6752	.6771	.6790	.6808	.6827	.6846
5.4	1.6864	1.6883	1.6901	1.6919	1.6938	1.6956	1.6975	1.6993	1.7011	1.7029

$$\log_e N = 2.30259 \log_{10} N$$
$$\log_{10} N = 0.43429 \log_e N$$

	.00	.01	.02	.03	.04	.05	.06	.07	.08	.09
5.5	1.7048	1.7066	1.7084	1.7102	1.7120	1.7138	1.7156	1.7174	1.7192	1.7210
5.6	.7228	.7246	.7263	.7281	.7299	.7317	.7334	.7352	.7370	.7387
5.7	.7405	.7422	.7440	.7457	.7475	.7492	.7509	.7527	.7544	.7561
5.8	.7579	.7596	.7613	.7630	.7647	.7664	.7682	.7699	.7716	.7733
5.9	.7750	.7767	.7783	.7800	.7817	.7834	.7851	.7868	.7884	.7901
6.0	.7918	.7934	.7951	.7968	.7984	.8001	.8017	.8034	.8050	.8067
6.1	.8083	.8099	.8116	.8132	.8148	.8165	.8181	.8197	.8213	.8229
6.2	.8246	.8262	.8278	.8294	.8310	.8326	.8342	.8358	.8374	.8390
6.3	.8406	.8421	.8437	.8453	.8469	.8485	.8500	.8516	.8532	.8547
6.4	.8563	.8579	.8594	.8610	.8625	.8641	.8656	.8672	.8687	.8703
6.5	.8718	.8733	.8749	.8764	.8779	.8795	.8810	.8825	.8840	.8856
6.6	.8871	.8886	.8901	.8916	.8931	.8946	.8961	.8976	.8991	.9006
6.7	.9021	.9036	.9051	.9066	.9081	.9095	.9110	.9125	.9140	.9155
6.8	.9169	.9184	.9199	.9213	.9228	.9243	.9257	.9272	.9286	.9301
6.9	.9315	.9330	.9344	.9359	.9373	.9387	.9402	.9416	.9431	.9445
7.0	.9459	.9473	.9488	.9502	.9516	.9530	.9545	.9559	.9573	.9587
7.1	.9601	.9615	.9629	.9643	.9657	.9671	.9685	.9699	.9713	.9727
7.2	.9741	.9755	.9769	.9782	.9796	.9810	.9824	.9838	.9851	1.9865
7.3	1.9879	1.9892	1.9906	1.9920	1.9933	1.9947	1.9961	1.9974	1.9988	2.0001
7.4	2.0015	2.0028	2.0042	2.0055	2.0069	2.0082	2.0096	2.0109	2.0122	.0136
7.5	.0149	.0162	.0176	.0189	.0202	.0216	.0229	.0242	.0255	.0268
7.6	.0282	.0295	.0308	.0321	.0334	.0347	.0360	.0373	.0386	.0399
7.7	.0412	.0425	.0438	.0451	.0464	.0477	.0490	.0503	.0516	.0528
7.8	.0541	.0554	.0567	.0580	.0592	.0605	.0618	.0631	.0643	.0656
7.9	.0669	.0681	.0694	.0707	.0719	.0732	.0744	.0757	.0769	.0782
8.0	.0794	.0807	.0819	.0832	.0844	.0857	.0869	.0882	.0894	.0906
8.1	.0919	.0931	.0943	.0956	.0968	.0980	.0992	.1005	.1017	.1029
8.2	.1041	.1054	.1066	.1078	.1090	.1102	.1114	.1126	.1138	.1151
8.3	.1163	.1175	.1187	.1199	.1211	.1223	.1235	.1247	.1259	.1270
8.4	.1282	.1294	.1306	.1318	.1330	.1342	.1354	.1365	.1377	.1389
8.5	.1401	.1412	.1424	.1436	.1448	.1459	.1471	.1483	.1494	.1506
8.6	.1518	.1529	.1541	.1552	.1564	.1576	.1587	.1599	.1610	.1622
8.7	.1633	.1645	.1656	.1668	.1679	.1691	.1702	.1713	.1725	.1736
8.8	.1748	.1759	.1770	.1782	.1793	.1804	.1816	.1827	.1838	.1849
8.9	.1861	.1872	.1883	.1894	.1905	.1917	.1928	.1939	.1950	.1961
9.0	.1972	.1983	.1994	.2006	.2017	.2028	.2039	.2050	.2061	.2072
9.1	.2083	.2094	.2105	.2116	.2127	.2138	.2149	.2159	.2170	.2181
9.2	.2192	.2203	.2214	.2225	.2235	.2246	.2257	.2268	.2279	.2289
9.3	.2300	.2311	.2322	.2332	.2343	.2354	.2365	.2375	.2386	.2397
9.4	.2407	.2418	.2428	.2439	.2450	.2460	.2471	.2481	.2492	.2502
9.5	.2513	.2523	.2534	.2544	.2555	.2565	.2576	.2586	.2597	.2607
9.6	.2618	.2628	.2638	.2649	.2659	.2670	.2680	.2690	.2701	.2711
9.7	.2721	.2732	.2742	.2752	.2762	.2773	.2783	.2793	.2803	.2814
9.8	.2824	.2834	.2844	.2854	.2865	.2875	.2885	.2895	.2905	.2915
9.9	2.2925	2.2935	2.2946	2.2956	2.2966	2.2976	2.2986	2.2996	2.3006	2.3016

$$\log_e 10 = 2.30259$$
$$\log_e (10^k N) = \log_e N + 2.30259k$$

TABLE VI. AMOUNT OF AN ANNUITY OF 1 PER ANNUM   505

$$\frac{(1 + r)^n - 1}{r}$$

n	$\frac{5}{12}\%$	$\frac{1}{2}\%$	$\frac{7}{12}\%$	$\frac{3}{4}\%$	1%
1	1.000 000	1.000 000	1.000 000	1.000 000	1.000 000
2	2.004 167	2.005 000	2.005 833	2.007 500	2.010 000
3	3.012 517	3.015 025	3.017 534	3.022 556	3.030 100
4	4.025 070	4.030 100	4.035 136	4.045 225	4.060 401
5	5.041 841	5.050 251	5.058 675	5.075 565	5.101 005
6	6.062 848	6.075 502	6.088 184	6.113 631	6.152 015
7	7.088 110	7.105 879	7.123 698	7.159 484	7.213 535
8	8.117 644	8.141 409	8.165 253	8.213 180	8.285 671
9	9.151 467	9.182 116	9.212 883	9.274 779	9.368 527
10	10.189 599	10.228 026	10.266 625	10.344 339	10.462 213
11	11.232 055	11.279 167	11.326 514	11.421 922	11.566 835
12	12.278 855	12.335 562	12.392 585	12.507 586	12.682 503
13	13.330 017	13.397 240	13.464 875	13.601 393	13.809 328
14	14.385 559	14.464 226	14.543 420	14.703 404	14.947 421
15	15.445 499	15.536 548	15.628 257	15.813 679	16.096 896
16	16.509 855	16.614 230	16.719 422	16.932 282	17.257 864
17	17.578 646	17.697 301	17.816 952	18.059 274	18.430 443
18	18.651 891	18.785 788	18.920 884	19.194 718	19.614 748
19	19.729 607	19.879 717	20.031 256	20.338 679	20.810 895
20	20.811 814	20.979 115	21.148 105	21.491 219	22.019 004
21	21.898 529	22.084 011	22.271 469	22.652 403	23.239 194
22	22.989 773	23.194 431	23.401 386	23.822 296	24.471 586
23	24.085 564	24.310 403	24.537 894	25.000 963	25.716 302
24	25.185 921	25.431 955	25.681 032	26.188 471	26.973 465
25	26.290 862	26.559 115	26.830 838	27.384 884	28.243 200
26	27.400 407	27.691 911	27.987 351	28.590 271	29.525 631
27	28.514 575	28.830 370	29.150 610	29.804 698	30.820 888
28	29.633 386	29.974 522	30.320 656	31.028 233	32.129 097
29	30.756 859	31.124 395	31.497 526	32.260 945	33.450 388
30	31.885 012	32.280 017	32.681 262	33.502 902	34.784 892
31	33.017 866	33.441 417	33.871 902	34.754 174	36.132 740
32	34.155 441	34.608 624	35.069 488	36.014 830	37.494 068
33	35.297 755	35.781 667	36.274 060	37.284 941	38.869 009
34	36.444 829	36.960 575	37.485 659	38.564 578	40.257 699
35	37.596 683	38.145 378	38.704 325	39.853 813	41.660 276
36	38.753 336	39.336 105	39.930 101	41.152 716	43.076 878
37	39.914 808	40.532 785	41.163 026	42.461 361	44.507 647
38	41.081 119	41.735 449	42.403 144	43.779 822	45.952 724
39	42.252 291	42.944 127	43.650 496	45.108 170	47.412 251
40	43.428 342	44.158 847	44.905 124	46.446 482	48.886 373
41	44.609 293	45.379 642	46.167 070	47.794 830	50.375 237
42	45.795 165	46.606 540	47.436 378	49.153 291	51.878 989
43	46.985 979	47.839 572	48.713 090	50.521 941	53.397 779
44	48.181 754	49.078 770	49.997 250	51.900 856	54.931 759
45	49.382 511	50.324 164	51.288 900	53.290 112	56.481 075
46	50.588 271	51 575 785	52.588 086	54.689 788	58.045 885
47	51.799 056	52.833 664	53.894 850	56.099 961	59.626 344
48	53.014 885	54.097 832	55.209 236	57.520 711	61.222 608
49	54.235 781	55.368 321	56.531 290	58.952 116	62.834 834
50	55.461 763	56.645 163	57.861 056	60.394 257	64.463 182

$$\frac{(1 + r)^n - 1}{r}$$

n	$\frac{5}{12}\%$	$\frac{1}{2}\%$	$\frac{7}{12}\%$	$\frac{3}{4}\%$	1%
51	56.692 854	57.928 389	59.198 579	61.847 214	66.107 814
52	57.929 074	59.218 031	60.543 904	63.311 068	67.768 892
53	59.170 445	60.514 121	61.897 077	64.785 901	69.446 581
54	60.416 989	61.816 692	63.258 143	66.271 796	71.141 047
55	61.668 726	63.125 775	64.627 149	67.768 834	72.852 457
56	62.925 679	64.441 404	66.004 140	69.277 100	74.580 982
57	64.187 869	65.763 611	67.389 165	70.796 679	76.326 792
58	65.455 319	67.092 429	68.782 268	72.327 654	78.090 060
59	66.728 049	68.427 891	70.183 498	73.870 111	79.870 960
60	68.006 083	69.770 031	71.592 902	75.424 137	81.669 670
61	69.289 442	71.118 881	73.010 527	76.989 818	83.486 367
62	70.578 148	72.474 475	74.436 422	78.567 242	85.321 230
63	71.872 223	73.836 847	75.870 634	80.156 496	87.174 443
64	73.171 691	75.206 032	77.313 213	81.757 670	89.046 187
65	74.476 573	76.582 062	78.764 207	83.370 852	90.936 649
66	75.786 892	77.964 972	80.223 664	84.996 134	92.846 015
67	77.102 671	79.354 797	81.691 636	86.633 605	94.774 475
68	78.423 932	80.751 571	83.168 170	88.283 357	96.722 220
69	79.750 698	82.155 329	84.653 318	89.945 482	98.689 442
70	81.082 993	83.566 105	86.147 129	91.620 073	100.676 337
71	82.420 838	84.983 936	87.649 654	93.307 223	102.683 100
72	83.764 259	86.408 856	89.160 944	95.007 028	104.709 931
73	85.113 276	87.840 900	90.681 049	96.719 580	106.757 031
74	86.467 915	89.280 104	92.210 022	98.444 977	108.824 601
75	87.828 198	90.726 505	93.747 914	100.183 314	110.912 847
76	89.194 149	92.180 138	95.294 777	101.934 689	113.021 975
77	90.565 791	93.641 038	96.850 663	103.699 199	115.152 195
78	91.943 149	95.109 243	98.415 625	105.476 943	117.303 717
79	93.326 245	96.584 790	99.989 716	107.268 021	119.476 754
80	94.715 104	98.067 714	101.572 989	109.072 531	121.671 522
81	96.109 751	99.558 052	103.165 498	110.890 575	123.888 237
82	97.510 208	101.055 842	104.767 297	112.722 254	126.127 119
83	98.916 500	102.561 122	106.378 440	114.567 671	128.388 390
84	100.328 653	104.073 927	107.998 981	116.426 928	130.672 274
85	101.746 689	105.594 297	109.628 975	118.300 130	132.978 997
86	103.170 633	107.122 268	111.268 477	120.187 381	135.308 787
87	104.600 511	108.657 880	112.917 543	122.088 787	137.661 875
88	106.036 346	110.201 169	114.576 229	124.004 453	140.038 494
89	107.478 164	111.752 175	116.244 590	125.934 486	142.438 879
90	108.925 990	113.310 936	117.922 684	127.878 995	144.863 267
91	110.379 848	114.877 490	119.610 566	129.838 087	147.311 900
92	111.839 764	116.451 878	121.308 294	131.811 873	149.785 019
93	113.305 763	118.034 137	123.015 926	133.800 462	152.282 869
94	114.777 871	119.624 308	124.733 519	135.803 965	154.805 698
95	116.256 112	121.222 430	126.461 131	137.822 495	157.353 755
96	117.740 512	122.828 542	128.198 821	139.856 164	159.927 293
97	119.231 098	124.442 684	129.946 647	141.905 085	162.526 565
98	120.727 894	126.064 898	131.704 670	143.969 373	165.151 831
99	122.230 927	127.695 222	133.472 947	146.049 143	167.803 349
100	123.740 222	129.333 698	135.251 539	148.144 512	170.481 383

TABLE VI. AMOUNT OF AN ANNUITY OF 1 PER ANNUM   507

$$\frac{(1 + r)^n - 1}{r}$$

n	$1\frac{1}{8}\%$	$1\frac{1}{4}\%$	$1\frac{1}{2}\%$	$1\frac{3}{4}\%$	2%
1	1.000 000	1.000 000	1.000 000	1.000 000	1.000 000
2	2.011 250	2.012 500	2.015 000	2.017 500	2.020 000
3	3.033 877	3.037 656	3.045 225	3.052 806	3.060 400
4	4.068 008	4.075 627	4.090 903	4.106 230	4.121 608
5	5.113 773	5.126 572	5.152 267	5.178 089	5.204 040
6	6.171 303	6.190 654	6.229 551	6.268 706	6.308 121
7	7.240 730	7.268 038	7.322 994	7.378 408	7.434 283
8	8.322 188	8.358 888	8.432 839	8.507 530	8.582 969
9	9.415 813	9.463 374	9.559 332	9.656 412	9.754 628
10	10.521 741	10.581 666	10.702 722	10.825 399	10.949 721
11	11.640 110	11.713 937	11.863 262	12.014 844	12.168 715
12	12.771 061	12.860 361	13.041 211	13.225 104	13.412 090
13	13.914 736	14.021 116	14.236 830	14.456 543	14.680 332
14	15.071 277	15.196 380	15.450 382	15.709 533	15.973 938
15	16.240 828	16.386 335	16.682 138	16.984 449	17.293 417
16	17.423 538	17.591 164	17.932 370	18.281 677	18.639 285
17	18.619 553	18.811 053	19.201 355	19.601 607	20.012 071
18	19.829 023	20.046 192	20.489 376	20.944 635	21.412 312
19	21.052 099	21.296 769	21.796 716	22.311 166	22.840 559
20	22.288 935	22.562 979	23.123 667	23.701 611	24.297 370
21	23.539 686	23.845 016	24.470 522	25.116 389	25.783 317
22	24.804 507	25.143 078	25.837 580	26.555 926	27.298 984
23	26.083 558	26.457 367	27.225 144	28.020 655	28.844 963
24	27.376 998	27.788 084	28.633 521	29.511 016	30.421 862
25	28.684 989	29.135 435	30.063 024	31.027 459	32.030 300
26	30.007 695	30.499 628	31.513 969	32.570 440	33.670 906
27	31.345 282	31.880 873	32.986 678	34.140 422	35.344 324
28	32.697 916	33.279 384	34.481 479	35.737 880	37.051 210
29	34.065 768	34.695 377	35.998 701	37.363 293	38.792 235
30	35.449 008	36.129 069	37.538 681	39.017 150	40.568 079
31	36.847 809	37.580 682	39.101 762	40.699 950	42.379 441
32	38.262 347	39.050 441	40.688 288	42.412 200	44.227 030
33	39.692 798	40.538 571	42.298 612	44.154 413	46.111 570
34	41.139 342	42.045 303	43.933 092	45.927 115	48.033 802
35	42.602 160	43.570 870	45.592 088	47.730 840	49.994 478
36	44.081 434	45.115 505	47.275 969	49.566 129	51.994 367
37	45.577 350	46.679 449	48.985 109	51.433 537	54.034 255
38	47.090 095	48.262 942	50.719 885	53.333 624	56.114 940
39	48.619 859	49.866 229	52.480 684	55.266 962	58.237 238
40	50.166 832	51.489 557	54.267 894	57.234 134	60.401 983
41	51.731 209	53.133 177	56.081 912	59.235 731	62.610 023
42	53.313 185	54.797 341	57.923 141	61.272 357	64.862 223
43	54.912 959	56.482 308	59.791 988	63.344 623	67.159 468
44	56.530 730	58.188 337	61.688 868	65.453 154	69.502 657
45	58.166 700	59.915 691	63.614 201	67.598 584	71.892 710
46	59.821 076	61.664 637	65.568 414	69.781 559	74.330 564
47	61.494 063	63.435 445	67.551 940	72.002 736	76.817 176
48	63.185 871	65.228 388	69.565 219	74.262 784	79.353 519
49	64.896 712	67.043 743	71.608 698	76.562 383	81.940 590
50	66.626 800	68.881 790	73.682 828	78.902 225	84.579 401

$$\frac{(1 + r)^n - 1}{r}$$

n	$1\frac{1}{8}\%$	$1\frac{1}{4}\%$	$1\frac{1}{2}\%$	$1\frac{3}{4}\%$	2%
51	68.376 352	70.742 812	75.788 070	81.283 014	87.270 989
52	70.145 585	72.627 097	77.924 892	83.705 466	90.016 409
53	71.934 723	74.534 936	80.093 765	86.170 312	92.816 737
54	73.743 989	76.466 623	82.295 171	88.678 292	95.673 072
55	75.573 609	78.422 456	84.529 599	91.230 163	98.586 534
56	77.423 812	80.402 736	86.797 543	93.826 690	101.558 264
57	79.294 830	82.407 771	89.099 506	96.468 658	104.589 430
58	81.186 897	84.437 868	91.435 999	99.156 859	107.681 218
59	83.100 249	86.493 341	93.807 539	101.892 104	110.834 843
60	85.035 127	88.574 508	96.214 652	104.675 216	114.051 539
61	86.991 772	90.681 689	98.657. 871	107.507 032	117.332 570
62	88.970 430	92.815 210	101.137 740	110.388 405	120.679 222
63	90.971 347	94.975 400	103.654 806	113.320 202	124.092 806
64	92.994 775	97.162 593	106.209 628	116.303 306	127.574 662
65	95.040 966	99.377 125	108.802 772	119.338 614	131.126 155
66	97.110 177	101.619 339	111.434 814	122.427 039	134.748 679
67	99.202 666	103.889 581	114.106 336	125.569 513	138.443 652
68	101.318 696	106.188 201	116.817 931	128.766 979	142.212 525
69	103.458 532	108.515 553	119.570 200	132.020 401	146.056 776
70	105.622 440	110.871 998	122.363 753	135.330 758	149.977 911
71	107.810 692	113.257 898	125.199 209	138.699 047	153 977 469
72	110.023 563	115.673 621	128.077 197	142.126 280	158 057 019
73	112.261 328	118.119 542	130.998 355	145.613 490	162.218 159
74	114.524 268	120.596 036	133.963 331	149.161 726	166.462 522
75	116.812 666	123.103 486	136.972 781	152.772 056	170.791 773
76	119.126 808	125.642 280	140.027 372	156.445 567	175.207 608
77	121.466 985	128.212 809	143.127 783	160.183 364	179.711 760
78	123.833 488	130.815 469	146.274 700	163.986 573	184.305 996
79	126.226 615	133.450 662	149.468 820	167.856 338	188.992 115
80	128.646 665	136.118 795	152.710 852	171.793 824	193.771 958
81	131.093 940	138.820 280	156.001 515	175.800 216	198.647 397
82	133.568 746	141.555 534	159.341 538	179.876 720	203.620 345
83	136.071 395	144.324 978	162.731 661	184.024 563	208.692 752
84	138.602 198	147.129 040	166.172 636	188.244 992	213.866 607
85	141.161 473	149.968 153	169.665 226	192.539 280	219.143 939
86	143.749 539	152.842 755	173.210 204	196.908 717	224.526 818
87	146.366 722	155.753 289	176.808 357	201.354 620	230.017 354
88	149.013 347	158.700 206	180.460 482	205.878 326	235.617 701
89	151.689 747	161.683 958	184.167 390	210.481 196	241.330 055
90	154.396 257	164.705 008	187.929 900	215.164 617	247.156 656
91	157.133 215	167.763 820	191.748 849	219.929 998	253.099 789
92	159.900 964	170.860 868	195.625 082	224.778 773	259.161 785
93	162.699 849	173.996 629	199.559 458	229.712 401	265.345 021
94	165.530 223	177.171 587	203.552 850	234.732 369	271.651 921
95	168.392 438	180.386 232	207.606 142	239.840 185	278 084 960
96	171.286 853	183.641 059	211.720 235	245.037 388	284.646 659
97	174.213 830	186.936 573	215.896 038	250.325 542	291.339 592
98	177.173 735	190.273 280	220.134 479	255.706 239	298.166 384
99	180.166 940	193.651 696	224.436 496	261.181 099	305.129 712
100	183.193 818	197.072 342	228.803 043	266.751 768	312.232 306

TABLE VI. AMOUNT OF AN ANNUITY OF 1 PER ANNUM   509

$$\frac{(1 + r)^n - 1}{r}$$

n	3%	4%	5%	6%	7%
1	1.000 000	1.000 000	1.000 000	1.000 000	1.000 000
2	2.030 000	2.040 000	2.050 000	2.060 000	2.070 000
3	3.090 900	3.121 600	3.152 500	3.183 600	3.214 900
4	4.183 627	4.246 464	4.310 125	4.374 616	4.439 943
5	5.309 136	5.416 323	5.525 631	5.637 093	5.750 739
6	6.468 410	6.632 975	6.801 913	6.975 319	7.153 291
7	7.662 462	7.898 294	8.142 008	8.393 838	8.654 021
8	8.892 336	9.214 226	9.549 109	9.897 468	10.259 803
9	10.159 106	10.582 795	11.026 564	11.491 316	11.977 989
10	11.463 879	12.006 107	12.577 893	13.180 795	13.816 448
11	12.807 796	13.486 351	14.206 787	14.971 643	15.783 599
12	14.192 030	15.025 805	15.917 127	16.869 941	17.888 451
13	15.617 790	16.626 838	17.712 983	18.882 138	20.140 643
14	17.086 324	18.291 911	19.598 632	21.015 066	22.550 488
15	18.598 914	20.023 588	21.578 564	23.275 970	25.129 022
16	20.156 881	21.824 531	23.657 492	25.672 528	27.888 054
17	21.761 588	23.697 512	25.840 366	28.212 880	30.840 217
18	23.414 435	25.645 413	28.132 385	30.905 653	33.999 033
19	25.116 868	27.671 229	30.539 004	33.759 992	37.378 965
20	26.870 374	29.778 079	33.065 954	36.785 591	40.995 492
21	28.676 486	31.969 202	35.719 252	39.992 727	44.865 177
22	30.536 780	34.247 970	38.505 214	43.392 290	49.005 739
23	32.452 884	36.617 889	41.430 475	46.995 828	53.436 141
24	34.426 470	39.082 604	44.501 999	50.815 577	58.176 671
25	36.459 264	41.645 908	47.727 099	54.864 512	63.249 038
26	38.553 042	44.311 745	51.113 454	59.156 383	68.676 470
27	40.709 634	47.084 214	54.669 127	63.705 766	74.483 823
28	42.930 923	49.967 583	58.402 583	68.528 112	80.697 691
29	45.218 850	52.966 286	62.322 712	73.639 798	87.346 529
30	47.575 416	56.084 938	66.438 848	79.058 186	94.460 786
31	50.002 678	59.328 335	70.760 790	84.801 677	102 073 041
32	52.502 759	62.701 469	75.298 829	90.889 778	110.218 154
33	55.077 841	66.209 527	80.063 771	97.343 165	118.933 425
34	57.730 177	69.857 909	85.066 959	104.183 755	128.258 765
35	60.462 082	73.652 225	90.320 307	111.434 780	138.236 878
36	63.275 944	77.598 314	95.836 323	119 120 867	148.913 460
37	66.174 223	81.702 246	101.628 139	127 268 119	160.337 402
38	69.159 449	85.970 336	107.709 546	135 904 206	172.561 020
39	72.234 233	90.409 150	114.095 023	145.058 458	185.640 292
40	75.401 260	95.025 516	120.799 774	154.761 966	199.635 112
41	78.663 298	99.826 536	127.839 763	165.047 684	214.609 570
42	82.023 196	104.819 598	135.231 751	175.950 545	230.632 240
43	85.483 892	110.012 382	142.993 339	187.507 577	247.776 496
44	89.048 409	115.412 877	151.143 006	199.758 032	266.120 851
45	92.719 861	121.029 392	159.700 156	212.743 514	285.749 311
46	96.501 457	126.870 568	168.685 164	226.508 125	306.751 763
47	100.396 501	132.945 390	178 119 422	241.098 612	329.224 386
48	104.408 396	139.263 206	188.025 393	256.564 529	353.270 093
49	108.540 648	145.833 734	198.426 663	272.958 401	378.999 000
50	112.796 867	152.667 084	209.347 996	290.335 905	406.528 929

$$\frac{(1 + r)^n - 1}{r}$$

n	3%	4%	5%	6%	7%
51	117.180 773	159.773 767	220.815 396	308.756 059	435.985 955
52	121.696 197	167.164 718	232.856 165	328.281 422	467.504 971
53	126.347 082	174.851 306	245.498 974	348.978 308	501.230 319
54	131.137 495	182.845 359	258.773 922	370.917 006	537.316 442
55	136.071 620	191.159 173	272.712 618	394.172 027	575.928 593
56	141.153 768	199.805 540	287.348 249	418.822 348	617.243 594
57	146.388 381	208.797 762	302.715 662	444.951 689	661.450 646
58	151.780 033	218.149 672	318.851 445	472.648 790	708.752 191
59	157.333 434	227.875 659	335.794 017	502.007 718	759.364 844
60	163.053 437	237.990 685	353.583 718	533.128 181	813.520 383
61	168.945 040	248.510 313	372.262 904	566.115 872	871.466 810
62	175.013 391	259.450 725	391.876 049	601.082 824	933.469 487
63	181.263 793	270.828 754	412.469 851	638.147 793	999.812 351
64	187.701 707	282.661 904	434.093 344	677.436 661	1070.799 216
65	194.332 758	294.968 380	456.798 011	719.082 861	1146.755 161
66	201.162 741	307.767 116	480.637 912	763.227 832	1228.028 022
67	208.197 623	321.077 800	505.669 807	810.021 502	1314.989 983
68	215.443 551	334.920 912	531.953 298	859.622 792	1408.039 282
69	222.906 858	349.317 749	559.550 963	912.200 160	1507.602 032
70	230.594 064	364.290 459	588.528 511	967.932 170	1614.134 174
71	238.511 886	379.862 077	618.954 936	1027.008 100	1728.123 566
72	246.667 242	396.056 560	650.902 683	1089.628 586	1850.092 216
73	255.067 259	412.898 823	684.447 817	1156.006 301	1980.598 671
74	263.719 277	430.414 776	719 670 208	1226.366 679	2120.240 578
75	272.630 856	448.631 367	756.653 718	1300.948 680	2269.657 419
76	281.809 781	467.576 621	795.486 404	1380.005 601	2429.533 438
77	291.264 075	487.279 686	836.260 725	1463.805 937	2600.600 779
78	301.001 997	507.770 873	879.073 761	1552.634 293	2783.642 833
79	311.032 057	529.081 708	924.027 449	1646.792 350	2979.497 831
80	321.363 019	551.244 977	971.228 821	1746.599 891	3189.062 680
81	332.003 909	574.294 776	1020.790 262	1852.395 885	3413.297 067
82	342.964 026	598.266 567	1072.829 776	1964.539 638	3653.227 862
83	354.252 947	623.197 230	1127.471 264	2083.412 016	3909.953 812
84	365.880 536	649.125 119	1184.844 828	2209.416 737	4184.650 579
85	377.856 952	676.090 123	1245.087 069	2342.981 741	4478.576 120
86	390.192 660	704.133 728	1308.341 422	2484.560 646	4793.076 448
87	402.898 440	733.299 078	1374.758 493	2634.634 285	5129.591 799
88	415.985 393	763.631 041	1444.496 418	2793.712 342	5489.663 225
89	429.464 955	795.176 282	1517.721 239	2962.335 082	5874.939 651
90	443.348 904	827.983 334	1594.607 301	3141.075 187	6287.185 427
91	457.649 371	862.102 667	1675.337 666	3330.539 698	6728.288 407
92	472.378 852	897.586 774	1760.104 549	3531.372 080	7200.268 595
93	487.550 217	934.490 245	1849.109 777	3744.254 405	7705.287 397
94	503.176 724	972.869 854	1942.565 266	3969.909 669	8245.657 515
95	519.272 026	1012.784 648	2040.693 529	4209.104 250	8823.853 541
96	535.850 186	1054.296 034	2143.728 205	4462.650 505	9442.523 288
97	552.925 692	1097.467 876	2251.914 616	4731.409 535	10104.499 919
98	570.513 463	1142.366 591	2365.510 346	5016.294 107	10812.814 913
99	588.628 867	1189.061 254	2484.785 864	5318.271 753	11570.711 957
100	607.287 733	1237.623 705	2610.025 157	5638.368 059	12381.661 794

TABLE VII. PRESENT VALUE OF 1 PER ANNUM   511

$$\frac{1 - (1 + r)^{-n}}{r}$$

n	$\frac{5}{12}\%$	$\frac{1}{2}\%$	$\frac{7}{12}\%$	$\frac{3}{4}\%$	1%
1	0.995 851	0.995 025	0.994 200	0.992 556	0.990 099
2	1.987 569	1.985 099	1.982 635	1.977 723	1.970 395
3	2.975 173	2.970 248	2.965 337	2.955 556	2.940 985
4	3.958 678	3.950 496	3.942 340	3.926 110	3.901 966
5	4.938 103	4.925 866	4.913 677	4.889 440	4.853 431
6	5.913 463	5.896 384	5.879 381	5.845 598	5.795 476
7	6.884 777	6.862 074	6.839 484	6.794 638	6.728 195
8	7.852 060	7.822 959	7.794 019	7.736 613	7.651 678
9	8.815 329	8.779 064	8.743 018	8.671 576	8.566 018
10	9.774 602	9.730 412	9.686 513	9.599 580	9.471 305
11	10.729 894	10.677 027	10.624 537	10.520 675	10.367 628
12	11.681 222	11.618 932	11.557 120	11.434 913	11.255 077
13	12.628 603	12.556 151	12.484 295	12.342 345	12.133 740
14	13.572 053	13.488 708	13.406 093	13.243 022	13.003 703
15	14.511 588	14.416 625	14.322 545	14.136 995	13.865 053
16	15.447 224	15.339 925	15.233 682	15.024 313	14.717 874
17	16.378 978	16.258 631	16.139 534	15.905 025	15.562 251
18	17.306 867	17.172 768	17.040 133	16.779 181	16.398 269
19	18.230 904	18.082 356	17.935 510	17.646 830	17.226 008
20	19.151 108	18.987 419	18.825 693	18.508 020	18.045 553
21	20.067 494	19.887 979	19.710 714	19.362 799	18.856 983
22	20.980 077	20.784 059	20.590 602	20.211 215	19.660 379
23	21.888 873	21.675 681	21.465 387	21.053 315	20.455 821
24	22.793 898	22.562 866	22.335 099	21.889 146	21.243 387
25	23.695 169	23.445 638	23.199 767	22.718 755	22.023 156
26	24.592 699	24.324 018	24.059 421	23.542 189	22.795 204
27	25.486 505	25.198 028	24.914 089	24.359 493	23.559 608
28	26.376 603	26.067 689	25.763 800	25.170 713	24.316 443
29	27.263 007	26.933 024	26.608 583	25.975 893	25.065 785
30	28.145 733	27.794 054	27.448 467	26.775 080	25.807 708
31	29.024 796	28.650 800	28.283 480	27.568 318	26.542 285
32	29.900 212	29.503 284	29.113 650	28.355 650	27.269 589
33	30.771 995	30.351 526	29.939 006	29.137 122	27.989 693
34	31.640 161	31.195 548	30.759 575	29.912 776	28.702 666
35	32.504 725	32.035 371	31.575 385	30.682 656	29.408 580
36	33.365 701	32.871 016	32.386 464	31.446 805	30.107 505
37	34.223 105	33.702 504	33.192 840	32.205 266	30.799 510
38	35.076 951	34.529 854	33.994 538	32.958 080	31.484 663
39	35.927 254	35.353 089	34.791 587	33.705 290	32.163 033
40	36.774 029	36.172 228	35.584 014	34.446 938	32.834 686
41	37.617 290	36.987 291	36.371 845	35.183 065	33.499 689
42	38.457 053	37.798 300	37.155 107	35.913 713	34.158 108
43	39.293 330	38.605 274	37.933 826	36.638 921	34.810 008
44	40.126 138	39.408 232	38.708 029	37.358 730	35.455 454
45	40.955 490	40.207 196	39.477 742	38.073 181	36.094 508
46	41.781 401	41.002 185	40.242 991	38.782 314	36.727 236
47	42.603 885	41.793 219	41.003 803	39.486 168	37.353 699
48	43.422 956	42.580 318	41.760 201	40.184 782	37.973 959
49	44.238 628	43.363 500	42.512 213	40.878 195	38.588 079
50	45.050 916	44.142 786	43.259 864	41.566 447	39.196 118

$$\frac{1 - (1 + r)^{-n}}{r}$$

n	$\frac{5}{12}\%$	$\frac{1}{2}\%$	$\frac{7}{12}\%$	$\frac{3}{4}\%$	1%
51	45.859 834	44.918 195	44.003 179	42.249 575	39.798 136
52	46.665 394	45.689 747	44.742 183	42.927 618	40.394 194
53	47.467 613	46.457 459	45.476 901	43.600 614	40.984 351
54	48.266 502	47.221 353	46.207 358	44.268 599	41.568 664
55	49.062 077	47.981 445	46.933 579	44.931 612	42.147 192
56	49.854 350	48.737 757	47.655 588	45.589 689	42.719 992
57	50.643 337	49.490 305	48.373 410	46.242 868	43.287 121
58	51.429 049	50.239 109	49.087 069	46.891 184	43.848 635
59	52.211 501	50.984 189	49.796 588	47.534 674	44.404 589
60	52.990 706	51.725 561	50.501 994	48.173 374	44.955 038
61	53.766 678	52.463 245	51.203 308	48.807 319	45.500 038
62	54.539 431	53.197 258	51.900 554	49.436 545	46.039 642
63	55.308 977	53.927 620	52.593 757	50.061 086	46.573 903
64	56.075 330	54.654 348	53.282 940	50.680 979	47.102 874
65	56.838 502	55.377 461	53.968 126	51.296 257	47.626 608
66	57.598 509	56.096 976	54.649 338	51.906 955	48.145 156
67	58.355 361	56.812 912	55.326 600	52.513 107	48.658 571
68	59.109 074	57.525 285	55.999 934	53.114 746	49.166 901
69	59.859 658	58.234 115	56.669 362	53.711 907	49.670 199
70	60.607 129	58.939 418	57.334 909	54.304 622	50.168 514
71	61.351 497	59.641 212	57.996 595	54.892 925	50.661 895
72	62.092 777	60.339 514	58.654 444	55.476 849	51.150 391
73	62.830 982	61.034 342	59.308 478	56.056 426	51.634 051
74	63.566 123	61.725 714	59.958 719	56.631 688	52.112 922
75	64.298 214	62.413 645	60.605 189	57.202 668	52.587 051
76	65.027 267	63.098 155	61.247 909	57.769 397	53.056 486
77	65.753 295	63 779 258	61.886 902	58.331 908	53.521 274
78	66.476 310	64.456 973	62.522 190	58.890 231	53.981 459
79	67.196 325	65.131 317	63.153 792	59.444 398	54.437 088
80	67.913 353	65.802 305	63.781 732	59.994 440	54.888 206
81	68.627 406	66.469 956	64.406 030	60.540 387	55.334 858
82	69.338 495	67.134 284	65.026 708	61.082 270	55.777 087
83	70.046 634	67.795 308	65.643 786	61.620 119	56.214 937
84	70.751 835	68.453 042	66.257 285	62.153 965	56.648 453
85	71.454 109	69.107 505	66.867 226	62.683 836	57.077 676
86	72.153 470	69.758 711	67.473 630	63.209 763	57.502 650
87	72.849 929	70.406 678	68.076 517	63.731 774	57.923 415
88	73.543 497	71.051 421	68.675 908	64.249 900	58.340 015
89	74.234 188	71.692 956	69.271 822	64.764 169	58.752 490
90	74.922 013	72.331 300	69.864 280	65.274 609	59.160 881
91	75.606 984	72.966 467	70.453 303	65.781 250	59.565 229
92	76.289 113	73.598 475	71.038 909	66.284 119	59.965 573
93	76.968 411	74.227 338	71.621 119	66.783 245	60.361 954
94	77.644 891	74.853 073	72.199 953	67.278 655	60.754 410
95	78.318 563	75.475 694	72.775 430	67.770 377	61.142 980
96	78.989 441	76.095 218	73.347 569	68.258 439	61.527 703
97	79.657 534	76.711 660	73.916 390	68.742 867	61.908 617
98	80.322 856	77.325 035	74.481 912	69.223 689	62.285 759
99	80.985 416	77.935 358	75.044 154	69.700 932	62.659 168
100	81.645 228	78.542 645	75.603 136	70.174 623	63.028 879

TABLE VII. PRESENT VALUE OF 1 PER ANNUM   513

$$\frac{1 - (1 + r)^{-n}}{r}$$

n	$1\frac{1}{8}\%$	$1\frac{1}{4}\%$	$1\frac{1}{2}\%$	$1\frac{3}{4}\%$	2%
1	0.988 875	0.987 654	0.985 222	0.982 801	0.980 392
2	1.966 749	1.963 115	1.955 883	1.948 699	1.941 561
3	2.933 745	2.926 534	2.912 200	2.897 984	2.883 883
4	3.889 982	3.878 058	3.854 385	3.830 943	3.807 729
5	4.835 582	4.817 835	4.782 645	4.747 855	4.713 460
6	5.770 662	5.746 010	5.697 187	5.648 998	5.601 431
7	6.695 339	6.662 726	6.598 214	6.534 641	6.471 991
8	7.609 730	7.568 124	7.485 925	7.405 053	7.325 481
9	8.513 948	8.462 345	8.360 517	8.260 494	8.162 237
10	9.408 107	9.345 526	9.222 185	9.101 223	8.982 585
11	10.292 318	10.217 803	10.071 118	9.927 492	9.786 848
12	11.166 693	11.079 312	10.907 505	10.739 550	10.575 341
13	12.031 340	11.930 185	11.731 532	11.537 641	11.348 374
14	12.886 369	12.770 553	12.543 382	12.322 006	12.106 249
15	13.731 885	13.600 546	13.343 233	13.092 880	12.849 264
16	14.567 995	14.420 292	14.131 264	13.850 497	13.577 709
17	15.394 804	15.229 918	14.907 649	14.595 083	14.291 872
18	16.212 414	16.029 549	15.672 561	15.326 863	14.992 031
19	17.020 928	16.819 308	16.426 168	16.046 057	15.678 462
20	17.820 448	17.599 316	17.168 639	16.752 881	16.351 433
21	18.611 074	18.369 695	17.900 137	17.447 549	17.011 209
22	19.392 904	19.130 563	18 620 824	18 130 269	17.658 048
23	20.166 036	19.882 037	19.330 861	18.801 248	18.292 204
24	20.930 567	20.624 235	20.030 405	19.460 686	18.913 926
25	21.686 593	21.357 269	20.719 611	20.108 782	19.523 456
26	22.434 208	22.081 253	21.398 632	20.745 732	20.121 036
27	23.173 506	22.796 299	22.067 617	21.371 726	20.706 898
28	23.904 579	23.502 518	22.726 717	21.986 955	21.281 272
29	24.627 520	24.200 018	23.376 076	22.591 602	21.844 385
30	25.342 418	24.888 906	24.015 838	23.185 849	22.396 456
31	26.049 362	25.569 290	24.646 146	23.769 877	22.937 702
32	26.748 442	26.241 274	25.267 139	24.343 859	23 468 335
33	27.439 745	26.904 962	25.878 954	24.907 970	23.988 564
34	28.123 357	27.560 456	26.481 728	25.462 378	24.498 592
35	28.799 365	28.207 858	27.075 595	26.007 251	24.998 619
36	29.467 851	28.847 267	27.660 684	26.542 753	25.488 842
37	30.128 901	29.478 783	28.237 127	27.069 045	25.969 453
38	30.782 597	30.102 501	28.805 052	27.586 285	26.440 641
39	31.429 020	30.718 520	29.364 583	28.094 629	26.902 589
40	32.068 253	31.326 933	29.915 845	28.594 230	27.355 479
41	32.700 373	31.927 835	30.458 961	29.085 238	27.799 489
42	33.325 462	32.521 319	30.994 050	29.567 801	28.234 794
43	33.943 596	33.107 475	31.521 232	30.042 065	28.661 562
44	34.554 854	33.686 395	32.040 622	30.508 172	29.079 963
45	35.159 312	34.258 168	32.552 337	30.966 263	29.490 160
46	35.757 045	34.822 882	33.056 490	31.416 474	29.892 314
47	36.348 129	35.380 624	33.553 192	31.858 943	30.286 582
48	36.932 637	35.931 481	34.042 554	32.293 801	30.673 120
49	37.510 642	36.475 537	34.524 683	32.721 181	31.052 078
50	38.082 217	37.012 876	34.999 688	33.141 209	31.423 606

$$\frac{1 - (1 + r)^{-n}}{r}$$

n	$1\frac{1}{8}\%$	$1\frac{1}{4}\%$	$1\frac{1}{2}\%$	$1\frac{3}{4}\%$	2%
51	38.647 433	37.543 581	35.467 673	33.554 014	31.787 849
52	39.206 362	38.067 734	35.928 742	33.959 719	32.144 950
53	39.759 072	38.585 417	36.382 997	34.358 446	32.495 049
54	40.305 634	39.096 708	36.830 539	34.750 316	32.838 283
55	40.846 115	39.601 687	37.271 467	35.135 445	33.174 788
56	41.380 584	40.100 431	37.705 879	35.513 951	33.504 694
57	41.909 106	40.593 019	38.133 871	35.885 947	33.828 131
58	42.431 749	41.079 524	38.555 538	36.251 545	34.145 226
59	42.948 577	41.560 024	38.970 973	36.610 855	34.456 104
60	43.459 656	42.034 592	39.380 269	36.963 986	34.760 887
61	43.965 050	42.503 301	39.783 516	37.311 042	35.059 693
62	44.464 820	42.966 223	40.180 804	37.652 130	35.352 640
63	44.959 031	43.423 430	40.572 221	37.987 351	35.639 843
64	45.447 744	43.874 992	40 957 853	38.316 807	35.921 415
65	45.931 020	44.320 980	41.337 786	38.640 597	36.197 466
66	46.408 920	44.761 462	41.712 105	38.958 817	36.468 103
67	46.881 503	45.196 506	42.080 891	39.271 565	36.733 435
68	47.348 829	45.626 178	42.444 228	39.578 934	36.993 564
69	47.810 955	46.050 547	42.802 195	39.881 016	37.248 592
70	48.267 941	46.469 676	43.154 872	40.177 903	37.498 619
71	48.719 843	46.883 630	43.502 337	40.469 683	37.743 744
72	49.166 717	47.292 474	43.844 667	40.756 445	37.984 063
73	49.608 620	47.696 271	44.181 938	41.038 276	38.219 670
74	50.045 607	48.095 082	44.514 224	41.315 259	38.450 657
75	50.477 733	48.488 970	44.841 600	41.587 478	38.677 114
76	50.905 051	48.877 995	45.164 138	41.855 015	38.899 132
77	51.327 615	49.262 218	45.481 910	42.117 951	39.116 796
78	51.745 478	49.641 696	45.794 985	42.376 364	39.330 192
79	52.158 693	50.016 490	46.103 433	42.630 334	39.539 404
80	52.567 311	50.386 657	46.407 323	42.879 935	39.744 514
81	52.971 383	50.752 254	46.706 723	43.125 243	39.945 602
82	53.370 960	51.113 337	47.001 697	43.366 332	40.142 747
83	53.766 091	51.469 963	47.292 313	43.603 275	40.336 026
84	54.156 827	51.822 185	47.578 633	43.836 142	40.525 516
85	54.543 216	52.170 060	47.860 722	44.065 005	40.711 290
86	54.925 306	52.513 639	48.138 643	44.289 931	40.893 422
87	55.303 145	52.852 977	48.412 456	44.510 989	41.071 982
88	55.676 782	53.188 125	48.682 222	44.728 244	41.247 041
89	56.046 261	53.519 136	48.948 002	44.941 764	41.418 668
90	56.411 630	53.846 060	49.209 855	45.151 610	41.586 929
91	56.772 935	54.168 948	49.467 837	45.357 848	41.751 891
92	57.130 220	54.487 850	49.722 007	45.560 539	41.913 619
93	57.483 530	54.802 815	49.972 421	45.759 743	42.072 175
94	57.832 910	55.113 892	50.219 134	45.955 521	42.227 623
95	58.178 403	55.421 127	50.462 201	46.147 933	42.380 023
96	58.520 052	55.724 570	50.701 675	46.337 035	42.529 434
97	58.857 901	56.024 267	50.937 611	46.522 884	42.675 916
98	59.191 991	56.320 264	51.170 060	46.705 537	42.819 525
99	59.522 364	56.612 606	51.399 074	46.885 049	42.960 319
100	59.849 063	56.901 339	51.624 704	47.061 473	43.098 352

TABLE VII. PRESENT VALUE OF 1 PER ANNUM   515

$$\frac{1 - (1 + r)^{-n}}{r}$$

n	3%	4%	5%	6%	7%
1	0.970 874	0.961 538	0.952 381	0.943 396	0.934 579
2	1.913 470	1.886 095	1.859 410	1.833 393	1.808 018
3	2.828 611	2.775 091	2.723 248	2.673 012	2.624 316
4	3.717 098	3.629 895	3.545 951	3.465 106	3.387 211
5	4.579 707	4.451 822	4.329 477	4.212 364	4.100 197
6	5.417 191	5.242 137	5.075 692	4.917 324	4.766 540
7	6.230 283	6.002 055	5.786 373	5.582 381	5.389 289
8	7.019 692	6.732 745	6.463 213	6.209 794	5.971 299
9	7.786 109	7.435 332	7.107 822	6.801 692	6.515 232
10	8.530 203	8.110 896	7.721 735	7.360 087	7.023 582
11	9.252 624	8.760 477	8.306 414	7.886 875	7.498 674
12	9.954 004	9.385 074	8.863 252	8.383 844	7.942 686
13	10.634 955	9.985 648	9.393 573	8.852 683	8.357 651
14	11.296 073	10.563 123	9.898 641	9.294 984	8.745 468
15	11.937 935	11.118 387	10.379 658	9.712 249	9.107 914
16	12.561 102	11.652 296	10.837 770	10.105 895	9.446 649
17	13.166 118	12.165 669	11.274 066	10.477 260	9.763 223
18	13.753 513	12.659 297	11.689 587	10.827 603	10.059 087
19	14.323 799	13.133 939	12.085 321	11.158 116	10.335 595
20	14.877 475	13.590 326	12.462 210	11.469 921	10.594 014
21	15.415 024	14.029 160	12.821 153	11.764 077	10.835 527
22	15.936 917	14.451 115	13.163 003	12.041 582	11.061 240
23	16.443 608	14.856 842	13.488 574	12.303 379	11.272 187
24	16.935 542	15.246 963	13.798 642	12.550 358	11.469 334
25	17.413 148	15.622 080	14.093 945	12.783 356	11.653 583
26	17.876 842	15.982 769	14.375 185	13.003 166	11.825 779
27	18.327 031	16.329 586	14.643 034	13.210 534	11.986 709
28	18.764 108	16.663 063	14.898 127	13.406 164	12.137 111
29	19.188 455	16.983 715	15.141 074	13.590 721	12.277 674
30	19.600 441	17.292 033	15.372 451	13.764 831	12.409 041
31	20.000 428	17.588 494	15.592 811	13.929 086	12.531 814
32	20.388 766	17.873 551	15.802 677	14.084 043	12.646 555
33	20.765 792	18.147 646	16.002 549	14.230 230	12.753 790
34	21.131 837	18.411 198	16.192 904	14.368 141	12.854 009
35	21.487 220	18.664 613	16.374 194	14.498 246	12.947 672
36	21.832 252	18.908 282	16.546 852	14.620 987	13.035 208
37	22.167 235	19.142 579	16.711 287	14.736 780	13.117 017
38	22.492 462	19.367 864	16.867 893	14.846 019	13.193 473
39	22.808 215	19.584 485	17.017 041	14.949 075	13.264 928
40	23.114 772	19.792 774	17.159 086	15.046 297	13.331 709
41	23.412 400	19.993 052	17.294 368	15.138 016	13.394 120
42	23.701 359	20.185 627	17.423 208	15.224 543	13.452 449
43	23.981 902	20.370 795	17.545 912	15.306 173	13.506 962
44	24.254 274	20.548 841	17.662 773	15.383 182	13.557 908
45	24.518 713	20.720 040	17.774 070	15.455 832	13.605 522
46	24.775 449	20.884 654	17.880 066	15.524 370	13.650 020
47	25.024 708	21.042 936	17.981 016	15.589 028	13.691 608
48	25.266 707	21.195 131	18.077 158	15.650 027	13.730 474
49	25.501 657	21.341 472	18.168 722	15.707 572	13.766 799
50	25.729 764	21.482 185	18.255 925	15.761 861	13.800 746

$$\frac{1 - (1 + r)^{-n}}{r}$$

n	3%	4%	5%	6%	7%
51	25.951 227	21.617 485	18.338 977	15.813 076	13.832 473
52	26.166 240	21.747 582	18.418 073	15.861 393	13.862 124
53	26.374 990	21.872 675	18.493 403	15.906 974	13.889 836
54	26.577 660	21.992 957	18.565 146	15.949 976	13.915 735
55	26.774 428	22.108 612	18.633 472	15.990 543	13.939 939
56	26.965 464	22.219 819	18.698 545	16.028 814	13.962 560
57	27.150 936	22.326 749	18.760 519	16.064 919	13.983 701
58	27.331 005	22.429 567	18.819 542	16.098 980	14.003 458
59	27.505 831	22.528 430	18.875 754	16.131 113	14.021 924
60	27.675 564	22.623 490	18.929 290	16.161 428	14.039 181
61	27.840 353	22.714 894	18.980 276	16.190 026	14.055 309
62	28.000 343	22.802 783	19.028 834	16.217 006	14.070 383
63	28.155 673	22.887 291	19.075 080	16.242 458	14.084 470
64	28.306 478	22.968 549	19.119 124	16.266 470	14.097 635
65	28.452 892	23.046 682	19.161 070	16.289 123	14.109 940
66	28.595 040	23.121 810	19.201 019	16.310 493	14.121 439
67	28.733 049	23.194 048	19.239 066	16.330 654	14.132 186
68	28.867 038	23.263 507	19.275 301	16.349 673	14.142 230
69	28.997 124	23.330 296	19.309 810	16.367 617	14.151 617
70	29.123 421	23.394 515	19.342 677	16.384 544	14.160 389
71	29.246 040	23.456 264	19.373 978	16.400 513	14.168 588
72	29.365 088	23.515 639	19.403 788	16.415 578	14.176 251
73	29.480 667	23.572 730	19.432 179	16.429 791	14.183 412
74	29.592 881	23.627 625	19.459 218	16.443 199	14.190 104
75	29.701 826	23.680 408	19.484 970	16.455 848	14.196 359
76	29.807 598	23.731 162	19.509 495	16.467 781	14.202 205
77	29.910 290	23.779 963	19.532 853	16.479 039	14.207 668
78	30.009 990	23.826 888	19.555 098	16.489 659	14.212 774
79	30.106 786	23.872 008	19.576 284	16.499 679	14.217 546
80	30.200 763	23.915 392	19.596 460	16.509 131	14.222 005
81	30.292 003	23.957 108	19.615 677	16.518 048	14 226 173
82	30.380 586	23.997 219	19.633 978	16.526 460	14.230 069
83	30.466 588	24.035 787	19.651 407	16.534 396	14 233 709
84	30.550 086	24.072 872	19.668 007	16.541 883	14.237 111
85	30.631 151	24 108 531	19.683 816	16.548 947	14 240 291
86	30 709 855	24 142 818	19 698 873	16 555 610	14 243 262
87	30.786 267	24.175 787	19 713 212	16.561 896	14.246 040
88	30.860 454	24.207 487	19.726 869	16.567 827	14.248 635
89	30.932 479	24.237 969	19.739 875	16.573 421	14.251 061
90	31.002 407	24.267 278	19.752 262	16.578 699	14.253 328
91	31.070 298	24.295 459	19 764 059	16.583 679	14.255 447
92	31.136 212	24.322 557	19 775 294	16.588 376	14.257 427
93	31.200 206	24.348 612	19.785 994	16 592 808	14.259 277
94	31.262 336	24.373 666	19.796 185	16.596 988	14.261 007
95	31.322 656	24.397 756	19 805 891	16.600 932	14.262 623
96	31.381 219	24.420 919	19.815 134	16.604 653	14.264 134
97	31.438 077	24.443 191	19.823 937	16.608 163	14.265 546
98	31.493 279	24.464 607	19.832 321	16 611 475	14.266 865
99	31.546 872	24.485 199	19.840 306	16.614 599	14.268 098
100	31.598 905	24.504 999	19.847 910	16.617 546	14.269 251

ANSWERS TO ODD-NUMBERED EXERCISES

CHAPTER I

Section 3

1. **a.** p: Jack is late; q: I am going to town; $p \wedge q$.
   b p: Mathematics is difficult; q: English is easy; $p \vee q$.
   d. p: John is studious; q: He will pass his French exam; $p \rightarrow q$.
   f. p: Smith is dull; q: Jones is happy; $p \wedge (\sim q)$.
3. **(d)** and **(f)**.
5. **a.** History is difficult and Math is uninteresting.
   History is difficult or Math is uninteresting.
   If History is difficult, Math is uninteresting.
   If Math is uninteresting, then history is difficult.
   c. 7 is a prime and $2 + 3 = 6$.
   7 is a prime or $2 + 3 = 6$.
   If 7 is a prime, then $2 + 3 = 6$.
   If $2 + 3 = 6$, then 7 is a prime.
   e. 7 is not a prime and $2 + 3 = 6$.
   7 is not a prime or $2 + 3 = 6$.
   If 7 is not a prime, then $2 + 3 = 6$.
   If $2 + 3 = 6$, then 7 is not a prime.
7. **a.** The diagonals of some rectangles are not perpendicular.
   c. The lines are parallel.
   e. Some blondes are not beautiful.
   g. All triangles are isosceles.

517

9.

p	q	$p \to q$	$\sim q$	$\sim p$	$\sim q \to \sim p$
T	T	T	F	F	T
T	F	F	T	F	F
F	T	T	F	T	T
F	F	T	T	T	T

11.

p	q	$p \wedge q$	$\sim(p \wedge q)$	$\sim p$	$\sim q$	$(\sim p) \vee (\sim q)$
T	T	T	F	F	F	F
T	F	F	T	F	T	T
F	T	F	T	T	F	T
F	F	F	T	T	T	T

13.

p	q	r	$p \wedge r$	$q \wedge r$	$p \vee r$	$q \vee r$	$p \wedge (q \wedge r)$	$p \wedge (q \vee r)$	$p \vee (q \wedge r)$
T	T	T	T	T	T	T	T	T	T
T	T	F	F	F	T	T	F	T	T
T	F	T	T	F	T	T	F	T	T
T	F	F	F	F	T	F	F	F	T
F	T	T	F	T	T	T	F	F	T
F	T	F	F	F	F	T	F	F	F
F	F	T	F	F	T	T	F	F	F
F	F	F	F	F	F	F	F	F	F

15. 2^4; 2^n.

Section 4

1.

p	q	$p \to q$	$q \to p$	$(p \to q) \wedge (q \to p)$	$p \leftrightarrow q$
T	T	T	T	T	T
T	F	F	T	F	F
F	T	T	F	F	F
F	F	T	T	T	T

3.

p	q	$p \leftrightarrow q$	$\sim(p \leftrightarrow q)$	$\sim q$	$p \leftrightarrow (\sim q)$	$\sim p$	$\sim p \leftrightarrow q$
T	T	T	F	F	F	F	F
T	F	F	T	T	T	F	T
F	T	F	T	F	T	T	T
F	F	T	F	T	F	T	F

5. No. The husband's statement is equivalent to the statement "If I do not get a raise I will not buy you a car."

7. **a.** $p: 7x + 3 = 10$; $q: x = 1$; $p \to q$.
  c. $p:$ a triangle is a right triangle; $q:$ no angle is greater than $90°$; $p \to q$.
  e. $p:$ a triangle is equiangular; $q:$ a triangle is equilateral; $p \leftrightarrow q$.

Section 7

1. **a.** Finite; $M = 26$.
  c. Finite; $M = 9$.

  e. Not well defined.

  g. Finite; $M = 1$.

3. **a.** {Maine, Md., Mass., Mich., Minn., Miss., Mo., Mont.}.

  c. {1, 4, 9, 16, 25, 36, 49}.

  f. {Ala., Ga., Ky., La., Miss., Mo., N.C., Va.}.

5. **a.** T.   **c.** F.   **e.** T.   **g.** F.

Section 11

1. **a.** Equal.   **c.** Equivalent.   **e.** Equivalent.

3. {1}, {2}, {3}, {4}, {1, 2}, {1, 3}, {1, 4}, {2, 3}, {2, 4}, {3, 4}, {1, 2, 3}, {1, 2, 4}, {1, 3, 4}, {2, 3, 4}, {1, 2, 3, 4}, { } $\cdots$ 16.

5.

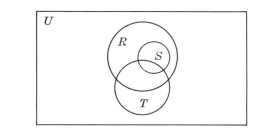

7.

$$
\begin{array}{ccccc}
1 & 2 & 3 & \cdots & n & \cdots \\
\updownarrow & \updownarrow & \updownarrow & & \updownarrow \\
5 & 10 & 15 & \cdots & 5n & \cdots
\end{array}
$$

  $T \sim N$ and $T \subset N$ is true.

9. $U = $ {all triangles}, $R = $ {all right triangles}.

  $I = $ {all isosceles triangles}, $E = $ {all equilateral triangles}.

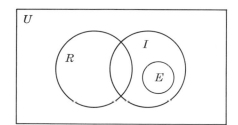

11. **b.** Yes.   **f.** Yes; $C = $ {1, 2, 3, 4, 5}, $A = $ {1, 3, 5}, $B = $ {2, 4}.

  d. Yes.

17. **a.**

$$
\begin{array}{ccccc}
1 & 2 & 3 & \cdots & n & \cdots \\
\updownarrow & \updownarrow & \updownarrow & & \updownarrow \\
7 & 14 & 21 & \cdots & 7n & \cdots
\end{array}
$$

  c.

$$
\begin{array}{ccccc}
1 & 2 & 3 & \cdots & n & \cdots \\
\updownarrow & \updownarrow & \updownarrow & & \updownarrow \\
\frac{1}{2} & \frac{2}{3} & \frac{3}{4} & \cdots & \dfrac{n}{n+1} & \cdots
\end{array}
$$

  e.

$$
\begin{array}{ccccccccc}
1 & 2 & 3 & 4 & 5 & 6 & \cdots & n & \cdots \\
\updownarrow & \updownarrow & \updownarrow & \updownarrow & \updownarrow & \updownarrow & & \updownarrow \\
4 & 9 & 14 & 19 & 24 & 29 & \cdots & 5n - 1 & \cdots
\end{array}
$$

Section 12

1. a. $\{1, 2, 3, 4, 5, 7, 9\}$.   **g.** $\{1, 2, 3, 4, 5, 7\}$.
c. $\{2, 3, 5, 6, 7, 8, 9\}$.   **i.** $\{2, 3, 5\}$.
e. $\{5, 7\}$.

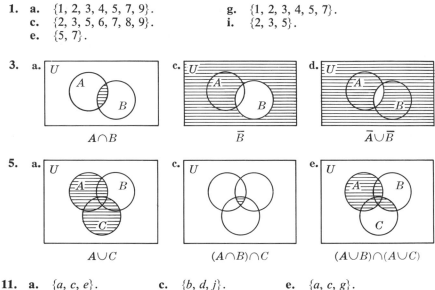

3. a. $A \cap B$ **c.** $\bar{B}$ **d.** $\bar{A} \cup \bar{B}$

5. a. $A \cup C$ **c.** $(A \cap B) \cap C$ **e.** $(A \cup B) \cap (A \cup C)$

11. a. $\{a, c, e\}$.   **c.** $\{b, d, j\}$.   **e.** $\{a, c, g\}$.
15. a. 2.   **b.** 7.   **c.** 14.   **d.** 10.   **e.** 13.

Section 13

1. a. $A \times B = \{(3, 2), (3, 7), (4, 2), (4, 7), (5, 2), (5, 7)\}$.
   $B \times A = \{(2, 3), (2, 4), (2, 5), (7, 3), (7, 4), (7, 5)\}$.
   $A \times A = \{(3, 3), (3, 4), (3, 5), (4, 3), (4, 4), (4, 5), (5, 3), (5, 4), (5, 5)\}$.
3. $\{H, T\} \times \{H, T\} = \{(H, H), (H, T), (T, H), (T, T)\}$.
5. $A = B$.
7. a. $\{(1, 1), (1, 2), (1, 3), (1, 4), (2, 1), (2, 2), (2, 3), (2, 4), (3, 1), (3, 2), (3, 3), (3, 4)\}$.
   b. $\{(1, 2), (1, 4)\}$.   **e.** $\{\ \}$.
   c. $\{(1, 1), (2, 2), (3, 3), (4, 4)\}$.   **f.** $\{(4, 1), (4, 2), (5, 1), (5, 2)\}$.
   d. $\{(1, 3), (2, 2), (3, 1)\}$.
9. a. $\{(\text{John, Alice}), (\text{John, Mary}), (\text{Paul, Alice}), (\text{Paul, Mary})\}$.
   b. $\{(\text{John, Alice}), (\text{John, Mary}), (\text{Paul, Alice}), (\text{Paul, Mary})\}$;
   $\{(\text{John, Alice}), (\text{John, Mary}), (\text{Paul, Alice})\}$;
   $\{(\text{John, Alice}), (\text{John, Mary}), (\text{Paul, Mary})\}$;
   $\{(\text{John, Alice}), (\text{Paul, Alice}), (\text{Paul, Mary})\}$;
   $\{(\text{John, Mary}), (\text{Paul, Alice}), (\text{Paul, Mary})\}$;
   $\{(\text{John, Alice}), (\text{John, Mary})\}$;
   $\{(\text{John, Alice}), (\text{Paul, Alice})\}$;
   $\{(\text{John, Alice}), (\text{Paul, Mary})\}$;
   $\{(\text{John, Mary}), (\text{Paul, Alice})\}$;
   $\{(\text{John, Alice}), (\text{Paul, Mary})\}$;
   $\{(\text{Paul, Alice}), (\text{Paul, Mary})\}$;
   $\{(\text{John, Alice})\}$;
   $\{(\text{John, Mary})\}$;
   $\{(\text{Paul, Alice})\}$;
   $\{(\text{Paul, Mary})\}$;
   $\{\ \}$.

Section 15

1. **a.** $\{2, 5, 7\}$.
   c. $\{-4\}$.
   e. {Cardinals, Dodgers, Mets, Cubs, Braves, Astros, Giants, Reds}.
3. **a.** For all prime numbers x greater than 2, $x + 1$ is an even integer.
   c. For all x such that $x > 2$, then $x^2 > 4$.
   e. For all x, x an odd integer, x^2 is an odd integer.
5. **a.** $5x = 10$. **c.** $x + 5 = x + 7$.
   b. $(x - 1)(x - 2) = 0$. **d.** $x < 2$.
7. **a.** $\forall_x [x$ a prime; $x + 1$ is not a prime number].
   c. $\forall_x (x^2 \neq 1)$.
   e. $\forall_x [1 - 17x - 5x^2$ is negative].

CHAPTER II

Section 2

1. $\{2, 3, 5, 7, 11, 13, 17, 19, 23, 29, 31, 37, 41, 43, 47, 53, 59, 61, 67, 71, 73, 79,$
   $83, 87, 89, 91, 97\}$.
3. **a.** 2, 4. **b.** 2, 5, 10. **c.** 5, 25.
5. **(a), (b), (c), (d), (e)** and **(f)** are rational; **(g)** is irrational since it is a non-repeating infinite decimal.
11. $N = $ {all natural numbers},
    $I = $ {all integers},
    $J = $ {all rational numbers},
    $K = $ {all irrational numbers}.

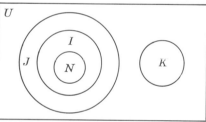

Section 4

1. $a + b + c = (a + b) + c$ Definition 2.9,
   $\qquad\qquad = a + (b + c)$ Axiom 5,
   $\qquad\qquad = a + (c + b)$ Axiom 3,
   $\qquad\qquad = (c + b) + a$ Axiom 3,
   $\qquad\qquad = c + b + a$ Definition 2.9.
3. Axiom 7.
9. **a.** $\{3, 6, 9, 12, \cdots\}$. **e.** {all the integers}.
   c. $\{1, 2, 3, \cdots\}$. **g.** {all the integers}.
11. **a.** $14, -8, 4, 2$. **b.** Yes. **c.** False.
13. **a.** $x(x + y)$. **c.** $(x + a)(y + z)$. **e.** $8(7 + 11)$.
15. No. Division by zero not valid.

Section 7

1. $a + c = b + c$, $b + c = b + d$, then $a + c = b + d$.
3. $-(a - b) = (-1)[a + (-b)] = (-1)(a) + (-1)(-b) = -a + b$.
5. **a.** 4. **e.** 30. **i.** 0.
   c. -231. **g.** Impossible. **k.** 16.

7. a. (-15).   **c.** -16.   **e.** 21.   **g.** -12.   **i.** 10.

9. $-0 = (-0) + 0, (-0) + 0 = 0, 0 = 0 + 0, (-0) + 0 = 0 + 0, (-0) = 0,$
$-0 = 0.$

11. $0 - a = 0 + (-a) = (-a) = -a.$

13. No.

15. 924 lots, 80 lots.

Section 10

1. a. $\frac{7}{12}$.   **c.** $\frac{3}{7}$.   **e.** $\frac{1}{6}$.   **g.** $\frac{15}{52}$.

3. a. $\frac{11}{14}$.   **c.** $\frac{1}{6}$.   **e.** $\frac{5}{12}$.   **g.** $\frac{121}{105}$.

5. a. 1.   **c.** $\frac{9}{5}$.   **e.** 1.

7. a. $a + (b - c)$.   **c.** $a + b + (-c - d)$.

9. a. $-\dfrac{7}{3}$.   **c.** -2.   **e.** $\dfrac{a - b}{a + b}$.

Section 13

1. b. $-2 < 5$.   **d.** $-2 < 1$.   **f.** $12.3 < 12\frac{1}{3}$.   **h.** $-8 < 0$.

3. a. $ac < bc$.   **c.** $bc < ac$.   **e.** $ac < bc$.

12. $5, 8, \frac{3}{4}, \pi, 189, 17, 2.5$.

Section 14

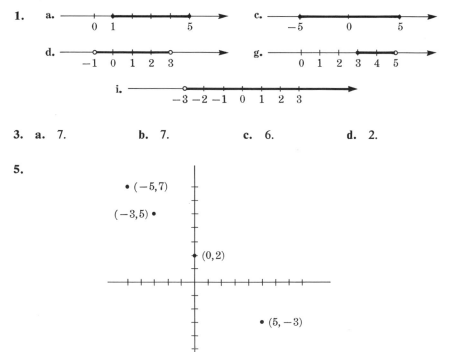

3. a. 7.   **b.** 7.   **c.** 6.   **d.** 2.

5.

They all lie on same straight line.

7. a. On a line through the origin and making 45° angle with x-axis.
   b. On a straight line through the origin but not the 45° line.

Section 15

1. a. $9 + 14i.$ **c.** $-3 + 6i.$ **e.** $8 + 0i.$ **g.** $7 - 8i.$
3. a. $-7 + 26i.$ **c.** $2.$ **e.** $8 - 27i.$ **g.** $2i.$
6. a. $x = 2, y = -2.$ **c.** $x = 4, y = 7.$
   b. $x = 3, y = 2.$ **d.** $x = 1, y = -3.$
9.

number	additive inverse	conjugate
$2 + 3i$	$-2 - 3i$	$2 - 3i$
$5 - 7i$	$-5 + 7i$	$5 + 7i$
$-4 - 2i$	$4 + 2i$	$-4 + 2i$
$1/i$	i	i
$\dfrac{2 + i}{1 - i}$	$-\dfrac{1}{2} - \dfrac{3}{2}i$	$\dfrac{1}{2} - \dfrac{3}{2}i$

CHAPTER III

Section 2

1. $6xy.$ **5.** $4a^2 + 5a - 1.$ **9.** $-14x + 6y.$
3. $-7y + 3z.$ **7.** $3x^2 + 3x + 7.$ **11.** $2x^2 - 9xy - 2y^2.$

13. a. $8.$ **b.** $8.$ **c.** $-4.$ **d.** $-12.$
15. $x^2 - 16x - 8.$ **21.** $9 - 4x.$
17. $2x^2 - 8xy + 3y^2 - x.$ **23.** $8, 9, 81, -8, 0, -1, 1024.$
19. $6x - 11y.$

Section 3

1. a. $256.$ **e.** $-\frac{1}{3}.$ **i.** $3.$
   c. $\frac{1}{25}.$ **g.** $-16.$ **k.** $64.$

3. a. $x^{10}.$ **c.** $x^3.$ **e.** $1.$ **g.** $x^{10}.$ **i.** $\dfrac{a}{b^4}.$

5. a. $2\sqrt{5}.$ **e.** $-3\sqrt[3]{2}.$ **i.** $20\sqrt{2}.$
   c. $2\sqrt[3]{3}.$ **g.** $9\sqrt{2}.$ **k.** $2\sqrt{17}.$

7. a. $2.$ **c.** $\frac{1}{2}.$ **e.** $\frac{4}{7}\sqrt{2}.$ **g.** $|x|.$ **i.** $3\sqrt{3}.$

Section 4

1. $72a^7.$
3. $12a^4b^5.$
5. $3x^3y - 3x^2y^3 + 3x^2y.$
7. $2x^4 - 7x^3y + 5x^2y^2 - 3xy^3 + 3y^4.$
9. $7x^2 + 39xy - 18y^2.$
11. $8x^3 - 27y^3.$
13. $a^2 - 2ab + b^2 - 4.$
15. $9x^2 - 25y^2.$

17. $60x^2 + 44xy - 56y^2.$
19. $3 - x.$
21. $x^4 - 5x^3 + 3x^2 + 20x - 28.$
23. $4x^2 - 20xy + 25y^2.$
25. $9x^2 + 24x + 16.$
27. $4x^4 - 100y^4.$
29. $6xy + 15x^2y^4.$
31. $x - y.$

Section 5

3. $3ax(1 - 3ax)$.

5. $5(3x - 4y)(3x + 4y)$.

7. $(2x - 5y)^2$.

9. $(x - y)(x^2 + xy + y^2)$.

11. $(x - 2)(x + 1)$.

13. $(x - 2)(x + 2)(x^2 + 4)$.

15. $(x + y - 2)(x + y + 2)$.

17. $(x - 2)(x - 3)$.

19. $(x - 6)(x + 1)$.

21. $(10x - 7)^2$.

23. $(x - y)(x + y)(x^2 + xy + y^2)(x^2 - xy + y^2)$.

25. $x^2(x - 3)(x + 1)$.

27. $(x - 1)(x + 1)(x - 3)(x + 3)$.

29. $(3x - 4y)(2x + 7y)$.

31. $(a + b + c - d)(a + b - c + d)$.

33. $6(x - 2)(x + 1)$.

35. $2m(2m + 1)(4m^2 - 2m + 1)$.

37. $(x - 2)^2(x + 2)$.

39. $(.2x - 1.3y)(.2x + 1.3y)$.

41. $2(x - 9)^2$.

43. $(x - 4)(\sqrt{3}x - \sqrt{2})(\sqrt{3}x + \sqrt{2})$.

45. $(3x - 4)(2x + 5)$.

47. $(4a - 1)(16a^2 + 4a + 1)$.

49. $(x - 2)(x^2 + 5)$.

Section 6

1. $3ax^2$.

3. $-3xy^2$.

5. $2x - 1$.

7. $2x + 10$, $R = 5$.

9. $x^3 - 9x^2 + 23x - 15$.

11. $x^2 + 2x + 2$.

13. $x^3 + 11x^2 + 39x + 45$.

15. $x^3 + 2x - 5$.

17. $4x^2 - 4xy + y^2$.

19. $\frac{3}{2}x^2 - \frac{5}{4}x + \frac{3}{8}$, $R = -\frac{5}{8}$.

21. $x^3 - x^2 + x - 1$, $R = 2$.

Section 7

1. $\dfrac{11}{19}$.

3. $\dfrac{3}{11}$.

5. $\dfrac{1}{4}$.

7. $\dfrac{x}{x + 2}$.

9. $\dfrac{x - 2y}{x}$.

11. $x + y$.

13. $\dfrac{7}{10}$.

15. $\dfrac{33}{29}$.

17. $\dfrac{-x + 3y}{6}$.

19. $\dfrac{8x - 1}{12}$.

21. $\dfrac{2}{x + 1}$.

23. $\dfrac{x + 3y}{x^2y}$.

Section 9

1. **a.** 30. **b.** 35. **c.** 2160.

3. **a.** $(k - 1)(k - 2)$. **b.** $\dfrac{1}{k - r}$. **c.** $(k + r + 1)(k + r)$.

5. **a.** 10. **b.** 1. **c.** 45. **d.** 45.

7. $a^3 + 3a^2h + 3ah^2 + h^3$.

9. $a^5 + 5a^4h + 10a^3h^2 + 10a^2h^3 + 5ah^4 + h^5$.

11. $32x^5 - 80x^4y + 80x^3y^2 - 40x^2y^3 + 10xy^4 - y^5$.

13. $a^5 - 10a^4b + 40a^3b^2 - 80a^2b^3 + 80ab^4 - 32b^5$.

15. $a^8 + 4a^6b + 6a^4b^2 + 4a^2b^3 + b^4$.

17. $729x^6 - 1458x^5y + 1215x^4y^2 - 540x^3y^3 + 135x^2y^4 - 18xy^5 + y^6$.

19. $x^{10} - \dfrac{5x^7}{2} + \dfrac{5x^4}{2} - \dfrac{5x}{4} + \dfrac{5}{16x^2} - \dfrac{1}{32x^5}$.

21. $x^8 + 8x^6\sqrt{x} + 28x^5 + 56x^3\sqrt{x} + 70x^2 + 56\sqrt{x} + \dfrac{28}{x} + \dfrac{8}{x^2\sqrt{x}} + \dfrac{1}{x^4}$.

23. $a^{20} - 20a^{19}b + 190a^{18}b^2 - 1140a^{17}b^3 + \cdots$.

25. $1 - 12x^2 + 66x^4 - 220x^6 + \cdots$.

27. 1.21899. **31.** 1.80611. **35.** 2.98597.

29. 1.50363. **33.** 1.64463.

CHAPTER IV

Section 4

1. $x^2 + 4x + 4$. **9.** $x = 5$. **17.** $x = -2$.

3. $\frac{9}{15}x$. **11.** $y = 3$. **19.** $x = 1$.

5. $(x - 3)(x + 2)$. **13.** $x = -9$. **21.** $x = \frac{384}{67}$.

7. $(2a - 5b)(a + b)$. **15.** $x = 1$.

Section 6

1. $3, -2$. **9.** $1, \frac{2}{3}$. **17.** $2, \frac{1}{2}$. **25.** $\frac{1}{5}, \frac{4}{3}$.

3. $0, \frac{5}{3}$. **11.** $-2, -5$. **19.** $4, -\frac{1}{3}$. **27.** $\frac{7}{2}, -2$.

5. ± 7. **13.** $1, \frac{5}{2}$. **21.** $-3, -3$. **29.** $-\frac{3}{2}, -\frac{2}{3}$.

7. $-\dfrac{3}{2}, -\dfrac{3}{2}$. **15.** $a, -b$. **23.** $1, \dfrac{5}{2}$. **31.** $\dfrac{1}{a}, -a$.

33. **a.** $x^2 - 2x - 3 = 0$. **e.** $x^2 - (m + n)x + mn = 0$.

   c. $x^2 + 4x + 4 = 0$. **g.** $x^2 - 6x + 4 = 0$.

Section 7

1. 4. **9.** $-2 \pm \sqrt{6}$. **17.** $-1 \pm \sqrt{2}$.

3. $\dfrac{4}{9}$. **11.** $\dfrac{2 \pm \sqrt{7}}{3}$. **19.** $\dfrac{a}{2}(-1 \pm \sqrt{5})$.

5. $\dfrac{25}{36}$. **13.** $\dfrac{-5 \pm \sqrt{61}}{6}$. **21.** $\dfrac{11 \pm \sqrt{61}}{6}$.

7. $\dfrac{a^2}{4}$. **15.** $\dfrac{-3 \pm \sqrt{21}}{2}$. **23.** $1 \pm 2i$.

Section 8

1. $\dfrac{3 \pm \sqrt{5}}{2}$.

3. $2 \pm i\sqrt{6}$.

5. $6 \pm 3\sqrt{3}$.

7. $2, \dfrac{1}{5}$.

9. $\dfrac{-7 \pm \sqrt{109}}{20}$.

11. $\frac{13}{25}, \frac{1}{24}$.

13. $\dfrac{4 \pm 2i\sqrt{11}}{3}$.

15. $\dfrac{a}{2}, \dfrac{a}{6}$.

17. $-\frac{2}{5}, -\frac{5}{2}$.

19. $\dfrac{4 \pm i\sqrt{26}}{6}$.

21. $\dfrac{-6 \pm 4\sqrt{6}}{4}$.

23. $\dfrac{-5 \pm i\sqrt{71}}{6}$.

25. $x, \dfrac{x-3}{2}$.

27. $1 - x, -2x$.

29. $5 + 2x, 3 + x$.

31. $2x + 3, 2 - x$.

Section 10

1. $D = 9$, real, unequal, rational.
3. $D = 0$, real, equal, rational.
5. $D = -55$, imaginary.
7. $D = 89$, real, unequal, irrational.
9. $D = 20$, but $b = -2i$, roots are imaginary.
11. Imaginary.
13. $D = 0$, real, equal.
15. $D = -36$, imaginary.

17. $k = \pm 4$.
19. $k = \pm 4$.
21. $-2, \frac{7}{3}$.

23. $\pm 3, \pm 2i$.
25. $4, 9$.
27. $\frac{25}{4}$.

29. $\frac{3}{2}, \frac{2}{5}$.
31. $3, \frac{7}{2}$.
33. $5, 3$.

35. $4, -5$.
37. $\frac{7}{4}, 0$.

Section 14

1. 11.
3. -2.
5. -6.
7. Yes.

9. Yes.
11. No.
13. Yes.
15. $q(x) = 4x^2 + 2x + 1, R = 4$.

17. $q(x) = x^3 - 2x^2 + 5x - 10, R = 21$.
19. $q(x) = x^7 - 3x^6 + 9x^5 - 27x^4 + 81x^3 - 243x^2 + 729x - 2187, R = 0$.
21. $q(x) = x^4 + 3x, R = -4$.
23. $q(x) = x^5 - x^4 + x^3 - x^2 + x - 1, R = 2$.

27. $k = 3$.

29. Yes.

Section 18

1. Upper limit 3, lower limit -1.
3. Upper limit 2, lower limit -3.

5. Upper limit 3, lower limit -1.
7. Upper limit 3, lower limit -2.

9. One positive root less than 3; no negative root or two negative roots greater than -1.
11. One positive root not greater than 2, one negative root not less than -2, two nonreal roots.

13. Zero, two, or four positive roots less than 1; no negative roots; zero, two, or four imaginary roots.

15. One negative root greater than -2, four nonreal roots.

Section 19

1. 1, 2, 3.

3. $\frac{2}{3}, \pm i\sqrt{2}$.

5. $-3, \pm 5$.

7. $\pm 1, 5, -2$.

9. $\frac{3}{4}, -\frac{1}{2}, -2, -2$.

11. $\pm 2, \frac{3}{2}$.

13. $\pm \frac{1}{2}, 1 \pm 3i$.

15. $0, 4, -1, -2$.

17. $2, 2, -3$.

19. $2, 2, 2, 3$.

21. $20, \frac{5}{4}(1 \pm \sqrt{33})$.

23. $2, 2, 3, -1, -1$.

25. $1, 1, 1, -\frac{3}{2}$.

27. $6, \dfrac{3 \pm i\sqrt{2}}{2}$.

29. None.

31. $(x + 1)(x - 2)(x - 4)$.

33. $(2x - 1)(2x + 3)(x^2 + 2)$.

35. $(4x + 1)(x^2 + x + 3)$.

37. $(x + 2)(x - 2)(x^2 - 2x + 4)(x^2 + 2x + 4)$.

39. $(2x - 1)(4x^2 + 2x + 1)$.

41. $x^3 - 6x^2 + 11x - 6 = 0$.

43. $x^3 - 2x^2 - 3x + 6 = 0$.

45. $x^4 - 6x^3 + 12x^2 - 6x - 5 = 0$.

47. $6x^3 - 25x^2 + 2x + 8 = 0$.

Section 20

1. $2, -1$.

3. $\frac{1}{2}$.

5. $3, -\frac{2}{5}$.

7. $x = 5$.

9. $x = 3$.

11. $x = 4$.

13. $y = 6$.

15. $x = \frac{13}{3}$.

17. $x = \pm 2$.

19. $-1, -\frac{1}{2}$.

21. $x = -\frac{4}{5}$.

Section 21

1. 6.

3. 7, 10.

5. 5.

7. 10.

9. 4, 20.

11. $\frac{13}{4}$.

13. 4.

15. $x = 3$.

Section 22

1.

(a)

1.

(c)

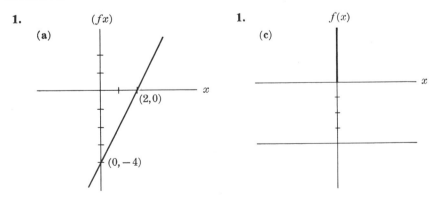

1.   (e) $f(x)$

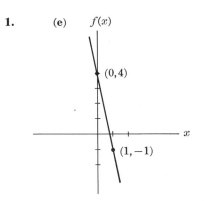

7.

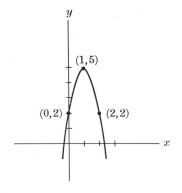

3.

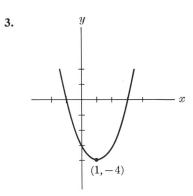

11.

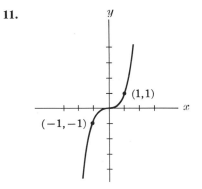

5.

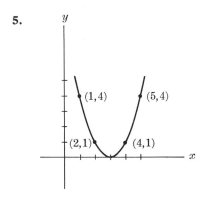

13.

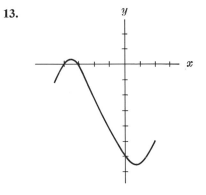

Section 23

1.   2.2, -2.3, -0.4.

3.   1.4, 2.7, -0.7, -1.4.

5.   0.6, two nonreal roots.

7.   2.196.

9.   1.587.

11.   1.565.

Section 25

1. $(-\infty, 2)$

3. $(-\infty, 3]$

5. $(-\infty, -2)$

7. $(3, \infty)$

9. $(-\infty, -3) \cup (3, \infty)$

11. $(-3, 5)$

13. $(-5, 1)$

15. $[-\frac{19}{3}, 1]$

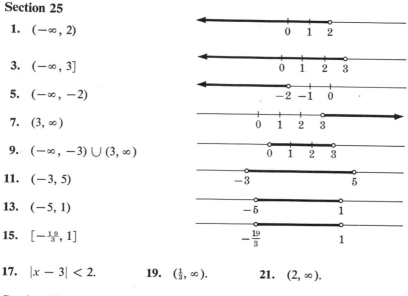

17. $|x - 3| < 2.$ 19. $(\frac{1}{3}, \infty).$ 21. $(2, \infty).$

Section 27

1. $(-3, 2).$
3. $[-\frac{7}{3}, \frac{5}{2}].$
5. $(-2, 5).$
7. $(-\frac{1}{3}, 3).$
9. $(-4, 1).$
11. $(-\infty, \frac{1}{2}) \cup (\frac{1}{2}, \infty).$
13. $(-\infty, \infty).$
15. $(-\infty, 2) \cup (3, \infty).$
17. $(1 - \sqrt{5}, 1 + \sqrt{5}).$

19. $(-\infty, -2) \cup (2, 4).$
21. $(-\infty, -\frac{1}{3}] \cup [\frac{1}{2}, 3].$
23. $(-\frac{1}{2}, 2) \cup (3, \infty).$
25. $(-1, 2).$
27. $(-3, -1) \cup (1, 2) \cup (4, \infty).$
29. $(-\infty, -2) \cup (2, 4).$
31. $(-1, 1) \cup (3, 5).$
33. $(-\infty, \frac{11}{5}) \cup (\frac{5}{2}, 3).$
35. $(-\infty, 0) \cup (\frac{2}{3}, \frac{12}{7}) \cup (2, \infty).$

CHAPTER V

Section 7

1. C is a function. Domain $= \{-5, -3, 0, 1, 3, 5\}$, Range $= \{2\}$.
   D is a function. Domain $= \{5, 8, 10, 13, 15\}$, Range $= \{17, 21, 27, 31, 42\}$.
3. $f(0) = -4, f(-1) = -2, f(a) = 2a^2 - 4, f(\frac{1}{2}) = -3.5, f(-\frac{2}{3}) = -\frac{28}{9}.$
5. $f(0) = 1, f(1) = 0, f(-1) = 0.$
7. Yes. Domain $= \{1, 2, 3\}$, Range $= \{0, 4\}$.
9. a. $x^2 + 2xh + h^2 + 5x + 5h - 3.$ c. $2x + 5 + h.$
   b. $h^2 + 5h + 2xh.$

11. a. $\dfrac{4}{5}.$ b. $\dfrac{4}{5 + h}.$ c. $-\dfrac{4h}{5(5 + h)}.$ d. $-\dfrac{4}{5(5 + h)}.$

13. a. $A = S^2.$ c. $A = \dfrac{S^2}{4}\sqrt{3}.$ e. $S = \pi r^2 + \dfrac{200\pi}{r}.$

15. Yes.   a. 2.1540.   b. 2.1817.

Section 9

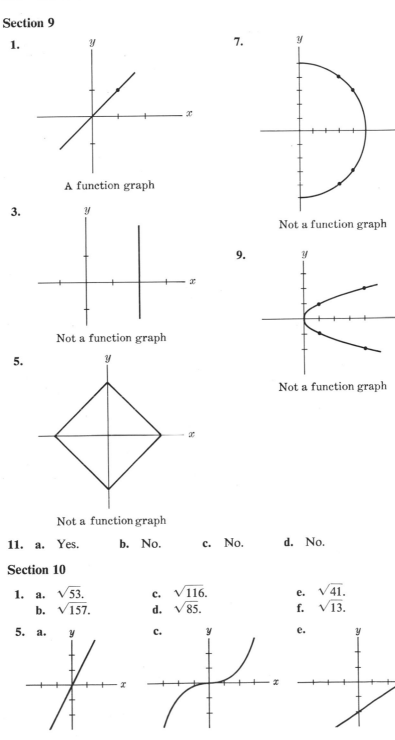

1.

A function graph

3.

Not a function graph

5.

Not a function graph

7.

Not a function graph

9.

Not a function graph

11.   **a.**   Yes.   **b.**   No.   **c.**   No.   **d.**   No.

Section 10

1.   **a.** $\sqrt{53}$.   **c.** $\sqrt{116}$.   **e.** $\sqrt{41}$.
     b. $\sqrt{157}$.   **d.** $\sqrt{85}$.   **f.** $\sqrt{13}$.

5.   **a.**   **c.**   **e.**

7. $3\sqrt{2} + 2\sqrt{2} = 5\sqrt{2}$.

9. **a.** $(-3, 1)$.   **b.** $(8, 5)$.

11. **a.** $c = 1$.   **b.** $c = 7$.

13. 5 units.   **15.** $(3, -2)$ or $(3, 14)$.

Section 11

1. **a.** $m = \frac{3}{4}$.   **c.** $m = -\frac{3}{4}$.   **e.** $m = -\frac{17}{4}$.
   b. $m = 2$.   **d.** $m = \frac{1}{7}$.   **f.** $m = (d - b)/(c - a)$.

3. **a.** $10, \frac{3}{4}, (3, 4)$.   **b.** $\sqrt{136}, \frac{5}{3}, (6, 3)$.

5. **a.**   **c.**   **e.**

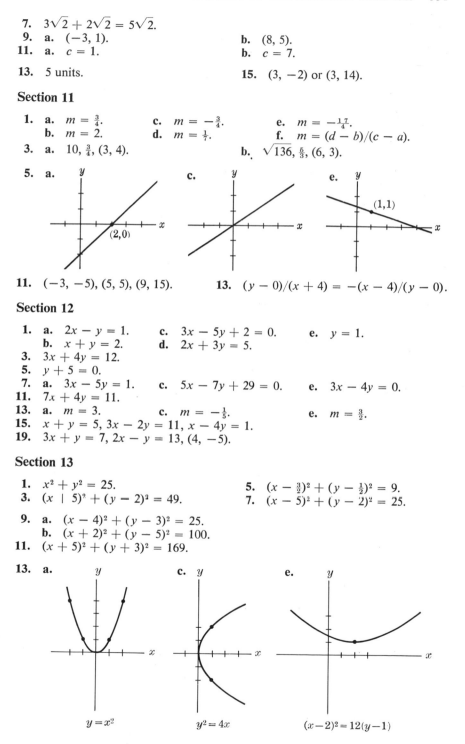

11. $(-3, -5), (5, 5), (9, 15)$.   **13.** $(y - 0)/(x + 4) = -(x - 4)/(y - 0)$.

Section 12

1. **a.** $2x - y = 1$.   **c.** $3x - 5y + 2 = 0$.   **e.** $y = 1$.
   b. $x + y = 2$.   **d.** $2x + 3y = 5$.

3. $3x + 4y = 12$.

5. $y + 5 = 0$.

7. **a.** $3x - 5y = 1$.   **c.** $5x - 7y + 29 = 0$.   **e.** $3x - 4y = 0$.

11. $7x + 4y = 11$.

13. **a.** $m = 3$.   **c.** $m = -\frac{1}{5}$.   **e.** $m = \frac{3}{2}$.

15. $x + y = 5, 3x - 2y = 11, x - 4y = 1$.

19. $3x + y = 7, 2x - y = 13, (4, -5)$.

Section 13

1. $x^2 + y^2 = 25$.   **5.** $(x - \frac{3}{2})^2 + (y - \frac{1}{2})^2 = 9$.

3. $(x + 5)^2 + (y - 2)^2 = 49$.   **7.** $(x - 5)^2 + (y - 2)^2 = 25$.

9. **a.** $(x - 4)^2 + (y - 3)^2 = 25$.
   b. $(x + 2)^2 + (y - 5)^2 = 100$.

11. $(x + 5)^2 + (y + 3)^2 = 169$.

13. **a.**   **c.**   **e.**

$y = x^2$ $y^2 = 4x$ $(x-2)^2 = 12(y-1)$

15. a.

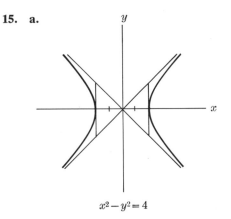

$$x^2 - y^2 = 4$$

d.

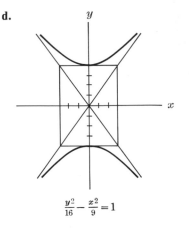

$$\frac{y^2}{16} - \frac{x^2}{9} = 1$$

Section 14

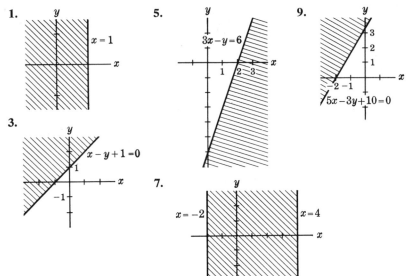

1.

$x = 1$

3.

$x - y + 1 = 0$

5.

$3x - y = 6$

7.

$x = -2$ $x = 4$

9.

$5x - 3y + 10 = 0$

CHAPTER VI

Section 2

1. **a.** $\bar{R} = 7$.   **b.** $\bar{R} = 4$.   **c.** $\bar{R} = 11$.   **d.** $\bar{R} = -2$.

3. **a.** $\bar{R} = 0.55$.   **b.** $R = 0.5$.

5. **a.** $R = 28$ in.³/sec.   **b.** $\bar{R} = 34$ in.³/sec.

7. **a.** 10 deg/min.   **b.** 10 deg/min.   **c.** 10 deg/min.

9. **a.** .02 gal/mph.   **c.** .21 gal/mph.
   b. .12 gal/mph.   **d.** .13 gal/mph.

11. **a.** 27.5 lb/mo.   **c.** 7.5 lb/mo.
   b. 27 lb/mo.   **d.** 23 lb/mo.

Section 3

1. **a.** 32 ft/sec.   **b.** 48 ft/sec.   **c.** 80 ft/sec.
3. No; 10.5 hrs.
5. **a.** 60 mph.   **b.** 150 mph.   **c.** Impossible.

Section 4

1. $(-7 - 2h)$ units/unit.

3. $-\dfrac{4}{25 + 5h} \dfrac{\text{units}}{\text{unit}}$.

5. **a.** 22 ft/sec.   **b.** 25 ft/sec.
7. **a.** 48 ft/sec.   **c.** -272 ft/sec.
   b. 0 ft/sec.   **d.** $(80 - 16h)$ ft/sec.
9. **a.** 8 units/unit.   **b.** $(8 + 2h)$ units/unit.

11. **a.** $-\dfrac{5}{72} \dfrac{\text{hr}}{\text{mph}}$.   **b.** $-\dfrac{25}{2(160 + h)} \dfrac{\text{hr}}{\text{mph}}$.

13. **a.** $-\dfrac{16}{9}$ dynes/cm.   **b.** $-\dfrac{300 + 50h}{9(3 + h)^2}$ dynes/cm.

Section 9

1. -2.   5. 75.   9. 13.   13. $\frac{2}{3}$.   17. $-\frac{3}{2}$.
3. 9.   7. 4.   11. 3.   15. 1.   19. $3x^2$.

Section 14

1. **a.** $(28 - 3h)$ ft/sec.   **b.** 28 ft/sec.

3. **a.** $m = 6x - 5$.   **b.** $m = -1/x^2$.   **c.** $m = \dfrac{1}{(x + 1)^2}$.

5. **a.** $R = -100/x^3$ dynes/cm.   **c.** F is decreasing at $x = 2$.
   b. $R = -12.5$ dynes/cm.
7. $-\frac{3}{4}$ units/unit.
9. **a.** $m = 2$.   **b.** $2x - y = 9$.
11. $A = 36$.
13. **a.** $\overline{A} = -0.4 - 0.07h - 0.002h^2$.   **b.** $A = -0.4$.

CHAPTER VII

Section 2

1. 5.

11. $\frac{1}{2}x^{-1/2}$ or $\dfrac{1}{2\sqrt{x}}$.

19. $\dfrac{2}{(x + 1)^2}$.

3. $6x - 8$.

13. $\frac{1}{3}x^{-2/3}$ or $\dfrac{1}{3\sqrt[3]{x^2}}$.

21. $3x^2 + 3$.

5. $20x + 13$.
7. $3x^2$.
9. $21x^2 - 5$.

15. $16x - 7$.
17. $-4(1 - 2x)$.

23. -1.
25. 40π.

Section 3

1. 7.

3. $500x^{99}$.

5. $40t - 20t^3$.

7. $8\pi r$.

9. $2ax + b$.

11. $\dfrac{3x^2 + 2x}{a + b}$.

13. $12x^2(2x^3 - 5)$.

15. $3x^2 - 4$.

17. $4u^3 - 6u^2 + 3$.

19. $51x^{16} - 36x^8$.

23. **a.** $-10/x^3$.   **b.** $-28/x^5$.   **c.** $40/x^{11}$.   **d.** $-600/x^{101}$.

Section 4

1. $-6x^{-3}$.

3. $-30x^{-4}$.

5. $-2/(x - 1)^2$.

7. $(2)(2x + 1)^2(x^2 - 1)^3(11x^2 + 4x - 3)$.

9. $4(2 - 2x)(2x - x^2)^3$.

11. $\dfrac{3x^2 + 4x}{(3x + 2)^2}$.

13. $\dfrac{-20x}{(1 + x^2)^2}$.

15. $-20/(1 + x)^3$.

17. $\dfrac{-10(x + 2)}{(x - 3)^2}$.

19. $-\frac{3}{4}$.

21. 16.

23. $3 \times 3 \times 2$.

Section 5

1. $-15x^{-6}$.

3. $x(-5x^3 - 15x + 2)$.

5. $\dfrac{-29}{(5x - 7)^2}$.

7. $30x^2(x^3 + 1)^9$.

9. $2x - 7/x^2 + 1/2\sqrt{x}$.

11. $(x)(x^2 + 1)^{-1/2}(3x^2 + 2)$.

13. $\frac{9}{2}x^2(x^3 + 7)^{1/2}$.

15. $-\dfrac{2x}{3y}$.

17. $\dfrac{1}{2\sqrt{x}} - \dfrac{1}{2x^{3/2}}$.

19. $\dfrac{-10(x + 2)}{(x - 3)^3}$.

21. $\dfrac{2x - 3y}{3x + 4y}$.

23. $-\dfrac{y + 3}{x - 2}$.

25. $40(x + 1)(x^2 + 2x)^{19}$.

27. $-12(1 + x)^{-4}$.

29. $-5(2x + 3)^{-3/2}$.

31. $(x - 1)(x^2 - 2x + 5)^{-1/2}$.

33. $-\dfrac{\sqrt[3]{y}}{\sqrt[3]{x}}$ or $-\sqrt[3]{\dfrac{y}{x}}$.

Section 7

1. a. $80 - 32t$.
    b. -32.
    c. 80.

    d. 196 ft, 16 ft/sec, -32 ft/sec²,
        4 ft, -112 ft/sec, -32 ft/sec².

3. $t = 6$ hr, 180 mi.
5. 8 ft/sec, -4 ft/sec, 50 ft.
7. $20,000, 35/unit.

9. 0.
11. 3.

13. 0.
15. -8.

17. $\frac{4}{3}$.
19. $\frac{1}{2}$.

21. $\frac{3}{4}$.
23. $4\pi r^2$.

25. (3, 3).

Section 9

1. a. $360x^2$.   b. $-120x$.   c. $120x - 2x$.   d. 24.
3. -1, 6, decreasing.
5. 12 ft/sec, 12 ft/sec², -12 ft/sec².
7. 4, 9, -12.
9. a. $20x^{-3}$.   b. $4(x - 1)^{-3}$.   c. $2 + 2/x^3$.
11. Increasing $x < 2$, decreasing $x > 2$, concave downward in $(-\infty, \infty)$, $x = 2$.
13. For $x > 0$, increasing, for $x < 0$, decreasing, concave upward, (0, 0).
15. $x > 1$ increasing, $x < 1$ increasing, $x > 1$ concave upward, $x < 1$ concave downward, $x = 1$.
17. $x > 1$ increasing in $(1, \infty)$, decreasing in $(-\infty, 1)$, concave upward for $x > \frac{2}{3}$ or $x < 0$, concave downward in $(0, \frac{2}{3})$, $x = 0$, $x = 1$.
19. Increasing in $(-2, 0)$, decreasing in $(0, 2)$, concave downward in $(-2, 2)$, $x = 0$.

Section 10

1. Rel max (3, 9).
3. Rel max $(-1, 3)$; rel min $(1, -1)$.
5. Rel max $(0, -20)$; rel min $(4, -52)$.
7. Inflection point (1, 2).
9. Rel min (1, 0).
11. Rel max (1, 2), rel min $(-1, -6)$; inflection point $(0, -2)$.
13. Rel min (2, 4), rel max $(-2, -4)$.
15. Rel max (4, 4).
17. Absolute max $(-1, 15)$, absolute min $(3, -17)$.

Section 11

1. 10×20.
3. $u = 4$.
5. $10 \times 10 \times 5$.

7. 15×20.
9. 2 weeks from now.
11. 20×20.

13. $2.16.
15. $r = 5, h = 10$.
17. $20.

Section 13

1. 0.27 ft/min.
3. 0.25 in./min.

5. 50 mph.
7. 0.4 ft/min.

9. 80 cu ft/min.
11. $\dfrac{1}{4\pi}$ in./min.

CHAPTER VIII

Section 3

1. $\dfrac{3}{8}x^8 + c.$

3. $\dfrac{x^4}{4} + \dfrac{7x^3}{3} - \dfrac{5}{2}x^2 - 4x + c.$

5. $-1/x^2 + c.$

7. $\dfrac{x^4}{4} - \dfrac{x^2}{2} + c.$

9. $2x^{20} + c.$

11. $\dfrac{x^7}{7} + \dfrac{3}{5}x^5 + x^3 + x + c.$

13. $x^5 - x^3 + 2x + 7.$

15. $80t - 16t^2 + c.$

17. $50 - 32t.$

19. $V = \frac{4}{3}\pi r^3.$

Section 5

1. 384, 384, no.
3. 92 ft/sec, 165 ft.

5. 40, $-20.$
7. 21.

9. 128 ft/sec.
11. 192 ft/sec.

Section 6

1. $y = x^2 + c.$
3. $y = 3x^3 - 6x^2 + c.$
5. $y = -5x + c.$
7. $y = x^3 - 7.$

9. $y = 4x + 2.$
11. $6y = 2x^3 + 3x^2 - 6x - 26.$
13. $25 + .002x^2.$
15. $y = 2 + 6x - 6x^2.$

Section 8

1. $\dfrac{x^6}{6} + c.$

3. $t^4 + c.$

5. $y + c.$

7. $x^5 + 2x^4 - x^3 + 3x^2 - 7x + c.$
9. $7y + 2y^2 - 3y^3 + c.$
11. $-10x^{-1} + c.$

13. $\dfrac{(x + 1)^4}{4} + c.$

15. $\dfrac{10x^3}{3} + \dfrac{x^6}{6} + c.$

17. $-(4 - x^2)^{1/2} + c.$

19. $\dfrac{t^{20}}{20} - \dfrac{7t^9}{9} + 4t + c.$

21. $\dfrac{ax^3}{3} + \dfrac{bx^2}{2} + cx + d.$

23. $(2y + 1)^{1/2} + c.$
25. $y^2 = x^2 + 10x - 23.$
27. $4y - y^2 = 8x + x^2 + 3.$

29. $-\dfrac{1}{y} = \dfrac{x^3}{3} - \dfrac{4}{3}.$

Section 9

1. 35.
3. 90.

5. $\frac{8}{3}.$
7. 2.

9. $-6.$
11. 16.

13. 40.
15. $\frac{32}{3}.$

17. $\frac{125}{6}.$
19. $\frac{27}{6}.$

Section 10

1. 10.49π (units)^3. **3.** $250\pi/3$. **5.** $\frac{4}{3}\pi a^3$. **7.** 54π (ft)^3.

CHAPTER IX

Section 3

1. $x = 3, y = 2$.
3. No solution.
5. Equations are equivalent.
7. $x = -3, y = 1$.
9. $x = -5, y = 10$.
11. $x = -\frac{3}{2}, y = \frac{5}{4}$.
13. $x = -\frac{1975}{4453}, y = \frac{7675}{4453}$.

15. $x = \frac{3}{4}, y = -1$.
17. $x = 3, y = 2, z = 1$.
19. $x = 1, y = -2, z = 3$.
21. $x = 3, y = 2, z = -1$.
23. 9, 16.
25. 290 mph and 60 mph.
27. 14 nickels, 6 dimes, and 8 quarters.

Section 4

1. 2.
3. 0.
5. -5.

7. -11.
9. 30.
11. -12.

13. $x = \frac{2}{3}, y = -\frac{1}{2}$.
15. $x = 3, y = 2, z = 2$.
17. $x = 6, y = 3, z = 12$.

Section 5

1.
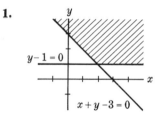

3.
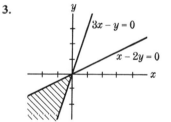

5.
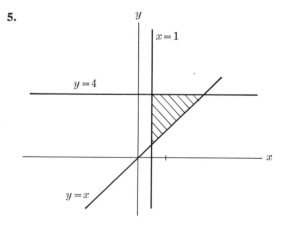

7.

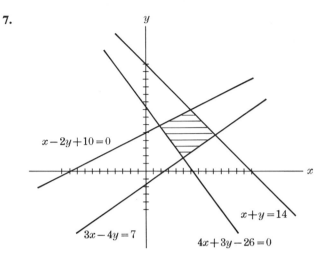

9.

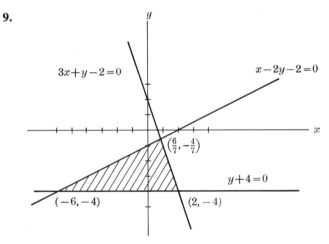

Section 6

1. 25.
3. Maximum value is 69, minimum is -31.
5. $2x + 11y - 16 \leq 0$,
   $7x - 11y - 10 \leq 0$,
   $4x + \quad y - 13 \geq 0$,
   $5x - \quad y - \quad 5 \geq 0$.
7. 29. Yes. At all points of the segment joining (7, 0) and (0, 7), since the graph of $f(x, y) = 3x + 3y + 8 = k$ is parallel to one side of the convex polygon.
9. Max. 0, min. -61; max. 20, min. -65; max. 39, min. -17.

CHAPTER X

Section 2

3. 57.29933°, 0.017453 radians.

5. **a.** 41°.   **b.** 119°50′52″.   **c.** $\dfrac{13\pi}{24}$.

Section 3

		SINE	COSINE	TANGENT	COTANGENT	SECANT	COSECANT
1.		$\dfrac{3}{5}$	$\dfrac{4}{5}$	$\dfrac{3}{4}$	$\dfrac{4}{3}$	$\dfrac{5}{4}$	$\dfrac{5}{3}$
3.		$\dfrac{3}{\sqrt{10}}$	$-\dfrac{1}{\sqrt{10}}$	-3	$-\dfrac{1}{3}$	$-\sqrt{10}$	$\dfrac{\sqrt{10}}{3}$
5.		$-\dfrac{5}{\sqrt{29}}$	$\dfrac{2}{\sqrt{29}}$	$-\dfrac{5}{2}$	$-\dfrac{2}{5}$	$\dfrac{\sqrt{29}}{2}$	$-\dfrac{\sqrt{29}}{5}$
7.		$\dfrac{b}{\sqrt{a^2+b^2}}$	$\dfrac{a}{\sqrt{a^2+b^2}}$	$\dfrac{b}{a}$	$\dfrac{a}{b}$	$\dfrac{\sqrt{a^2+b^2}}{a}$	$\dfrac{\sqrt{a^2+b^2}}{b}$
9.	**a.**	$\dfrac{1}{2}$	$\dfrac{\sqrt{3}}{2}$	$\dfrac{1}{\sqrt{3}}$	$\sqrt{3}$	$\dfrac{2\sqrt{3}}{3}$	2
	b.	$\dfrac{\sqrt{3}}{2}$	$\dfrac{1}{2}$	$\sqrt{3}$	$\dfrac{1}{\sqrt{3}}$	2	$\dfrac{2\sqrt{3}}{2}$
	c.	$\dfrac{\sqrt{2}}{2}$	$\dfrac{\sqrt{2}}{2}$	1	1	$\sqrt{2}$	$\sqrt{2}$
	d.	$\dfrac{\sqrt{3}}{2}$	$-\dfrac{1}{2}$	$-\sqrt{3}$	$-\dfrac{\sqrt{3}}{3}$	-2	$\dfrac{2\sqrt{3}}{3}$
	e.	$\dfrac{1}{2}$	$-\dfrac{\sqrt{3}}{2}$	$-\dfrac{\sqrt{3}}{3}$	$-\sqrt{3}$	$-\dfrac{2\sqrt{3}}{3}$	2
	f.	$-\dfrac{\sqrt{3}}{2}$	$-\dfrac{1}{2}$	$\sqrt{3}$	$\dfrac{\sqrt{3}}{3}$	-2	$-\dfrac{2\sqrt{3}}{3}$
	g.	$-\dfrac{\sqrt{3}}{2}$	$\dfrac{1}{2}$	$-\sqrt{3}$	$-\dfrac{\sqrt{3}}{3}$	2	$-\dfrac{2\sqrt{3}}{3}$
11.		$\pm\dfrac{15}{17}$	$-\dfrac{8}{17}$	$\pm\dfrac{15}{8}$	$\pm\dfrac{8}{15}$	$-\dfrac{17}{8}$	$\pm\dfrac{17}{15}$
13.		$-\dfrac{3}{5}$	$\dfrac{4}{5}$	$-\dfrac{3}{4}$	$-\dfrac{4}{3}$	$\dfrac{5}{4}$	$-\dfrac{5}{3}$

Section 4

1. $70°$, $9°17'$, $35°27'43''$, $23°18'$, $\dfrac{\pi}{3}$, .083, $\dfrac{7\pi}{15}$.

	SINE	COSINE	TANGENT	COTANGENT	SECANT	COSECANT
3.	$\dfrac{24}{25}$	$\dfrac{7}{25}$	$\dfrac{24}{7}$	$\dfrac{7}{24}$	$\dfrac{25}{7}$	$\dfrac{25}{24}$
5.	$\dfrac{3\sqrt{10}}{10}$	$-\dfrac{\sqrt{10}}{10}$	-3	$-\dfrac{1}{3}$	$-\sqrt{10}$	$\dfrac{\sqrt{10}}{3}$
7.	$\dfrac{2\sqrt{5}}{5}$	$-\dfrac{\sqrt{5}}{5}$	-2	$-\dfrac{1}{2}$	$-\sqrt{5}$	$\dfrac{\sqrt{5}}{2}$

9. **a.** $\sin 150° = \sin 30°$
$\cos 150° = -\cos 30°$
$\tan 150° = -\tan 30°.$

   g. $\sin(-140°) = -\sin 40°$
$\cos(-140°) = -\cos 40°$
$\tan(-140°) = \tan 40°.$

   c. $\sin 315° = -\sin 45°$
$\cos 315° = \cos 45°$
$\tan 315° = -\tan 45°.$

   i. $\sin 1475° = \sin 35°$
$\cos 1475° = \cos 35°$
$\tan 1475° = \tan 55°.$

   e. $\sin(-250°) = \sin 70°$

   $\cos(-250°) = -\cos 70°$

   $\tan(-250°) = -\cos 70°.$

   j. $\sin \dfrac{11\pi}{6} = -\sin \pi/6$

   $\cos \dfrac{11\pi}{6} = \cos \pi/6$

   $\tan \dfrac{11\pi}{6} = -\tan \pi/6.$

Section 5

7. $\dfrac{\pm\sqrt{5}}{5}.$

9. $1.$

11. $\cos \theta.$

13. $\cos \theta.$

15. $\sin \theta.$

17. $2 \sec \theta.$

19. $\csc \theta.$

21. $1.$

Section 7

1. $0.24841.$
3. $0.86849.$
5. $0.92388.$
7. $0.31537.$
9. $0.70401.$

11. $0.99750.$
13. $0.53597.$
15. $0.88884.$
17. $17°46'.$
19. $30°24'.$

21. $56°26'.$
23. $52°6'.$
25. $77°23'.$
27. $45°.$
29. $36°11'21''.$

Section 8

1. $B = 63°50'$, $b = 244.2$, $c = 272.1.$
3. $A = 47°59.3'$, $B = 42°0.7'$, $b = 133.9.$
5. $B = 48°40'$, $a = 92.46$, $b = 105.12.$
7. $A = 3°49.3'$, $B = 86°10.7'$, $b = 0.9702.$
9. $B = 17°30'$, $a = 475.7$, $c = 498.8.$
11. $A = 45°25'$, $a = 712.2$, $b = 702.$
13. $A = 39°$, $B = 51°$, $c = 772.$

15. $A = 45°, B = 45°, c = 707.11.$
17. (1) 14,650; (3) 9841; (5) 9722; (7) 0.0314; (9) 35,680; (11) 249,980; (13) 145,800; (15) 250,000.

Section 9

1. 27.8 ft.
3. 220 ft.
5. 109 ft.

7. 92.6 ft or 419.2 ft.
9. 10:16 A.M.
11. 265 yd from O, 424 yd.

Section 10

1. $V = 21.2, H = 33.9.$
3. $36°52'.$

5. 111.8 lb, $26°34'.$
7. 34.2 lb.

Section 11

1. $B = 43°50', a = 21.13, b = 15.39.$
3. $A = 30°, b = 196.96, c = 187.94.$
5. $B = 30°, a = 37.59, c = 25.71.$
7. $a = 36.06, B = 46°7', C = 73°53'.$

9. $A = 56°, B = 84°, c = 15.5.$
11. 140 lbs, $21°47'$ from 100 lb force.
13. 10.26 ft.
19. 19.15, 37.35.

Section 12

1. a. $\frac{36}{85}.$ c. $-\frac{77}{85}.$ e. $-\frac{36}{77}.$ g. $-\frac{7}{25}.$ i. $\frac{161}{289}.$

3. a. $\dfrac{1}{2}.$ c. $\dfrac{\sqrt{3}}{2}.$ e. $\dfrac{1}{2}.$ g. 1.

5. a. 2.   b. $\frac{4}{7}.$
7. Sin $(A + B) = \frac{56}{65}$, cos $(A - B) = \frac{63}{65}.$

CHAPTER XI

Section 2

1. a. $\frac{1}{U6}.$ b. $\frac{1}{8}.$ c. $\frac{5}{4}.$ d. $\frac{7}{100}.$ e. $\frac{1}{6}.$
3. a. 12.5%.   c. 40%.   e. 68%.
      b. $33\frac{1}{3}\%.$ d. 175%.
5. a. 46.   b. 13.75.   c. 7.8.   d. 197.34.
7. a. 5000.   b. 80.   c. 25.2.   d. 350.

9. $360.   **11.** $7000.   **13.** 50 lb.   **15.** 100 gal.

Section 3

1. $168, $968.   **5.** $4\frac{1}{2}\%.$ **9.** 9 mo.
3. 10 mo.   **7.** 1.25 yr.

Section 4

1. $297.52.
3. a. $983.61.   b. $991.74.   c. $1000.00.   d. $1016.67.

5. $592.36, $27.64.   **7.** $404.15.

Section 7

1. **a.** $402.44.   **b.** $406.56.   **c.** $408.70.
3. **a.** $1104.02, $604.02.   **d.** $3519.99, $3019.99.
   b. $1631.02, $1131.02.   **e.** $5142.86, $4642.86.
   c. $2400.51, $1900.51.
5. $12,795.12.   **7.** 3.2435.

Section 8

1. $153.80.   **3.** $886.69.   **5.** $1567.05.

7. **a.** 691.07.   **b.** $695.65.

9. $1133.30.   **11.** $1200 due in 2 years.

Section 9

1. **a.** $493.16.   **c.** $576.92.   **e.** $648.98
   b. $533.40.   **d.** $600.

3. $333.16.   **5.** $2331.09.   **7.** $865.43.   **9.** $958.00.

CHAPTER XII

Section 3

1. $d = 1, L = 50, S_n = 1275.$ **9.** $a = 10.4, d = 0.4.$
3. $d = -3, L = -47, S_n = -370.$ **11.** $a + b.$
5. $d = -0.20, L = -3.80, S_n = 4.$ **13.** $d = -5.$
7. $d = 1.5, L = 8.5, S_n = 17.5.$ **15.** 17,157.

Section 5

1. $L = 512, S_n = 1023.$ **9.** $L = 123.2358, S_n = 1954.13.$
3. $L = \frac{1}{128}, S_n = \frac{255}{128}.$ **11.** $L = (0.02)^5, S_n = 1.020408.$
5. $L = -\frac{1}{64}, S_n = \frac{341}{64}.$ **13.** $r = \pm\frac{1}{2}, S_n = 508$ or $172.$
7. $L = 1.456811, S_n = 24.2974.$ **15.** $r = \pm\sqrt{6}/2.$

Section 6

1. 33.066.   **7.** 16.   **13.** $\frac{179}{55}.$
3. 12.17.   **9.** $\frac{2}{3}.$ **15.** $313.75.
5. 121.5.   **11.** $\frac{19}{11}.$ **17.** $12, $102.

19. 13, 15.   **27.** $1586.87.
21. $12, \frac{1}{3}.$ **29.** 156.
23. $10,737, 418.23.   **31.** $5229.90.
25. $8052.55, $38,578.05.   **33.** 30 mo, $1293.

Section 9

1. $1214.86.   **3.** $2292.78.   **5.** $7439.56.

Section 10

1. **a.** $558.24.   **b.** $564.80.   **c.** $568.18.

3. $1103.72.   **5.** $63.06.   **7.** $3644.61.   **9.** $n = 24$.

Section 11

1. **a.** $896.63.   **c.** $1089.86.   **e.** $2157.86.
   b. $1037.97.   **d.** $1460.52.   **f.** $2265.75.

3. $109.73.   **7.** 27^+ quarters.   **11.** $329.33.
5. $3572.09.   **9.** $368.21.   **13.** $21,835.40.

Section 12

1. $142.46.
3. $n = 35$.
5. $R = 1065.52, $3867.73, $154.71 int., $910.81 reduction of principal.
7. **a.** $25.51.   **b.** $460.34.   **c.** $4.60 int., $20.91 prin.
9. $R = 1528.43, $8197.87.   **13.** $116.49.

CHAPTER XIII

Section 3

1. **a.** 1.0725.   **c.** 2490.   **e.** 0.0000527.
   b. 0.95123.   **d.** 20,952.   **f.** 10.434.
   g. 0.19515.
3. **a.** $2000e^{0.06t}$, $3644.20.   **b.** $3612.22.
5. $12,130.60.
7. $S = 100e^{0.03t}$, 948.77.   **9.** $y = 40e^{2x}$, 16137.2, 14.715.

Section 5

1. **a.** 1.1184.   **c.** 2.0643.   **e.** 1.3878.
   b. 1.7440.   **d.** 1.9072.   **f.** 2.1158.
3. **a.** 1.5644.   **c.** 33.43.   **e.** -15.07.
   b. 0.3432.   **d.** -1.3218.

Section 6

1. **a.** 6.2767.   **c.** -0.7236.   **e.** 10.7685.   **g.** 6.8698.
   b. 8.8159.   **d.** -2.4316.   **f.** -5.5561.
3. 1790.
5. 0.05487.
7. **a.** 17.26.   **b.** 73.29.   **c.** 3.512.

Section 8

1. $10e^{2x}$.

9. $\dfrac{4}{4x+5}$.

17. $\frac{1}{2}e^{x^2} + C$.

3. $(1 + x)e^x$.

11. $\dfrac{2\ln x}{x}$.

19. $-\frac{1}{3}e^{x^3} + C$.

5. $\dfrac{1}{x}$.

13. $\dfrac{2x^2 - 1}{x(x^2 - 1)}$.

21. $\ln |x + 1| + C$.

7. $\left(\dfrac{1}{x} + \ln x\right)e^x$.

15. $-\dfrac{15}{e^{3x}}$.

23. $\ln (4 + e^x) + C$.

25. $-1/(x + 1) + C$.
27. a. 1.3863.   **b.** 3.4366.

Section 9

1. 2.

7. 4.

13. 10.

19. $\log \dfrac{x^2 y^3}{z^5}$.

3. -3.

9. 2.

15. $\dfrac{1}{16}$.

21. $\log \dfrac{x^3 y^2}{z\sqrt{w}}$.

5. -3.

11. $\frac{1}{25}$.

17. $\log ab^2$.

CHAPTER XIV

Section 2

1. $\frac{5}{26}$.
3. a. $\frac{1}{4}$.   **b.** $\frac{1}{2}$.
5. a. $\frac{2}{3}$.   **b.** $\frac{1}{2}$.
7. a. $\frac{5}{36}$.   **b.** $\frac{15}{36}$.   **c.** 7.
9. No.

Section 3

1. 120, 60.

9. 210.

17. $\frac{11}{4165}$.

3. 840.

11. 84, 84.

19. $\frac{89}{110}$.

5. 48.

13. 9900.

21. $\dfrac{C(3, 2)C(12, 4)}{C(15, 6)}$.

7. 90.

15. 280, 280(9!).

Section 4

1. $\dfrac{1}{108,290}$.

5. $\dfrac{625}{11,664}$.

9. 0.416.

13. $\dfrac{1}{4}, \dfrac{3}{14}$.

3. $\frac{7}{12}, \frac{1}{6}$.

7. 0.12.

11. $\frac{4083}{4096}$.

Section 5

1. 7.   **3.** −$1.70.   **5.** −60 cents.   **7.** 9.5 cents.

Section 6

1.

x_i	0	1	2
$P_r(x_i)$	.9025	.0950	.0025

$P_r(x_i) = C(2, x_i)(.05)^{x_i}(0.95)^{2-x_i}$, $\{x_i\} = \{0, 1, 2\}$.

3. 0.1178.   **5.** 0.0002.

Section 7

1. $\mu = 5.8$, $\sigma^2(x) = 3.0267$, $\sigma(x) = 1.74$.
3. $\mu = \frac{49}{8}$, $\sigma^2(x) = \frac{7}{64}$, $\sigma(x) = \sqrt{7}/8$.
5. $\{-.707, .707, 1.414, 0, -2.121, .707, -.707, -.707, .707\}$.

Section 8

1. $s^2 = .80$, $\sigma^2 = .75$.   **3. b.** $\mu = 3.5$, $\sigma^2 = \frac{35}{12}$.

Section 9

1. .5328, .9332.   **3. b.** 4.80 cents per rod.   **5.** .1118.

INDEX

Abel, N. H., 133
Abscissa, 73
Absolute inequalities, 157
Absolute maximum value, 272
Absolute minimum value, 272
Absolute value, 66
Acceleration, 238-239, 262
   angular, 344
Accumulation factor, 386
Acute angle, 343
Addition:
   algebraic expressions, 81
   algebraic fractions, 97-98
   cancellation, 50-51
   cancellation law for, 50-51
   complex numbers, 76
   fractions, 60
Algebra:
   fundamental theorem of, 138
   terminology of, 80-81
Algebraic expressions, 80
   addition, 81
   division, 94
   multiplication, 89-93
   subtraction, 81-82
Algebraic fractions, 96-100
Algebraic processes, elementary,
   80-110

Amortization, 411-412
Amount:
   annuity, 404
     Tables, 505-510
   compound, 384
     formula for, 385-387
     Table, 485-490
Analytic geometry, 189
Angles, 341-344
   acute, 343
   central, 343
   complementary, 351
   coterminal, 345
   of depression, 360
   of elevation, 360
   initial side of, 341
   magnitude of, 341
   obtuse, 343
   quadrantal, 345
   related, 348-350
   right, 342
   straight, 343
   terminal side of, 341
   vertex of, 341
Angular acceleration, 344
Angular velocity, 344
Annuities, 401-411
   amount of, 404

Tables, 505-510
certain, 402-404
contingent, 402
defined, 401
present value of, 404-406
Tables, 511-516
simple, 402
types of, 401-402
value of, 402, 407-410
Applications:
maximum value, 277
minimum value, 277
Arbitrary constant, 113
Area:
between two curves, 306-308
found by integration, 301-308
under a curve, 301-308
Arithmetic means, 395
Arithmetic progressions, 393-394
Associative law for the union of
three sets, 27
Associative Laws, 47
Average rates, 217-218, 222-226
over a flexible interval, 224-225
Average slope, 240
Average speed, 237
Axioms, 1
defining identity elements, 48
defining inverse elements, 48
of mathematical induction, 101
order, 63-64

Base, 83
logarithm, 428
Binomial, 80
Binomial expansion, 437-440
Binomial probability distribution,
443
Binomial Theorem, 105-109
Body, freely falling, 290-292
Braces, 61
Brackets, 61
Broken-line graph, 185

Cancellation law:
for addition, 50-51
for multiplication, 52
Cartesian product of two sets, 32-34
Central angle, 343
Chain rule of differentiation, 280-281

Chuck-a-luck, 439, 442
Circles, equations of, 203-205
Closed interval, 70
Closure Laws, 46
Coefficient:
numerical, 81
variable, 81
Cofactor, 323
Combinations, 435-436
Common factor, 42
Common difference, 393
Common logarithms, 429
Commutative law for the union of
two sets, 27
Commutative Laws, 47
Commuting obligation, 389
Complementary angles, 351
Completing the square, 122-124
Complex fractions, 99-100
Complex numbers, 75-78
imaginary part, 76
real part, 76
Components of vectors, 365-366
Composites, 41
Compound amount, 384
formula for, 385-387
Table, 485-490
Compound interest, 378
defined, 384
Compound interest law, 418
Compound propositions, 3, 4-7
logically equivalent, 7
Compounding continuously, 415-418
Concavity, 268-270
Conclusions, 1, 2
Condition, initial, 288
Conditional connective, 7
Conditional equations, 114
Conditional inequalities, 157
Conjunctions, 4
Connectives, 3-10
conditional, 7
Constant, 14-15
arbitrary, 113
derivative of a, 247
Constant function, 177
Constraints, 338
Contingent annuity, 402
Continuous compounding, 415-418
Continuous functions, 232
Contradictory inequalities, 157
Contrapositive of the implication, 8
Converse of the implication, 8

Conversion, frequency of, 385
Conversion period, 384, 385
Converted interest, 384
Convex polygon, 332
Convex set, 331
Cosecant, 351
Cosines, 351
   law of, 370
Cost, marginal, 263
Cotangent, 350, 351
Coterminal, 345
Counting numbers, 41
Countable sets, 23-25
Cramer's Rule, 325-327
Critical point, 274
Critical value of x, 274
Cube, 81
Cube root, 81
Cubes, two, factoring the sum or
   difference of, 92
Curve(s):
   area between two, 306-308
   area under, 301-306
   equation of, 292-294

Date, focal, 389
Debt, amortization, 411-412
Decimals, repeating, 42, 399
Decreasing function, 266-271
Definite integral, 304
Degree, 342
Delta notation, 245
Delta process, 246
Denominator, 96
   lowest common, 59, 98
Dependent variable, 173
Depression, angle of, 360
Derivative(s), 425
   of a constant, 247
   delta process for finding, 246
   of a function, 244-245
   interpretations of, 262-264
   of a power function, 253-255
   of a product, 251-252
   of a quotient, 252-253
Descartes' rule of signs, 140-141
Determinants, 319-329
   elements, 322
   entries, 322
   second order, 319
   third order, 321

Deviation, standard, 448-453
   sample, 453
Difference:
   common, 393
Differential equation, 299
Differential of a function, 297-301
Differentiation, 172, 244-283
   chain rule, 280-281
   defined, 245
   implicit, 256-259
   of polynomials, 249
   rules for, 247-250
   successive, 265-266
Discriminant, 127
Disjoint sets, 18, 19
Disjunctions, 4-5
   exclusive, 4-5
   inclusive, 4-5
Distance, 74, 288
Distance formula, 190
Distribution(s):
   binomial probability, 443
   normal probability, 455-460
   standard normal, 446
Distributions, probability, 443-448
Distributive Law, 48
Division:
   algebraic expressions, 94
   algebraic fractions, 97
   complex numbers, 77
   fractions, 57
   synthetic, 135-136
Domain of definition of the function,
   173
Domain of definition of the relation,
   172
Double Angle Formulas, 376

Elements, 12-16
Element, determinant, 322
Elevation, angle of, 360
Elimination method, 314-317
Ellipses, equations of, 207-211
Empty set, 16, 18
Entry, determinant, 322
Equal sets, 18
Equality, properties of, 45-46
Equation(s), 37, 112-114
   of circles, 203-205
   conditional, 114
   containing fractions, 145-149

of a curve, 292-294
derived, 115-116
differential, 299
of ellipses, 207-211
equivalent, 115-116
functions defined by, 176-177
of hyperbolas, 211-213
identity, 114
involving radicals, 149-151
involving two variables, graph of, 185-189
involving variables, 113-114
left member of, 114
linear, 312
numerical, 113
of parabolas, 205-207
polynomial, 114
quadratic, *see* Quadratic equations
in quadratic form, 128-130
right member of, 114
root of, 115
solution of, 115
solution set of, 115-116
solving, 116-119
of straight lines, 198-202
of value, 389-390
Equilateral triangle, 344
Equivalences, 10-11
Equivalent equations, 115-116
Equivalent fractions, 58-59
Equivalent sets, 21-23
Euclidean geometry, 344
Evaluation of the determinant by minors of the first column, 323
Exclusive disjunction, 4-5
Existential quantifiers, 38
Expansion, binomial, 437-440
Expectation, mathematical, 441-443
Exponent, 81, 83
laws of, 83-87
Exponential functions, 418-419
Table, 497-502
Expressions, algebraic (*see* Algebraic expressions)
Extremes, 395

F (truth value), 2, 3
Factor, 41, 81
accumulation, 386
common, 42
Factoring, 90-93

solution of equations, 120-122
Factor Theorem, 134
Falling bodies, freely, 290-292
Field, 49
Finite geometric series, 398
Finite series, 392
Finite set, 15
First Derivative Test, 275
Focal date, 389
Formula:
compound amount, 385-387
distance, 190
double angle, 376
functions defined by, 176-177
integration, 285-287
midpoint, 191-193
quadratic, 124-127, 133
Fractions, 41, 42
addition, 60
algebraic, 96-100
complex, 99-100
division, 57
equations containing, 145-149
equivalent, 58-59
fundamental principle of, 57-58, 84
inequalities involving, 165-170
multiplication, 57
rational, 146
simple, 99
subtraction, 60
Freely falling bodies, 290-292
Frequency, of conversion, 385
Function(s), 173
constant, 177
continuous, 232
decreasing, 266-271
defined by a formula or an equation, 176-177
defined by a table of values, 178-181
definition of, 173
derivative of, 244-245
differential of, 297-301
exponential, 418-419
Table, 497-502
graphs of, 181-185
increasing, 266-271
polynomial, 232-234
power, 418
rules used in defining, 176
trigonometric, 341-377
value of, 173

Function-graph, 184
Functional notation, 174-176
Fundamental theorem of algebra, 138

Geometric means, 397-398
Geometric progressions, 396-397
Geometric series, 398-399
Geometry:
    analytic, 189
    Euclidean, 344
Graphs:
    broken-line, 185
    of equations involving two
        variables, 185-189
    function, 184
    of functions, 181-185
    of linear inequalities in two
        variables, 214-216
    of polynomials, 151-154
    of relations, 181-185
Graphical interpolation, 183
Greatest common monomial factor,
    91
Grouping:
    factoring by, 93
    symbols of, 61-63
Growth, law of, 418

Half-open interval, 71
Histogram, 456
Hyperbolas, equations of, 211-213

Identity, 114
    numerical, 113
Implication, 7-8
    contrapositive of the, 8
    converse of the, 8
    inverse of the, 8
Implicit differentiation, 256-259
Inclusive disjunction, 4-5
Increasing function, 266-271
Indefinite integral, 304
Independent variable, 173
Index of radical, 86
Induction, mathematical, 101-104
Inequalities, 37, 64, 157
    absolute, 157
    conditional, 157

contradictory, 157
    involving fractions, 165-170
    linear, 329
        in one variable, 159-161
        in two variables, graphs of,
            214-216
    in one variable, 157-170
    quadratic, 161-165
    solution of, 157
    solution set of, 157
    solving, 158
Inference, statistical, 459
Infinite geometric series, 398
Infinite series, 392
Infinite set, 15, 24
Infinity, 235-237
Inflection, point of, 270
Initial condition, 288
Initial side of angle, 341
Instantaneous rates, 218-220, 226,
    224
    in general, 241-242
Instantaneous speed, 237-238
Integers, positive, 41
Integral, 426
    definite, 304
    indefinite, 304
Integral notation, 294-296
Integration, 172, 284-311
    areas found by, 301-308
    defined, 285
    formulas, 285-287
    lower limit of, 303-304
    upper limit of, 304
Interest, 378-391
    compound, 378, 384
        law of, 418
    defined, 378
    simple, 378, 381-384
Interest rate, 378
Intermediate Value Theorem, 259
Interpolation:
    graphical, 183
    by proportional parts, 179
Interval:
    closed, 70
    half-open, 70
    open, 70
Interval of time, 226
Inverse of the implication, 8
Irrational number, 42
Irrational roots of polynomial
    equations, 154-157

Isosceles triangle, 344

Law(s):
   associative, 47
   Closure, 46
   commutative, 47
   compound interest, 418
   cosines, 370
   distributive, 48
   exponents, 83-87
   growth, 418
   natural logarithms, 422-424
   sines, 367
Left member of equation, 114
Limiting process, 228
Limits, 226-231
   concept of, 226-230
   theorems concerning, 230-231
Line(s):
   number, 67
   parallel, 195
   perpendicular, 195-197
   secant, 239
   slope of a, 193-198
   straight, equations of, 198-202
Line segment, length and midpoint of
a, 189-193
Linear equations:
   determinants method of solving
     systems of, 319-329
   elimination method for solving
     systems of, 314-317
   graphical method for solving
     systems of, 313
   systems of, 312
Linear inequalities:
   in one variable, 159-161
   systems of, 329-332
Linear programming, 332-340
Location principle, 155
Logarithms:
   common, 429
   derivative, 425
   integral, 426
   natural, 420-429
     Table, 503-504
Logic, 1, 2
   symbolic, 4
Lower limit, of roots, 139
Lower limit of integration, 303-304
Lowest common denominator, 59, 98

Magnitude of the angle, 341
Marginal cost, 263
Marginal revenue, 263
Mathematical expectation, 441-443
Mathematical induction, 101-104
Mathematical systems, 44-45
Maturity value, 382
Maximum value, 271
   application, 277
Mean, sample, 453
Mean value, 448-453
Mean Value Theorem, 260
Means:
   arithmetic, 395
   geometric, 397-398
Midpoint formulas, 191-193
Midpoint of a line segment, 189-193
Minimum value, 271
   application, 277
Minor, 322
Minute (angular measure), 342
Monomial, 80
Multinomial, 80
Multiplication:
   algebraic expressions, 89-93
   algebraic fractions, 97
   cancellation law for, 52
   complex numbers, 76-77
   fractions, 57
   of nonzero numbers, 55-56
Multiplicity of roots, 138

Natural logarithms, 420-429
   table, 421, 503-504
Natural numbers, 41-42
Negations, 3, 5-6
Negative numbers, 41
Normal probability distributions,
   455-460
Notation:
   delta, 245-246
   functional, 174-176
   integral, 294-296
Null set, 16, 18
Number line, 67
Number systems, 40-79
Numbers:
   complex, 75-78
   counting, 41
   irrational, 42
   natural, 41-42

negative, 41
rational, 41, 42
real, 40-43
    absolute value, 66
    comparing, 63-65
    sequence of, 392
Numerator, 96
Numerical coefficient, 81
Numerical equations, 113
Numerical identity, 113

Oblique triangle, 344, 367-371
Obtuse angle, 343
One-dimensional-coordinate system, 70
One-to-one correspondence, 21
Open interval, 70
Optimal point, 338
Order, axioms, 63-64
Order relations, 63-65
Ordered pairs, 32-34, 69
Ordinate, 73
Origin, 71
Overlapping sets, 18, 19

Parabolas, equations of, 205-207
Parallel lines, 195
Parentheses, 61
Percent, 379
Percentage, 379-381
Period:
    conversion, 384, 385
    interest, 384
Permutations, 433-435
Perpendicular, 342
Perpendicular lines, 195-197
Perpetuity, 402
Plotting the point, 74
Point of inflection, 270
Point of tangency, 239
Point(s):
    optimal, 338
    relative maximum, 273
    relative minimum, 273
Points, set of, 183
Polygons, 332
    convex, 332
Polynomial equations:
    complex roots of, 137-138
    irrational roots of, 154-157

in one variable, 114
    upper and lower limits of real
        roots of, 139-140
Polynomial functions, 232-234
Polynomials:
    differentiating, 249
    graphs of, 151-154
    in one variable, 111-112
    real, 112
    two major problems, 130-131
    zeros of, 132-134
Population, 453
Positive integers, 41
Power, 81
Power function, 418
    derivative of, 253-255
Present value, 387-388
    Tables, 491-496
    of annuity, 404-406
        Tables, 511-516
Primes, 41
Principal, 378
Principle of mathematical induction, 101, 102
Probability, 430
    distribution, 443-448
        binomial, 443
        normal, 455-460
    rules, 437-440
Product, 89
    derivative of, 251-252
Programming, linear, 332-340
Progressions:
    arithmetic, 393-394
    geometric, 396-397
Projections, 362-363
    length of, 363
Proper subsets, 17, 19
Propositions, 2, 4, 37
    combinations of, 3
    compound, 3, 4-7
        logically equivalent, 7
    equivalent, 10-11
    negation of, 5-6
    simple, 3
Pythagorean Theorem, 190

Quadrants, 74, 345
Quadrantal angle, 345
Quadratic equations:
    facts about roots of, 127-128

in one variable, 119-120
Quadratic form, equations in, 128-130
Quadratic formula, 124-127, 133
Quadratic-formula method, 124-127
Quadratic inequalities, 161-165
Quantifiers, 37-39
Quantity, 172
    vector, 363
Quotient, derivative of, 252-253

Radian, 343
Radical, 86
Radicals:
    equations involving, 149-151
    laws of, 87
Radicand, 86
Range of the function, 173
Range of the relation, 172
Rate problem, 172, 217
Rate(s):
    average, 217-218, 222-226
    instantaneous, 218-220, 226,
       241-242, 244
    interest, 378
    related, 281-283
Rational fraction, 146
Rational numbers, 41, 42
Rational roots, 142-145
Real numbers, 40-43
    absolute value, 66
    comparing, 63-65
    system of, 45-49
Real polynomial, 112
Reasoning, logical, 1, 2
Rectangular coordinate system, 69-74
Related angles, 348-350
Related-Angle Theorem, 348
Related rates, 281-283
Relations, 172
    graph of, 181-185
Relative maximum, 271
Relative minimum value, 272
Remainder Theorem, 134
Repeating decimals, 42, 399
Resultant, 364
Revenue, marginal, 263
Right angle, 342
Right member of equation, 114
Right triangle, 344
    solution of, 358-359
Rolle's Theorem, 260

Roots, 81
    complex, of polynomial
      equations, 137-138
    irrational, of polynomial
      equations, 154-157
    multiplicity of, 138
    number of, 138
    rational, 142-145
Rule of signs, Descartes', 140-141
Rules, probability, 437-440

Sample mean, 453
Samples, 453
Sample standard deviation, 453
Sample variance, 453
Scalars, 363
Secant, 350
Secant line, 239
Second (angular measure), 342
Second Derivative Test, 276
Sequences, 392-393
Series, 392
    finite, 392
    geometric, 398-399
    infinite, 392
Set-forming operations, 26-29
Sets, 12-16
    Cartesian product of two, 32-34
    complement of, 28-29
    concept of, 1
    constructing, methods of, 13-15
    convex, 331
    countable, 23-25
    defined, 12-13
    disjoint, 18, 19
    empty, 16, 18
    equal, 18
    equivalent, 20-23
    finite, 15
    infinite, 15, 24
    intersection of two, 28
    language of, 1
    null, 16, 18
    operations on, 26-29
    of points, 183
    overlapping, 18, 19
    solution, 37, 115
    union of two, 27
    universal, 15-16, 19
    Venn diagrams and, 19-20
Signs, Descartes' Rule of, 140-141

Simple annuity, 402
Simple fraction, 100
Simple interest, 378
    defined, 381
    present value at, 382-383
Simple proposition, 3
Sines, 350
Slash, 6
Slope, average, 240
Slope of a curve at a point, 240
Slope of a line, 193-198
Solids, volume of, 309-311
Solution, 115
    of inequality, 157
    right triangles, 358-359
Solution set, 37, 115-116
    of inequality, 157
Special products, 90
Speed, 288
    average, 237
    instantaneous, 237-238
Square, 81
    completing the, 122-124
Square root, 81, 85
Standard deviation, 448-453
    sample, 453
Standard normal distribution, 446
Statement, verbal, 176
Statements, 1, 2
    open, 35-37
Statistical inference, 459
Straight angle, 343
Straight lines, equations of, 198-202
Subsets, 17-18, 19
    proper, 17, 19
Substitution principle, 45
Substitution synthetic, 131-132
Subtraction:
    algebraic expressions, 81-82
    algebraic fractions, 98
    complex numbers, 76
    fractions, 60
Successive differentiation, 265-266
Sum, of vectors, 364
Symbols, of grouping, 61-63
Synthetic division, 135-136
Synthetic substitution, 131-132
System(s):
    complex number, 75-78
    Cramer's Rule, 325-327
    linear equations, 312
    linear inequalities, 329-332
    mathematical, 44-45

    number, 40-79
    real number, 45-49

T (truth value), 2, 3
Table:
    amount of annuity, 505-510
    of annuity, 511-516
    compound amount, 485-490
    exponential, 497-502
    natural logarithm, 421
    present value, 491-496
    trigonometric functions, 355-357,
      462-484
    of values, functions defined by,
      178-181
Tangent, 350
Tangent line to a curve at a point,
    239-240
Terms, 80
Terminal side of angle, 341
Theorems, 1, 10-11
    basic, 50-53
    binomial, 105-109
    Factor, 134
    fundamental, of Algebra, 138
    intermediate value, 259
    mean value, 260
    Pythagorean, 190
    Related-Angle, 348
    Remainder, 134
    Rolle's, 260
    Unique Factorization, 41
Time, interval of, 226
Triangles, 344-345
    equilateral, 344
    isosceles, 344
    oblique, 344, 367-371
    right, 344
      solution of, 358-359
Trigonometric functions, 341-377
    tables of, 355-357, 462-484
Trigonometry, 346
Trinomial, 80
Truth value, 2, 3, 4
Truths
    assumed, 1
    deduced, 1

Unique Factorization Theorem, 41
Universal quantifier, 37
Universal set, 15-16, 19

Upper limit of integration, 304
Upper limit of roots, 139

Value:
   absolute, 66
   of annuity, 402, 407-410
   equation, 389-390
   of function, 173
   maturity, 382
   maximum, 271
   mean, 448-453
   minimum, 271
   present, 387-388
    of annuity, 404-406
    Table, 491-496
   table of, functions defined by,
    178-181
Variable, 14, 36, 80
   dependent, 173

   independent, 173
Variable coefficient, 81
Variance, 448-453
   sample, 453
Vector quantity, 363
Vectors, 363-367
   components of, 365-366
Velocity, angular, 344
Venn diagrams, 19-20
Venn, John, 19
Verbal statement, 176
Vertex, angle, 341
Volumes of solids, 309-311

Zero, 41, 48
   of polynomial, 132-134
   products and quotients involving,
    53-54
   square root of, 85